BASIC PRINCIPLES
AND CALCULATIONS
IN CHEMICAL ENGINEERING

PRENTICE-HALL INTERNATIONAL SERIES
IN THE PHYSICAL AND CHEMICAL ENGINEERING SCIENCES

NEAL R. AMUNDSON, EDITOR, *University of Minnesota*

ADVISORY EDITORS

ANDREAS ACRIVOS, *Stanford University*
JOHN DAHLER, *University of Minnesota*
THOMAS J. HANRATTY, *University of Illinois*
JOHN M. PRAUSNITZ, *University of California*
L. E. SCRIVEN, *University of Minnesota*

AMUNDSON *Mathematical Methods in Chemical Engineering: Matrices and Their Application*
ARIS *Introduction to the Analysis of Chemical Reactors*
ARIS *Vectors, Tensors, and the Basic Equations of Fluid Mechanics*
BOUDART *Kinetics of Chemical Processes*
FREDRICKSON *Principles and Applications of Rheology*
HAPPEL AND BRENNER *Low Reynolds Number Hydrodynamics*
HIMMELBLAU *Basic Principles and Calculations in Chemical Engineering, 2nd ed.*
HOLLAND *Multicomponent Distillation*
HOLLAND *Unsteady State Processes with Applications in Multicomponent Distillation*
KOPPEL *Introduction to Control Theory with Applications to Process Control*
LEVICH *Physicochemical Hydrodynamics*
PETERSEN *Chemical Reaction Analysis*
PRAUSNITZ, ECKERT, ORYE, AND O'CONNELL *Computer Calculations for Multicomponent Vapor-Liquid Equilibria*
WHITAKER *Introduction to Fluid Mechanics*
WILDE *Optimum Seeking Methods*

PRENTICE-HALL, INC.
PRENTICE-HALL INTERNATIONAL, INC., UNITED KINGDOM AND EIRE
PRENTICE-HALL OF CANADA, LTD., CANADA

BASIC PRINCIPLES
AND CALCULATIONS
IN CHEMICAL ENGINEERING

Second Edition

DAVID M. HIMMELBLAU

Professor of Chemical Engineering
University of Texas

PRENTICE-HALL, INC.
Englewood Cliffs, New Jersey

PRENTICE-HALL INTERNATIONAL, INC. *London*
PRENTICE-HALL OF AUSTRALIA, PTY. LTD. *Sydney*
PRENTICE-HALL OF CANADA, LTD. *Toronto*
PRENTICE-HALL OF INDIA PRIVATE LTD. *New Delhi*
PRENTICE-HALL OF JAPAN, INC. *Tokyo*

Current Printing:

10 9 8 7 6 5 4

Library of Congress Catalog Card Number: 67—13068
Printed in the United States of America

PREFACE

This text is intended to serve as an introduction to the principles and techniques used in the field of chemical and petroleum engineering. To match the character of the problems that can be encountered, the chapters have been organized essentially into a review of fundamental terms, an explanation of how to make material and energy balances, and a review of certain aspects of applied physical chemistry.

Chemical engineers have always been proud of their flexibility and broad background. In line with this philosophy, the goal of this book is to help students achieve the ability to solve a variety of small-scale practical problems. More than that, it guides the reader into forming generalized patterns of attack in problem-solving which can be successfully used in connection with unfamiliar types of problems. The text is designed to acquaint the student with a sufficient number of fundamental concepts of chemical engineering so that he can (1) continue with his training, and (2) start finding solutions to new problems on his own. It offers practice in finding out what the problem is, defining it, collecting data, analyzing and breaking down information, assembling the basic ideas into patterns, and, in effect, doing everything but testing the solution.

I have found from experience that there is a vast difference between having a student understand a principle and establishing his ability to apply it. By the use of numerous detailed examples it is hoped that straightforward, orderly methods of procedure can be instilled along with some insight into physical principles. Furthermore, a wide variety of problems at the end of each chapter, about one fourth of which are accompanied by answers, offer practice in the application of these principles.

Emphasis has been placed on a few fundamental principles, stated both in words and mathematical symbols, rather than on technology or memorization of formulas. The text does not describe the chemical process industries per se, although certain aspects of these are introduced by the use of problems. Also, the topics of vapor-liquid equilibria, chemical equilibria, and kinetics have been omitted since it is believed that these can best be taken up after an introductory course in physical chemistry. On the other hand, the topic of real gases has been included because far too much attention is devoted in scientific courses to the ideal gases, leaving a very misleading impression. Discussion of unsteady-state (lumped) balances has been deferred until the final chapter because experience has shown that most students lack the mathematical and engineering maturity to absorb these problems simultaneously with the steady-state balances.

The topics are presented in order of easy assimilation rather than in a strictly logical order. The organization is such that easy material is alternated with difficult material in order to give a "breather" after passing over each hump. More topics have been included in the text than can be covered in one semester so that the instructor has some choice as to alternate routes of procedure. In almost every case, the text is followed by concrete examples illustrating the principle covered. Many references are given at the end of each chapter in the hope that those who need supplementary information will pursue their interest further.

I would indeed be ungrateful if I did not express may thanks to the hundreds of students who have participated in the preparation of both the original and the revised edition of this book. It has been used for six years as a text for the introductory course in chemical engineering at the University of Texas (given at the sophomore level), and many modifications have been introduced as a result of the experience of the students and faculty who have used it.

D. M. H.

CONTENTS

BASIC PRINCIPLES
AND CALCULATIONS
IN CHEMICAL ENGINEERING

Chapter 1

INTRODUCTION

TO ENGINEERING

CALCULATIONS

There are few concepts in this chapter that you have not already encountered in basic chemistry and physics courses. Why, then, the need for a review? First, from experience we have found it necessary to restate these familiar basic concepts in a somewhat more general and clearer fashion; second, you will need practice to develop your ability to analyze and work engineering problems. To read and understand the principles discussed in this chapter is relatively easy; to apply them to different unfamiliar situations is not. An engineer becomes competent in his profession by mastering the techniques developed by his predecessors—then, perhaps, he can pioneer new ones.

This chapter begins with a discussion of units, dimensions, and conversion factors, and then goes on to review some terms you should already be acquainted with such as:

(a) Mole and mole fraction
(b) Density and specific gravity
(c) Measures of concentration
(d) Temperature
(e) Pressure

It then provides some clues as to "how to solve problems" which should be of material aid in all the remaining portions of your work. Finally, the

1

principles of stoichiometry are reviewed, and the technique of handling incomplete reactions is illustrated.

1.1. Units and dimensions

At some time in every student's life comes the exasperating sensation of frustration in problem solving. Somehow, the answers or the calculations do not come out as expected. The use of units or dimensions along with the numbers in calculations requires more attention than you probably have been giving to your computations in the past, but it will help avoid such annoying experiences. The proper use of dimensions in problem solving is not only sound from a logical viewpoint—it will also be helpful in guiding you along an appropriate path of analysis from what is at hand through what has to be done to the final solution.

Dimensions are our basic concepts of measurement such as *length, time, mass, temperature,* etc; *units* are the means of expressing the dimensions, as *feet* or *centimeters* for length, or *hours* or *seconds* for time. It is necessary to attach units to certain quantities you may have previously considered dimensionless. A good example is *molecular weight*, which is really the mass of one substance per mole of that substance. This method of attaching units to all numbers which are not fundamentally dimensionless has the following very practical benefits:

(a) It diminishes the possibility of inadvertent inversion of any portion of the calculation.

(b) It reduces the calculation in many cases to simple ratios, which can be easily manipulated on the slide rule.

(c) It reduces the intermediate calculations and eliminates considerable time in problem solving.

(d) It enables you to approach the problem logically rather than by remembering a formula and plugging numbers into a formula.

(e) It demonstrates the physical meaning of the numbers you use.

The rule for handling units is essentially quite simple: treat the units as you would algebraic symbols. For example, you cannot add, subtract, multiply, or divide different units into each other and thus cancel them out—this may be done only for like units. You may be able to add pounds to pounds and calories to calories—subtract them, multiply them, or divide them—but you cannot divide 10 pounds by 5 calories and get 2 any more than you can change 2 apples into 2 bananas.

Example 1.1　Dimensions and Units

Add the following:

(a)　　　　　　　　　　　　　　　1 foot + 3 seconds
(b)　　　　　　　　　　　　　　　1 hp + 300 watts

Solution:

The operation indicated by

$$1 \text{ foot} + 3 \text{ seconds}$$

has no meaning since the dimensions of the two terms are not the same. One foot has the dimensions of length, whereas 3 seconds has the dimensions of time. In the case of

$$1 \text{ hp} + 300 \text{ watts}$$

the dimensions are the same (energy per unit time) but the units are different. You must transform the two quantities into like units, such as hp, watts, or something else, before the addition can be carried out. Since 1 hp = 745.7 watts,

$$745.7 \text{ watts} + 300 \text{ watts} = 1045.7 \text{ watts}$$

Example 1.2　Conversion of Units

If a plane travels at twice the speed of sound (the speed of sound is about 1100 ft/sec), how fast is it going in miles per hour?

Solution:

$$\frac{2}{} \left| \frac{1100 \text{ ft}}{\text{sec}} \right| \frac{1 \text{ mi}}{5280 \text{ ft}} \left| \frac{60 \text{ sec}}{1 \text{ min}} \right| \frac{60 \text{ min}}{1 \text{ hr}} = 1500 \frac{\text{mi}}{\text{hr}}$$

or

$$\frac{\dfrac{2}{} \left| 1100 \text{ ft} \right| 60 \dfrac{\text{mi}}{\text{hr}}}{\text{sec} \quad \left| 88 \dfrac{\text{ft}}{\text{sec}} \right.} = 1500 \frac{\text{mi}}{\text{hr}}$$

You will note in Example 1.2 the use of what is called the *dimensional equation.* It contains both units and numbers. The initial speed, 2200 ft/sec, is multiplied by a number of ratios (termed *conversion factors*) of equivalent values of combinations of time, distance, etc., to arrive at the final desired answer. The ratios used are simple well-known values and thus the conversion itself should present no great problem. Of course, it is possible to look up conversion ratios, which will enable the length of the calculation to be reduced; for instance, in Example 1.2 we could have used the conversion factor of 60 mi/hr equals 88 ft/sec. However, it usually takes less time to use values you know than to look up short-cut conversion factors in a handbook. Common conversion ratios are listed in Appendix A.

The dimensional equation has vertical lines set up to separate each ratio, and these lines retain the same meaning as an $\times$ or multiplication sign placed between each ratio. The dimensional equation will be retained in this form throughout most of this text to enable you to keep clearly in mind the significance of units in problem solving. It is suggested that units always be written down next to the associated numerical value (unless the calculation is very simple) until you become quite familiar with the use of units and dimensions and can carry them in your head.

At any point in the dimensional equation you can determine the consolidated net units and see what conversions are still required. This may be carried out formally, as shown below by drawing slanted lines below the dimensional equation and writing the consolidated units on these lines, or it may be done by eye, mentally canceling and accumulating the units.

$$\frac{2 \times 1100 \text{ ft}}{\text{sec}} \left| \frac{1 \text{ mi}}{5280 \text{ ft}} \right| \frac{60 \text{ sec}}{1 \text{ min}} \left| \frac{60 \text{ min}}{1 \text{ hr}} \right.$$

$$\frac{\text{mi}}{\text{sec}} \qquad \frac{\text{mi}}{\text{min}}$$

Example 1.3   Use of Units

Change 400 in.^{3}/day to cm^3/min.

Solution:

$$\frac{400 \text{ in.}^3}{\text{day}} \left| \left(\frac{2.54 \text{ cm}}{1 \text{ in.}} \right)^3 \right| \frac{1 \text{ day}}{24 \text{ hr}} \left| \frac{1 \text{ hr}}{60 \text{ min}} \right. = 4.56 \frac{\text{cm}^3}{\text{min}}$$

In this example note that not only are the numbers raised to a power but the units also are raised to the same power.

Example 1.4   Units

What are the units of the universal gas constant R in the ideal gas equation $pv = nRT$?

Solution:

We will discuss the ideal gas equation in Chap. 3. However, we can see by rearrangement that

$$R = \frac{pV}{nT}$$

and many sets of units will be satisfactory, such as

$$\frac{\text{(atm)(liter)}}{\text{(g mole)(}^\circ\text{K)}} \quad \text{or} \quad \frac{\text{(mm Hg)(ft}^3\text{)}}{\text{(lb mole)(}^\circ\text{R)}}$$

The numerical value associated with R, of course, will change with the set of units selected. Example 3.5 in Chap. 3 illustrates the numerical calculation of R.

There are quite a variety of systems of units in use, just as there are a variety of monetary systems—based on the American dollar, the English pound, and the French franc. The most common systems are shown in Table 1.1. Note that the cgs, the fps (English absolute), and the British engineering systems all have three basically defined units and that the fourth unit is derived from these three defined units. Only the American engineering system has four basically defined units, and consequently in this system it is necessary to use the conversion factor, g_c, a constant, to make the units come out properly. This peculiarity exists because of the way in which force is defined in the various systems of units. According to Newton's law:

$$F = Cma \tag{1.1}$$

where F = force

m = mass

a = acceleration

C = a constant whose numerical value and units depend upon those selected for F, m, and a

In the cgs system the unit of force is defined as follows:

$$\frac{1 \text{ g} \times 1 \text{ cm}}{1 \text{ sec}^2} = 1 \text{ dyne} \qquad C = 1\frac{\text{dyne}}{\text{(g)(cm)/sec}^2} \tag{1.2}$$

In the English absolute system the unit of force is defined this way:

$$\frac{1 \text{ ft} \times 1 \text{ lb}_m}{1 \text{ sec}^2} = 1 \text{ poundal} \qquad C = 1\frac{\text{poundal}}{\text{(ft)(lb}_m)/\text{sec}^2} \tag{1.3}$$

In the British engineering system it is the unit of mass which is derived from the three basic units: pound weight, feet, and seconds.

$$1 \text{ slug} = \frac{1 \text{ lb weight}}{1 \text{ ft/sec}^2} \qquad C = 1\frac{\text{lb weight}}{\text{(slug)(ft)/sec}^2} \tag{1.4}$$

A *slug* is the mass associated with a 1-lb weight in the earth's gravitational field accelerating at the rate of 1 ft/sec². A 1-lb mass times an acceleration of 32.2 ft/sec² (i.e., the acceleration of gravity, g) is also equal to a 1-lb weight so that the slug is 32 times the mass of a 1-lb mass. In the American engineering system we want the numerical value of the force and mass to be the same so we say:

$$1 \text{ lb}_m \times g\frac{\text{ft}}{\text{sec}^2} \times C = 1 \text{ lb}_f \tag{1.5}$$

TABLE 1.1 COMMON SYSTEMS OF UNITS

	Length	Time	Mass	Force	Energy	Remarks
Absolute Systems						
Cgs	cm	sec	gram	dyne*	erg, joule, or calorie	common scientific
Fps (foot-lb-sec or English absolute)	ft	sec	lb	poundal*	ft poundal	
Gravitational Systems						
British engineering	ft	sec	slug*	pound weight	Btu ft-lb	
American engineering	ft	sec	pound (mass)	pound (force)	ft-lb$_f$, Btu or hp-hr	used by chemical and petroleum engineers

*Unit derived from basic units; all energy units are derived.

where g = acceleration of gravity, about 32.2 ft/sec², depending on location on earth

$C = 1/g_c$ = a conversion factor constant, where g_c is equal to

$$32.174 \frac{(\text{ft})(\text{lb}_m)}{(\text{sec}^2)(\text{lb}_f)}$$

The numerical value 32.174 has been chosen because it equals the numerical value of the average acceleration of gravity at sea level at 45° latitude when the latter is expressed in ft/sec². The acceleration of gravity, you may recall, varies a few tenths of one per cent from place to place on the surface of the earth. By this selection of units and with the number 32.174 employed in the conversion factor g_c, you can see that in the American engineering system we have the convenience that the *numerical* value of a pound mass is also that of a pound force if the numerical value of the ratio g/g_c is equal to 1, as it is approximately in most cases. Similarly, a 1-lb mass also usually weighs 1 lb. However, you should be aware that these two quantities g and g_c are not the same. Note also that the pound (mass) and the pound (force) are not the same units in the American engineering system (the system used most frequently by chemical and petroleum engineers) even though we speak of "pounds" to express force, weight, or mass. Furthermore, if a satellite weighing 1 lb on the earth is shot up to a height of 200 miles, it will no longer "weigh" 1 lb although its mass will still be 1 lb (mass). Additional details concerning units and dimensions can be found in an article by Silberberg and McKetta,[1] and in various books.[2,3,4]

Example 1.5 Use of g_c

One hundred pounds of water are flowing through a pipe at the rate of 10 ft/sec. What is the kinetic energy of this water?

Solution:

$$\text{K.E.} = \tfrac{1}{2}mv^2$$

Assume the 100 lb of water means the mass of the water. (This would be numerically identical to the weight of the water if $g = g_c$.)

$$\text{K.E.} = \frac{1}{2} \left| \frac{100 \text{ lb}_m}{} \right| \left(\frac{10 \text{ ft}}{\text{sec}} \right)^2 \left| \frac{1}{32.174 \frac{(\text{ft})(\text{lb}_m)}{(\text{sec}^2)(\text{lb}_f)}} \right. = 155 \,(\text{ft})(\text{lb}_f)$$

[1] I. H. Silberberg and J. J. McKetta, Jr., *Petroleum Refiner*, v. 32, pp. 179–83 (April), 147–50 (May), 1953.

[2] D. C. Ipsen, *Units, Dimensions, and Dimensionless Numbers*, McGraw-Hill Book Co., New York, 1960.

[3] S. J. Kline, *Similitude and Approximation Theory*, McGraw-Hill Book Co., New York, 1965.

[4] H. E. Huntley, *Dimensional Analysis*, Dover Publications, Inc., New York, 1958.

Example 1.6   Use of g_c

What is the potential energy of a 100-lb drum hanging 10 ft above the surface of the earth?

Solution:

$$P.E. = mgh$$

Assume the 100 lb means 100 lb mass; g = acceleration of gravity = 32.2 ft/sec².

$$P.E. = \frac{100\ lb_m}{\ } \left| \frac{32.2\ ft}{sec^2} \right| \frac{10\ ft}{\ } \left| \frac{1}{32.174\ \frac{(ft)(lb_m)}{(sec^2)(lb_f)}} \right| = 1000\ (ft)(lb_f)$$

Notice that in the ratio of g/g_c, or 32.2 ft/sec² divided by 32.174 (ft/sec²) (lb_m/lb_f), the numerical values are almost equal. A good many people would solve the problem by saying 100 lb × 10 ft = 1000 (ft)(lb) without realizing that in effect they are canceling out the numbers in the g/g_c ratio.

You should develop some facility in converting units from the cgs system into the American engineering system and the reverse, since these are the two sets of units used in this text. Certainly you are familiar with the common conversions in the American engineering system from elementary and high school work. Similarly, you have used the cgs system in physics, chemistry, and mathematics. If you have forgotten, a short selection of essential conversion factors from Appendix A is listed in Table 1.2. Memorize these. Common abbreviations also appear in this table.

TABLE 1.2 BASIC CONVERSION FACTORS

Dimension	American engineering	Cgs	Equivalents
Length	12 in. = 1 ft 3 ft = 1 yd 5280 ft = 1 mi	10 mm = 1 cm 100 cm = 1 m	2.54 cm = 1 in.
Volume	1 ft³ = 7.48 gal	1000 cm³ = 1 l	use factor above
Density	1 ft³ H_2O = 62.4 lb_m	1 cm³ H_2O = 1 g	
Mass	1 ton = 2000 lb	1000 g = 1 kg	1 lb = 454 g
Time	1 min = 60 sec 1 hr = 60 min		

Other useful conversion factors will be discussed in subsequent sections of this book. A detailed discussion of systems of units can be found in Kayan.[5]

[5] C. F. Kayan, "Systems of Units—National and International Aspects, *Publ. Am. Assoc. Advan. Sci.*, Washington, D. C., 1959. For systems used in the USSR consult *Meas. Tech.* (USSR) (*English Trans.*), no. 10, Apr., 1964.

Example 1.7   Application of Dimensions

A simplified equation for heat transfer from a pipe to air is

$$h = 0.026\, G^{0.6}/D^{0.4}$$

where h = the heat transfer coefficient in Btu/(hr)(ft²)(°F)
G = mass rate of flow in lb_m/(hr)(ft²)
D = outside diameter of the pipe in ft
If h is to be expressed in cal/(min)(cm²)(°C), what should the new constant in the equation be in place of 0.026?

Solution:

To convert to cal/(min)(cm²)(°C) we set the expression up as follows:

$$h = \frac{0.026 G^{0.6}\,\text{Btu}}{D^{0.4}(\text{hr})(\text{ft}^2)(°\text{F})}\left|\frac{252\,\text{cal}}{1\,\text{Btu}}\right|\frac{1\,\text{hr}}{60\,\text{min}}\left|\left(\frac{1\,\text{ft}}{12\,\text{in.}}\right)^2\right.$$

$$\left|\left(\frac{1\,\text{in.}}{2.54\,\text{cm}}\right)^2\right|\frac{1.8°\text{F}}{1°\text{C}} = 2.11 \times 10^{-4}\,\frac{G^{0.6}\,\text{cal}}{D^{0.4}(\text{min})(\text{cm}^2)(°\text{C})}$$

(*Note:* See Sec. 1.4 for a detailed discussion of temperature conversion factors.)

If G and D are to be used in units of

$$G' : \frac{\text{g}}{(\text{min})(\text{cm}^2)}$$

$$D' : \text{cm}$$

than an additional conversion is required,

$$h' = \frac{2.11 \times 10^{-4}\left|\left[\frac{G'(\text{g})}{(\text{min})(\text{cm}^2)}\left|\frac{1\,\text{lb}_m}{454\,\text{g}}\right|\frac{60\,\text{min}}{1\,\text{hr}}\left|\left(\frac{2.54\,\text{cm}}{1\,\text{in.}}\right)^2\right|\left(\frac{12\,\text{in.}}{1\,\text{ft}}\right)^2\right]^{0.6}}{1}$$

$$\overline{\left[D'(\text{cm})\left|\left(\frac{1\,\text{in.}}{2.54\,\text{cm}}\right)\right|\left(\frac{1\,\text{ft}}{12\,\text{in.}}\right)\right]^{0.4}} = 1.42 \times 10^{-2}\,\frac{(G')^{0.6}\,\text{cal}}{(D')^{0.4}(\text{min})(\text{cm}^2)(°\text{C})}$$

Dimensional considerations can also be used to help identify the dimensions of terms or quantities in terms in an equation. Equations must be dimensionally consistent, i.e., each term in an equation must have the same net dimensions and units as every other term to which it is added or subtracted. The use of dimensional consistency can be illustrated by an equation which represents gas behavior and is known as van der Waals' equation, an equation which will be discussed in more detail in Chap. 3:

$$\left(p + \frac{a}{V^2}\right)(V - b) = RT$$

Inspection of the equation shows that the constant a must have the dimensions of [(pressure)(volume)^2] in order for the expression in the first parenthesis to be consistent throughout. If the units of pressure are atm and those of volume are cm^3, then a will have the units specifically of [(atm)(cm)^6]. Similarly b must have the same units as V, or in this particular case the units of cm^3.

1.2 The mole unit

What is a mole? One convenient answer is that a *mole* is a certain number of molecules.[6] In the cgs system the mole contains a different number of molecules than it does in the American engineering system. In the cgs system a mole has about 6.02×10^{23} molecules; this is called a *gram mole* (abbreviated *g mole*). In the American engineering system the *pound mole* (abbreviated *lb mole*) has $6.02 \times 10^{23} \times 454$ molecules. Thus the pound mole and the gram mole represent two different quantities. Here is another way to look at the mole unit:

$$\text{the g mole} = \frac{\text{mass in g}}{\text{molecular weight}} \tag{1.6}$$

$$\text{the lb mole} = \frac{\text{mass in lb}}{\text{molecular weight}} \tag{1.7}$$

or

$$\text{mass in g} = (\text{mol. wt})(\text{g mole}) \tag{1.8}$$

$$\text{mass in lb} = (\text{mol. wt})(\text{lb mole}) \tag{1.9}$$

The values of the molecular weights are built up from the tables of atomic weights based on an arbitrary scale of the relative masses of the elements. The term "atomic weight" is universally used by chemists and engineers instead of the more accurate term, "atomic mass." Since weighing was the original method for determining the comparative atomic masses, as long as they were calculated in a common gravitational field, the values obtained for "atomic weights" were identical with those of the "atomic masses." There have always been and are today some questions in issue about the standard reference element and its atomic weight. Many of the old standards such as H (atomic hydrogen) = 1, O (atomic oxygen) = 100, O = 1 and O = 16 have been discarded, and now $C^{12} = 12$ exactly is used as the reference point on the chemist's scale, i.e., 12.000 grams of carbon 12 contain 1 g mole or 6.023×10^{23} atoms.

On this scale of atomic weights, hydrogen is 1.008, carbon is 12.01, etc.

---

[6] For a discussion of the requirements of the mole concept, refer to the series of articles in *J. Chem. Educ.*, v. 38, pp. 549–556 (1961).

(In most of our calculations we will round these off to 1 and 12, respectively.) In your calculations you may attach any unit of mass you desire to these atomic weights, as, for example, a gram atom, a pound atom, a ton atom, etc. Thus a gram atom of oxygen is 16.00 grams, a pound atom of oxygen is 16.00 pounds, and a kilogram atom of hydrogen is 1.008 kilograms.

A compound is composed of more than one atom, and the molecular weight of the compound is nothing more than the sum of the weights of the atoms of which it is composed. Thus H_2O consists of 2 hydrogen atoms and 1 oxygen atom, and the molecular weight of water is $(2)(1.008) + 16.000 = 18.02$. These weights are all relative to the C^{12} atom as 12.0000, and again, any mass unit can be attached to the molecular weight of water, such as 18.02 grams per gram mole, 18.02 pounds per pound mole, etc.

You can compute average molecular weights for mixtures of constant composition even though they are not chemically bonded if their compositions are known accurately. Thus later on in Example 1.12 we will show how to calculate the average molecular weight of air. Of course, for a material such as fuel oil or coal whose composition may not be exactly known, you cannot determine an exact molecular weight, although you might estimate an approximate average molecular weight good enough for engineering calculations.

Example 1.8   Molecular Weights

If a bucket holds 2 lb of NaOH (mol. wt = 40), how many
(a) lb moles of NaOH does it contain?
(b) g moles of NaOH does it contain?

Solution:

Basis: 2 lb NaOH

(a) $\dfrac{2 \text{ lb NaOH} \mid 1 \text{ lb mole NaOH}}{40 \text{ lb NaOH}} = 0.05 \text{ lb mole NaOH}$

(b₁) $\dfrac{2 \text{ lb NaOH} \mid 1 \text{ lb mole NaOH} \mid 454 \text{ g mole}}{40 \text{ lb NaOH} \mid 1 \text{ lb mole}} = 22.7 \text{ g mole}$

or

(b₂) $\dfrac{2 \text{ lb NaOH} \mid 454 \text{ g} \mid 1 \text{ g mole NaOH}}{1 \text{ lb} \mid 40 \text{ g NaOH}} = 22.7 \text{ g mole}$

Example 1.9   Molecular Weights

How many lb of NaOH are in 7.5 g moles of NaOH?

Solution:

Basis: 7.5 g mole NaOH

$$\frac{7.5 \text{ g mole NaOH}}{} \left| \frac{1 \text{ lb mole}}{454 \text{ g mole}} \right| \frac{40 \text{ lb NaOH}}{1 \text{ lb mole NaOH}} = 0.66 \text{ lb NaOH}$$

1.3 Conventions in methods of analysis and measurement

There are certain definitions and conventions which we should mention at this time since they will be constantly used throughout this book. If you memorize them now, you will immediately have a clearer perspective and save considerable trouble later on.

1.3-1 Density. Density is the ratio of mass per unit volume, as for example, gram/cm^3 or lb/ft^3. It has both a numerical value and units. To determine the density of a substance, you must find both its volume and its mass or weight. If the substance is a solid, a common method to determine its volume is to displace a measured quantity of inert liquid. For example, a known weight of a material can be placed into a container of liquid of known weight and volume, and the final weight and volume of the combination measured. The density (or specific gravity) of a liquid is usually measured with a hydrometer (a known weight and volume is dropped into the liquid and the depth to which it penetrates into the liquid is noted) or a Westphal balance (the weight of a known slug is compared in the unknown liquid with that in water). Gas densities are quite difficult to measure; one device used is the Edwards balance, which compares the weight of a bulb filled with air to the same bulb when filled with the unknown gas.

In most of your work using liquids and solids, density will not change very much with temperature or pressure, but for precise measurements for common substances you can always look up in a handbook the variation of density

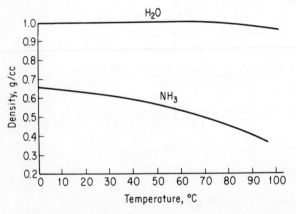

Fig. 1.1. Densities of liquid H_2O and NH_3 as a function of temperature.

with temperature. This change is illustrated in Fig. 1.1 for liquid water and liquid ammonia. Density also varies with composition. In the winter you may put antifreeze in your car radiator. The service station attendant checks the concentration of antifreeze by measuring the specific gravity and, in effect, the density of the radiator solution after it is mixed thoroughly. He has a little thermometer in his hydrometer kit in order to be able to read the density at the proper temperature.

1.3-2 Specific Gravity. Specific gravity is commonly thought of as a dimensionless ratio. Actually, it should be considered as the ratio of two densities—that of the substance of interest, A, to that of a reference substance. In symbols:

$$\text{sp gr} = \text{specific gravity} = \frac{(\text{lb/ft}^3)_A}{(\text{lb/ft}^3)_{\text{ref}}} = \frac{(\text{g/cm}^3)_A}{(\text{g/cm}^3)_{\text{ref}}} = \frac{(\text{ton/liter})_A}{(\text{ton/liter})_{\text{ref}}} \quad (1.10)$$

The reference substance for liquids and solids is normally water. Thus the specific gravity is the ratio of the density of the substance in question to the density of water. The specific gravity of gases frequently is referred to air, but may be referred to other gases, as will be discussed in more detail in Chap. 3. Liquid density can be considered to be nearly independent of pressure for most common calculations, but, as just mentioned, it varies somewhat with temperature; therefore, to be very precise when referring to specific gravity, state the temperature at which each density is chosen. Thus

$$\text{sp gr} = 0.73 \frac{20°}{4°}$$

can be interpreted as: the specific gravity at 20°C referred to that of water at 4°C is 0.73. Since the density of water at 4°C is very close to 1.0000 in the cgs system, the numerical values of the specific gravity and density in this system are essentially equal. Since densities in the American engineering system are expressed in lb/ft³ and the density of water is about 62.4 lb/ft³, it can be seen that the specific gravity and density values are not numerically equal.

In the petroleum industry the specific gravity of petroleum products is usually reported in terms of a hydrometer scale called °API. The equation for the API scale is

$$°\text{API} = \frac{141.5}{\text{sp gr} \frac{60°}{60°}} - 131.5 \quad (1.11)$$

or

$$\text{sp gr} \frac{60°}{60°} = \frac{141.5}{°\text{API} + 131.5} \quad (1.12)$$

The volume and therefore the density of petroleum products vary with temperature, and the petroleum industry has established 60°F as the standard temperature for volume and API gravity. The National Bureau of Standards has published the National Standard Petroleum Oil Tables, NBS Circular C410 (1936), which relates API, density, specific gravity, and temperature for all petroleum oils. Thus you may convert any of the above properties at any temperature to any other temperature.

There are many other systems of measuring density and specific gravity which are somewhat specialized as, for example, the Baume (°Be) and the Twaddell (°Tw) systems. Relationships among the various systems of density may be found in standard reference books.

1.3-3 Specific Volume. The specific volume of any compound is its volume expressed on a per-unit mass or unit amount of material basis. Units of specific volume might be ft^3/lb, ft^3/lb mole, cm^3/gram, bbl/lb, or similar ratios. The specific volume is nothing more than the reciprocal of the density.

1.3-4 Mole Fraction and Weight Fraction. Mole fraction is simply the moles of a particular substance divided by the total number of moles present. This holds for gases, liquids, and solids. Similarly, the weight fraction is nothing more than the weight of the substance divided by the total weight of all substances present. Mathematically these ideas can be expressed as:

$$\text{mole fraction} = \frac{\text{moles of } A}{\text{total moles}} \tag{1.13}$$

$$\text{weight fraction} = \frac{\text{weight of } A}{\text{total weight}} \tag{1.14}$$

Mole per cent and weight per cent are the respective fractions times 100.

1.3-5 Analyses. The analyses of gases such as air, combustion products, and the like are usually on a dry basis—i.e., water vapor is excluded from the analysis. Such an analysis is called an *Orsat* analysis. In practically all cases the analysis of the gas is on a volume basis, which for the ideal gas is the same as a mole basis. A typical gas analysis is that of air, which is approximately

$$
\begin{array}{l}
21\% \text{ oxygen} \\
\underline{79\% \text{ nitrogen}} \\
100\% \text{ total}
\end{array}
$$

This means that any sample of air will contain 21 per cent oxygen by volume and also 21 mole per cent oxygen. Per cent, you should remember, is nothing more than the fraction times 100; consequently the mole fraction of oxygen is 0.21.

Analyses of liquids and solids are usually given by weight per cent, but occasionally by mole per cent. In this text analyses of liquids and solids will always be assumed to be weight per cent unless otherwise stated.

Example 1.10   Mole Fraction and Weight Fraction

A bottle is found to contain 5 lb of water and 5 lb of NaOH. What is the weight fraction and mole fraction of each component in the bottle?

Solution:

Basis: 10 lb total solution

component	lb	weight fraction	mol. wt	lb moles	mole fraction
H_2O	5	$\frac{5}{10} = 0.5$	18	0.278	$\frac{0.278}{0.403} = 0.69$
NaOH	5	$\frac{5}{10} = 0.5$	40	0.125	$\frac{0.125}{0.403} = 0.31$
total	10	1.0		0.403	1.00

The lb moles are calculated as follows:

$$\frac{5 \text{ lb } H_2O}{} \left| \frac{1 \text{ lb mole } H_2O}{18 \text{ lb } H_2O} \right. = 0.278 \text{ lb mole } H_2O$$

$$\frac{5 \text{ lb NaOH}}{} \left| \frac{1 \text{ lb mole NaOH}}{40 \text{ lb NaOH}} \right. = 0.125 \text{ lb mole NaOH}$$

Adding these quantities together gives the total lb moles.

Example 1.11   Density and Specific Gravity

If dibromopentane has a specific gravity of 1.57, what is its density in lb/ft^3 and in g/cm^3?

Solution:

Our reference substance is water.

(a)
$$\frac{1.57 \frac{g \text{ DBP}}{cm^3}}{1.00 \frac{g \text{ } H_2O}{cm^3}} \left| 1.00 \frac{g \text{ } H_2O}{cm^3} \right. = 1.57 \frac{g \text{ DBP}}{cm^3}$$

(b)
$$\frac{1.57 \frac{lb \text{ DBP}}{ft^3}}{1.00 \frac{lb \text{ } H_2O}{ft^3}} \left| 62.4 \frac{lb \text{ } H_2O}{ft^3} \right. = 97.9 \frac{lb \text{ DBP}}{ft^3}$$

Note how the units of specific gravity as used here clarify the calculation.

Example 1.12   Compute the Average Molecular Weight of Air

Basis: 100 lb mole of air

component	moles = %	mol. wt	lb	weight %
O_2	21	32	672	23.17
N_2*	79	28.2	2228	76.83
total	100		2900	100.00

* Includes Ar, CO_2, Kr, Ne, Xe, and is called atmospheric nitrogen. The molecular weight is 28.2.

The average molecular weight is 2900 lb/100 lb mole = 29.00.

1.3-6 Basis. Have you noted in the previous illustrations that the word *basis* has appeared at the top of the computations? This concept of basis is vitally important both to your understanding of how to solve a problem and also to your solving it in the most expeditious manner. The basis is the reference chosen by you for the calculations you plan to make in any particular problem, and a proper choice of basis frequently makes the problem much easier to solve. The basis may be a period of time—for example, hours, or a given weight of material—such as 5 lb of CO_2 or some other convenient quantity. In selecting a sound basis (which in many problems is predetermined for you but in some problems is not so clear), you should ask yourself the following questions:

(a) What do I have to start with?
(b) What do I want to find out?
(c) What is the most convenient basis to use?

These questions and their answers will suggest suitable bases. Sometimes, when a number of bases seem appropriate, you may find it is best to use a unit basis of 1 or 100 of something, as, for example, pounds, hours, moles, cubic feet, etc. Many times for liquids and solids when a weight analysis is used, a convenient basis is 1 or 100 lb; similarly 1 or 100 moles is often a good choice if a mole analysis is used for a gas. The reason for these choices is that per cent automatically equals the number of pounds or moles, respectively, and one step in the calculations is saved.

Example 1.13   Choosing a Basis

An oil is 80% C and 20% H. What is the C and H ratio in moles?

Solution:

If a basis of 100 lb of oil is selected, then the per cent = pounds.

Basis: 100 lb oil

component	lb = %	mol. wt	lb moles
C	80	12	6.67
H	20	1	20
	100		

Consequently the C/H ratio in moles is

$$C/H = 6.67/20 = 0.33$$

Example 1.14   Choosing a Basis

A tank contains 200 lb of gas of the following composition: CS_2, 30%; CO, 40%; CH_4, 30%. What is the average molecular weight of this gas?

Solution:

The obvious basis is 200 lb of gas ("What I have to start with") but a little reflection will show that such a basis is of no use. You cannot multiply *mole per cent* of this gas times pounds and expect the answer to mean anything. Thus the next step is to choose a "convenient basis" which is 100 moles of gas, and proceed as follows:

Basis: 100 lb moles of gas

composition	% = lb moles	mol. wt	lb
CS_2	30	76	2280
CO	40	28	1120
CH_4	30	16	480
	100		3880

$$\text{average molecular weight} = \frac{3880 \text{ lb}}{100 \text{ lb moles}} = 38.8 \text{ lb/lb mole}$$

It is important that your basis be indicated at the beginning of the problem so that you will keep clearly in mind the real nature of your calculations and so that anyone checking your problem will be able to understand on what basis they are performed. If you change bases in the middle of the problem, a new basis should be indicated at that time. Many of the problems which we will encounter will be solved on one basis and then at the end will be shifted to another basis to give the desired answer. The significance of this type of manipulation will become considerably clearer as you accumulate more experience. The ability to choose the basis that requires the fewest steps in solution can only come with practice. As you look at each problem illustrated in this text, determine first in your own mind what the basis should be; then compare it with the selected basis, and you will quickly obtain the knack of choosing a sound basis.

Example 1.15   Changing Bases

In Example 1.14, how many lb moles were in the tank?

Solution:
From the calculation in Example 1.14 you know there are 38.8 lb in the tank per lb mole. Choose a new basis now of the original 200 lb of gas in the tank.

Basis: 200 lb gas mixture

$$\frac{200 \text{ lb gas}}{} \left| \frac{1 \text{ lb mole gas}}{38.8 \text{ lb gas}} = 5.15 \text{ lb moles} \right.$$

1.3-7 Concentrations. Concentration means the quantity of some solute per fixed amount of solvent or solution, as, for example:

(a) Weight per unit volume (lb/ft^3, g/l, lb/bbl).
(b) Moles per unit volume (lb $mole/ft^3$, g $mole/l$, g $mole/cm^3$).
(c) Parts per million—a method of expressing the concentration of extremely dilute solutions, commonly found in water analysis—for example, the parts per million (ppm) of chloride ion. This is a weight fraction because the total amount of material is of a much higher order of magnitude than the solute.
(d) Other methods of expressing concentration with which you should be familiar are: molarity (moles/liter), normality (equivalents/liter), and molality (moles/1000 g of solvent).

It is important to remember that in an ideal solution, such as a simple mixture of hydrocarbons or compounds of like chemical nature, the volumes of the components may be added without great error to get the total volume of the mixture. For the so-called nonideal mixtures this rule does not hold, and the total volume of the mixture is bigger or smaller than the sum of the volumes of the components.

1.4 Temperature

Our concept of temperature probably originated with our physical sense of hot or cold. Attempts to be more specific and quantitative led to the idea of a temperature scale and the thermometer—a device to measure how hot or cold something is. We are all familiar with the thermometer used in laboratories which holds mercury sealed inside a glass tube or the alcohol thermometer used to measure outdoor temperatures.

Although we do not have the space to discuss in detail the many methods of measuring temperature, we can point out some of the other more common techniques with which you are probably already familiar:

(a) The voltage produced by a junction of two dissimilar conductors changes with temperature and is used as a measure of temperature (the *thermocouple*).

(b) The property of changing electrical resistance with temperature gives us a device known as the *thermistor*.

(c) Two thin strips of metal bonded together at one end expand at different rates with change of temperature. These strips assist in the control of the flow of water in the radiator of an automobile and in the operation of air conditioners and heating systems.

(d) High temperatures can be measured by devices called *pyrometers* which note the radiant energy leaving a hot body.

Figure 1.2 illustrates the appropriate ranges for various temperature-measuring devices.

As you also know, the temperature of a substance is normally measured in degrees Fahrenheit or Centigrade. The common scientific scale is the *Centigrade* scale,[7] where 0° is the ice point of water and 100° is the normal boiling point of water. In the early 1700's Fahrenheit, a glassblower by trade, was able to build mercury thermometers that gave temperature measurements in reasonable agreement with each other. The *Fahrenheit* scale is the one commonly used in everyday life in this country. Its reference points are of more mysterious origin, but it is reported that the fixed starting point, or 0° on Fahrenheit's scale, was the temperature of an ice-salt mixture, and 96°, the temperature of the blood of a healthy man, was selected as the upper point because it is easily divisible by 2, 3, 4, 6, and 8, whereas 100° is not. In any case, as now standardized, 32°F represents the ice point and 212°F represents the normal boiling point of water.

These two scales, Fahrenheit and Centigrade, are *relative* scales; that is, their zero points were arbitrarily fixed by their inventors. Quite often it is necessary to use *absolute* temperatures instead of relative temperatures. Absolute temperature scales have their zero point at the lowest possible temperature which man believes can exist. As you may know, this lowest temperature is related both to the ideal gas laws and to the laws of thermodynamics. The absolute scale which is based on degree units the size of those

---

[7] As originally devised by Celsius in 1742, the freezing point was designated as 100°. Officially, °C now stands for *degrees Celsius*.

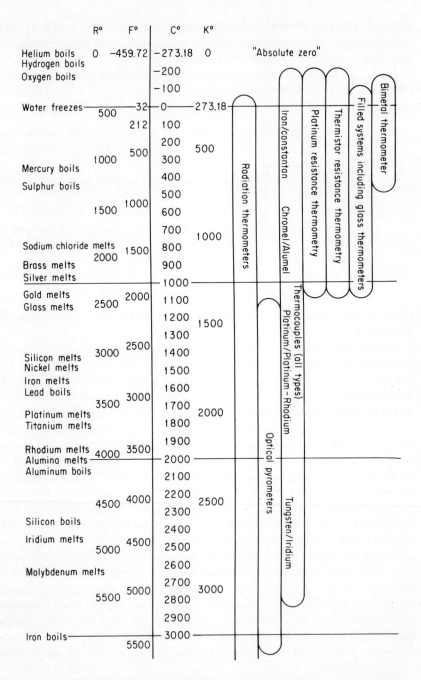

Fig. 1.2. Temperature measuring instruments span the range from near absolute zero to beyond 3000°K. The chart indicates the preferred methods of thermal instrumentation for various temperature regions.

in the Centigrade scale is called the *Kelvin* scale, after its inventor Lord Kelvin; the absolute scale which corresponds to the Fahrenheit degree scale is called the *Rankine* scale in honor of a Scottish engineer. The relations between relative temperature and absolute temperature are illustrated in Fig. 1.3 and are mathematically stated as follows:[8]

Fahrenheit:

$$T(°F) = 32(°F) + T(°C)\left[\frac{1.8(°F)}{1(°C)}\right] \qquad (1.15)$$

Centigrade:

$$T(°C) = [T(°F) - 32(°F)]\left[\frac{1(°C)}{1.8(°F)}\right] \qquad (1.16)$$

Rankine:

$$T(°R) = T(°F)\left[\frac{1(°R)}{1(°F)}\right] + 460(°R) = T(°K)\left[\frac{1.8(°R)}{1(°K)}\right] \qquad (1.17)$$

Kelvin:

$$T(°K) = T(°C)\left[\frac{1(°K)}{1(°C)}\right] + 273(°K) = T(°R)\left[\frac{1(°K)}{1.8(°R)}\right] \qquad (1.18)$$

After you have used these equations a bit, they will become so familiar that temperature conversion will become an automatic reflex. During your "learning period," in case you forget them, just think of the appropriate scales side by side as in Fig. 1.3, and put down the values for the freezing and boiling points of water.

Besides understanding how to change the numerical value of the temperature from one scale to another, you should also be aware of the relationship among the unit temperature differences. For example, the units of the heat capacity, which we will take up in Chap. 4, might be Btu/(lb)(°F). Actually, this °F is a Δ°F, or unit temperature *difference*. In words we might say, "Btu per pound per degree Fahrenheit difference." Consequently,

$$\frac{\text{Btu}}{\text{(lb)(°F)}} = \frac{\text{Btu}}{\text{(lb)(°R)}} \quad \text{since} \quad Δ°F = Δ°R \qquad (1.19)$$

and

$$\frac{\text{cal}}{\text{(g)(°C)}} = \frac{\text{cal}}{\text{(g)(°K)}} \quad \text{since} \quad Δ°C = Δ°K \qquad (1.20)$$

and since

$$\frac{Δ°C}{Δ°F} = 1.8 = \frac{Δ°K}{Δ°R} \qquad (1.21)$$

---

[8] Absolute zero on the Rankine scale of $-459.58°F$ has been rounded off to $-460°F$; similarly, $-273.15°C$ has been rounded off to $-273°C$.

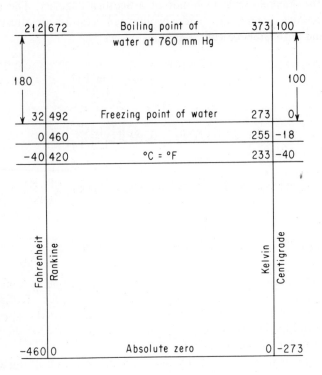

Fig. 1.3. Temperature scales.

(remember that the $\Delta°C$ is larger than the $\Delta°F$.)
then

$$\frac{1 \text{ Btu}}{(\text{lb})(°F)} \left| \frac{1.8°F}{1°C} \right. = 1.8 \frac{\text{Btu}}{(\text{lb})(°C)} \tag{1.22}$$

Unfortunately, the symbol $\Delta°C$ is not in standard usage, and consequently the proper meaning of the symbol $°C$ as either the temperature or the temperature difference must be interpreted from the context of the equation or sentence being examined.

In Fig. 1.3 you will notice that $-40°$ is a common temperature on both the Centigrade and Fahrenheit scales. Therefore, the following relationships exist:

$$T(°F) = [T(°C) + 40(°C)]\frac{1.8°F}{1°C} - 40(°F) \tag{1.23}$$

$$T(°C) = [T(°F) + 40(°F)]\frac{1°C}{1.8°F} - 40(°C) \tag{1.24}$$

In Fig. 1.3 all values have been rounded off, but more exact agreement could be obtained if additional significant figures were used. 0°C and its equivalents are known as *standard conditions of temperature.*

Example 1.16   Temperature Conversion

Convert 100°C to (a) °K, (b) °F, (c) °R.

Solution:

(a)
$$(100°C + 273°C)\frac{1°K}{1°C} = 373°K$$

(b)
$$(100°C)\frac{1.8°F}{1°C} + 32°F = 212°F$$

(c)
$$(212°F + 460°F)\frac{1°R}{1°F} = 672°R$$

$$\text{or } (373°K)\ \frac{1.8°R}{1°K} = 672°R$$

Example 1.17   Temperature Conversion

The thermal conductivity of aluminum at 32°F is 117 Btu/(hr)(ft²)(°F/ft). Find the equivalent value at 0°C in terms of Btu/(hr)(ft²)(°K/ft).

Solution:

Since 32°F is identical to 0°C, the value is already at the proper temperature. The "°F" in the denominator of the thermal conductivity actually stands for Δ°F so that the equivalent value is

$$\frac{117(\text{Btu})(\text{ft})}{(\text{hr})(\text{ft}^2)(°F)}\ \Bigg|\ \frac{1.8°F}{1°C}\ \Bigg|\ \frac{1°C}{1°K} = 211\ (\text{Btu})/(\text{hr})(\text{ft}^2)(°K/\text{ft})$$

1.5 Pressure

Pressures, like temperatures, can also be expressed by either absolute or relative scales. Pressure is defined as "force per unit area." A cube of water contained in a tank 1 ft² on a side (see Fig. 1.4) has a density of about 62.4 lb_m/ft^3 and exerts a force on the bottom of the tank (in addition to any pressure exerted by the atmosphere above the water) of

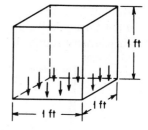

Fig. 1.4. Pressure.

$$F = \frac{62.4\ \text{lb}_m}{1\ \text{ft}^3}\ \Bigg|\ \frac{g\ \text{ft}}{\text{sec}^2}\ \Bigg|\ g_c\frac{(\text{ft})(\text{lb}_m)}{(\text{sec}^2)(\text{lb}_f)}\ \Bigg|\ 1\ \text{ft}^3$$

$$= 62.4\ \text{lb}_f$$

Observe that the numerical value of $g/g_c = 1.0$. The pressure exerted on the sides of the tank varies with the depth of the water in the tank. The pressure on the bottom of the tank is

$$p = \frac{F}{A} = \frac{62.4 \text{ lb}_f}{1 \text{ ft}^2} = 62.4 \text{ lb}_f/\text{ft}^2$$

Whether relative or absolute pressure is measured depends upon the nature of the instrument used to take the measurements. For example, an open-end manometer (Fig. 1.5) would measure a relative pressure, since the reference for the open end is the pressure of the atmosphere at the open end

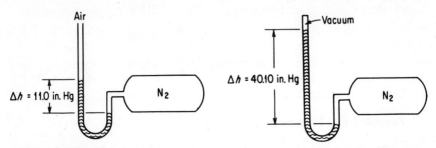

Fig. 1.5. Open-end manometer showing a pressure above atmospheric pressure.

Fig. 1.6. Absolute pressure manometer.

of the manometer. On the other hand, closing off the end of the manometer (Fig. 1.6) and creating a vacuum in it results in a measurement against a complete vacuum, or against "no pressure." This measurement is called *absolute pressure*. Since absolute pressure is based on a complete vacuum, a fixed reference point which is unchanged regardless of location or temperature or weather or other factors, absolute pressure then establishes a precise, invariable value which can be readily identified. Thus the zero point for an absolute pressure scale corresponds to a perfect vacuum, whereas the zero point for a relative pressure scale usually corresponds to the pressure of the air which surrounds us at all times, and, as you know, varies slightly.

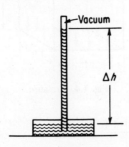

Fig. 1.7. A barometer.

If the mercury reading is set up as in Fig. 1.7, the device is called a *barometer* and the reading of atmospheric pressure termed *barometric pressure*.

An understanding of the principle upon which a manometer operates will aid you in recognizing the nature of the pressure measurement taken from it. As shown in Fig. 1.5 for an open-end, U-tube manometer, if the pressure measured is greater than atmospheric, the liquid is forced downward in the leg to which the pressure source is connected and upward in the open leg. Eventually a point of hydrostatic balance is reached in which the manometer stabilizes, and the difference in height of the fluid in the open leg is exactly equal to the difference between the atmospheric pressure and the applied pressure in the opposite leg. If vacuum were applied instead of pressure to the same leg of the manometer, the fluid column would rise on the vacuum side. Nevertheless, the difference in pressure between the pressure source in the tank and atmospheric pressure is balanced by the difference in the height of the two columns of fluid. Water and mercury are commonly used indicating fluids for manometers; the readings thus are expressed in "inches of water" or "inches of mercury."

If a fluid twice as heavy as water is used, then the movement of the fluid in the indicating tube will be one-half as great as that you would expect to get from water. If the indicating fluid has a specific gravity less than that of water, it will move a proportionally greater distance than water. (In ordinary engineering calculations we ignore the vapor pressure of mercury and minor changes in the density of mercury due to temperature changes in making pressure measurements.)

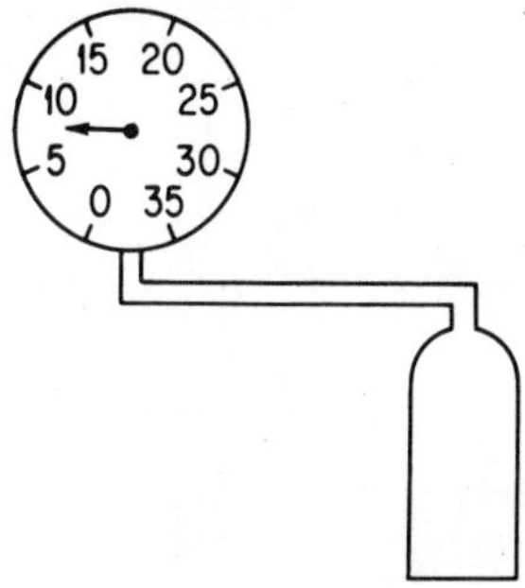

Fig. 1.8. Bourdon gauge.

A third type of common measuring device is the visual *Bourdon gauge*[9] (Fig. 1.8), which normally (but not always) measures a reading of zero pressure when open to the atmosphere.

Pressure scales may be temporarily somewhat more confusing than temperature scales since the reference point or zero point for the relative pressure scales is not constant, whereas in the temperature scales the boiling point or the freezing point of water is always a fixed value. However, you will become accustomed to this feature of the pressure scale with practice.

The relationship between relative and absolute pressure is illustrated in Figs. 1.9 and 1.10 and is also given by the following expression:

$$\text{Gauge pressure} + \text{barometer pressure} = \text{absolute pressure} \quad (1.25)$$

Equation (1.25) can be used only with consistent units. Note that you must add the atmospheric pressure, i.e., the barometric pressure, to the gauge, or relative pressure (or manometer reading if open on one end), in order to get the absolute pressure.

Another method of measuring pressure which is illustrated in Figs. 1.9

[9] The pressure-sensing device in the Bourdon gauge is a thin metal tube with an elliptical cross section closed at one end which has been bent into an arc. As the pressure increases at the open end of the tube, it tries to straighten out, and the movement of the tube is converted into a dial movement by gears and levers.

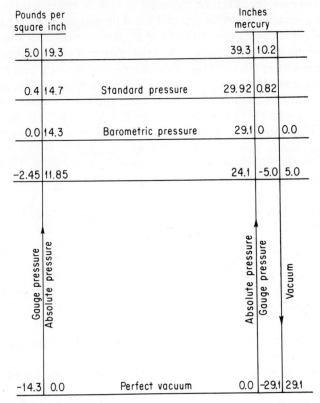

Fig. 1.9. Pressure comparisons when barometer reading is 29.1 in. Hg.

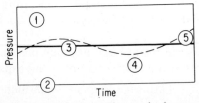

Fig. 1.10. Pressure terminology. The standard atmosphere is shown by the heavy horizontal line. The broken line illustrates the atmospheric (barometric) pressure which changes from time to time. 1 in the figure is a pressure of 19.3 lb/sq in. referred to a complete vacuum or 5 lb/sq in. referred to the barometric pressure. 2 is the complete vacuum while 3 represents the standard atmosphere. 4 illustrates a negative relative pressure or a pressure less than atmospheric. This type of measurement is described in the text as a vacuum type of measurement. 5 also indicates a vacuum measurement, but one which is equivalent to an absolute pressure above the standard atmosphere.

and 1.10 is that of "vacuum." In effect, when the engineer measures pressure as "inches of mercury vacuum," he is reversing the usual direction of measurement and measures from the barometric pressure down to the vacuum, in which case a perfect vacuum would be the highest pressure that he could achieve. This procedure would be the same as evacuating the air at the top of a mercury barometer and watching the mercury rise up in the barometer as the air is removed. The vacuum system of measurement of pressure is commonly used in apparatus which operates at pressures less than atmospheric—such as a vacuum evaporator or vacuum filter. A pressure which is only slightly below barometric pressure may sometimes be expressed as a "draft" (which is identical to the vacuum system) in inches of water, as, for example, in the air supply to a furnace or a water cooling tower.

As to the units of pressure, we have shown in Fig. 1.9 two of the most common systems: pounds per square inch (psi) and inches of mercury (in. Hg). Pounds per square inch absolute is normally abbreviated "psia," and "psig" stands for "pounds per square inch gauge." Figure 1.9 compares the relative and absolute pressure scales in terms of these two systems of measurement when the barometric pressure is 29.1 in. of mercury (14.3 psia). Other systems of expressing pressure exist; in fact you will discover there are as many different units of pressure as there are means of measuring pressure. Some of the most frequently used systems are:

> Millimeters of mercury   (mm Hg)
>
> Feet of water   (ft H_2O)
>
> Atmospheres   (atm)

To sum up our discussion of pressure and its measurement, you should now be acquainted with:

(a) Atmospheric pressure—the pressure of the air and the atmosphere surrounding us which changes from day to day
(b) Barometric pressure—the same as atmospheric pressure, called "barometric pressure" because a barometer is used to measure atmospheric pressure
(c) Absolute pressure—a measure of pressure referred to a complete vacuum, or zero pressure
(d) Gauge pressure—pressure expressed as a quantity measured from (above) atmospheric pressure (or some other reference pressure)
(e) Vacuum—a method of expressing pressure as a quantity below atmospheric pressure (or some other reference pressure)

You definitely must not confuse the standard atmosphere with atmospheric pressure. The *standard atmosphere* is defined as the pressure (in a standard gravitational field) equivalent to 14.696 psi or 760 mm mercury at

0°C or other equivalent value, whereas atmospheric pressure is a variable and must be obtained from a barometer each time you need it. The standard atmosphere may not actually exist in any part of the world except perhaps at sea level on certain days, but it is extremely useful in converting from one system of pressure measurement to another (as well as being useful in several other ways to be considered later).

Expressed in various units, the standard atmosphere is equal to:

  1.000   atmospheres (atm)
  33.91   feet of water (ft H_2O)
  14.7   (14.696, more exactly) pounds per square inch absolute (psia)
  29.92   (29.921, more exactly) inches of mercury (in. Hg)
  760.0   millimeters of mercury (mm Hg)

In order to convert from one set of pressure units to another, it is convenient to use the relationships among the standard pressures as shown in the examples below.

If pressures are measured by means of the height of a column of liquid[10] other than mercury or water (for which the standard pressure is known), it is easy to convert from one liquid to another by means of the following expressions:

$$p = \rho \frac{g}{g_c} h \qquad (1.26)$$

where ρ = density of the liquid
     g = acceleration of gravity

By taking the ratio of this expression for two different substances, you will get the ratio between the heights of two columns of liquid. If one of these liquids is water, it is then easy to convert to any of the more commonly used systems as follows (with CCl_4 as the example):

$$\frac{\text{ft of } H_2O}{\text{ft of } CCl_4} = \frac{\text{density of } CCl_4}{\text{density of } H_2O} \qquad (1.27)$$

Example 1.18   Pressure Conversion

Convert 35 psia to inches of mercury.

Solution:
It is desirable to use the ratio of 14.7 psia to 29.92 in. Hg, an identity, to carry out this conversion.

Basis: 35 psia

$$\frac{35 \text{ psia}}{} \left| \frac{29.92 \text{ in. Hg}}{14.7 \text{ psia}} \right. = 71.25 \text{ in. Hg}$$

an identity

---

[10] Sometimes these liquid columns are referred to as "heads" of liquid.

Example 1.19 Pressure Conversion

Convert 340 mm Hg to inches of water.

Solution:

$$\text{Basis: 340 mm Hg}$$

$$\frac{340 \text{ mm Hg}}{} \left| \frac{33.91 \text{ ft H}_2\text{O}}{760 \text{ mm Hg}} \right| \frac{12 \text{ in.}}{1 \text{ ft}} = 182 \text{ in. H}_2\text{O}$$

Example 1.20 Pressure Conversion

The pressure gauge on a tank of CO_2 used to fill soda water bottles reads 51.0 psi. At the same time the barometer reads 28.0 in. Hg. What is the absolute pressure in the tank in psia?

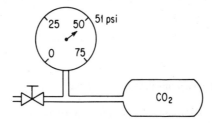

Solution:

The pressure gauge is reading psig, not psia.

From Eq. (1.25) the absolute pressure is the sum of the gauge pressure and the atmospheric (barometric) pressure expressed in the same units.

$$\text{Basis: Barometric pressure} = 28.0 \text{ in. Hg}$$

$$\text{atmospheric pressure} = \frac{28.0 \text{ in. Hg}}{} \left| \frac{14.7 \text{ psia}}{29.92 \text{ in. Hg}} \right| = 13.78 \text{ psia}$$

(*Note:* Atmospheric pressure does not equal 1 standard atm.) The absolute pressure in the tank is

$$51.0 + 13.78 = 64.78 \text{ psia}$$

Example 1.21 Pressure Conversion

Air is flowing through a duct under a draft of 4.0 in. H_2O. The barometer indicates that the atmospheric pressure is 730 mm Hg. What is the absolute pressure of the gas in inches Hg?

Solution:

Again we have to employ consistent units, and it appears in this case that the best units are those of inches of mercury.

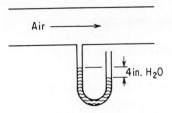

Basis: 730 mm Hg pressure

$$\text{atmospheric pressure} = \frac{730 \text{ mm Hg} \mid 29.92 \text{ in. Hg}}{760 \text{ mm Hg}} = 28.9 \text{ in. Hg}$$

Basis: 4.0 in. H_2O draft (under atmospheric)

$$\frac{4 \text{ in. } H_2O \mid 1 \text{ ft} \mid 29.92 \text{ in. Hg}}{12 \text{ in.} \mid 33.91 \text{ ft } H_2O} = 0.29 \text{ in. Hg}$$

Since the reading is 4.0 in. H_2O draft (under atmospheric), the absolute reading in uniform units is

$$28.9 - 0.29 = 28.6 \text{ in. Hg absolute}$$

Example 1.22   Vacuum Pressure Reading

A mercury manometer is attached to a tank as shown. The tank is known to be below atmospheric pressure. If the manometer reads 25.4 in. Hg and the barometer reads 14.79 psia, what is the absolute pressure in the tank?

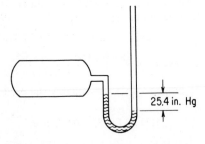

Solution:

Basis: 25.4 in. Hg below atmospheric

We will assume $g/g_c \cong 1.00$ and ignore any temperature corrections to convert the mercury to 0°C. Then, since the vacuum reading on the tank is 25.4 in. Hg below atmospheric, the absolute pressure in the tank is

$$14.79 \text{ psia} - \frac{25.4 \text{ in. Hg} \mid 14.7 \text{ psia}}{29.92 \text{ in. Hg}} = 14.79 - 12.49 = 2.3 \text{ psia}$$

1.6 Physical and chemical properties of compounds and mixtures

If you know the chemical formula for a pure compound, you can look up many of its physical properties in standard reference books, such as:

(a) *The International Critical Tables*[11]
(b) Perry's *Chemical Engineers' Handbook*[12]
(c) *Handbook of Physics and Chemistry*[13]
(d) Lange's *Handbook*[14]

Also, specialized texts in your library frequently list properties of compounds. For example, the book *Fuel Flue Gases*[15] lists considerable data on gas mixtures which are primarily of concern in the gas utility field. Appendix D in this text tabulates the chemical formula, molecular weight, melting point, boiling point, etc., for most, but not all, of the compounds involved in the problems you will find at the end of the chapters.

Many of the materials we talk about and use every day are not pure compounds, and it is considerably more trouble to obtain information about the properties of these materials. Fortunately, for materials such as coal, coke, petroleum products, and natural gas—which are the main sources of energy in this country—tables and formulas are available in reference books and handbooks which list some of the specific gross properties of these mixtures. Some typical examples of natural gas analyses and ultimate analyses of petroleum and petroleum products as shown in Tables 1.3 and 1.4 point out the variety of materials which can be found.

Since petroleum and petroleum products represent complex mixtures of hydrocarbons and other organic compounds of various types together with various impurities, if the individual components cannot be identified, then the mixture is treated as a uniform compound. Usually, the components in natural gas can be identified, thus their individual physical properties can be looked up in the reference books mentioned above or in the Appendix in this text. As will be discussed in Chap. 3 under gases, many times the properties of a pure gas when mixed with another gas are the sum of the properties of the pure components. On the other hand, liquid petroleum crude oil and petroleum fractions are such complicated mixtures that their physical properties are hard to estimate from the pure components (even if known) unless the mixture is very simple. As a result of the need for methods

[11] *The International Critical Tables*, McGraw-Hill Book Co., New York, 1928.
[12] J. H. Perry, ed, *Chemical Engineers' Handbook*, 4th ed., McGraw-Hill Book Co., New York, 1963.
[13] *Handbook of Chemistry and Physics*, Chemical Rubber Publishing Co., Cleveland, Ohio, annually.
[14] N. A. Lange, *Handbook of Chemistry*, McGraw-Hill Book Co., New York annually.
[15] *Fuel Flue Gases*, American Gas Association, New York, 1941.

TABLE 1.3 TYPICAL DRY GAS ANALYSES*
Analysis (volume %—excluding water vapor)

Type	CO_2	O_2	N_2	CO	H_2	CH_4	C_2H_6	C_3H_8	C_4H_{10}	$C_5H_{12}^+$
Natural gas	6.5					77.5	16.0			
Natural gas, dry†	0.2		0.6			99.2				
Natural gas, wet†	1.1					87.0	4.1	2.6	2.0	3.4
Natural gas, sour‡	(H_2S 6.4)					58.7	16.5	9.9	5.0	3.5
Butane							2.0	3.3	75.4	n-butane
									18.1	isobutane

Illuminants

Type	CO_2	O_2	N_2	CO	H_2	CH_4	C_2H_6	Illuminants
Reformed refinery oil	2.3	0.7	4.9	20.8	49.8	12.3	5.5	3.7
Coal gas, by-product	2.1	0.4	4.4	13.5	51.9	24.3		3.4
Producer gas	4.5	0.6	50.9	27.0	14.0	3.0		
Blast furnace gas	5.4	0.7	8.3	37.0	47.3	1.3		
Sewage gas	22.0		6.0		2.0	68.0		

*Fuel Flue Gases, American Gas Association, New York, 1941, p. 20.
† Dry gas contains much less propane (C_3H_8) and higher hydrocarbons than wet gas does.
‡ "Sour" implies that the gas contains significant amounts of hydrogen sulfide.

TABLE 1.4 ULTIMATE ANALYSIS OF PETROLEUM CRUDE*

Type	Sp gr	At °C	Weight per cent				
			C	H	N	O	S
Pennsylvania	0.862	15	85.5	14.2			
Humbolt, Kan.	0.921		85.6	12.4			0.37
Beaumont, Tex.	0.91		85.7	11.0	2.61		0.70
Mexico	0.97	15	83.0	11.0	1.7		
Baku, U.S.S.R.	0.897		86.5	12.0		1.5	

* Data from W. L. Nelson, Petroleum Refinery Engineering, 4th ed., McGraw-Hill Book Co., New York, 1958.

of predicting the behavior of petroleum stocks, empirical correlations have been developed in recent years for many of the physical properties we want to use. These correlations are based upon the °API, the Universal Oil Products characterization factor K, the boiling point, and the apparent molecular weight of the petroleum fraction. These parameters in turn are related to five or six relatively simple tests of the properties of oils. Some of the details of these tests, the empirical parameters, and the properties that can be predicted from these parameters will be found in the reference to Table 1.4 and in Appendix K.

1.7 Technique of solving problems

If you can form good habits of problem solving early in your career, you will save considerable time and avoid many frustrations in all aspects of your work in and out of school. In solving material and energy balance problems, you should:

(a) Read the available material through thoroughly and understand what is required for an answer. Sometimes, as in life, the major obstacle is to find out what the problem really is.

(b) Determine what additional data are needed, if any, and obtain this information.

(c) Draw a simplified picture of what is taking place and write down the available data. You may use boxes to indicate processes or equipment, and lines for the flow of streams.

(d) Pick a basis on which to start the problem, as discussed in Sec. 1.3-6.

(e) If a chemical equation is involved, write it down and make sure it is balanced.

By this time you should have firmly in mind what the problem is and a reasonably clear idea of what you are going to do about it; however, if you have not seen exactly how to proceed from what is available to what is wanted, then you should:

(f) Decide what formulas or principles are governing in this specific case and what types of calculations and intermediate answers you will need to get the final answer. If alternative procedures are available, try to decide which are the most expedient. If an unknown cannot be found directly, give it a letter symbol, and proceed as if you knew it.

(g) Make the necessary calculations in good form, being careful to check the arithmetic and units as you proceed.

(h) Determine whether the answer seems reasonable in view of your experience with these types of calculations.

Problems which are long and involved should be divided into parts and attacked systematically piece by piece.

If you can assimilate this procedure and make it a part of yourself—so that you do not have to think about it step by step—you will find that you will be able to materially improve your speed, performance, and accuracy in problem solving.

The major difference between problems solved in the classroom and in the plant lies in the quality of the data available for the solution. Plant data may be of poor quality, inconclusive, inadequate, or actually conflicting, depending on the accuracy of sampling, the type of analytical procedures employed, the skill of the technicians in the operation of analytical apparatus, and many other factors. The ability of an engineer to use the stoichiometric principles for the calculation of problems of material balance is only partly exercised in the solution of problems, even of great complexity, if solved from adequate and appropriate data. The remainder of the test lies in his ability to recognize poor data, to request and obtain usable data, and if necessary, to make accurate estimates in lieu of incorrect or insufficient data.[16]

1.8 The chemical equation and stoichiometry

As you already know, the chemical equation provides a variety of qualitative and quantitative information essential for the calculation of the combining weights of materials involved in a chemical process. Take for example the combustion of heptane as shown below. What can we learn from this equation?

$$C_7H_{16} + 11\ O_2 \longrightarrow 7\ CO_2 + 8\ H_2O \qquad (1.28)$$

We can see that 1 mole (*not* pound) of heptane will react with 11 moles of oxygen to give 7 moles of carbon dioxide plus 8 moles of water. These may be pound moles or gram moles or any other type of mole as shown in Fig. 1.11. One mole of CO_2 is formed from each 1/7 mole of C_7H_{16}. Also, 1 mole of H_2O is formed with each 7/8 mole of CO_2. Thus the equation tells us in terms of moles (*not* pounds) the ratios among reactants and products.

Stoichiometry (stoi-ki-om-e-tri)[17] deals with the combining weights of elements and compounds. The ratios obtained from the numerical coefficients in the chemical equation are the stoichiometric ratios that permit you to calculate the moles of one substance as related to the moles of another substance in the chemical equation. You should use the following method in solving problems involving chemical equations: (a) Calculate the number of moles of the substance represented by the basis, (b) change this to the moles of the desired product by multiplying by the proper stoichiometric ratio, as determined by the chemical equation, and (c) then change the moles of product to a weight basis. These steps are indicated in Fig. 1.12 for the above reaction. You can combine these steps in a single dimensional equation, as shown in the examples below for ease of slide rule calculations; however, the order of operations should be kept the same.

An assumption implicit in the above is that the reaction takes place exactly as written in the equation and proceeds to 100 per cent completion. When reactants, products, or degree of completion of the actual reaction differ from the assumptions of the equation, additional data must be made available to indicate the actual status or situation.

---

[16] B. E. Lauer, *The Material Balance*, Work Book Edition 1954, p. 89.
[17] From the Greek *stoicheion*, basic constituent, and *metrein*, to measure.

C_7H_{16}	$+$	$11\ O_2$	$\longrightarrow$	$7\ CO_2$	$+$	$8\ H_2O$

Qualitative information:

heptane	reacts with	oxygen	to give	carbon dioxide	and	water

Quantitative information:

1 molecule of heptane	reacts with	11 molecules of oxygen	to give	7 molecules of carbon dioxide	and	8 molecules of water

6.023×10^{23} molecules of C_7H_{16}	$+$	$11(6.023 \times 10^{23})$ molecules of O_2	$\longrightarrow$	$7(6.023 \times 10^{23})$ molecules of CO_2	$+$	$8(6.023 \times 10^{23})$ molecules of H_2O
1 g mole of C_7H_{16}	$+$	11 g moles of O_2	$\longrightarrow$	7 g moles of CO_2	$+$	8 g moles of H_2O
1 lb mole of C_7H_{16}	$+$	11 lb moles of O_2	$\longrightarrow$	7 lb moles of CO_2	$+$	8 lb moles of H_2O
1 ton mole of C_7H_{16}	$+$	11 ton moles of O_2	$\longrightarrow$	7 ton moles of CO_2	$+$	8 ton moles of H_2O
$1(100)$ g of C_7H_{16}	$+$	$11(32)$ g of O_2	$=$	$7(44)$ g of CO_2	$+$	$8(18)$ g of H_2O

100 g	352 g	308 g	144 g

452 g	$=$	452 g
452 kg	$=$	452 kg
452 ton	$=$	452 ton
452 lb	$=$	452 lb

Fig. 1.11. The chemical equation.

Basis: 10 lb C_7H_{16}

Component	Mol. wt
C_7H_{16}	100
O_2	32
CO_2	44
H_2O	18

1 lb mole   7 lb mole

$$C_7H_{16} \quad + \quad 11\ O_2 \quad \longrightarrow \quad 7CO_2 \quad + \quad 8\ H_2O$$

$$\frac{10\ \text{lb}\ C_7H_{16}}{100\ \text{lb}\ C_7H_{16}} = 0.1\ \text{lb mole}\ C_7H_{16} \longrightarrow \frac{0.7\ \text{lb mole}\ CO_2}{1\ \text{lb mole}\ CO_2} = 30.8\ \text{lb}\ CO_2$$

10 lb C_7H_{16} yields 30.8 lb CO_2

Fig. 1.12. Stoichiometry.

Example 1.23   Stoichiometry

In the combustion of heptane, CO_2 is produced. Assuming it is desired to produce 500 lb of dry ice per hour and that 50 per cent of the CO_2 can be converted into dry ice, how many pounds of heptane must be burned per hour?

Solution:

$$\text{Basis: 500 lb dry ice (or 1 hr)}$$

Mol. wt heptane $= 100$

$$\text{Chemical equation as in Fig. 1.10}$$

$$\frac{500 \text{ lb dry ice}}{} \left| \frac{1 \text{ lb } CO_2}{0.5 \text{ lb dry ice}} \right| \frac{1 \text{ lb mole } CO_2}{44 \text{ lb } CO_2} \left| \frac{1 \text{ lb mole } C_7H_{16}}{7 \text{ lb mole } CO_2} \right.$$

$$\left| \frac{100 \text{ lb } C_7H_{16}}{1 \text{ lb mole } C_7H_{16}} = 325 \text{ lb } C_7H_{16} \right.$$

Since the basis of 500 lb dry ice is identical to 1 hr, 325 lb of C_7H_{16} must be burned per hour. Note that pounds are converted first to moles, then the chemical equation is applied, and finally moles are converted to pounds again for the final answer.

Example 1.24   Stoichiometry

Sodium sulfite removes oxygen from boiler feedwater by the following reaction:

$$2 \text{ Na}_2SO_3 + O_2 \longrightarrow 2 \text{ Na}_2SO_4$$

How many pounds of sodium sulfite are theoretically required to remove the oxygen from 8,330,000 lb of water (10^6 gal) containing 10.0 parts per million of dissolved oxygen and at the same time maintain a 35 per cent excess of sodium sulfite?

Solution:

Additional data: mol. wt of Na_2SO_3 is 126.

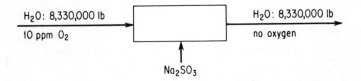

Chemical equation: $2\ Na_2SO_3 + O_2 \longrightarrow 2\ Na_2SO_4$

Basis: 8,330,000 lb H_2O with 10 ppm O_2 or 83.3 lb O_2

$$\frac{8{,}330{,}000\ \text{lb}\ H_2O}{}\ \bigg|\ \frac{10\ \text{lb}\ O_2}{\underbrace{(1{,}000{,}000 - 10\ \text{lb}\ O_2)\ \text{lb}\ H_2O}_{\text{effectively same as 1,000,000}}} = 83.3\ \text{lb}\ O_2$$

$$\frac{8{,}330{,}000\ \text{lb}\ H_2O}{}\ \bigg|\ \frac{10\ \text{lb}\ O_2}{10^6\ \text{lb}\ H_2O}\ \bigg|\ \frac{1\ \text{lb mole}\ O_2}{32\ \text{lb}\ O_2}\ \bigg|\ \frac{2\ \text{lb mole}\ Na_2SO_3}{1\ \text{lb mole}\ O_2}$$

$$\bigg|\ \frac{126\ \text{lb}\ Na_2SO_3}{1\ \text{lb mole}\ Na_2SO_3}\ \bigg|\ \frac{1.35}{1} = 885\ \text{lb}\ Na_2SO_3$$

Example 1.25   Stoichiometry

A limestone analyzes

$CaCO_3$	92.89
$MgCO_3$	5.41
Insoluble	1.70

(a) How many pounds of calcium oxide can be made from 5 tons of this limestone?

(b) How many pounds of CO_2 can be recovered per pound of limestone?

(c) How many pounds of limestone are needed to make 1 ton of lime?

Solution:

Read the problem carefully to fix in mind exactly what is required. Lime will include all the impurities present in the limestone which remain after the CO_2 has been driven off. Next draw a picture of what is going on in this process.

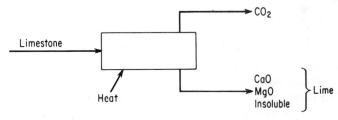

To complete the preliminary analysis you need the following chemical equations:

$$CaCO_3 \longrightarrow CaO + CO_2$$

$$MgCO_3 \longrightarrow MgO + CO_2$$

Additional data are:

	$CaCO_3$	$MgCO_3$	CaO	MgO	CO_2
Mol. wt	100	84.3	56.0	40.3	44

Basis: 100 lb limestone

This basis was selected because lb = %.

comp.	lb = %	lb moles	$\longrightarrow$	lime	lb	CO_2 (lb)
$CaCO_3$	92.89	0.9289		CaO	52.0	40.9
$MgCO_3$	5.41	0.0641		MgO	2.59	2.82
insol.	1.70			insol.	1.70	
total	100.00	0.9930		total	56.3	43.7

Note that the total pounds of products equal the 100 lb of entering limestone. Now to calculate the quantities originally asked for:

(a) CaO produced $= \dfrac{52.0 \text{ lb CaO}}{100 \text{ lb stone}} \Big| \dfrac{2000 \text{ lb}}{1 \text{ ton}} \Big| \dfrac{5 \text{ ton}}{} = 5200 \text{ lb CaO}$

(b) CO_2 recovered $= \dfrac{43.7 \text{ lb CO}_2}{100 \text{ lb stone}} = 0.437 \text{ lb}$ or,

$\dfrac{0.9930 \text{ lb mole CaCO}_3 + \text{MgCO}_3}{100 \text{ lb stone}} \Big| \dfrac{1 \text{ lb mole CO}_2}{1 \text{ lb mole CaCO}_3 + \text{MgCO}_3}$

$\Big| \dfrac{44 \text{ lb CO}_2}{1 \text{ lb mole CO}_2} = 0.437 \text{ lb}$

(c) limestone required $= \dfrac{100 \text{ lb stone}}{56.3 \text{ lb lime}} \Big| \dfrac{2000 \text{ lb}}{1 \text{ ton}} = 3560 \text{ lb stone}$

In industrial reactions you will rarely find exact stoichiometric amounts of materials used. In order to make a desired reaction take place or to use up a costly reactant, excess reactants are nearly always used. This excess material comes out together with, or perhaps separately from, the product—and sometimes can be used again. Even if stoichiometric quantities of reactants are used, but if the reaction is not complete or there are side reactions, the products will be accompanied by side-products or reactants. In these circumstances some new definitions must be understood:

(a) *Limiting reactant* is the reactant which is present in the smallest stoichiometric amount.
(b) *Excess reactant* is a reactant in excess of the limiting reactant. The *per cent excess* of a reactant is based on the amount of any excess reactant above the amount required to react with the limiting reactant according to the chemical equation, or

$$\% \text{ excess} = \frac{\text{moles in excess}}{\text{moles required to react with limiting reactant}} 100$$

where the moles in excess frequently can be calculated as the total available moles of a reactant less the moles required to react with the limiting reactant. A common term, "excess air," is used in combustion reactions; it means the amount of air available to react that is in excess of the air theoretically required to *completely* burn the combustible material. The *required* amount of a reactant is established by the limiting reactant and is for all other reactants the corresponding stoichiometric amount. **Even if only part of the limiting reactant actually reacts, the required and excess quantities are based on the entire amount of the limiting reactant.**

(c) *Per cent conversion* is the percentage of the amount of any reactant converted into products. This is related to the *degree of completion* of a reaction which is usually the percentage or fraction of the limiting reactant converted into products. The basis for the per cent conversion or degree of completion always has to be clearly specified since sometimes it is intended to include a desired product only, whereas in other cases it may be based on the desired product plus other by-products.

(d) *Yield,* for a single reactant and product, is the weight or moles of final product divided by the weight or moles of initial reactant (P pounds of product A per R pounds of reactant B). If more than one product and more than one reactant are involved, the reactant upon which the yield is to be based must be clearly stated.

The employment of these concepts can best be illustrated by examples.

Example 1.26   Limiting Reactant and Incomplete Reaction

If 10 kg of PbS and 3 kg of O_2 react to yield 6 kg of Pb and 1 kg of PbO_2, and the only other product of the reaction that takes place is SO_2, what is:

(a) The amount of PbS that does not react?
(b) The amount of SO_2 formed?
(c) The per cent conversion of PbS into Pb?

Solution:
The equation for the reaction in unbalanced form is

$$PbS + O_2 \longrightarrow Pb + PbO_2 + SO_2$$

The g moles of each substance can be computed as follows:

		kg	*mol. wt*	*g moles*
	PbS	10	239	41.9
	O_2	3	32	93.7
Basis:	Pb	6	207	29.0
	PbO_2	1	239	4.19
	SO_2		64	

(a) In order to find the limiting reactant and the amount of PbS that does not react, let us look at the following two balanced equations and assume the over-all reaction is composed of these two simultaneous reactions:

$$PbS + O_2 \longrightarrow Pb + SO_2$$

$$PbS + 2\,O_2 \longrightarrow PbO_2 + SO_2$$

For either of these equations the O_2 is in excess and the PbS is the limiting reactant. You can see that the PbS which reacts must appear in the products as Pb or PbO_2. According to these two equations this amounts to

Pb   PbO$_2$

$$29.0 + 4.19 = 33.19 \text{ g moles PbS react}$$

Since 41.9 g moles of PbS are available to react, 41.9–33.19 or 8.7 g moles of PbS do not react. This quantity is equivalent to

$$\frac{8.7 \text{ g mole}}{} \left| \frac{239 \text{ g}}{1 \text{ g mole}} \right| \frac{1 \text{ kg}}{1000 \text{ g}} = 2.08 \text{ kg PbS}$$

Thus, the limiting reactant is PbS, but not all of the available limiting reactant actually reacts. Furthermore, if the amount of O_2 available was considerably less than 93.7 g moles, the limiting reactant might be O_2 based on the second equation, or PbS based on the first equation. Which equation was the basis would have to be clearly specified. The term "per cent excess oxygen" here is not completely clear, but based on the first equation it is

$$\frac{\text{total } O_2 \text{ available} - \text{required } O_2}{\text{required } O_2} = \frac{93.7 - 41.9}{41.9}\,100 = 124\%$$

Based on the second equation in which both the Pb and the S are oxidized it is

$$\frac{93.7 - 2(41.9)}{2(41.9)}\,100 = 11.8\%$$

Based on the amount of PbS that actually reacts, the excess O_2 is

$$\frac{93.7 - [29.0 + 2(4.19)]}{[29.0 + 2(4.19)]}\,100 = 150\%$$

This latter basis of computation is not commonly used.

(b) The SO_2 formed must come from the oxidation of PbS, and for every mole of S in the PbS that reacts, 1 mole of SO_2 is formed. Consequently, 33.19 g moles of SO_2 are formed, or

$$\frac{33.19 \text{ g mole}}{} \left| \frac{64 \text{ g}}{1 \text{ g mole}} \right| \frac{1 \text{ kg}}{1000 \text{ g}} = 2.12 \text{ kg SO}_2$$

(c) Of the original 10 kg of PbS, only 6 kg of Pb are formed. The per cent conversion to Pb based on the total PbS provided is 69.4%.

$$100 \times \frac{29.0 \text{ g mole Pb}}{41.9 \text{ g mole Pb possible}} = 69.4\%$$

Incidentally, to complete the analysis, the over-all per cent conversion of the PbS into products is

$$\frac{33.19 \text{ g mole PbS reacting}}{41.9 \text{ g mole available to react}} \times 100 = 79.2\%$$

Another way to handle this problem would be to write separate balanced equations for the individual reactions forming the over-all reaction:

$$29.0 \text{ PbS} + 29.0 \text{ O}_2 \longrightarrow 29.0 \text{ Pb} + 29.0 \text{ SO}_2$$

$$4.19 \text{ PbS} + 8.38 \text{ O}_2 \longrightarrow 4.19 \text{ PbO}_2 + 4.19 \text{ SO}_2$$

The computations would be identical to those presented above. Notice especially that the addition of the two equations immediately above would not yield an equation tantamount to the one given at the start of this example if it were balanced in the form of

$$2 \text{ PbS} + 3 \text{ O}_2 \longrightarrow \text{Pb} + \text{PbO}_2 + 2 \text{ SO}_2$$

Why would it not do so?

You should remember that the chemical equation does not indicate the true mechanism of the reaction, nor how fast or to what extent the reaction will take place. For example, a lump of coal in air will sit unaffected at room temperature, but at higher temperatures will readily burn. All the chemical equation indicates is the stoichiometric amounts required for the reaction and obtained from the reaction if it proceeds in the manner in which it is written.

WHAT YOU SHOULD HAVE LEARNED FROM THIS CHAPTER

1. You should have memorized the common conversion units.
2. You should be able to convert units from the American engineering system to the cgs system and the reverse with ease, and understand the significance of g_c.
3. You should understand *moles, molecular weights, density, specific gravity, mole* and *weight fraction, temperature,* and *pressure,* and be able to work problems involving these concepts.
4. You should have well in mind the proper approach to problem solving and be able to effectively put into practice the principles discussed in the chapter.
5. You should know how to apply the principles of stoichiometry to problems involving chemical reactions.

NOMENCLATURE

(Units are discussed in the text)

a = acceleration
A = area
$°API$ = specific gravity of oil defined in Eq. (1.11)

C = constant in Eq. (1.1)

F = force

g = acceleration of gravity

g_c = conversion factor, $32.174 \dfrac{(\text{ft})(\text{lb}_m)}{(\text{sec}^2)(\text{lb}_f)}$

h = height above a datum plane

K.E. = kinetic energy

m = mass

mol. wt = molecular weight

p = pressure

P.E. = potential energy

R = universal gas constant

sp gr = specific gravity

v = volume or specific volume

ρ = density

SUPPLEMENTARY REFERENCES

1. Anderson, H. V., *Chemical Calculations*, McGraw-Hill Book Company, New York, 1955.
2. Benson, S. W., *Chemical Calculations*, 2nd ed., John Wiley & Sons, Inc., New York, 1963.
3. Felsing, W. A., and G. W. Watt, *General Chemistry*, McGraw-Hill Book Company, New York, 1951.
4. Henley, E. J., and H. Bieber, *Chemical Engineering Calculations*, McGraw-Hill Book Company, New York, 1959.
5. Hougen, O. A., K. M. Watson, and R. A. Ragatz, *Chemical Process Principles*, Part I, 2nd ed., John Wiley & Sons, Inc., New York, 1956.
6. Littlejohn, C. E., and F. G. Meenaghan, *An Introduction to Chemical Engineering*, Reinhold Publishing Corp., New York, 1959.
7. Williams, E. T., and R. C. Johnson, *Stoichiometry for Chemical Engineers*, McGraw-Hill Book Company, New York, 1958.

PROBLEMS

1.1. AP Service—If you want a glass of water in a New York City restaurant, you'll have to ask for it. The water conservation measure was ordered because the drought is continuing to lower levels in the city's reservoirs. The ban on serving water in restaurants will save 12 to 15 million gal a day, estimates the commissioner of water supply, gas and electricity.

How many servings of 8-oz. glasses make up the 12 to 15 million gal (to be divided among 7 million New Yorkers and visitors)?

1.2. Hollywood (AP)—Blonde Jan Eastlund from Europe, a loser in last year's Miss Universe pageant, came up a winner this week with a studio contract and a starring role in her first movie. Jan speaks English with a slight accent, and is baffled by our units of measure. Asked for her measurements, she answered, "My bust is 92, waist 58, and my hips 92." A studio press agent gave an imitation of a man suffering apoplexy. "That can't be right," he cried. "When you say '92', what do you mean—92 what!" "Centimeters, of course," Jan answered. "Is that so bad?" Help out the distraught publicist by providing the correct dimensions in inches.

1.3. In a stolen-oil case, Frank Sigafooe has been caught with a truck containing 12,000 gal of oil taken from someone's storage tank. The law says that grand larceny must amount to a theft of more than $1000; petit larceny is the theft of any lesser amount. If oil sells in the field for $2.45/bbl, should Frank be indicted for grand or petit larceny?

1.4. Find:
(a) The acceleration produced when 20 poundals act on a mass of 2 slugs
(b) The weight in lb_f of 2 slugs
(c) The energy expended in $(ft)(lb_f)$ when a force of 5 poundals acts on a mass of $10 \, lb_m$ for a distance of 6.44 ft

1.5. Show that 1 g/liter $= 1 \, oz/ft^3$.

1.6. If a rocket uses 2 liters of liquid oxygen per second as an oxidizer, how many cubic feet per hour of liquid oxygen are used?

1.7. Convert:
(a) 60 mi/hr to ft/sec
(b) 50 $lb/in.^2$ to kg/cm^2
(c) 6.2 cm/hr^2 to ft/sec^2

1.8. A pipeline moving 6142 bbl of oil per hour is moving the equivalent of how many cubic meters per second? (42 gal $= 1$ bbl.)

1.9. Change the following to the desired units:
(a) 235 grams   to pounds
(b) 610 liters   to cubic feet
(c) $30 \frac{grams}{liter}$ to pounds/cubic feet
(d) 14.7 $lb/in.^2$ to kg/cm^2

1.10. $\dfrac{(100)(in.)(mm)^2}{(year)(sec)(wk)(barrel)}$ would be how much in the units $\dfrac{(miles)(ft)^2}{(min)^3(cm)^3}$?

1.11. $1000 \dfrac{cm}{(sec)^3}$ would be how much in the units $\dfrac{yards}{(hr)(week)(min)}$?

1.12. An elevator which weighs 10,000 lb is pulled up 10 ft between the first and second floors of a building 100 ft high. The greatest velocity the elevator attains is 3 ft/sec. How much kinetic energy does the elevator have in $(ft)(lb_f)$ at this velocity?

1.13. The density of a certain liquid is 93.6 lb/ft^3. Calculate the weight in grams of 2.0 liters of the liquid.

1.14. Water is flowing through a pipe of 3.355-in.^{2} cross-sectional area at the rate of 60 gal/min. Find the velocity, ft/sec.

1.15. An electric heater uses 1100 watts. How much heat (Btu) does it produce in 2 min?

1.16. Find the kinetic energy of a ton of water moving at 60 mph expressed as (a) (ft)(lb$_f$), (b) ergs, (c) joules, (d) (hp)(sec), (e) (watt)(sec), and (f) (liter)(atm).

1.17. Evaluate the unitless ratio $C\mu/k$ from the following data:

$$C = 1.0 \text{ Btu/(lb)(°F)}, \qquad \mu = 0.020 \text{ g/(sec)(cm)}$$

$$k = 0.34 \text{ (Btu)(ft)/(hr)(ft}^2\text{)(°F)}$$

1.18. Calculate the kinetic and potential energy of a missile moving at 12,000 mi/hr above the earth where the acceleration due to gravity is 30 ft/sec^2.

1.19. On September 19, 1957, the first completely contained nuclear explosion was fired at the Nevada test site. The explosion had an energy release equivalent to 1700 tons of high explosive, which was calculated as a total energy release of 1.7×10^{12} calories. The code name "Rainier" was assigned to this burst, and the amount of U^{235} fissioned was only 80 g. From this description, calculate the Btu released per pound of U^{235} used.

1.20. Densities may sometimes be expressed as linear functions of temperature, such as

$$\rho = \rho_0 + At$$

where ρ = lb/ft^3 at temperature t
        ρ_0 = lb/ft^3 at temperature t_0
        t = temperature in °F
If the equation is dimensionally consistent, what must the units of A be?

1.21. The equation for pressure drop due to friction for fluids flowing in a pipe is

$$\Delta p = \frac{2fL\rho v^2}{D}$$

where Δp = pressure drop
       v = velocity
       L = length of the pipe
       ρ = density of the fluid
       D = diameter of the pipe
Is the equation dimensionally consistent? What are the units of the "friction factor" f? Use units of the ft-lb-sec system for Δp, L, ρ, v, and D; is the equation then consistent?

1.22. The equation for the velocity of a fluid stream measured with a Pitot tube is

$$v = \sqrt{\frac{2\Delta p}{\rho}}$$

where v = velocity

  Δp = pressure drop

  ρ = density of fluid stream = 1.20 g/cm³

The equation is dimensionally consistent. If the pressure drop is 15 mm Hg and the density of Hg is 13.6 g/cm³, calculate the velocity in cm/sec.

1.23. The density of a certain liquid is given by an equation of the following form:

$$\rho = (A + Bt)e^{CP}$$

where ρ = density in gm/cm³

  t = temp. in °C

  P = pressure in atm

(a) The equation is dimensionally consistent. What are the units of A, B, and C?

(b) In the units above,

$$A = 1.096$$
$$B = 0.00086$$
$$C = 0.000953$$

Find A, B, and C if ρ is expressed in lb/ft³, t in °R, and P in $lb_f/in.^2$

1.24. The equation for the flow of water through a nozzle is as follows:

$$q = C\sqrt{\frac{2g}{1 - (d_2/d_1)^4}}\left(A\sqrt{\frac{\Delta p}{\rho}}\right)$$

where q = volume flowing per unit time

  g = local gravitational acceleration

  d_1 = smaller nozzle diameter

  d_2 = larger nozzle diameter

  A = area of nozzle outlet

  Δp = pressure drop across nozzle

  ρ = density of fluid flowing

  C = dimensionless constant

State whether this equation is dimensionally consistent. Show how you arrived at your conclusion.

1.25. Countercurrent gas centrifuges have been used to separate U^{235} from U^{238}. The rate of diffusive transport is $K = 2\pi D\rho\bar{r}$.

If K = rate of transport of light component to the center of the centrifuge, g moles/(sec) (cm of height)

  D = diffusion coefficient

  ρ = molar density, g moles/cm³

  $\bar{r}$ = log mean radius, $(r_2 - r_1)/\ln(r_2/r_1)$, with r in cm

what are the units of D?

1.26. A useful dimensionless number called the *Reynolds number* is

$$\frac{DU\rho}{\mu}$$

where D is the diameter or length

  U is some characteristic velocity

ρ is the fluid density

μ is the fluid viscosity

Calculate the Reynolds number for the following cases:

	1	2	3	4
D	2 in.	20 ft	ft	2 mm
U	10 ft/sec	10 mph	1 m/sec	3 cm/sec
ρ	62.4 lb/ft³	1 lb/ft³	12.5 kg/m³	25 lb/ft³
μ	0.3 lb$_m$/(hr)(ft)	0.14 × 10⁻⁴ lb$_m$/(sec)(ft)	2 × 10⁻⁶ centipoise	1 × 10⁻⁶ centipoise

1.27. The Colburn equation for heat transfer is

$$\left(\frac{h}{CG}\right)\left(\frac{C\mu}{k}\right)^{2/3} = \frac{0.023}{(DG/\mu)^{0.2}}$$

where C = heat capacity, Btu/(lb of fluid)(°F)

μ = viscosity, lb/(hr)(ft)

k = thermal conductivity, Btu/(hr)(ft²)(°F)/ft

D = pipe diameter, ft

G = mass velocity, lb/(hr)(ft²) cross section

What are the units of the heat transfer coefficient h?

1.28. Suppose you measure the density of a uranium oxide slurry and find that the variation in density is best expressed by the following equation:

$$\rho = C_0[1 + C_1 t] + C_2 e^{C_3 x}$$

In the formula, ρ = density, lb$_m$/ft³

t = temperature, °F

x = weight fraction uranium oxide

and C_0, C_1, C_2, and C_3 are empirically determined constants. If the equation is to be dimensionally sound, what do the units of C_0, C_1, C_2, and C_3 have to be?

1.29. (a) How many g moles are represented by 100 g of CO_2?

(b) Calculate the weight in pounds of 3.5 g moles of nitrogen.

1.30. Write the formula and calculate the pound molecular weight of: (a) carbon, i.e., C = 12.01 lb/lb mole; (b) sodium chloride; (c) carbon dioxide; (d) calcium carbonate; (e) ferric sulfate, anhydrous; (f) sodium alum; (g) sulfur.

1.31. Write the formula and calculate the kilogram molecular weight of: (a) carbon, i.e., C = 12.01 kg/kg mole; (b) carbon monoxide; (c) ammonium chloride; (d) sodium nitrate; (e) aluminum sulfate, anhydrous; (f) potassium ferrocyanide; (g) potassium alum.

1.32. Write the name and calculate the weight of the following amounts of material in the units indicated: (a) 1.50 g moles P (in g), (b) 0.37 lb mole SO_2 (in lb), (c) 5.68 kg moles $FeSO_4 \cdot 7 H_2O$ (in kg), (d) 2.17 lb moles $Fe_4(Fe(CN)_6)_3$ (in lb).

1.33. (a) How many lb moles are there in 100 lb of each of the following compounds? Meta-arsenic acid; arsenous selenide; calcium carbonate; ferric formate; ferric potassium oxalate trihydrate; ferrous perchlorate; magnesium bromide (commercial); manganese chloride (commercial); nickel ammonia nitrate dihydrate; hydantoin (glycolyl urea).

(b) How many g moles are there in 100 g of the compounds listed in (a)?

1.34. Comment on the statement "a mole is an amount of substance containing the same number of atoms as 12 g of pure carbon-12."

1.35. How many pounds of compound are contained in each of the following?
(a) 130 g moles sodium hydroxide (anhydrous)
(b) 300 g moles sodium oleate
(c) 165 lb moles sodium perchromate
(d) 62 lb moles pure nitric acid
(e) 36 g moles cupric tartrate
(f) 36 lb moles cuprous phosphide (Cu_6P_2)
(g) 72 lb moles nickel bromide
(h) 12 g moles nitrogen sulfide (N_4S_4)
(i) 120 lb moles potassium nitrate
(j) 11 g moles stannic fluoride

1.36. Convert the following:
(a) 120 g moles of NaCl to g
(b) 120 g NaCl to g moles
(c) 120 lb moles of NaCl to lb
(d) 120 lb of NaCl to lb moles
(e) 120 lb moles of NaCl to g
(f) 120 g moles of NaCl to lb
(g) 120 lb of NaCl to g moles
(h) 120 g of NaCl to lb moles
(i) 120 g moles of NaCl to lb moles
(j) 120 g of NaCl to lb

1.37. The lifting power of a balloon is proportional to the weight lost by replacing air with some other gas. Calculate the lifting power of helium as a percentage of the lifting power of hydrogen.

1.38. A liquid has a specific gravity of 2.0. Calculate its density in lb_m/ft^3.

1.39. What is the density of oil which has a specific gravity of 0.782? Express your answer in lb_m/ft^3 and g/cm^3.

1.40. For a mixture of 50 gal of benzene with 50 gal of n-octane, calculate (a) mol. wt of the mixture, (b) API of the mixture, (c) sp gr of the mixture.

Data:

benzene mol. wt $= 78$ °API $= 28.5$ sp gr $= 0.8844$

n-octane mol. wt $= 114$ °API $= 68.6$ sp gr $= 0.7072$

1.41. A solution of sulfuric acid at 60°F is found to have a sp gr of 1.22. From the tables in Perry's *Chemical Engineer's Handbook*, this is found to be 30% by weight H_2SO_4. What is the concentration of H_2SO_4 in: (a) lb mole/gal, (b) lb/ft^3, (c) g/l, (d) lb H_2SO_4/lb H_2O, (e) lb mole H_2O/lb mole total solution?

1.42. *Fortune*, Feb., 1965, p. 209—Union's hydrocracker produces no by-product fuel oil; it converts 100 barrels of feedstock to 120 barrels of gasoline. The weight of product is the same as that of the feed but since the gasoline weighs less than the crude the volume is greater.

Comment on the above statement. How accurate is it?

1.43. Two immiscible liquids are allowed to separate in a vessel. One liquid has a specific gravity of 0.936; the second liquid weighs 9.63 lb/gal. A block which is 9 by 9 by 9 in. and weighs 25.8 lb is dropped into the vessel. Will the block float at the top, stop at the interface where the two liquids are separated, or sink? What fraction of the volume of the block is in one or both of the liquids?

1.44. A hydrometer has a glass stem 12 in. long. The stem is made of glass tubing which weighs 0.042 lb/ft and is 0.400 in. in diameter on the outside. The bulb has a volume of 60 cm^3. The entire hydrometer, including the lead shot which is placed in the bulb, weighs 63.0 g. The stem of the hydrometer is graduated in inches from 0 at the top to 12 at the bottom.

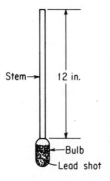

Find the calibration equation of the hydrometer, giving the density G in g/cm^3 as a function of the reading R from 0 to 12. (The hydrometer is read at the interface of the liquid sample on the stem.) Also give the upper and lower limits of densities in g/cm^3 for which this hydrometer may be used.

1.45. You have 100 lb of gas of the following composition:

CH_4	30%
H_2	10%
N_2	60%

What is the average molecular weight of this gas?

1.46. Calculate the average molecular weight of the following gas mixture (volume % is given in the column to the right):

CO_2	2.0
CO	10.0
O_2	8.0
N_2	75.0
H_2O	5.0
	100.0%

1.47. Charcoal pellets contain 10% moisture and 70% C. What is the per cent C on a dry (moisture-free) basis?

1.48. Analysis of a salt solution indicates 10% Na_2SO_4 and the remainder, water. What is the mole fraction and mole percent of each component in the solution?

1.49. What is the weight per cent water in the salt $Na_2SO_4 \cdot 10\ H_2O$; what is the per cent Na_2O?

1.50. The waste gas from a process analysis is 50% CO_2, 10% C_2H_4, and 40% H_2. What is its average molecular weight? What is the composition in weight per cent?

1.51. Calculate the mole percentage of each constituent in 675 g of a mixture having the following composition:

$CaCO_3$	22%
$MgCO_3$	18
CaO	23
NaCl	30
K_2SO_4	7

1.52. A gas mixture has the following composition by volume:

CH_4	60%
C_2H_6	15
C_3H_8	15
H_2	5
N_2	5

(a) What is the mole per cent of each constituent?
(b) What is the weight per cent of each constituent?

1.53. Calculate the percentage composition by weight of a stainless steel alloy melted in an electric furnace if the charge consisted of 2000 lb of iron, 506 lb of Cr, 225 lb of Ni, and 85 lb of Mo. Look up the specific gravities of these elements in your handbook, and calculate the percentage composition by volume (assuming the volumes are additive). What is the specific gravity of the alloy? What is its density in lb/ft³?

1.54. Ten pounds each of liquid propane, isobutane, n-butane, and n-hexane are mixed. What is the percentage composition by volume? What is the density of the mixture in lb/ft³? Repeat, taking 10 g of each hydrocarbon.

1.55. Repeat Prob. 1.54, taking 10 gal of each hydrocarbon and calculate the composition by weight. What is the density of the mixture in lb/ft³? What is its API gravity?

1.56. Five thousand barrels of 28° API gas oil are blended with 20,000 bbl of 15° API fuel oil. What is the °API (API gravity) of the mixture? What is the density in lb/gal and lb/ft³?

1.57. One barrel each of gasoline (55°API), kerosene (40°API), gas oil (31°API), and isopentane are mixed. What is the composition of the mixture expressed in weight per cent and volume per cent? What is the API gravity and the density of the mixture in g/cm³ and lb/gal?

1.58. If 100 cm³ of ethyl alcohol is added to 100 cm³ of water at 20°C, the total volume of the mixture is only 193 cm³. In other words, volumes are not additive for this system as they are for hydrocarbon mixtures.

(a) If the proof of alcohol-water mixtures is defined as twice the volume per cent alcohol, and volume per cent is defined as the volumes of pure alcohol obtainable from 100 volumes of mixture, determine accurately the weight and mole per cent alcohol in a 100-proof mixture. The sp gr of the mixture is 0.9303, of pure alcohol 0.7893, and of pure water 0.9982, all at 20°C.

(b) Why is it unscientific to express compositions as "volume per cent" in this system? Why is it done commercially?

1.59. Show that:

(a) $\quad T(°F) = 2\{T(°C) + \frac{1}{10}[160°C - T(°C)]\}$

(b) $\quad T(°F) = \{[T(°C) \times 2] - \frac{1}{10}[T(°C) \times 2]\} + 32$

1.60. When the first people from Earth landed on the planet Mercury, they found the people there used a temperature scale based on the freezing and boiling points of mercury: 0°M was defined as the freezing point of mercury and 1000°M as the boiling point of mercury. In our system the freezing point of Hg is −38.9°C and the normal boiling point is 356.9°C. Set up an equation which will show the relation between °F and °M. Do the same for °R and °M.

1.61. Calculate all temperatures from the one value given:

	(a)	(b)	(c)	(d)	(e)	(f)	(g)	(h)
°F	140				1000			
°R			500			1000		
°K		298					1000	
°C				−40				1000

1.62. The emissive power of a black body depends on the fourth power of the temperature and is given by

$$W = AT^4$$

where W = emissive power in Btu/(ft²)(hr)

$\quad A$ = Stefan-Boltzmann constant, 0.171×10^{-8} Btu/(ft²)(hr)(°R)⁴

$\quad T$ = temperature in °R

What is the value of A in the units erg/(cm²)(sec)(°K)⁴?

1.63. The temperature scale we use at present is linear, forming an ordered sequence of numbers starting at $0°K$,

$$+0°K \ldots 273.16°K \ldots + \infty°K$$

Kelvin proposed the relation

$$T = e^{\psi}$$

where ψ depends on the thermal properties of the system and T is the absolute temperature ($°K$). It is possible to construct another temperature scale, the ψ scale, or the logarithmic scale. The logarithmic nature of the ψ scale assures that the zero value on the linear absolute scale (T scale) will be reached asymptotically, i.e., $T = 0°K$, when $\psi = -\infty$. Comparing both these scales, the inaccessibility of the absolute zero follows generically, being not imaginable from the linear T scale alone.

Plot the ψ vs. T scales, and calculate the value of ψ for $T = 1°K$, and $273°K$.

1.64. According to a letter to the editor of *Chemical and Engineering News*, May 17, 1965, the flashing rate of a firefly and the chirping rate of a cricket are both linearly related to temperature:

$$T(°F) = 0.25x_1 + 39.0 \qquad x_1 = \text{chirps/min}$$
$$T(°F) = 2.32x_2 + 48.1 \qquad x_2 = \text{flashes/min}$$

Estimate the temperature in $°R$ for 132 chirps/min; 11 flashes/min; the average of the two predictions.

1.65. The pressure gauge on a compressed air tank indicates 125.0 psig. The barometer reading is 745.0 mm Hg. Calculate the absolute pressure in the tank in atmospheres.

1.66. A manometer uses kerosene, specific gravity 0.82, as the fluid. A reading of 5 in. on the manometer is equivalent to how many mm Hg?

1.67. The barometer reading is 28.40 in. Hg. What is the maximum height over which water can be siphoned, i.e., how high can the siphon be raised above the source of water? $T = 60°F$.

1.68. The pressure gauge on the steam condenser for a turbine indicates 26.2 in. Hg of vacuum. The barometer reading is 30.4 in. Hg. What is the pressure in the condenser in psia?

1.69. A building has a water tank on top of it; the water is 275 ft above the faucets in the basement. A pressure gauge at the faucet will show what reading in psig? If the faucet is opened, will the reading be greater, equal, or less than the reading when closed? Why?

1.70. A pressure gauge on a tank shows a pressure of 28.0 psig. The barometric pressure is 28.3 in. Hg. Calculate the absolute pressure in the tank in the following units: (a) psi, (b) lb per sq ft, (c) atm, (d) in. Hg, (e) ft water, (f) g/cm².

1.71. At the bottom of a river 50 ft below the surface of the water (at $50°F$), what is the pressure in psi? The density of water can be assumed to be 62.4 lb_m/ft^3.

1.72. A two-stage air compressor takes suction at 0 lb/in.^{2} gauge and has a final discharge pressure of 100 lb/in.^{2} gauge. The interstage pressure on most compressors is the geometric mean of absolute suction and discharge pressures. Calculate the interstage gauge pressure in psig if the barometer reads (a) 770 mm Hg, (b) 28.0 in. Hg, (c) 0.79 atm.

1.73. (a) If the piston-manometer system is full of water, what has to be the pressure at A in psia to give a reading of   36 in. of water at B? The barometer reads 760 mm Hg.

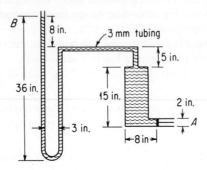

(b) If the Bourdon gauge reads 30 psi, what is the pressure of the gas? What is Δh? The barometer reads 745 mm Hg.

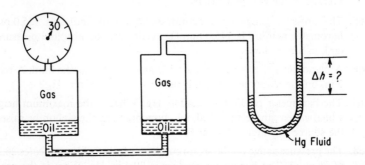

1.74. An open-end mercury manometer attached to a tank reads 27.38 in. Hg at 70°F. The barometer reads 14.77 psia. The density of Hg is 13.59 g/cm^3. The man who read the manometer said the pressure was 1.3 psia in the tank. His assistant said he was crazy and that the pressure was 28.2 psia. Since there seemed to be a question, you have been asked to arbitrate this point. Can 1.3 psia be right?

1.75. A sight-glass level gauge is connected to a tank as shown on the figure. The volume of liquid in the tank as determined by a meter scale placed by the level gauge was, for one observation, 2% different than the volume as determined by the calibration stick in the tank. What reasons can be offered for this difference, and how might you offset the error?

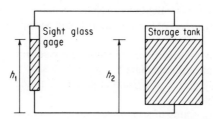

1.76. Logarithmic scales are not new; they are found for hydrogen ion concentration (pH), decibels (signal power), etc. They encompass wide ranges of a variable on a reasonably compact scale. The deciboyle (dB_o) has been proposed as a pressure unit to encompass the 30 decades over which pressure measurements take place,

$$dB_o = 10 \log_{10} p + 0.0572$$

where p is in atm. Plot dB_o vs. p, and compute the values of dB_o for a high vacuum, 10^{-14} atm, and for 60 kilobars (the pressure used in making diamonds).

1.77. (a) An orifice is used to measure the flow rate of a gas through a pipe as shown in the figure. The pressure drop across the orifice is measured with a mercury manometer, both legs of which are constructed of $\frac{1}{4}$-in. inner diameter (ID) glass tubing. If the pressure drop across the orifice is equivalent to 4.65 in. of Hg, calculate h_2 and h_3 (both in inches) if h_1 is equal to 13.50 in.

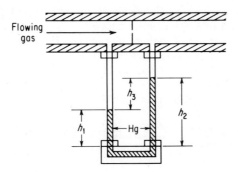

(b) The right glass leg of the manometer above becomes dirty and is replaced with glass tubing which is $\frac{3}{8}$-in. ID. The manometer is filled with the same volume of mercury as in part (a). For the same pressure drop as in part (a), calculate h_2 and h_3 (both in inches).

1.78. John Long says he calculated from a formula that the pressure at the top of Pikes Peak is 9.75 psia. John Green says that it is 504 mm of Hg because he looked it up in a table. Which John is right?

1.79. $BaCl_2 + Na_2SO_4 \longrightarrow BaSO_4 + 2\,NaCl$

    (a) How many grams of barium chloride will be required to react with 5.00 g of sodium sulfate?

    (b) How many grams of barium chloride are required for the precipitation of 5.00 g of barium sulfate?

    (c) How many grams of barium chloride are needed to produce 5.00 g of sodium chloride?

    (d) How many grams of sodium sulfate are necessary for the precipitation of the barium of 5.00 g of barium chloride?

    (e) How many grams of sodium sulfate have been added to barium chloride if 5.00 g of barium sulfate are precipitated?

    (f) How many pounds of sodium sulfate are equivalent to 5.00 lb of sodium chloride?

    (g) How many pounds of barium sulfate are precipitated by 5.00 lb of barium chloride?

    (h) How many pounds of barium sulfate are precipitated by 5.00 lb of sodium sulfate?

    (i) How many pounds of barium sulfate are equivalent to 5.00 lb of sodium chloride?

1.80. $AgNO_3 + NaCl \longrightarrow AgCl + NaNO_3$

    (a) How many grams of silver nitrate will be required to react with 5.00 g of sodium chloride?

    (b) How many grams of silver nitrate are required for the precipitation of 5.00 g of silver chloride?

    (c) How many grams of silver nitrate are equivalent to 5.00 g of sodium nitrate?

    (d) How many grams of sodium chloride are necessary for the precipitation of the silver of 5.00 g of silver nitrate?

    (e) How many grams of sodium chloride have been added to silver nitrate if 5.00 g of silver chloride are precipitated?

    (f) How many pounds of sodium chloride are equivalent to 5.00 lb of sodium nitrate?

    (g) How many pounds of silver chloride are precipitated by 5.00 lb of silver nitrate?

    (h) How many pounds of silver chloride are precipitated by 5.00 lb of sodium chloride?

    (i) How many pounds of silver chloride are equivalent to 5.00 lb of silver nitrate?

1.81. How many grams of chromic sulfide will be formed from 0.718 g of chromic oxide according to the equation

$$2\,Cr_2O_3 + 3\,CS_2 \longrightarrow 2\,Cr_2S_3 + 3\,CO_2$$

1.82. How many grams of tin must be treated with nitric acid to obtain 10 kg of stannic oxide ($Sn \longrightarrow SnO_2$)?

1.83. What weight of Cu_2O would be required to furnish 40 lb of Cu?

1.84. Phosphate rock contains 80 per cent of the compound $3 Ca_3(PO_4)_2 \cdot CaF_2$.
    (a) How much phosphorus is contained in 100 lb of phosphate rock?
    (b) How much phosphoric anhydride, P_2O_5, is contained in 100 lb of phosphate rock?

1.85. Oxygen is prepared according to the equation

$$2 KClO_3 \longrightarrow 2 KCl + 3 O_2$$

    (a) What is the yield of oxygen when 7.07 g of potassium chlorate are decomposed?
    (b) How many grams of potassium chlorate must be decomposed to liberate 2.0 g of oxygen?

1.86. In the compound $CaCO_3 \cdot 3 Ca_3(PO_4)_2$:
    (a) How much phosphorus is contained in 4.00 g?
    (b) How much phosphoric anhydride in the same amount?

1.87. When sodium nitrate is treated with sulfuric acid, the two most important reactions which occur are

(1) $2 NaNO_3 + H_2SO_4 \longrightarrow Na_2SO_4 + 2 HNO_3$
(2) $NaNO_3 + H_2SO_4 \longrightarrow NaHSO_4 + HNO_3$

For a given weight of sulfuric acid, which reaction yields the most nitric acid? Which reaction would be used commercially? Explain, with reference to your source of information.

1.88. What is the difference in cost per pound, as a source of HCN, between KCN (98%) at 50 cents per pound and a mixture of KCN (65%) and NaCN (25%) at 60 cents per pound (for the mixture)?

1.89. To neutralize 5 gal of waste iron pickle liquor, 1.25 lb of sodium hydroxide is used. How many pounds of slacked lime, 94% $Ca(OH)_2$, are required for 1000 gal of the same liquor?

1.90. Sulfur dioxide may be produced by the reaction

$$Cu + 2 H_2SO_4 \longrightarrow CuSO_4 + 2 H_2O + SO_2$$

(a) How much copper and (b) how much 94% H_2SO_4 must be used to obtain 32 lb of sulfur dioxide?

1.91. The reactions for the preparation of oxygen from potassium chlorate and mercuric oxide are

$$2 KClO_3 \longrightarrow 2 KCl + 3 O_2 \quad \text{and} \quad 2 HgO \longrightarrow 2 Hg + O_2$$

If (a) mercuric oxide costs $5.40 and (b) potassium chlorate costs $0.80 per kilogram, what is the cost of producing 10.00 g of oxygen from these compounds?

1.92. A limestone is analyzed as $CaCO_3$, 93.12%; $MgCO_3$, 5.38%; and insoluble matter, 1.50%.
    (a) How many pounds of calcium oxide could be obtained from 5 tons of the limestone?

(b) How many pounds of carbon dioxide are given off per pound of this limestone?

1.93. In the unbalanced equation,

$$Na_2CO_3 + Ca(OH)_2 \longrightarrow NaOH + CaCO_3$$

(a) If 22 tons of Na_2CO_3 are causticized:
  1) How many pounds of NaOH are produced?
  2) How many pounds of CaO will be required for complete reaction?
  3) How many kilograms of $CaCO_3$ are precipitated?
(b) If 22 tons of 16% aqueous Na_2CO_3 are causticized:
  1) What is the weight, in pounds, of the NaOH yielded?
  2) What would be the concentration of NaOH, in weight per cent, if the products were filtered and the $CaCO_3$ removed in a dry state (all water remaining in NaOH solution)?

1.94. Sulfuric acid is made according to the equation

$$2\,S + 3\,O_2 + 2\,H_2O \longrightarrow 2\,H_2SO_4$$

(a) If commercial sulfur is 97% pure, how much sulfuric acid is produced from 1 ton of sulfur?
(b) If pyrites containing 96% FeS_2 is used, how many tons are required to yield a ton of sulfuric acid?

1.95. If potassium alum is assumed to be $KAl(SO_4)_2 \cdot 12\,H_2O$, calculate the percentage composition in terms of the oxides Al_2O_3, K_2O, SO_3, and H_2O.

1.96. Oxygen can be produced by heating potassium chlorate, which costs 12 cents per pound, or potassium nitrate, which costs 8 cents per pound. Which one produces oxygen at the lower cost?

$$2\,KClO_3 \longrightarrow 2\,KCl + 3\,O_2$$

$$2\,KNO_3 \longrightarrow 2\,KNO_2 + O_2$$

1.97. A compound whose molecular weight is 119 analyzes as follows:

C	70.6%
H	4.2
N	11.8
O	13.4

What is the formula?

1.98. A compound whose molecular weight is 103 analyzes as follows:

C	81.5%
H	4.9
N	13.6

What is the formula?

1.99. Seawater contains 65 parts per million of bromine in the form of bromides. In the Ethyl-Dow recovery process, 0.27 lb 98% sulfuric acid is added per ton of water, together with the theoretical Cl_2 for oxidation; finally, ethylene

(C_2H_4) is united with the bromine to form $C_2H_4Br_2$. Assuming complete recovery and using a basis of 1 lb bromine, find the weights of acid, chlorine, seawater, and dibromide involved.

$$2\,Br^- + Cl_2 \longrightarrow 2\,Cl^- + Br_2$$
$$Br_2 + C_2H_4 \longrightarrow C_2H_4Br_2$$

1.100. An ammonia synthesis gas of composition

N_2	25.1% (volume)
H_2	74.6
Ar	0.3
	100.0%

passes through a catalytic converter. The only reaction is

$$N_2 + 3\,H_2 = 2\,NH_3$$

The resulting gas mixture contains 9.20% NH_3. Six tons per day of NH_3 are produced in this converter. Compute the:
(a) Tons per day of synthesis gas entering the converter
(b) Complete composition of the product gas leaving the converter in volume per cent

$$N_2 \quad H_2 \longrightarrow \boxed{CONVERTER} \longrightarrow \begin{matrix} N_2 \\ H_2 \\ Ar \\ NH_3 \end{matrix}$$

1.101. Ethane, C_2H_6, reacts with pure oxygen to form water and CO_2. If 3 lb moles of oxygen are mixed, and 80% of the ethane reacts:
(a) How many pound moles of C_2H_6 are present in the final mixture?
(b) How many pound moles of O_2 are present in the final mixture?
(c) How many pound moles of H_2O are present in the final mixture?
(d) How many pounds of total final mixture are there?
(e) Which reactant component, C_2H_6 or O_2, is in excess, and what is the per cent excess over the theoretical requirement for complete combustion?

1.102. In the old Weldon process, chlorine was made from by-product HCl by the reaction:

$$MnO_2 + 4\,HCl \longrightarrow MnCl_2 + Cl_2 + 2\,H_2O$$

Into a retort were charged 500 lb pyrolusite (86% MnO_2) and 3500 lb hydrochloric acid (sp gr 1.098, 20% HCl). The reaction was 92% complete. Calculate (a) pounds of Cl_2 produced, (b) per cent of excess reactant.

Data:

MnO_2	86.9
$MnCl_2$	125.8
HCl	36.5
Cl_2	71.0
H_2O	18.0

1.103. Antimony is obtained by heating pulverized stibnite with scrap iron and drawing off the molten antimony from the bottom of the furnace.

$$Sb_2S_3 + 3\,Fe \longrightarrow 2\,Sb + 3\,FeS$$

If 500 lb stibnite (90% pure) and 200 lb iron turnings are heated together, and 250 lb antimony metal is drawn off, calculate (a) the limiting reactant, (b) per cent excess reactant, (c) degree of completion.

Data:

Sb_2S_3	339.7
Sb	121.8
FeS	87.9
Fe	55.8

1.104. $H_2SO_4 + 2\,NaOH \longrightarrow Na_2SO_4 + 2\,H_2O$
  (a) If 5 lb of a 73.3% NaOH solution and 10 lb of 80% sulfuric acid are mixed together, how much sodium sulfate will be formed?
  (b) What is the limiting reactant?
  (c) What is the excess reactant? What is the per cent excess?
  (d) Why does this reaction go to completion?

1.105. A barytes composed of 100% $BaSO_4$ is fused with carbon in the form of coke containing 6% ash (which is infusible). The composition of the fusion mass is

$BaSO_4$	11.1%
BaS	72.8
C	13.9
Ash	2.2
	100.0%

Reaction:

$$BaSO_4 + 4C \longrightarrow BaS + 4\,CO$$

Find the excess reactant, the per cent of the excess reactant, and the degree of completion of the reaction.

1.106. Diborane, B_2H_6, a possible propellant for solid fuel rockets, can be made in a variety of different ways. One of the simplest, but not the cheapest, is to use lithium hydride as follows:

$$6\,LiH + 2\,BCl_3 \longrightarrow B_2H_6 + 6\,LiCl$$

Suppose 200 lb of LiH are mixed with 1000 lb of BCl_3 and 45.0 lb of B_2H_6 are recovered. Determine the following:
  (a) Per cent of conversion of LiH to B_2H_6 (based on the BCl_3 that actually reacts)
  (b) Yield of B_2H_6 based on the LiH charged
  (c) The pounds of LiCl formed

Note: Problems 1.79, 1.81, 1.85, 1.90, and 1.92 have been adapted from Hougen, Watson, and Ragatz, *Chemical Process Principles*, 2nd ed., Wiley, 1954.

Chapter 2

MATERIAL BALANCES

Lavoisier and many of the scientists who followed in his path studied chemical changes quantitatively. They found invariably that the sum of the weights of the substances entering into a reaction equaled the sum of the weights of the products of the reaction. This fundamental fact has been extended and summed up in the law of the conservation of matter. The only "proof" we have for this law is of a negative type—never in our previous experience has any process been observed which upon thorough examination has been found to contradict this principle. Of course, we must exclude processes involving nuclear transformations, or else extend our law to include the conservation of both energy and matter. (As far as we will be concerned here, the word *process* will be taken to mean a series of physical operations on or physical or chemical changes in some specified material.)

In this chapter we will discuss the principle of the conservation of matter, and how it can be applied to industrial calculations, making use of the background information discussed in Chap. 1. In approaching the solution of material balance problems, we will first consider how to analyze them in order to clarify the method and the procedure of solution. The aim will be to help you acquire a generalized approach to problem solving so that you may avoid looking upon each new problem, unit operation, or process as entirely new and unrelated to anything you have seen before. As you scrutinize the examples used to illustrate the principles involved in each section, explore the method of analysis, but avoid memorizing each example by rote, because, after all, they are only samples of the myriad of problems which exist or could be devised on the subject of material balances. Most of the principles we will consider are of about the same degree of complexity

59

as the law of compensation devised by some unknown, self-made philosopher who said, "Things are generally made even somewhere or some place. Rain always is followed by a dry spell, and dry weather follows rain. I have found it an invariable rule that when a man has one short leg, the other is always longer!"

In working these problems you will find it necessary to employ some engineering judgment. You think of mathematics as an exact science. For instance, suppose it takes one man ten days to build a brick wall; then ten men can finish it in one day. Therefore 240 men can finish the wall in 1 hour; 14,400 can do the job in a minute; and with 864,000 men the wall will be up before a single brick is in place! Your password to success is the famous IBM motto: THINK.

2.1 Material balance

The concept behind the generalized law of the conservation of matter is very simple. Equation (2.1) describes in words the principle of the very general material balance applicable to processes both with and without chemical reaction

$$
\left\{ \begin{array}{c} \text{accumulation} \\ \text{within} \\ \text{the} \\ \text{system} \end{array} \right\} = \left\{ \begin{array}{c} \text{input} \\ \text{through} \\ \text{system} \\ \text{boundaries} \end{array} \right\} - \left\{ \begin{array}{c} \text{output} \\ \text{through} \\ \text{system} \\ \text{boundaries} \end{array} \right\} + \left\{ \begin{array}{c} \text{generation} \\ \text{within} \\ \text{the} \\ \text{system} \end{array} \right\} - \left\{ \begin{array}{c} \text{consumption} \\ \text{within} \\ \text{the} \\ \text{system} \end{array} \right\}
$$

$$(2.1)$$

The accumulation may be positive or negative. Equation (2.1) reduces to Eq. (2.2) for cases in which there is no generation (or usage) of material within the system

$$\text{accumulation} = \text{input} - \text{output} \qquad (2.2)$$

and reduces further to Eq. (2.3) when there is in addition no accumulation within the system

$$\text{input} = \text{output} \qquad (2.3)$$

If there is no flow in and out of the system, and no generation (or usage), Eq. (2.1) reduces to the basic concept of the conservation of matter within an enclosed isolated system.

Inherent in the formulation of each of the above balances is the concept of a system for which the balance is made. By *system* we mean any arbitrary portion or whole of a process as set out specifically by the engineer for analysis. Figure 2.1 shows a system in which

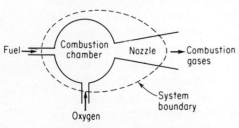

Fig. 2.1. A flow system with combustion

flow and reaction take place; note particularly the system boundary is formally circumscribed about the process itself to call attention to the importance of carefully delineating the system in each problem you work. In most of the problems in this text the mass accumulation term will be zero; that is, only *steady-state* problems will be considered. (See Chap. 6 for cases where the accumulation is not zero.) For a steady-state process we can say, "What goes in must come out." Illustrations of this principle can be found below. Although the problems we will take up deal with a balance on mass, at times we will use the word "weight" and refer to "weight balance" as well as "material balance," as is the common practice in ordinary engineering work.

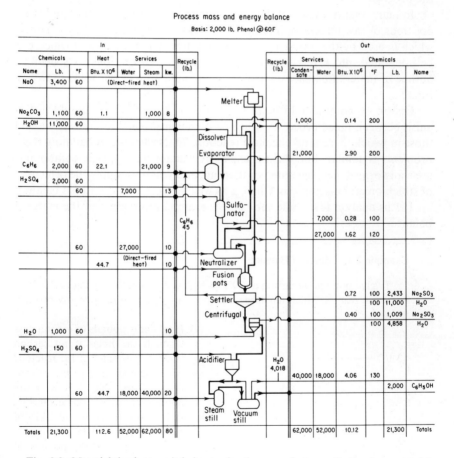

Fig. 2.2. Material (and energy) balances in the manufacture of phenol presented in the form of a ledger sheet. (Taken from *Chem. Eng.*, April 1961, p. 177. By permission.)

If every incoming and outgoing stream in a process can be measured and analyzed, then there is little need for a material balance except as a check on the experimental data. However, if there are one or more points in a process where it is impossible or uneconomical to collect data, then, if sufficient other data are available, by making a material balance on the process it is possible to get the information you need about the quantities and compositions at the inaccessible location. Another use of the material balance is to make calculations for prospective processes. For example, in the extraction of soybean oil from soybeans you could calculate the amount of solvent required per ton of soybeans, or the time needed to fill up the filter press, and use this information in the design of equipment or in the evaluation of the economics of the process.

In many plants a mass of data is accumulated on the quantities and compositions of raw materials, intermediates, wastes, products, and by-products which is used by the production and accounting departments and which can be integrated into a revealing picture of company operations. A schematic outline of material balance control in the manufacture of phenol is shown in Fig. 2.2.

One more point should be brought out at this time. You should distinguish between those processes in which a chemical reaction takes place and those in which there is no chemical reaction. The technique of handling these problems is similar, but when a chemical reaction takes place, compounds are transformed, i.e., generated or used up, and you must apply the principles of stoichiometry discussed in Chap. 1 as well as those of the material balance.

Let us analyze first some very simple examples in the use of the material balance.

Example 2.1   Material Balance

Twelve pounds of carbon at 70°F are placed in a recirculating cyclotronic revolving reactor which has large holes in the bottom to remove any product formed.

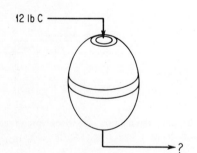

(a) How many pounds of carbon pass through the holes if no carbon sticks to the sides of the reactor?

(b) If the temperature in the reactor is raised to 1200°F, how many pounds of carbon come out?

(c) If 100 lb of oxygen and 24 lb of carbon are placed in the reactor at 600°F, how many pounds of carbon will come out; how many pounds of oxygen; how many pounds total?

Solution:

(a) Since 12 lb of carbon enter the reactor, 12 lb of carbon must leave the reactor if none remains inside.

(b) Changing the temperature will have no effect.

(c) Adding O_2 and C at a temperature sufficiently high for combustion to take place will have no effect on the total pounds of material leaving the reactor—124 lb will come out. Also 24 lb of carbon will leave, but in a combined form with oxygen. Assume combustion is complete according to the reaction $C + O_2 \longrightarrow CO_2$.

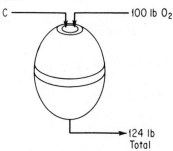

24 lb C ——————— 100 lb O_2

124 lb Total

Basis: 24 lb C

$$\frac{24 \text{ lb C}}{} \left| \frac{1 \text{ lb mole C}}{12 \text{ lb C}} \right| \frac{1 \text{ lb mole CO}_2}{1 \text{ lb mole C}} \left| \frac{44 \text{ lb CO}_2}{1 \text{ lb mole CO}_2} \right. = 88 \text{ lb CO}_2 \text{ leaving}$$

$$124 - 88 = 36 \text{ lb O}_2 \text{ leaving}$$

or

$$O_2 \text{ used} = \frac{24 \text{ lb C}}{} \left| \frac{1 \text{ lb mole C}}{12 \text{ lb C}} \right| \frac{1 \text{ lb mole O}_2}{1 \text{ lb mole C}} \left| \frac{32 \text{ lb O}_2}{1 \text{ lb mole O}_2} \right.$$

$$= 64 \text{ lb O}_2$$

$$100 - 64 = 36 \text{ lb O}_2 \text{ leaving}$$

Example 2.2   Material Balance

If in the previous problem (Example 2.1) 300 lb of air had been added to the carbon instead of oxygen, how many pounds of oxygen and how many total pounds of material would leave the reactor?

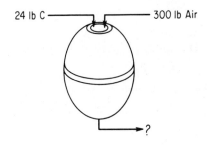

24 lb C ——————— 300 lb Air

?

Solution:

(a) The total material leaving the reactor would be 324 lb.

(b) Since air has 21% O_2 and 79% N_2:

Basis: 300 lb air

$$\frac{300 \text{ lb air}}{} \left| \frac{1 \text{ lb mole air}}{29 \text{ lb air}} \right| \frac{21 \text{ lb mole O}_2}{100 \text{ lb mole air}} = 2.18 \text{ lb mole O}_2$$

The oxygen required to completely burn 24 lb of C is 2 lb moles; consequently

$$2.18 - 2.00 = 0.18$$

is the number of moles of unused oxygen, and this is equivalent to $(0.18)(32) =$ 5.76 lb of O_2 as such leaving the reactor. In addition, 88 lb of CO_2 leave and

$$\frac{2.18 \text{ lb mole of } O_2}{} \left| \frac{79 \text{ lb mole } N_2}{21 \text{ lb mole } O_2} \right| \frac{28.2 \text{ lb } N_2}{1 \text{ lb mole } N_2} = 230 \text{ lb of } N_2$$

Summing up all exit streams we have

in	lb	out	lb
O_2	70	O_2	5.76
N_2	230	N_2	230
C	24	CO_2	88
	324 lb total		324 lb total

Note that in the examples above, although the total pounds put into a process and the total pounds recovered from a process have been shown to be equal, there is no such equality on the part of the *total* moles in and out, *if* a chemical reaction takes place. What is true is that the number of atoms of an element (such as C, O, or even oxygen expressed as O_2) put into a process must equal the atoms of the same element leaving the process. In Example 2.2 the total moles in and out are shown to be unequal:

total moles in		total moles out	
O_2	2.18	O_2	0.18
N_2	8.20	N_2	8.20
C	2.00	CO_2	2.00
	12.38		10.38

although the atoms of O in (expressed as moles of O_2) equal the atoms of O (similarly expressed as O_2) leaving:

	component moles in		component moles out	
O_2:	O_2	2.18	O_2	0.18
			O_2 in CO_2	2.00
	total $= O_2$	2.18	total $= O_2$	2.18
N_2:	N_2	8.20	N_2	8.20
C:	C	2.00	C in CO_2	2.00

Keeping in mind the above remarks for processes involving chemical reactions, we can summarize the applicability of Eqs. (2.1) and (2.3) to *steady-state processes* (no accumulation) as follows [Eq. (2.2) is the same as (2.3) for steady-state processes]:

	type of balance	steady-state process without chemical reaction	steady-state process with chemical reaction
	total mass	$(2.1) = (2.3)$	$(2.1) = (2.3)$
	total moles	$(2.1) = (2.3)$	(2.1) only
component balances	mass of a pure compound	$(2.1) = (2.3)$	(2.1) only
	moles of a pure compound	$(2.1) = (2.3)$	(2.1) only
	mass of an atomic species	$(2.1) = (2.3)$	$(2.1) = (2.3)$
	moles of an atomic species	$(2.1) = (2.3)$	$(2.1) = (2.3)$

Observe that the simpler equation (2.3) will prove to be quite useful if we restrict the balances to be made to a total mass balance and balances on the mass of each atomic species, since it applies even if a chemical reaction takes place.

We now turn to consideration of problems in which the accumulation term is zero. The basic task is to turn the problem, expressed in words, into a quantitative form, expressed in mathematical symbols and numbers.

2.2 Program of analysis of material balance problems

Much of the remaining portion of this chapter demonstrates the techniques of setting up and solving problems which call for material balances. Later portions of the text consider combined material and energy balances. Since these material balance problems all involve the same principle, although the details of the applications of the principle may be slightly different, we will first consider a generalized method of analyzing such problems which can be applied to the solution of any type of material balance problem.

We are going to discuss a method of analysis of material balance problems which will enable you to understand, first, how similar these problems are, and, secondly, how to solve them in the most expeditious manner. For some types of problems the method of approach is relatively simple; for others it is more complicated; but the important point is to regard problems in distillation, crystallization, evaporation, combustion, mixing, gas absorption, or drying not as being different from each other but as being related from the viewpoint of how to proceed to solve them.

An orderly method of analyzing problems and presenting their solutions represents training in logical thinking that is of considerably greater value than mere knowledge of how to solve a particular type of problem. Understanding how to approach these problems from a logical viewpoint will help you to develop those fundamentals of thinking that will assist you in your work as an engineer long after you have read this material.

If you want to make a material balance for a system, in general you have to have on hand information dealing with *two* fundamental concepts. One of these is the mass (weight) in all streams of the material entering and leaving the system and present in the system. The other information required is the composition of all the streams entering and leaving the system and the composition of the material in the system. Of course, if a chemical reaction takes place inside the system, the equation for the reaction is a third important piece of information.

Let us look at problems in general by means of the "black box" technique. All we do is draw a black box or line around the process and consider what is going into the process and what comes out of the process. This procedure defines the system, i.e., the process or body of matter set out to be analyzed. As previously mentioned, we will assume that the process is taking place at a steady rate, i.e., that there is no accumulation or depletion of material. Even if the process is of the batch type in which there is no flow in and out, let us pretend that the initial material is pushed into the black box and the final material is removed from the black box. By this hypothesis we can imagine a batch process converted into a fictitious flow process, and talk

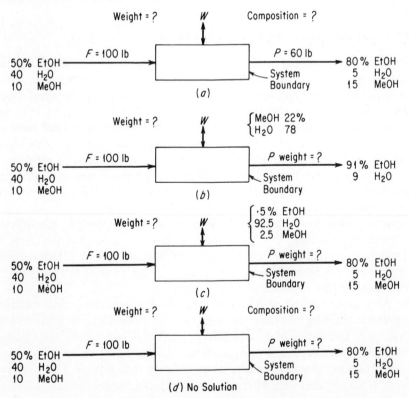

Fig. 2.3. Typical material balances (no chemical reaction involved).

about the "streams" entering and leaving even though in the real process nothing of the sort happens (except over a very long period of time). After you do this three or four times, you will see that it is a very convenient technique although at the beginning it may seem a bit illogical.

Let us start with a box with just three streams entering or leaving (all three cannot enter or leave, of course, in a steady-state process). In the examples in Figs. 2.3 and 2.4, F stands for the feed stream, P stands for

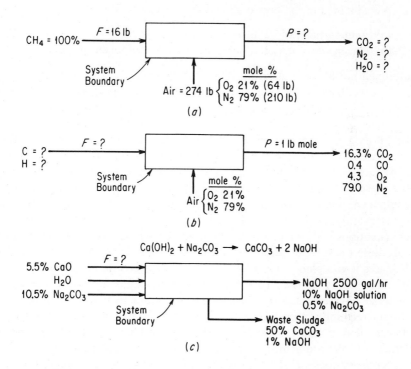

Fig. 2.4. Typical material balances (with chemical reaction).

product, and W stands for the third stream or "change," but any other symbols would do as well. The procedure of solution depends to some extent on which of the compositions and weights you know. All the problems in Figs. 2.3 and 2.4 have sufficient information shown to effect their solutions, except Fig. 2.3(*d*).

As a general rule, before making any calculations you should:

1. Draw a picture of the process.
2. Place all the available data on the picture.
3. See what compositions are known or can be immediately calculated for each stream.

4. See what weights are known or can easily be found for each stream. (One weight can be assumed as a basis.)
5. Select a suitable basis for the calculations. Every addition or subtraction *must* be made with the material on the *same* basis.
6. Make sure the system is well defined.

After this has been accomplished, you are ready to make the necessary number of material balances.

As explained in the previous section, you can write:

(a) A *total* material balance
(b) A *component* material balance for each component present

although not all the balances will be independent, as explained later.

For problems involving chemical reactions, the component to choose is an atomic specie or multiple thereof, i.e., hydrogen expressed as H_2. For problems without chemical reaction, any compound or atomic species may be selected for the component balance. If, for example, there are three components present, it is possible to write three component material balances. If we include the total material balance, it is possible to write four equations, but these equations are not independent inasmuch as the sum of the three component material balances will add up to the total material balance. Consequently, the number of degrees of freedom or the number of independent equations will be equal to the number of components. However, you can substitute the total material balance for any one of the component material balances if you plan to solve two or more equations simultaneously.

Since many of the problems you will encounter involving the use of material balances require you to solve for more than one unknown, you should remember that for each unknown, you need to have at least one independent material balance or other independent piece of information. Otherwise, the problem is indeterminate. For example, a problem in which the compositions of all the streams are known, and the weights of two streams are unknown, requires two independent material balances for its solution. What to do when more, or fewer, independent material balance equations are available than unknowns is discussed in Sec. 2.4.

Problems in which one weight and one composition are unknown can be solved without difficulty by direct addition or direct subtraction. Problems in which all the compositions are known and two or more of the weights are unknown require some more detailed calculations. If a tie element exists which makes it possible to establish the relationship between the unknown weights and the known weights, the problem solution may be simplified. (The tie element will be discussed in detail in Sec. 2.5.) When there is no direct or indirect tie element available, algebra must be used to relate the unknown weights to the known weight(s).

2.3 Problems with direct solutions

Problems in which one weight and one composition are unknown can be solved by direct addition or subtraction as shown in the examples below. There is no need to use algebraic techniques. You may find it necessary to make some brief preliminary calculations in order to decide whether or not all the information about the compositions and weights that you would like to have is available. Of course, in a stream containing just one component, the composition is known, because that component is 100 per cent of the stream.

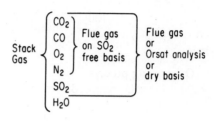

Fig. 2.5. Comparison of gas analyses on different bases.

In dealing with problems involving combustion you should become acquainted with a few special terms. These are:

(a) *Stack gas*—all the gases resulting from a combustion process including the water vapor, sometimes known as "wet basis."
(b) *Flue gas*—all the gases resulting from the combustion process not including the water vapor. Another way to state that water vapor is not included in the gas analysis is to give the analysis on a *dry basis* or give the *Orsat analysis*.

Pictorially, we can express this classification for a given gas as in Fig. 2.5. To convert from one analysis to another you have to ratio the percentages for the components as shown in Example 2.8.

(c) *Theoretical air* (or *theoretical oxygen*)—the amount of air (or oxygen) required to be brought into the process for *complete* combustion. Sometimes this quantity is called the *required* air (or oxygen).
(d) *Excess air* (or *excess oxygen*)—In line with the definition of excess reactant given in Chap. 1, excess air (or oxygen) would be the amount of air (or oxygen) **in excess of that required for complete combustion** as computed in (c).

Even if only partial combustion takes place, as, for example, C burning to both CO and CO_2, the excess air (or oxygen) is computed as if the process of combustion produced only CO_2. The per cent excess air is identical to the per cent excess O_2 (a more convenient method of calculation):

$$\% \text{ excess air} = 100 \frac{\text{excess air}}{\text{required air}} = 100 \frac{\text{excess } O_2/0.21}{\text{required } O_2/0.21} \qquad (2.4)$$

because the ratio 1/0.21 of air to O_2 cancels out in Eq. (2.4). Per cent excess air may also be computed as

$$\% \text{ excess air} = 100 \frac{O_2 \text{ entering process} - O_2 \text{ required}}{O_2 \text{ required}} \tag{2.5}$$

or

$$= 100 \frac{\text{excess } O_2}{O_2 \text{ entering} - \text{excess } O_2}$$

since

$$O_2 \text{ entering process}$$
$$= O_2 \text{ required for complete combustion} + \text{excess } O_2 \tag{2.6}$$

Example 2.3   Excess Air

A man comes to the door selling a service designed to check "chimney rot." He explains that if the CO_2 content of the gases leaving the chimney rises above 15%, it is dangerous to your health, is against the city code, and causes your chimney to rot. On checking the flue gas from the furnace he finds it is 30% CO_2. Suppose you are burning natural gas which is about 100% CH_4, and the air supply is adjusted to provide 130% excess air. Do you need his service?

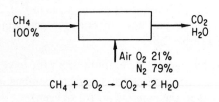

Solution:

Let us calculate the actual percentage of CO_2 in the gases from the furnace. The 130% excess air means 130% of the air required for complete combustion of CH_4. The chemical reaction is

$$CH_4 + 2 O_2 \longrightarrow CO_2 + 2 H_2O$$

Basis: 1 mole CH_4

On the basis of 1 mole of CH_4, 2 moles of O_2 are required for complete combustion, or

$$\frac{2 O_2 \mid 1.00 \text{ air}}{\mid 0.21 O_2} = 9.54 \text{ moles air required}$$

composed of 2 moles O_2 and 7.54 moles N_2. The excess air is 9.54(1.30) = 12.4 moles air, composed of 2.6 moles O_2 and 9.8 moles N_2.

Summing up our calculations so far we have entering the furnace:

	air	O_2	N_2
required	9.54	2.0	7.54
excess	12.4	2.6	9.8
total	21.94	4.6	17.34

Since 2 moles of the 4.6 moles of entering O_2 combine with the C and H of the CH_4 to form CO_2 and H_2O respectively, the composition of the gases from the furnace should contain the following:

	moles	%
CH_4	0	0
CO_2	1	4.4
H_2O	2	8.7
O_2	2.6	11.3
N_2	$\begin{cases}7.54\\9.8\end{cases}$	75.6
	22.94	100.0

The salesman's line seems to be rot all the way through.

Example 2.4   Excess Air

Suppose 20 lb of C_2H_4 are burned with 400 lb of air to 44 lb of CO_2 and 12 lb of CO. What is the per cent excess air?

Solution:

$$C_2H_4 + 3 O_2 \longrightarrow 2 CO_2 + 2 H_2O$$

$$\text{Basis: 20 lb } C_2H_4$$

Since the percentage of excess air is based on the complete combustion of C_2H_4 to CO_2 and H_2O, the fact that combustion is not complete has no influence on the definition of "excess air." The required O_2 is:

$$\frac{20 \text{ lb } C_2H_4}{} \left| \frac{1 \text{ lb mole } C_2H_4}{28 \text{ lb } C_2H_4} \right| \frac{3 \text{ lb mole } O_2}{1 \text{ lb mole } C_2H_4} = 2.14 \text{ lb mole } O_2$$

The entering O_2 is:

$$\frac{400 \text{ lb air}}{} \left| \frac{1 \text{ lb mole air}}{29 \text{ lb air}} \right| \frac{21 \text{ lb mole } O_2}{100 \text{ lb mole air}} = 2.90 \text{ lb mole } O_2$$

The per cent excess air is:

$$100 \times \frac{\text{excess } O_2}{\text{required } O_2} = 100\frac{\text{entering } O_2 - \text{required } O_2}{\text{required } O_2}$$

$$\% \text{ excess air} = \frac{2.90 \text{ lb mole } O_2 - 2.14 \text{ lb mole } O_2}{2.14 \text{ lb mole } O_2} \left| \frac{100}{} \right. = 35.5\%$$

Example 2.5   Drying

A wet paper pulp is found to contain 71% water. After drying it is found that 60% of the original water has been removed. Calculate:

(a) The composition of the dried pulp
(b) The weight of water removed per pound of wet pulp

Solution:

Basis: 1 lb wet pulp

Initially we know only the composition and weight (the chosen basis) of the wet pulp. However, we can easily calculate the composition (100% H_2O) and weight of water removed:

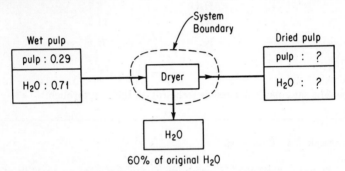

$$H_2O \text{ removed} = 0.60(0.71) = 0.426 \text{ lb}$$

Thus in essence we know two weights and two compositions.

(1) The final amount of pulp in the dried pulp is 0.29 lb and the associated water is:

$$\text{in} \quad - \quad \text{loss} \quad = \quad \text{remainder}$$
$$0.71 - 0.426 = 0.284 \text{ lb } H_2O \qquad water\ balance$$

or alternatively, since 40% of the H_2O was left in pulp:

$$0.40(0.71) = 0.284 \text{ lb } H_2O$$

(2) The composition of the dried pulp is:

	lb	%
pulp (dry)	0.29	50.5
H_2O	0.284	49.5
total	0.574	100.0

Example 2.6   Crystallization

A tank holds 10,000 lb of a saturated solution of $NaHCO_3$ at 60°C. You want to crystallize 500 lb of $NaHCO_3$ from this solution. To what temperature must the solution be cooled?

Solution:

A diagram of the process is:

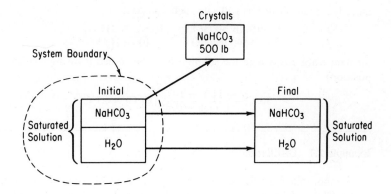

Additional data are needed on the solubility of $NaHCO_3$ as a function of temperature. From any handbook you can find:

	solubility
temp. (°C)	g $NaHCO_3$/100 g H_2O
60	16.4
50	14.45
40	12.7
30	11.1
20	9.6
10	8.15

Basis: 10,000 lb saturated $NaHCO_3$ solution at 60°C

We know both the weight of the initial solution and the weight of the crystals; we know the composition of both the initial solution and the crystals (100% $NaHCO_3$). Thus, the weight and composition of the final solution can be calculated by subtraction.

(a) Initial composition:

$$\frac{16.4 \text{ lb } NaHCO_3}{16.4 \text{ lb } NaHCO_3 + 100 \text{ lb } H_2O} = 0.141 \text{ or } 14.1\% \ NaHCO_3$$

$$100 - 14.1 = 85.9\% \ H_2O$$

(b) Material balance (component balance on the $NaHCO_3$):

initial $NaHCO_3$ − crystals $NaHCO_3$ = final $NaHCO_3$

0.141(10,000)   −   500   =   910 lb

(c) Final composition and weight:

$$H_2O = (0.859)10,000 = 8590\text{ lb}$$
$$NaHCO_3 = \qquad\qquad\quad \underline{\quad 910\text{ lb}}$$
$$\text{Total} \qquad\qquad\qquad\quad 9500\text{ lb}$$

Since the final solution is still saturated and has:

$$\frac{910\text{ lb NaHCO}_3}{8590\text{ lb H}_2O} = \frac{10.6\text{ g NaHCO}_3}{100\text{ g H}_2O}$$

the temperature to which the solution must be cooled is (using a linear interpolation)

$$30°C - \left[\frac{11.1 - 10.6}{11.1 - 9.6}\right][10°C] = 27°C$$

Example 2.7 Distillation

A moonshiner is having a bit of difficulty with his still. The operation is shown in the diagram. He finds he is losing too much alcohol in the bottoms (waste). Calculate the composition of the bottoms for him, and the weight of alcohol lost in the bottoms.

Solution:

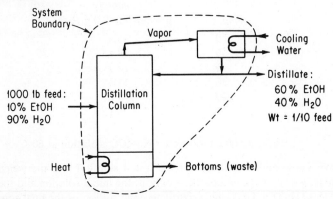

The information provided gives us the composition and weight of feed and distillate. The composition of the bottoms can be obtained by subtracting the distillate from the feed.

Basis: 1000 lb feed

	in			*out*	
				distillate	bottoms (*lb*)
component	*wt %*	*lb*		(*lb*)	(*by subtraction*)
EtOH	10	100		60	40*
H₂O	90	900		40	860
Total	100	1000		100	900

* Alcohol lost.

$$\frac{1000 \text{ lb feed}}{} \left| \frac{1 \text{ lb distillate}}{10 \text{ lb feed}} = 100 \text{ lb distillate} \right.$$

$$\frac{40 \text{ lb EtOH}}{900 \text{ lb bottoms}} \left| \frac{100}{} = 4.44\% \text{ EtOH} \right.$$

$$\frac{860 \text{ lb H}_2\text{O}}{900 \text{ lb bottoms}} \left| \frac{100}{} = 95.56\% \text{ H}_2\text{O} \right.$$

Example 2.8   Combustion

A gas containing 80% C_2H_6 and 20% O_2 is burned with 200% excess air. Eighty per cent of the ethane goes to CO_2, 10% goes to CO, and 10% remains unburned. Calculate the composition of the stack gas.

Solution:

We know the composition of the air and fuel gas; if a weight of fuel gas is chosen as the basis, the weight of air can easily be calculated. However, it is wasted effort to convert to a weight basis for this type of problem. Since the total moles entering and leaving the boiler are not equal, if we look at any one component and employ the stoichiometric principles previously discussed in Chap. 1 together with Eq. (2.1), we can easily obtain the composition of the stack gas. The net generation term in Eq. (2.1) can be evaluated from the stoichiometric equations listed below. The problem can be worked in the simplest fashion by choosing a basis of 100 moles of entering gas.

Basis: 100 lb moles of fuel

$$C_2H_6 + \tfrac{7}{2} O_2 \longrightarrow 2 CO_2 + 3 H_2O$$
$$C_2H_6 + \tfrac{5}{2} O_2 \longrightarrow 2 CO + 3 H_2O$$

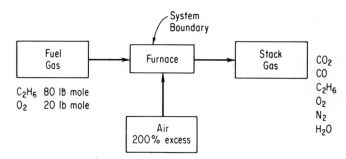

The total O_2 entering is 3.00 times the required O_2 (100% required plus 200% excess). Let us calculate the required oxygen:

O_2 (for complete combustion):

$$\frac{80 \text{ lb mole } C_2H_6}{} \left| \frac{3.5 \text{ mole } O_2}{1 \text{ lb mole } C_2H_6} = 280 \text{ lb mole } O_2 \right.$$

required O_2:

$$280 - 20 = 260 \text{ lb mole } O_2$$

(*Note:* The oxygen used to completely burn the fuel is reduced by the oxygen already present in the fuel to obtain the oxygen required in the entering air.)

Next we calculate the input of O_2 and N_2 to the system:

O_2 entering with air:

$$3(260 \text{ lb mole } O_2) = 780 \text{ lb mole } O_2$$

N_2 entering with air:

$$\frac{780 \text{ mole } O_2}{} \frac{79 \text{ lb mole } N_2}{21 \text{ lb mole } O_2} = 2930 \text{ lb mole } N_2$$

Now we apply our stoichiometric relations to find the components generated within the system:

$$\frac{80 \text{ lb mole } C_2H_6}{} \frac{2 \text{ lb mole } CO_2}{1 \text{ lb mole } C_2H_6} \frac{0.8}{} = 128 \text{ lb mole } CO_2$$

$$\frac{80 \text{ lb mole } C_2H_6}{} \frac{3 \text{ lb mole } H_2O}{1 \text{ lb mole } C_2H_6} \frac{0.8}{} = 192 \text{ lb mole } H_2O$$

$$\frac{80 \text{ lb mole } C_2H_6}{} \frac{2 \text{ lb mole } CO}{1 \text{ lb mole } C_2H_6} \frac{0.1}{} = 16 \text{ lb mole } CO$$

$$\frac{80 \text{ lb mole } C_2H_6}{} \frac{3 \text{ lb mole } H_2O}{1 \text{ lb mole } C_2H_6} \frac{0.1}{} = 24 \text{ lb mole } H_2O$$

To determine the O_2 remaining in the stack gas we have to find how much of the available (800 lb mole) O_2 combines with the C and H.

$$\frac{80 \text{ lb mole } C_2H_6}{} \frac{3.5 \text{ lb mole } O_2}{1 \text{ lb mole } C_2H_6} \frac{0.8}{} = 224 \text{ lb mole } O_2 \text{ to burn to } CO_2 \text{ and } H_2O$$

$$\frac{80 \text{ lb mole } C_2H_6}{} \frac{2.5 \text{ lb mole } O_2}{1 \text{ lb mole } C_2H_6} \frac{0.1}{} = 20 \text{ lb mole } O_2 \text{ to burn to } CO \text{ and } H_2O$$

244 lb mole O_2 total "used up" by reaction

By an oxygen (O_2) balance we get:

$$O_2 \text{ out} = 780 \text{ lb mole} + 20 \text{ lb mole} - 244 \text{ lb mole} = 556 \text{ lb mole } O_2$$

From a water balance we find:

$$H_2O \text{ out} = 192 \text{ lb mole} + 24 \text{ lb mole} = 216 \text{ lb mole } H_2O$$

The balances on the other compounds—C_2H_6, CO_2, CO, N_2—are too simple to be formally listed here.

Summarizing these calculations we have:

Example 2.8

Alternative Manner of Presentation

Initial component	Lb mole = %	Lb mole O_2 required	Actual lb mole O_2 used	Lb mole formed of				Reactions
				CO_2	H_2O	CO	C_2H_6 left	
C_2H_6	64 ⎫	$\frac{7}{2}(80) = 280$	$\frac{7}{2}(64) = 224$	128	192			$C_2H_6 + \frac{7}{2} O_2 \rightarrow 2\,CO_2 + 3\,H_2O$
C_2H_6	8 ⎬ 80		$\frac{5}{2}(8) = 20$		24	16		$C_2H_6 + \frac{5}{2} O_2 \rightarrow 2\,CO + 3\,H_2O$
C_2H_6	8 ⎭						8	$C_2H_6 \rightarrow C_2H_6$
O_2	20	-20						
	100	260	244	128	216	16	8	

O_2 entering with air: $3\,(260) = 780$

N_2 entering with air: $780\,\frac{79}{21} = 2930$

O_2 in exit gas:

air + fuel − used

$780 + 20 - 244 = 556$

Summary of Material Balances

Total moles in $\neq$ total moles out

Total lb in = total lb out   (each compound has to be multiplied by its molecular weight)

Balances on atomic species
- lb mole C in = lb mole C out: $2(80) = 128 + 16 + 2(8)$
- lb mole H_2 in = lb mole H_2 out: $3(80) = 216 + 3(8)$
- lb mole O_2 in = lb mole O_2 out: $20 + 780 = 128 + \frac{1}{2}(216) + \frac{1}{2}(16) + 556$
- lb mole N_2 in = lb mole N_2 out: $2930 = 2930$

Balances on compounds
- lb mole C_2H_6 in = lb mole C_2H_6 out + lb mole C_2H_6 consumed: $80 = 8 + 72 + 0$
- lb mole CO_2 in = lb mole CO_2 out − lb mole CO_2 generated: $0 = 128 - 128$
- lb mole CO in = lb mole CO out − lb mole CO generated: $0 = 16 - 16$
- lb mole H_2O in = lb mole H_2O out − lb mole H_2O generated: $0 = 216 - 216$
- lb mole N_2 in = lb mole N_2 out: $2930 = 2930 + 0$
- lb mole O_2 in = lb mole O_2 out + lb mole O_2 consumed: $800 = 556 + 244$

component	*fuel*	*air*	*stack gas*	*stack gas*
		lb moles		*% in*
C_2H_6	80	—	8	0.21
O_2	20	780	556	14.42
N_2	—	2930	2930	76.01
CO_2	—	—	128	3.32
CO	—	—	16	0.42
H_2O	—	—	216	5.62
	100	3710	3854	100.00

On a dry basis we would have (the water is omitted):

component	*lb moles*	*%*
C_2H_6	8	0.23
O_2	556	15.29
N_2	2930	80.52
CO_2	128	3.52
CO	16	0.44
	3638	100.00

Once you have become familiar with these types of problems, you will find the tabular form of solution illustrated on p. 77 a very convenient form to use.

2.4 Material balances using algebraic techniques

As illustrated in Figs. 2.3 and 2.4, problems can be posed or formulated in different ways depending upon the type of information available on streams and their respective compositions. The problems treated in the previous section were quite easy to solve, once the problem had been converted from words into numbers, because the missing information pertained to a single stream. Only simple addition or subtraction was required to find the unknown quantities. If the missing information pertains to different streams, then the standard method of solving material balances is to write the balance formally, assigning letters or symbols to represent the unknown quantities. Each unknown stream, or component, is assigned a letter to replace the unknown value in the total mass balance or the component mass balance, as the case may be. Keep in mind that for each unknown so introduced you will have to write one independent material balance if the set of equations you form is to have a unique solution.

If more than one piece of equipment or more than one junction point is involved in the problem to be solved, you can write material balances for each piece of equipment and a balance around the whole process. However, since the over-all balance is nothing more than the sum of the balances about each piece of equipment, not all of the balances will be independent.

Under some circumstances, particularly if you split a big problem into smaller parts to make the calculations easier, you may want to make a material balance about a "mixing point." As illustrated in Fig. 2.6, a mixing point is nothing more than a junction of three or more streams and can be designated as a system in exactly the same fashion as any other piece of equipment.

Fig. 2.6. A mixing point.

We now turn to some brief comments on the solution of sets of algebraic equations. If only two or three material balances are written, the unknowns can be solved for by substitution. With many simultaneous equations, computer routines are advantageous. If several *steady-state linear* material balances must be written, they will take the form:

$$a_{11}x_1 + a_{12}x_2 + \cdots + a_{1n}x_n = b_1$$
$$a_{21}x_1 + a_{22}x_2 + \cdots + a_{2n}x_n = b_2$$
$$\cdots$$
$$a_{m1}x_1 + a_{m2}x_2 + \cdots + a_{mn}x_n = b_m$$

(2.7)

or in compact matrix notation:

$$\mathbf{AX} = \mathbf{B}$$

(2.7a)

where $x_1, x_2, \ldots,$ represent the unknown variables, and the a_{ij} and the b_i represent the constants and known variables. With m equations in n unknown variables, three cases can be distinguished:

1. There is no set of x's which satisfies Eq. (2.7).
2. There is a unique set of x's which satisfies Eq. (2.7).
3. There are an infinite number of sets of x's which satisfy Eq. (2.7).

Case 1 is usually termed inconsistent, whereas cases 2 and 3 are consistent; but to the engineer who is interested in the solution of practical problems, case 3 is as unsatisfying as case 1. Hence, case 2 will be termed "determinate," and case 3 will be termed "indeterminate."

To insure that a system of equations represented by (2.7) has a unique solution, it is necessary to first show that (2.7) is consistent, i.e., that the coefficient matrix A and the augmented matrix [A + B] must have the same rank r. Then, if $n = r$, the system (2.7) is determinate, while, if $r < n$, as may be the case, then the number $(n - r)$ variables must be specified in some manner or determined by optimization procedures. If the equations are independent, $m = r$.

As an example, if a set of equations has 16 unknowns and only 10 equations are available so that $(n - m) = 6$, six more variables must be specified in some manner. Refer to Himmelblau and Bischoff[1] for details as to which variables should be selected for complicated systems.

The precise criteria used to determine case 2 for a linear system cannot be neatly extended to nonlinear systems of equations, because of the possibility of multiple roots and for other reasons. By making a balance for each component for each defined system, a set of independent equations can be obtained whether linear or nonlinear. Total mass balances may be substituted for one of the component mass balances. Likewise, an over-all balance around the entire system may be substituted for one of the subsystem balances. By following these rules, you should encounter no difficulty in generating sets of independent material balances for any process.

Illustrations of the use of algebraic techniques to solve material balance problems can be found below in this section and in the next section (on tie elements).

Example 2.9   Mixing

A tank of weak battery acid (H_2SO_4) solution contains 12.43% H_2SO_4 (and the remainder distilled water). If 200 lb of 77.7% H_2SO_4 are added to the tank, and the final solution is 18.63% H_2SO_4, how many pounds of battery acid have been made?

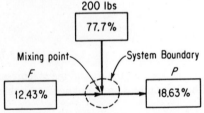

Solution:

In this problem one weight and three compositions are known; two weights are missing. To assist us, we will arbitrarily label the weights of the two unknown solutions F and P. With two unknowns it is necessary to set up two independent equations. However, we can write three material balances, any pair of which are independent equations.

Basis: 200 lb of 77.7% H_2SO_4 solution

type of balance	in	=	out	
Total	$F + 200$	=	P	(a)
component				
H_2SO_4	$F(0.1243) + 200(0.777)$	=	$P(0.1863)$	(b)
H_2O	$F(0.8757) + 200(0.223)$	=	$P(0.8137)$	(c)

Use of the total mass balance and one of the others is the easiest way to find P.

[1] D. M. Himmelblau and K. B. Bischoff, *Process Analysis and Simulation*, John Wiley & Sons, Inc., New York, 1967.

$$(P - 200)(0.1243) + 200(0.777) = P(0.1863)$$
$$P = 2110 \text{ lb of acid}$$
$$F = 1910 \text{ lb of acid}$$

Example 2.10   Distillation

A typical distillation column is shown in the diagram together with the known information for each stream. Calculate the pounds of distillate per pound of feed and per pound of waste.

Solution:

Inspection of the diagram shows all compositions are known, but three weights are unknown. Because only two independent balances can be written, one weight must be chosen as the basis for the problem to effect an algebraic solution.

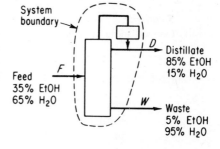

Basis: 1.00 lb feed

type of balance	in	=	out
total	1.00 =		$D + W$
EtOH	$1.00(0.35) = $		$D(0.85) + W(0.05)$
H₂O	$1.00(0.65) = $		$D(0.15) + W(0.95)$

Solving for D with $W = (1.00 - D)$,

$$1.00(0.35) = D(0.85) + (1.00 - D)(0.05)$$
$$D = 0.375 \text{ lb/lb feed}$$

Since $W = 1 - 0.375 = 0.625$ lb,

$$\frac{D}{W} = \frac{0.375}{0.625} = \frac{0.60 \text{ lb}}{\text{lb}}$$

Example 2.11   Multiple Equipment

In your first problem as a new company engineer you have been asked to set up an acetone recovery system and compute the cost of recovering acetone. The design of the proposed system is shown in the diagram. From the information given, list the flow rates (in lb/hr) of all the streams so that the size of the equipment can be determined, and calculate the composition of the feed to the still.

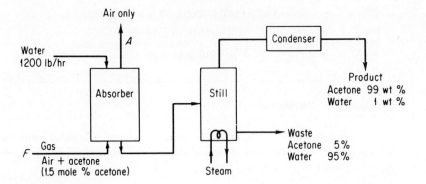

Solution:

Convert mole per cent of the air-acetone feed to weight per cent:

$$\text{mol. wt acetone} = 58, \qquad \text{mol. wt air} = 29$$

Basis: 100 lb mole gas feed

composition	lb mole	mol. wt	lb	wt %
acetone	1.5	58	87	2.95
air	98.5	29	2860	97.05
	100.0		2947	100.00

Now we know the compositions (on a weight basis) of all the streams. There are five streams entering and leaving the entire system, and the weight of only one is known, leaving as unknowns four weights.

Basis: 1 hr

Balances on complete system (over-all balances):

Let

$$\left.\begin{array}{l} F = \text{feed to absorber, lb} \\ A = \text{air leaving absorber, lb} \\ P = \text{product, lb} \\ W = \text{waste, lb} \end{array}\right\} \text{ the four unknowns}$$

total $F + 1200 = P + W + A$

acetone $F(0.0295) = P(0.99) + W(0.05)$

water $1200 = P(0.01) + W(0.95)$

air $F(0.9705) = A$

We now have four balances and four unknowns; however, only three of the equations are independent equations, as we can easily show by adding up the component balances to get the over-all balance. What is wrong? It seems as if there is not enough information available to solve this problem.

One additional bit of information would be enough to solve the problem as originally stated. This information might be, for example:

(a) The weight of entering gas/hr, product/hr, or waste/hour

(b) The composition of the feed into the still

With an extra piece of pertinent information available, a complete solution is possible; without it, only a partial solution can be effected. Observe that making additional balances about the individual pieces of equipment will not resolve the problem, since as many new unknowns are added as independent equations.

Example 2.12   Countercurrent Stagewise Mass Transfer

In many commercial processes such as distillation, extraction, absorption of gases in liquids, and the like, the entering and leaving streams flow in a direction opposite to each other, as shown in the figure. (The figure could just as well be laid on its side.)

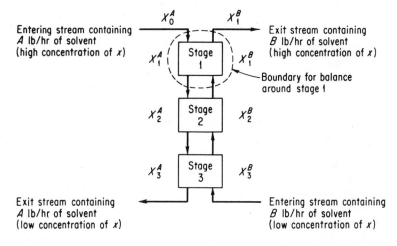

A, B = lb of stream less solute in the stream
= lb of solvent

This type of operation is known as *countercurrent* operation. If equilibrium is attained for the substance x between each stream at a number of points in the apparatus, many important calculations can be carried out related to the flow rates, concentration of products, size, and other design features of the apparatus. We will illustrate how a material balance can be made for such type of equipment. The letter X stands for the weight concentration of x in lb solute/lb of stream, solute free. The streams are assumed immiscible as in a liquid-liquid extraction process.

Around stage 1 the material balance is

$$\underset{\text{in}}{\frac{A\text{ lb}}{\text{hr}}\bigg|\frac{X_0^A\text{ lb}}{\text{lb }A} + \frac{B\text{ lb}}{\text{hr}}\bigg|\frac{X_2^B\text{ lb}}{\text{lb }B}} = \underset{\text{out}}{\frac{A\text{ lb}}{\text{hr}}\bigg|\frac{X_1^A\text{ lb}}{\text{lb }A} + \frac{B\text{ lb}}{\text{hr}}\bigg|\frac{X_1^B\text{ lb}}{\text{lb }B}}$$

or

$$A(X_0^A - X_1^A) = B(X_1^B - X_2^B) \tag{a}$$

Around stage 2 the material balance is

$$\underset{\text{in}}{\frac{A\text{ lb}}{\text{hr}}\bigg|\frac{X_1^A\text{ lb}}{\text{lb }A} + \frac{B\text{ lb}}{\text{hr}}\bigg|\frac{X_3^B\text{ lb}}{\text{lb }B}} = \underset{\text{out}}{\frac{A\text{ lb}}{\text{hr}}\bigg|\frac{X_2^A\text{ lb}}{\text{lb }A} + \frac{B\text{ lb}}{\text{hr}}\bigg|\frac{X_2^B\text{ lb}}{\text{lb }B}}$$

or

$$A(X_1^A - X_2^A) = B(X_2^B - X_3^B)$$

We could generalize that for any stage number n

$$A(X_{n-1}^A - X_n^A) = B(X_n^B - X_{n+1}^B)$$

Also a material balance could be written about the sum of stage 1 and stage 2 as follows:

$$\underset{\text{in}}{A(X_0^A) + B(X_3^B)} = \underset{\text{out}}{A(X_2^A) + B(X_1^B)} \tag{b}$$

or to generalize for an over-all material balance between the top end and the nth stage,

$$A(X_0^A - X_n^A) = B(X_1^B - X_{n+1}^B)$$

or for the $(n-1)$th stage,

$$A(X_0^A - X_{n-1}^A) = B(X_1^B - X_n^B)$$

Changing signs,

$$A(X_{n-1}^A - X_0^A) = B(X_n^B - X_1^B)$$

It we set this up in an equation assuming A, B, X_0^A, and X_1^B are constants (i.e., steady-state operation), and X^A and X^B are the variables as we go from stage to stage, we can write

$$X_{n-1}^A = \frac{B}{A}X_n^B + \left(X_0^A - \frac{B}{A}X_1^B\right) \tag{c}$$

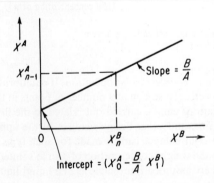

Equation (c) represents an unusual type of equation in that it gives the relationship between discrete points rather than continuous variables; it is called a "difference" equation. The locus of these points will fall upon a line with the slope B/A and an intercept $\left(X_0^A - \frac{B}{A}X_1^B\right)$, as shown in the diagram.

2.5 Problems involving tie elements

A *tie element* is material which goes from one stream into another without changing in any respect or having like material added to it or lost from it. In essence it is a single material balance equation which involves only two streams. To select a tie element, ask yourself the question, "What component passed through the process unchanged with constant weight (mass)?" The answer is the tie element. Frequently several components pass through a process with continuity so that there are many choices of tie elements. Sometimes the amounts of these components can be added together to give an over-all tie element which will result in a smaller percentage error in your calculations than if an individual tie element had been used. It may happen that a minor constituent passes through with continuity, but if the percentage error for the analysis of this component is large, you should not use it as a tie element. Sometimes you cannot find a tie element by direct examination of the problem, but you still may be able to develop a hypothetical tie element or a man-made tie element which will be equally effective as a tie element for a single material. A tie element is useful even if you do not know all the compositions and weights in any given problem because the tie element enables you to put two streams on the same basis. Thus a *partial solution* can be effected even if the entire problem is not resolved.

In solutions of problems involving tie elements it is not always advantageous to select as the basis "what you have." Frequently it turns out that the composition of one stream is given as a percentage composition, and then it becomes convenient to select as the basis 100 lb (or other weight) of the material because then pounds equal percentage and the same numbers can be used to represent both units. After you have carried out the computations on the basis of 100 lb (or another basis), then the answer can be transformed to the basis of the amount of material actually given by using the proper conversion factor. For example, if you had 32.5 lb of material, and you knew its composition on the basis of percentage, you then could take as your basis 100 lb of material, and at the end of the calculations convert your answer to the basis of 32.5 lb.

Tie-element problems can, of course, be worked by algebraic means, but in combustion problems and in some of the more complicated types of industrial chemical calculations so many unknowns and equations are involved that the use of a tie element greatly simplifies the calculations. Use of a tie element also clarifies the internal workings of a process. Consequently, rather than use algebra for simple problems which can also be solved by means of tie elements, the examples below illustrate the use of both tie-element and algebraic solutions. Become proficient in both techniques, as you will have to draw upon both of them in your career as an engineer. Examples follow.

Example 2.13   Drying

A dryer receives some cellulose pulp which is 80% water. After 100 lb of water are removed, it is found that the cellulose pulp is now 40% water. Calculate the weight of the original pulp.

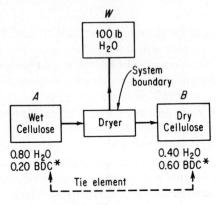

*Bone dry cellulose

Solution:
From the diagram we see that all the compositions and one weight are known and that there is a tie element.

To solve the problem by use of algebra requires the use of two independent material balance equations since there are two unknowns—A and B.

Basis: 100 lb water evaporated

$$\text{in} = \text{out}$$

$$\begin{array}{ll}
\text{total balance} & A = B + W = B + 100 \\
\text{cellulose balance} & 0.20A = 0.60B
\end{array} \left.\right\} \text{ mass balances}$$

Notice that because the cellulose balance involves only two streams, you can set up a direct ratio of A to B, which is the essence of the tie element:

$$B = \frac{0.20A}{0.60} = \frac{1}{3}A$$

Introduction of this ratio into the total balance gives

$$A = \tfrac{1}{3}A + 100$$

$$\tfrac{2}{3}A = 100$$

$$A = 150 \text{ lb initial pulp}$$

To solve the same problem by use of the tie element, take as a basis 100 lb of initial material (the 100 lb of H_2O will not serve as a useful basis).

Basis: 100 lb initial pulp

component	initial % = lb	− loss lb*	= final lb	%
H_2O	80	100	?	40
BDC	20 ← tie →		20	60
	100		?	100

* All H_2O.

In order to make either a total or a water material balance for this problem, all streams must be placed on the same basis (100 lb initial pulp was chosen as being the most convenient) by use of the tie element.

Tie final pulp to initial pulp by a tie element:

$$\frac{20\ lb\ \cancel{BDC}}{100\ lb\ initial\ pulp}\ \Big|\ \frac{100\ lb\ final\ pulp}{60\ lb\ \cancel{BDC}} = 33.3\ lb\ final\ pulp/100\ lb\ initial\ pulp$$

Notice that the BDC is the same (the tie element) in both the initial and final streams, and the units of BDC can be canceled. We have now used one independent material balance equation, the BDC balance. Our second balance will be total balance:

100 lb initial − 33.3 lb final = 66.7 lb of H_2O evap./100 lb initial pulp

An alternative way to obtain this same value is to use a water balance

$$\frac{20\ lb\ \cancel{BDC}}{100\ lb\ initial\ pulp}\ \Big|\ \frac{40\ lb\ H_2O\ in\ dry\ pulp}{60\ lb\ \cancel{BDC}\ in\ dry\ pulp}$$

$$= 13.3\ lb\ H_2O\ left/100\ lb\ initial\ pulp$$

80 lb initial H_2O − 13.3 lb final H_2O

$$= 66.7\ lb\ H_2O\ evap./100\ lb\ initial\ pulp$$

Next a shift is made to the basis of 100 lb H_2O evaporated as required by the problem statement

$$\frac{100\ lb\ initial\ pulp}{66.7\ lb\ H_2O\ evap.}\ \Big|\ \frac{100\ lb\ H_2O\ evap.}{} - 150\ lb\ initial\ pulp$$

Another suitable starting basis would be to use 1 lb of bone dry cellulose as the basis.

Basis: 1 lb BDC

component	initial fraction	− loss lb	= final fraction
H_2O	0.80	100	0.40
BDC	0.20		0.60
	1.00		1.00

$$\text{initial } H_2O - \quad \text{final } H_2O \quad = H_2O \text{ lost} \qquad \text{water balance}$$

$$\frac{0.80 \text{ lb } H_2O}{0.20 \text{ lb BDC}} - \frac{0.40 \text{ lb } H_2O}{0.60 \text{ lb BDC}} =$$

$$4.0 \quad - \quad 0.67 \quad = 3.33 \text{ lb } H_2O/\text{lb BDC}$$

Again we have to shift bases to get back to the required basis of 100 lb of H_2O evaporated:

$$\frac{1 \text{ lb } \cancel{BDC}}{3.33 \text{ lb } H_2O} \left| \frac{100 \text{ lb } H_2O \text{ evap.}}{} \right| \frac{1.0 \text{ lb initial pulp}}{0.2 \text{ lb } \cancel{BDC}} = 150 \text{ lb initial pulp}$$

You can see that the use of the tie element makes it quite easy to shift from one basis to another. If you now want to compute the pounds of final pulp, all that is necessary is to write:

$$\begin{array}{r} 150 \text{ lb initial pulp} \\ \underline{100 \text{ lb } H_2O \text{ evaporated}} \\ 50 \text{ lb final pulp} \end{array}$$

Now that we have examined some of the correct methods of handling tie elements, let us look at another method frequently attempted (not for long!) by some students before they become completely familiar with the use of the tie element. They try to say:

$$0.80 - 0.40 = 0.40 \text{ lb } H_2O \text{ evaporated}$$

$$\frac{100 \text{ lb}}{0.40 \text{ lb}} = 250 \text{ lb pulp}$$

On the surface this looks like an easy way to solve the problem—what is wrong with the method? More careful inspection of the calculation shows that two different bases were used in subtracting $(0.80 - 0.40)$. The 0.80 is on the basis of 1.00 lb of initial pulp while the 0.40 is on the basis of 1.00 lb of final pulp. You would not say $0.80/A - 0.40/B = 0.40/A$, would you? From our early discussion about units you can see that this subtraction is not a legitimate operation.

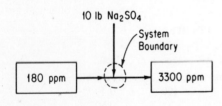

10 lb Na_2SO_4

System Boundary

180 ppm

3300 ppm

Example 2.14   Dilution

The water analysis in a flowing creek shows 180 ppm Na_2SO_4. If 10 lb of Na_2SO_4 are added to the stream uniformly over a 1-hr period, and the analysis downstream where mixing is complete indicates 3300 ppm Na_2SO_4, how many gallons of water are flowing per hour?

Tie-element Solution:

Basis: 100 lb initial solution (water + Na_2SO_4 initially present)

After choosing a basis of 100 lb of initial solution, we know three compositions and one weight. A tie element, the water, is present.

composition	initial lb = %		final %
H_2O	99.982	tie ⟵ ⟶ element	99.670
Na_2SO_4	0.018		0.330
	100.000		100.000

$$\frac{0.33 \text{ lb } Na_2SO_4}{99.67 \text{ lb } H_2O} \left| \frac{99.982 \text{ lb } H_2O}{100 \text{ lb initial solution}} \right.$$

$$= 0.331 \text{ lb } Na_2SO_4/100 \text{ lb initial solution}$$

The tie element of water comprises our first material balance. Now that the exit Na_2SO_4 concentration is on the same basis as the entering Na_2SO_4 concentration, by an Na_2SO_4 balance (our second balance) we find the Na_2SO_4 added is

$$0.331 - 0.0180 = 0.313 \text{ lb}/100 \text{ lb initial solution}$$

Including the Na_2SO_4 in the initial analysis, the flow of water per hour is

Basis: 1 hr

$$\frac{100 \text{ lb initial solution}}{0.313 \text{ lb } Na_2SO_4 \text{ added}} \left| \frac{10 \text{ lb added}}{1 \text{ hr}} \right| \frac{1 \text{ gal}}{8.35 \text{ lb}} = 383 \text{ gal/hr}$$

Algebraic Solution:
Let

$$x = \text{total lb flowing/hr initially}$$

$$y = \text{total lb flowing/hr after addition of } Na_2SO_4$$

total balance $\qquad x + 10 = y$ $\qquad\Big\}$ mass balances
water balance $\quad 0.99982x = 0.99670y$

$$x + 10 = \frac{0.99982x}{0.99670}$$

The water balance involves only two streams and provides a direct ratio between x and y. One of the difficulties in the solution of this problem using a water balance is that the quantity

$$\left[\frac{0.99982}{0.99670} - 1 \right] = 0.00313$$

has to be determined quite accurately. It would be more convenient to use an Na_2SO_4 balance,

$$0.00018x + 10 = 0.00330y$$

Solving the total balance and the Na_2SO_4 balance simultaneously,

$$x = 3210 \text{ lb/hr}$$

$$\frac{3210 \text{ lb}}{\text{hr}} \left| \frac{1 \text{ gal}}{8.35 \text{ lb}} \right. = 385 \text{ gal/hr}$$

Example 2.15   Crystallization

The solubility of barium nitrate at 100°C is 34 g/100 g H_2O and at 0°C is 5.0 g/100 g H_2O. If you start with 100 g of $Ba(NO_3)_2$ and make a saturated solution in water at 100°C, how much water is required? If this solution is cooled to 0°C, how much $Ba(NO_3)_2$ is precipitated out of solution?

Tie-element Solution:

Basis: 100 g $Ba(NO_3)_2$

The maximum solubility of $Ba(NO_3)_2$ in H_2O at 100°C is a saturated solution, or 34 g/100 g H_2O. Thus the amount of water required at 100°C is

$$\frac{100 \text{ g } H_2O}{34 \text{ g } Ba(NO_3)_2} \left| \frac{100 \text{ g } Ba(NO_3)_2}{} \right. = 295 \text{ g } H_2O$$

If the 100°C solution is cooled to 0°C, the $Ba(NO_3)_2$ solution will still be saturated, and the problem now can be pictured as in the diagram. The tie element is the water.

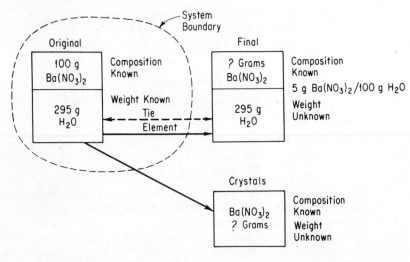

$$\frac{295 \text{ g } H_2O}{} \left| \frac{5 \text{ g } Ba(NO_3)_2}{100 \text{ g } H_2O} \right. = 14.7 \text{ g } Ba(NO_3)_2 \text{ in final solution}$$

original   —   final   =   crystals

$$100 \text{ g } Ba(NO_3)_2 - 14.7 \text{ g } Ba(NO_3)_2 = 85.3 \text{ g } Ba(NO_3)_2 \text{ precipitated}$$

Algebraic Solution:

Let

$$x = \text{g crystals}$$

$$y = \text{g final solution}$$

H₂O balance $\qquad 295 = y\left(\dfrac{100}{100 + 5}\right)\dfrac{\text{g } H_2O}{\text{g final solution}}$

Total balance $\qquad 395 = x + y$

$$y = 295\left(\frac{105}{100}\right) = 310$$

$$x = 395 - y = 85 \text{ g } Ba(NO_3)_2 \text{ crystals}$$

Example 2.16　Combustion

A fuel oil contains 88% C and 12% H₂ and is burned to a flue gas (fg) of the following composition:

CO₂	13.4
O₂	3.6
N₂	83.0
	100.0%

How many pound moles of fg are produced per 100 lb of fuel oil? What is the percentage of excess air used?

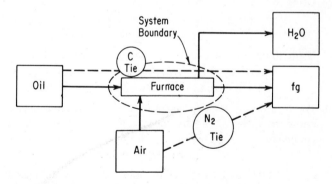

Tie-element Solution:

In this problem four streams are present all of whose compositions are known, two entering and two leaving. We have the weights of three streams as unknowns (if we choose one weight as the basis). However, since we do not have to answer any questions about the water stream, two tie elements to relate the oil, flue gas, and air streams to each other would be sufficient to solve the problem. In examining the data to determine whether a tie element exists, we see that the carbon goes directly from the oil to the flue gas, and nowhere else, so carbon will serve as one tie element. The N_2 in the air all shows up in the flue gas so N_2 can be used as another tie element. As explained before, there is no reason to convert all the available data to a weight basis, even though the moles of material entering and leaving the burner are not the same. Let us consider the moles of each atomic specie present. Then we have in 100 lb of oil:

$$C: \quad \tfrac{88}{12} = 7.33 \text{ lb mole}$$

$$H_2: \quad \tfrac{12}{2} = 6 \text{ lb mole}$$

We can say the pound moles of C entering the process equal the pound moles of C leaving the process since the molecular weight is a constant factor in both inlet and outlet material and can be canceled out. Thus,

$$\text{lb C in} = \text{lb C out}$$

$$\text{lb mole C in} = \text{lb mole C out}$$

In step (a) below both of these methods of attack are employed.

In the flue gas:

Basis: 100 lb mole fg

$$\frac{13.4 \text{ lb mole C}}{} \left| \frac{12 \text{ lb C}}{1 \text{ lb mole C}} = 161 \text{ lb C} \right.$$

In the fuel oil:

Basis: 100 lb of fuel oil

$$\frac{88 \text{ lb C}}{} \left| \frac{1 \text{ lb mole C}}{12 \text{ lb C}} = 7.33 \text{ lb mole C} \right.$$

(a_1) Using lb C = lb C as the tie element,

$$\frac{100 \text{ lb mole fg}}{161 \text{ lb C}} \left| \frac{88 \text{ lb C}}{100 \text{ lb oil}} = \frac{54.6 \text{ lb mole fg}}{100 \text{ lb oil}} \right.$$

(a_2) Using lb mole C = lb mole C as the tie element,

$$\frac{100 \text{ lb mole fg}}{13.4 \text{ lb mole C}} \left| \frac{7.33 \text{ lb mole C}}{100 \text{ lb oil}} = \frac{54.6 \text{ lb mole fg}}{100 \text{ lb oil}} \right.$$

(b) The N_2 serves as the tie element to tie the air to the flue gas, and since we know the excess O_2 in the flue gas, the percentage of excess air can be computed.

Basis: 100 lb mole of fg

$$\frac{83.0 \text{ lb mole } N_2}{} \left| \frac{1.00 \text{ lb mole air}}{0.79 \text{ lb mole } N_2} = \frac{105.0 \text{ lb mole air}}{100 \text{ lb mole fg}} \right.$$

$$(105.0)(0.21) = O_2 \text{ entering} = 22.1 \text{ lb mole } O_2$$

Or, saving one step,

$$\frac{83.0 \text{ lb mole } N_2}{} \left| \frac{0.21 \text{ lb mole } O_2 \text{ in air}}{0.79 \text{ lb mole } N_2 \text{ in air}} = \frac{22.1 \text{ lb mole } O_2 \text{ entering}}{100 \text{ lb mole fg}} \right.$$

$$\% \text{ excess air} = 100 \frac{\text{excess } O_2}{O_2 \text{ entering} - \text{excess } O_2} = \frac{(100)3.6}{22.1 - 3.6} = 19.4\%$$

To check this answer, let us work part (b) of the problem using as a basis:

Basis: 100 lb of oil

The required oxygen for complete combustion is:

comp.	lb	lb mole	lb mole O_2 required
C	88	7.33	7.33
H_2	12	6	3
			10.33

The excess oxygen is:

$$\frac{3.6 \text{ lb mole } O_2}{100 \text{ lb mole fg}} \left| \frac{54.6 \text{ lb mole fg}}{100 \text{ lb oil}} \right. = 1.97 \text{ lb mole}$$

$$\% \text{ excess air} = \frac{\text{excess } O_2}{\text{required } O_2} \; 100 = \frac{1.97(100)}{10.33} = 19.0\%$$

The answers computed on the two different bases agree reasonably well here, but in many combustion problems slight errors in the data will cause large differences in the calculated percentage of excess air. Assuming no mathematical mistakes have been made (it is wise to check), the better solution is the one involving the use of the most precise data. Frequently this turns out to be the method used in the check here—the one with a basis of 100 lb of oil.

If the flue-gas analysis had shown some CO in the flue gas, as in the following hypothetical analysis,

CO_2	11.9%
CO	1.6
O_2	4.1
N_2	82.4

then, on the basis of 100 moles of flue gas, we would calculate the excess air as follows:

O_2 entering with air:

$$\frac{82.4 \text{ lb mole } N_2}{} \left| \frac{0.21 \text{ lb mole } O_2}{0.79 \text{ lb mole } N_2} \right. = 21.9 \text{ lb mole } O_2$$

Excess O_2:

$$4.1 - \frac{1.6}{2} = 3.3 \text{ lb mole}$$

$$\% \text{ excess air} = 100 \, \frac{3.3}{21.9 - 3.3} = 17.7\%$$

Note that in order to get the true excess oxygen, the apparent excess oxygen in the flue gas, 4.1 lb mole, has to be reduced by the amount of the theoretical oxygen not combining with the CO. According to the reactions

$$C + O_2 \longrightarrow CO_2, \qquad C + \tfrac{1}{2} O_2 \longrightarrow CO$$

for each mole of CO in the flue gas, $\frac{1}{2}$ mole of O_2 which should have combined with the carbon to form CO_2 did not do so. This $\frac{1}{2}$ mole carried over into the flue gas and inflated the value of the true excess oxygen expected to be in the flue gas. In this example, 1.6 lb moles of CO are in the flue gas, so that (1.6/2) lb moles of theoretical oxygen are found in the flue gas in addition to the true excess oxygen.

Algebraic Solution:

An algebraic solution of the originally stated problem would proceed as follows:

Let

$$x = \text{lb of oil}$$

$$y = \text{lb moles of fg}$$

$$z = \text{lb moles of air}$$

$$w = \text{lb moles of } H_2O \text{ in the stack gas}$$

One of these unknowns can be replaced by the basis, say $x = 100$ lb oil. Since three unknowns will remain, it will be necessary to use in the solution three independent material balances from among the four component and one total balance that can be written. The balances are

total

$$100 + z = y + w$$

component

$$\text{C} \qquad 100(0.88) = \frac{y \text{ lb mole fg}}{} \left| \frac{0.134 \text{ lb mole C}}{1 \text{ lb mole fg}} \right| \frac{12 \text{ lb C}}{1 \text{ lb mole C}}$$

$$\text{H}_2 \qquad 100(0.12) = \frac{w \text{ lb mole } H_2O}{} \left| \frac{1 \text{ lb mole } H_2}{1 \text{ lb mole } H_2O} \right| \frac{1.008 \text{ lb } H_2}{1 \text{ lb mole } H_2}$$

$$\text{N}_2 \qquad 0.79z = 0.83y$$

$$\text{O}_2 \qquad 0.21z = \frac{w \text{ lb mole } H_2O}{} \left| \frac{0.5 \text{ lb mole } O_2}{1 \text{ lb mole } H_2O} \right.$$

$$+ \frac{y \text{ lb mole fg}}{} \left| \frac{0.036 \text{ lb mole } O_2}{1 \text{ lb mole fg}} \right.$$

Note that the balances for the tie elements C and N_2 (as well as H_2) involve only two streams, whereas the O_2 (and total) balance involves three streams. We will use the C and N_2 balances.

Basis: 100 lb fuel oil

$$y = \frac{88}{(0.134)(12)} = 54.6 \text{ lb mole fg}$$

$$z = \frac{0.83}{0.79}y \qquad = 105 \text{ lb mole air}$$

$$O_2 \text{ entering} = 105(0.21) = 22.1 \text{ lb mole}$$

The remainder of the calculations follow those described above. Can you demonstrate that the flue gas analysis is slightly inaccurate?

Example 2.17   Distillation

A continuous still is to be used to separate acetic acid, water, and benzene from each other. On a trial run the calculated data were as shown in the diagram. Data recording the benzene composition of the feed were not taken because of an apparatus defect. Calculate the benzene flow in the feed per hour.

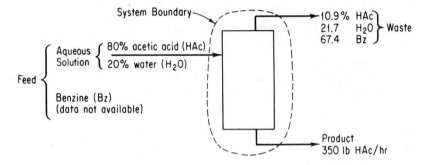

A quick inspection of the flow diagram shows that enough information about weights and compositions would be available to work this problem if only the benzene composition in the feed were known, but it is not. However, we have one added source of information not readily apparent on the surface, and that is there are *two* tie elements from the feed to the waste: water and benzene. A choice now must be made in procedure: The problem can be calculated using the tie elements (solution below) or using algebraic techniques (algebraic solution on next page).

Tie-element Solution:

Take a convenient basis of 100 lb of waste (100 lb of feed would involve more work since the benzene composition is unknown, but 100 lb of aqueous solution—80% HAc, 20% H_2O—would be a sound basis). Let x = lb of benzene in the feed/100 lb feed.

Basis: 100 lb waste

composition	feed lb	waste % = lb	product %
HAc	$(100 - x)0.80$	10.9	100
H_2O	$(100 - x)0.20$	21.7	
Bz	x	67.4	
total	100	100	

For an initial step let us calculate the quantity of feed per 100 lb of waste. We have the water in the feed (21.7 lb) and the benzene in the feed (67.4 lb); these two materials appear only in the waste and not in the product and can act as tie elements. All that is needed is the HAc in the feed. We can use water as the tie element to find this quantity.

$$\frac{21.7 \text{ lb } H_2O}{100 \text{ lb waste}} \left| \frac{0.80 \text{ lb HAc}}{0.20 \text{ lb } H_2O} \right. = 86.8 \text{ lb HAc/100 lb waste}$$

The product now is

HAc in feed — HAc in waste = HAc in product   *HAc balance*
    86.8   —   10.9   =   75.9

Take a new basis:

Basis: 350 lb HAc product ≡ 1 hr

$$\frac{67.4 \text{ lb Bz in feed}}{75.9 \text{ lb HAc in product}} \left| \frac{350 \text{ lb HAc product}}{hr} \right. = 311 \text{ lb Bz/hr}$$

Algebraic Solution:

To employ algebra in the solution of this problem we need an independent material balance for each unknown. The unknowns are

$$W = \text{waste, lb}$$

$$F = \text{feed, lb}$$

$$x = \text{lb benzene/100 lb feed}$$

Basis: 1 hr ≡ 350 lb HAc product

The equations are:

total balance $F = W + 350$

H₂O balance $F\left[\dfrac{0.20(100 - x)}{100}\right] = W(0.217)$

HAc balance $F\left[\dfrac{0.80(100 - x)}{100}\right] = W(0.109) + 350$

Bz balance $F\left[\dfrac{x}{100}\right] = W(0.674)$

Any three will be independent equations, but you can see the simultaneous solution of three equations involves more work than the use of tie elements.

Example 2.18   Economics

A chemical company buys coal at a contract price based on a specified maximum amount of moisture and ash. Since you have married the boss's daughter, your first job assignment is as purchasing agent. The salesman for the Higrade Coal Co. offers you a contract for 10 carloads per month of coal with a maximum moisture content of 3.2% and a maximum ash content of 5.3% at $4.85 per ton (weighed at delivery). You accept this contract price. In the first delivery the moisture content of the coal as reported by your laboratory is 4.5% and the ash content is 5.6%. The billed price for this coal is $4.85 per ton—as weighed by the railroad in the switchyards outside your plant. The accounting department wants to know if this billing price is correct. Calculate the correct price.

Solution:

What you really pay for is 91.5% combustible material with a maximum allowable content of ash and water. Based on this assumption, you can find the cost of the combustible material in the coal actually delivered.

Basis: 1 ton coal as delivered

composition	delivered	contract coal
combustible	0.899	0.915
moisture plus ash	0.101	0.085
	1.000	1.000

The contract calls for:

$$\frac{\$4.85}{\text{ton contract}} \left| \frac{1 \text{ ton contract}}{0.915 \text{ ton comb.}} \right| \frac{0.899 \text{ ton comb.}}{1 \text{ ton del.}} = \$4.76/\text{ton del.}$$

The billed price is wrong.

If the ash content had been below 5.3% but the water content above 3.2%, presumably an adjustment should be made in the billing for excess moisture even though the ash was low.

2.6 Recycle calculations

Processes involving "feedback" or recycle of part of the product are frequently encountered in the chemical and petroleum industry. For example, in some drying operations, the humidity in the air is controlled by recirculating part of the wet air which leaves the dryer. In chemical reactions, the unreacted material may be separated from the product and recycled, as in the synthesis of ammonia. Another example of the use of recycling operations is in fractionating columns where part of the distillate is refluxed through the column to enrich the product. A typical flow sheet for a recycle process is shown in Fig. 2.7.

The first point you should grasp concerning recycle calculations is one that may cause some confusion when you first look at Fig. 2.7. You should

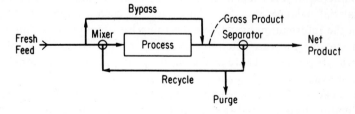

Fig. 2.7. A process with recycle.

realize that the process shown in Fig. 2.7 is in the *steady state*—no buildup or depletion of material takes place inside the reactor or in the recycle stream. The feed to the process is made up of two streams, the fresh feed and the recycle material. The gross product leaving the process is separated into two streams, the net product and the material to be recycled. In some cases the recycle stream may have the same composition as the gross product stream while in other instances the composition may be entirely different depending on how the separation takes place.

As discussed in Chap. 1, the term *conversion* as applied to Fig. 2.7 may be either the fraction or percentage of the fresh feed which reacts, or the fraction of the feed plus recycle. If 100 lb of substance A in the fresh feed are converted on an over-all basis into 40 lb of desired product, 30 lb of waste, 20 lb of a secondary product, and 10 lb of A pass through the process unchanged, the total conversion of A is 90 per cent based on the fresh feed. However, the *yield* of primary and secondary products is only 60 lb of products per 100 lb A. If, in addition, the recycle stream contains 100 lb of A, the total conversion of A on a once-through basis is only 45 per cent. You can see that the basis upon which the conversion and yield are calculated should always be clearly specified. When the fresh feed consists of more than one material, the yield and conversion must be stated for a single component, usually the limiting reactant, the most expensive reactant, or some similar compound.

Two additional commonly encountered terms are shown in Fig. 2.7:

(a) A by-pass stream—one which skips one stage of the process and goes directly to another stage.

(b) A purge stream—a stream bled off to remove an accumulation of inerts or unwanted material that might otherwise build up in the recycle stream. The purge rate is adjusted so that the amount of purged material remains below a specified level or so that the

$$\left\{ \begin{array}{c} \text{rate of} \\ \text{accumulation} \end{array} \right\} = 0 = \left\{ \begin{array}{c} \text{rate of entering material} \\ \text{and/or production} \end{array} \right\} - \left\{ \begin{array}{c} \text{rate of purge} \\ \text{and/or loss} \end{array} \right\}$$

Recycle problems have certain features in common, and the techniques you should use in solving these problems are the familiar ones previously encountered in this chapter in the use of material balances. You can make a material balance on a total basis, or for each component. Depending upon the information available concerning the amount and composition of each stream, you can determine the amount and composition of the unknowns. If tie elements are available, these simplify the calculations. If they are not available, then algebraic methods should be used.

If a chemical reaction is part of the problem, the stoichiometric equation, the limiting reactant, and the degree of completion all should be considered before beginning your calculations. Analysis of the problem frequently reveals a simplified method of solution (as illustrated in the following examples), but if such a simplification escapes you, or if there is none, then the standard procedure of setting up algebraic material balances will always be effective although perhaps long and involved. One psychological stumbling block is the stream of unknown weight or composition which is found to be essential for the solution and for which you have no information. By labeling this stream with a letter—R, X, or whatever—you can proceed to make material balances in the ordinary way and actually solve for the unknown stream. Of course, for each unknown you set up, you must write an independent equation; so from the viewpoint of the economic use of your time, it is advisable to minimize the number of unknowns. Some illustrations follow.

Example 2.19   Recycle Without Chemical Reaction

A distillation column separates 10,000 lb/hr of a 50% benzene–50% toluene mixture. The product recovered from the condenser at the top of the column contains 95% benzene, and the bottoms from the column contain 96% toluene. The stream entering the condenser from the top of the column is 8000 lb/hr. A portion of the product is returned to the column as reflux, and the rest is withdrawn for use elsewhere. Assume the compositions of the streams at the top of the column (V), the product withdrawn (D), and the reflux (R) are identical. Find the ratio of the amount refluxed to the product withdrawn.

Solution:

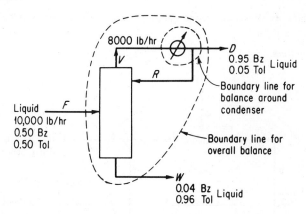

All the compositions are known and two weights are unknown. No tie elements are evident in this problem; thus an algebraic solution is mandatory. By making an over-all balance (ignoring the reflux stream for the moment) we can find D. With D known, a balance around the condenser will give us R.

Basis: 1 hr

Over-all material balances:
Total material:

$$F = D + W$$
$$10,000 = D + W \qquad\qquad (a)$$

Component (benzene):

$$FX_F = DX_D + WX_W$$
$$10,000(0.50) = D(0.95) + W(0.04) \qquad\qquad (b)$$

Solving (a) and (b) together:

$$5000 = (0.95)(10,000 - W) + 0.04W$$
$$W = 4950 \text{ lb/hr}$$
$$D = 5050 \text{ lb/hr}$$

Balance around the condenser:
Total material:

$$V = R + D$$
$$8000 = R + 5050$$
$$R = 2950 \text{ lb/hr}$$
$$\frac{R}{D} = \frac{1950}{5050} = 0.584$$

Example 2.20   Recycle Without Chemical Reaction

Data are presented in the diagram for an evaporator. What is the recycle stream in lb/hr?

Solution:

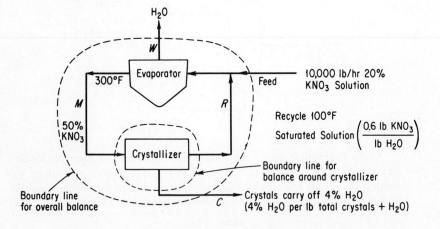

In this problem the compositions are all known except for the recycle stream, but this can be easily calculated. On the basis of 1 lb of water, the saturated recycle stream contains $(1.0 \text{ lb } H_2O + 0.6 \text{ lb } KNO_3) = 1.6$ lb total. The recycle stream composition is

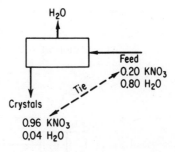

$$\frac{0.6 \text{ lb } KNO_3}{1 \text{ lb } H_2O} \Bigg| \frac{1 \text{ lb } H_2O}{1.6 \text{ lb solution}}$$

$$= 0.375 \text{ lb } KNO_3/\text{lb solution}$$

With all compositions known, a search for a tie element shows one exists on an over-all basis—the KNO_3. Temporarily ignoring the interior streams, we can draw a picture as shown. Now we can calculate the amount of crystals (and H_2O evaporated, if wanted).

$$\text{Basis: } 1 \text{ hr} \equiv 10,000 \text{ lb feed}$$

$$\frac{10,000 \text{ lb } F}{} \Bigg| \frac{0.20 \text{ lb } KNO_3}{1 \text{ lb } F} \Bigg| \frac{1 \text{ lb crystals}}{0.96 \text{ lb } KNO_3} = 2080 \text{ lb/hr crystals}$$

To determine the recycle stream R we need, in the absence of an additional tie element, either:

(a) A balance around the evaporator—or
(b) A balance around the crystallizer

The latter is easier since only three rather than four streams are involved.

Total balance on crystallizer:

$$M = C + R$$

$$M = 2080 + R$$

Component (KNO_3) balance on crystallizer:

$$Mx_M = Cx_C + Rx_R$$

$$0.5M = 0.96C + R(0.375)$$

Solving these two equations:

$$0.5(2080 + R) = 0.375R + 2000$$

$$R = 7680 \text{ lb/hr}$$

Example 2.21   Recycle With a Chemical Reaction

Metallic silver may be obtained from sulfide ores by roasting to sulfates, leaching with water, and precipitating the silver with copper. In the diagram below, the material leaving the second separator was found to contain 90% silver and 10% copper. What percentage of excess copper was used? (Base excess on fresh feed to reactor.) If the reaction goes to 75% completion based on the limiting reagent Ag_2SO_4, what is the recycle stream in pounds?

Data:

$$Ag_2SO_4 + Cu \longrightarrow 2\,Ag + CuSO_4$$

mol. wt   312   63.5   107.9   159.6

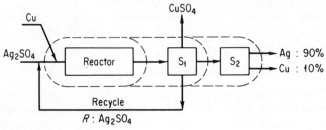

Solution:

Basis: 1000 lb of material leaving separator no. 2

What you have to find out in this problem is the amount of Cu put in the system above the stoichiometric amount called for in the chemical equation. The compositions of all streams are known, and one weight has been selected as the basis. On an over-all basis tie elements exist in the form of the element Ag and the SO_4^{-2}: the Ag in = the Ag out; also the SO_4^{-2} in = the SO_4^{-2} out.

(a) Find the lb Ag_2SO_4 required to be put into the system for each 900 lb of Ag leaving with the aid of an Ag tie element:

$$2\,Ag \longrightarrow 1\,Ag_2SO_4$$

$$\frac{900\,\text{lb Ag}}{} \left| \frac{1\,\text{lb mole Ag}}{107.9\,\text{lb Ag}} \right| \frac{1\,\text{lb mole Ag}_2SO_4}{2\,\text{lb mole Ag}} \left| \frac{312\,\text{lb Ag}_2SO_4}{1\,\text{lb mole Ag}_2SO_4} \right.$$

$$= 1300\,\text{lb Ag}_2SO_4$$

(b) Find the $CuSO_4$ leaving separator no. 1 with the aid of a SO_4^{-2} tie element:

$$\frac{1300\,\text{lb Ag}_2SO_4}{} \left| \frac{1\,\text{lb mole Ag}_2SO_4}{312\,\text{lb Ag}_2SO_4} \right| \frac{1\,\text{lb mole CuSO}_4}{1\,\text{lb mole Ag}_2SO_4} \left| \frac{159.6\,\text{lb CuSO}_4}{1\,\text{lb mole CuSO}_4} \right.$$

$$= 665\,\text{lb CuSO}_4$$

(c) Find the Cu introduced into the reactor from a Cu balance:

$$\frac{665\,\text{lb CuSO}_4}{} \left| \frac{1\,\text{lb mole CuSO}_4}{159.6\,\text{lb CuSO}_4} \right| \frac{1\,\text{lb mole Cu}}{1\,\text{lb mole CuSO}_4} \left| \frac{63.5\,\text{lb Cu}}{1\,\text{lb mole Cu}} \right.$$

$$= 265\,\text{lb Cu in the CuSO}_4$$

The total Cu in $= 265 + 0.10(1000) = 365$ lb

excess Cu $= 100$ lb

required Cu $= 265$ lb

% excess Cu $= \dfrac{100}{265}\,100 = 37.7\%$

(d) To calculate the amount of recycle, you would normally make a material balance which would cut the recycle stream. Various possible balances as indicated by the dashed lines in the original flow diagram, outlining successive systems are:

Balance about the reactor:

$$\overset{\text{in}}{\qquad} \overset{\text{out}}{\qquad}$$
$$Cu + Ag_2SO_4 + R = \text{output}$$

This equation is not of much help since it contains too many unknowns.

Balance about reactor and separator no. 1:

$$\overset{\text{in}}{\qquad} \overset{\text{out}}{\qquad}$$
$$Cu + Ag_2SO_4 + R = R + CuSO_4 + \text{stream to } S_2$$

The recycle stream cancels out.

Balance about reactor and separator no. 2:

$$\overset{\text{in}}{\qquad} \overset{\text{out}}{\qquad}$$
$$Cu + Ag_2SO_4 + R = R + CuSO_4 + Ag + Cu$$

This balance simply reduces to the over-all balance used earlier.

To make some progress in the required solution, we must use the information about the chemical reaction. We know that the reaction is 75% complete; consequently 25% of the limiting reagent (Ag_2SO_4) passes through the process unchanged and goes into S_1.

Let $R = $ lb recycle.

Ag_2SO_4 material balance around the reactor:

$$(R + Ag_2SO_4)(0.25) = R$$

This is known as the *once-through balance* and says that 25% of all the Ag_2SO_4 entering the reactor ($R + Ag_2SO_4$) leaves the reactor unchanged. In this problem it is all recycled, but in others only part of the unchanged material may be recycled, the rest passing on through the process to a different step.

$$0.25(1300 + R) = R$$
$$333 = 0.75R$$
$$R = 444 \text{ lb recycle}$$

Example 2.22   By-Pass Calculations

In the feed-stock preparation section of a plant manufacturing natural gasoline, isopentane is removed from butane-free gasoline. Assume for purposes of simplification that the process and components are as shown in the diagram.

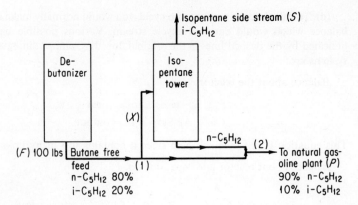

What fraction of the butane-free gasoline is passed through the isopentane tower?

Solution:

By examining the flow diagram you can see that part of the butane-free gasoline by-passes the isopentane tower and proceeds to the next stage in the natural gasoline plant. All the compositions are known. What kind of balances can we write for this process? We can write the following (each stream is designated by the letter F, S, or P):

Basis: 100 lb feed

(a) *Over-all balances* (all compositions are known; a tie element exists):
Total material balance:

$$\text{in} = \text{out}$$
$$100 = S + P \tag{1}$$

Component balance (n-C_5):

$$\text{in} = \text{out}$$
$$100(0.80) = S(0) + P(0.90) \tag{2}$$

Using (2):

$$P = 100\left(\frac{0.80}{0.90}\right) = 89 \text{ lb}$$

$$S = 100 - 89 = 11 \text{ lb}$$

The over-all balances will not tell us the fraction of the feed going to the isopentane tower; for this we need another balance.

(b) *Balance around isopentane tower:*
Let $x =$ lb of butane-free gas going to isopentane tower.
Total material:

$$\text{in} = \text{out}$$
$$x = 11 + n\text{-}C_5H_{12} \text{ stream} \qquad \text{(another unknown, } y) \tag{3}$$

Component (n-C_5):

$$x(0.80) = y \quad \text{(a tie element actually)} \tag{4}$$

Consequently, combining (3) and (4):

$$x = 11 + 0.8x$$

$$x = 55 \text{ lb, or the desired fraction is } 0.55$$

Another approach to this problem is to make a balance at points (1) or (2) called "mixing points." Although there are no pieces of equipment at those points, you can see that streams enter and leave the junction.

(c) *Balance around mixing point* (2):

$$\text{material into junction} = \text{material out}$$

Total material:

$$(100 - x) + y = 89 \tag{5}$$

Component (iso-C_5):

$$(100 - x)(0.20) + 0 = 89(0.10) \tag{6}$$

Equation (6) avoids the use of y. Solving,

$$20 - 0.2x = 8.9$$

$$x = 55 \text{ lb as before}$$

After a little practice you can size up a problem and visualize the simplest types of balances to make.

Up to now we have discussed material balances of a rather simple order of complexity. If you try to visualize all the operations which might be involved in even a moderate-sized plant, as illustrated in Fig. 2.2, the stepwise or simultaneous solution of material balances for each phase of the entire plant is truly a staggering task. However, an over-all plant balance can be composed of a number of individual, interlocking material balances which, however tedious they are to set up and solve, can be set down according to the principles and techniques discussed in this chapter. In a practical case there is always the problem of collecting suitable information and evaluating its accuracy, but this matter calls for detailed familiarity with any specific process and is not a suitable topic for discussion here. We can merely remark that some of the problems you will encounter have such conflicting data or so few useful data that the ability to perceive what kind of data are needed is the most important attribute you can bring to bear in their solution. By now, from working with simple problems, you should have some insight into the requirements for the solution of more complicated problems. In Chap. 5 you will encounter some of these more complex problems.

WHAT YOU SHOULD HAVE LEARNED FROM THIS CHAPTER

1. You should be able to analyze a material balance problem in order to:
   (a) Find out what the problem is.
   (b) Draw a picture of the process.
   (c) Put down all the compositions of the entering and leaving streams.
   (d) Decide which weights are known and unknown.
   (e) Find a tie element and/or set up mass balances involving the un-
       knowns.
   (f) Solve for the required values.

2. You should understand the once-through balance for recycle problems
   involving chemical reactions.

NOMENCLATURE

a = constant
A = coefficient matrix
b = constant
D = distillate product
fg = flue gas
F = feed
m = number of equations
n = number of unknown variables
P = product
r = rank of a matrix
R = recycle stream
sg = stack gas
W = waste stream
x = unknown variable

SUPPLEMENTARY REFERENCES

1. Anderson, H. V., *Chemical Calculations*, McGraw-Hill Book Company, New York, 1955.

2. Benson, S. W., *Chemical Calculations*, 2nd ed., John Wiley & Sons, Inc., New York, 1963.

3. Felsing, W. A., and G. W. Watt, *General Chemistry*, McGraw-Hill Book Company, New York, 1951.

4. Henley, E. J., and H. Bieber, *Chemical Engineering Calculations*, McGraw-Hill Book Company, New York, 1959.

5. Hougen, O. A., K. M. Watson, and R. A. Ragatz, *Chemical Process Principles*, Part I, 2nd ed., John Wiley & Sons, Inc., New York, 1956.

6. Littlejohn, C. E., and G. F. Meenaghan, *An Introduction to Chemical Engineering*, Reinhold Publishing Corp., New York, 1959.

7. Schmidt, A. X., and H. L. List, *Material and Energy Balances*, Prentice-Hall, Inc., Englewood Cliffs, N.J., 1962.

8. Williams, E. T., and R. C. Johnson, *Stoichiometry for Chemical Engineers*, McGraw-Hill Book Company, New York, 1958.

PROBLEMS

2.1. By use of an over-all steady-state material balance determinine whether or not the petrochemical process indicated in the accompanying diagram has

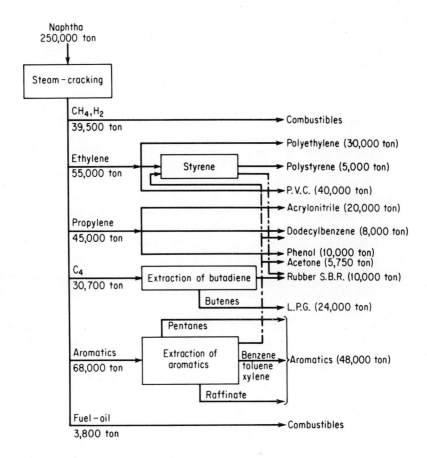

been properly formulated. The block diagrams represent the steam cracking of naphtha into various products, and all flows are on an annual basis, i.e., per year.

2.2. A schematic diagram is shown for the production of aromatics, synthetic fibers, and plastics using naphtha as a feed stock. Check the over-all steady-state material balance to see that the annual flows are correctly represented in the diagram.

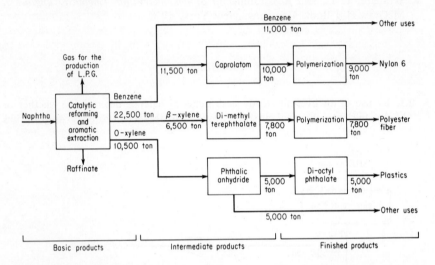

2.3. Consider a lake as a system, and discuss the material balance on (a) water, (b) salts, and (c) plant life which might be made for such a lake. What quantities can be measured, and what quantities must be calculated?

2.4. Hydrogen-free carbon in the form of coke is burnt (a) with complete combustion using theoretical air, (b) with complete combustion using 50% excess air, and (c) using 50% excess air but with 10% of the carbon burning to CO only. In each case calculate the gas analysis which will be found by testing the flue gases with an Orsat apparatus.

2.5. If dry hydrogen gas at atmospheric pressure is burnt completely in a furnace with 32% excess air, calculate the Orsat analysis of the flue gas from this furnace.

2.6. If moist hydrogen containing 4% of water by volume is burnt completely in a furnace with 32% excess air, calculate the Orsat analysis of the resulting flue gas.

2.7. (a) If pure methane is burnt completely in a furnace with theoretical air, calculate (1) the analysis of the resulting flue gas and (2) the analysis of the stack gas.

(b) Repeat part (a) on the assumption that 32% excess air is employed.

2.8. Aviation gasoline is isooctane, C_8H_{18}. If it is burned with 20% excess air and 30% of the carbon forms carbon monoxide, what is the flue-gas analysis?

2.9. "Flammo" is liquified propane (C_3H_8) and is used for gas heating. If it were burned with 25% excess air and 15% of the carbon formed carbon monoxide, what would be the flue-gas analysis?

2.10. Propane (C_3H_8) is a liquified gas used extensively for gas heating. If it were burned with 40% excess air and 10% of the carbon formed carbon monoxide, what would be the flue-gas analysis?

2.11. A steel-annealing furnace burns a fuel oil, the composition of which can be represented as $(CH_2)_n$. It is planned to burn this fuel with 12% excess air. Assuming complete combustion, calculate the Orsat analysis of the flue gas. Repeat this problem on the assumption that 5% of the carbon in the fuel is burnt to CO only.

2.12. A gas of the following analysis is being burned under a boiler with 100% excess air: CH_4, 10%; CS_3, 30%; CO_2, 10%; H_2, 10%; N_2, 40%. Calculate the flue-gas analysis on an SO_2 free basis.

2.13. A natural gas analyzes CH_4, 80.0% and N_2, 20.0%. It is burned under a boiler and most of the CO_2 is scrubbed out of the flue gas for the production of dry ice. The exit gas from the scrubber analyzes CO_2, 1.2%; O_2, 4.9%; and N_2, 93.9%. Calculate the:
(a) Per cent of the CO_2 absorbed
(b) Per cent excess air used

2.14. A natural gas that analyzes 80% CH_4 and 20% N_2 is burned, and the CO_2 scrubbed out of the resulting products for use in the manufacture of dry ice. The exit gases from the scrubber analyze 6% O_2 and 94% N_2. Calculate the:
(a) Air to gas ratio
(b) Per cent excess air

2.15. The U.B.T. Development Company is selling a fuel cell which generates electrical energy by direct conversion of coal into electrical energy. The cell is quite simple—it works on the same principle as a storage battery and produces energy free from the Carnot cycle limitation. To make clear the outstanding advantages of the fuel cell, we can consider the reaction:

$$\text{fuel} + \text{oxygen} = \text{oxidation products} \qquad (1)$$

Reaction (1) is intended to apply to any fuel and always to 1 mole of the fuel. The fuel cell is remarkable in that it can convert chemical energy directly into work and by-pass the wasteful intermediate conversion into heat. A typical fuel consists of:

C	65%
H	5
O	10
S	4
ash	16

Assume no carbon is left in the ash and that the S is oxidized to SO_2.
(a) If 20% excess air is used for oxidation of the fuel, calculate the compositions of all the oxidation products.

(b) If the same fuel were burned with 20% excess air in a furnace and 80% of the C went to CO_2, 15% to CO, and 5% remained as C in the ash (unburned), what would be the composition of the resulting flue gas? (The ash does not go into the flue gas.)

2.16. A producer gas analyzing CO_2, 4.5%; CO, 26%; H_2, 13%; CH_4, 0.5%; N_2, 56%, is burned in a furnace with 10% excess air. Calculate the Orsat analysis of the flue gas.

2.17. A producer gas made from coke has the following composition in mole per cent: CO, 27.3%; CO_2, 5.4%; O_2, 0.6%; N_2, 66.7%. This gas is burned with such a quantity of air that the oxygen entering is 20% in excess of that required to combine with the gas. If the combustion is 98% complete, calculate the weight and composition of the gaseous products formed per 100 lb of gas used.

2.18. The Deacon process can be reversed and HCl formed from Cl_2 and steam by removing the O_2 formed with hot coke as follows:

$$2Cl_2 + 2H_2O + C \longrightarrow 4HCl + CO_2$$

If chlorine cell gas analyzing 90% Cl_2 and 10% air is mixed with 5% excess steam and the mixture passed through a hot coke bed at 900°C, the conversion of Cl_2 will be 80% complete but all the O_2 in the air will react. Calculate the composition of the exit gases from the converter, assuming no CO formation.

2.19. A coke-fired furnace uses a fuel containing 81% C, 0.8% H, and the rest ash. This furnace is designed to operate with 60% excess air. Calculate the flue-gas analysis, assuming complete combustion, and repeat, assuming that 5% of the carbon is burnt to CO only.

2.20. Your assistant reports the following data: A hydrocarbon oil is burned in a furnace with 10% excess air yielding a flue gas containing CO_2, 11.8%; CO, 2%; H_2, 1.5%; O_2, 4%; N_2 by difference. Would you compliment him on his work or not?

2.21. Twelve hundred pounds of $Ba(NO_3)_2$ are dissolved in sufficient water to form a saturated solution at 90°C, at which temperature the solubility is 30.6 g/100 g water. The solution is then cooled to 20°C at which temperature the solubility is 8.6 g/100 g water.

(a) How many pounds of water are required for solution at 90°C, and what weight of crystals is obtained at 20°C?

(b) How many pounds of water are required for solution at 90°C, and what weight of crystals is obtained at 20°C, assuming that 10% more water is to be used than necessary for a saturated solution at 90°C?

(c) How many pounds of water are required for solution at 90°C, and what weight of crystals is obtained at 20°C, assuming that the solution is to be made up 90% saturated at 90°C?

(d) How many pounds of water are required for solution at 90°C, and what weight of crystals is obtained at 20°C, assuming that 5% of the water evaporates on cooling and that the crystals hold saturated solution mechanically in the amount of 5% of their dry weight?

2.22. How much water must be evaporated from 100 gal of Na_2CO_3 solution, containing 50 g/liter at 30°C, so that 70% of the Na_2CO_3 will crystallize out when the solution is cooled to 0°C?

2.23. The solubility of magnesium sulfate at 20°C is 35.5 g/100 g H_2O. How much $MgSO_4 \cdot 7 H_2O$ must be dissolved in 100 lb of H_2O to form a saturated solution?

2.24. The solubility of manganous sulfate at 20°C is 62.9 g/100 g H_2O. How much $MnSO_4 \cdot 5 H_2O$ must be dissolved in 100 lb of water to give a saturated solution?

2.25. An evaporator is fed with a 25% NaCl solution. It is to produce 14,670 lb of dry salt per hour. The salt removed carries 20% of its weight of brine (26.9% salt). How many pounds of feed solution are fed to the evaporator per hour?

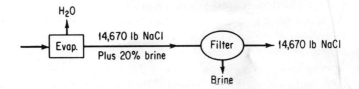

2.26. If 100 g of Na_2SO_4 is dissolved in 200 g of H_2O and the solution is cooled until 100 g of $Na_2SO_4 \cdot 10 H_2O$ crystallizes out, find:
(a) The composition of the remaining solution ("mother liquor")
(b) The grams of crystals recovered per 100 g of initial solution

2.27. The feed to a small continuous distillation unit is 20 gal/min. If the feed, product, and waste average 20.0%, 83.0%, and 2.0% ethanol, by weight, calculate the respective rates in gallons per minute at which the product and the waste must be removed. Data for alcohol are as follows:

% by weight	specific gravity
2.0	0.996
20.0	0.971
83.0	0.840

2.28. Fourteen hundred and eighty gallons of 95.2% by weight ethyl alcohol at 60°F, having a sp gr of 0.8080, is diluted with water to 2777 gal at the same temperature, the sp gr of the product being 0.9309. How many gallons of water at 60°F are required (sp gr = 1.000)?

2.29. A gas containing 80% CH_4 and 20% He is sent through a quartz diffusion tube to recover the helium. Twenty per cent by weight of the original gas is recovered, and its composition is 50% He. Calculate the composition of the waste gas if 100 lb moles of gas are processed per minute. The initial gas pres-

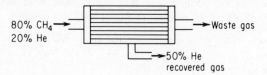

sure is 17 psia, and the final gas pressure is 2 psig. The barometer reads 740 mm Hg. The temperature of the process is 70°F.

2.30. A set of sugar evaporators handles 120 short tons/24 hr of pure cane sugar, fed to the evaporators as 38% solution and discharged by them as 74% solution. How many pounds of water do these units evaporate per day?

2.31. As dug from the ground, peat has the following composition:

moisture	88.0%
volatile matter	8.05
fixed carbon	3.18
ash	0.77

For use as a domestic fuel this peat is dried until it contains only 10% water. A process for drying by artificial heat is developed whereby water may be evaporated at a cost of 2.5 cents/100 lb of water removed. Calculate the drying cost per ton of product.

2.32. A 50 ml sample of a sodium carbonate solution is found to weigh 53.03 g at 20°C, and on titration with 1N acid 60.0 ml are used. The original solution is to be evaporated in a vacuum evaporator at 60°C until saturated and then cooled until 70% of the sodium carbonate has crystallized out. Calculate the:
(a) Per cent reduction in weight on evaporation
(b) Temperature to which the solution must be cooled
Use solubility data from the literature.

2.33. After drying, a batch of leather is found to weigh 900 lb and to contain 7% of moisture. During drying, the leather lost 59.1% of its original weight when wet. Calculate the:
(a) Percentage of "bone-dry," or moisture-free," leather in the original stock
(b) Number of pounds of water removed in the drying process per pound of bone-dry leather
(c) Percentage of the water removed based on the water originally present

2.34. Paper pulp is sold on the basis that it contains 12% moisture; if the moisture exceeds this value, the purchaser can deduct any charges for the excess moisture and also deduct for the freight costs of the excess moisture. A shipment of pulp became wet and was received with a moisture content of 22%. If the original price for the pulp was $40/ton of air-dry pulp and if the freight is $1.00/100 lb shipped, what price should be paid per ton of pulp delivered?

2.35. In order to meet certain specifications, a dealer mixes bone-dry glue, selling at 25 cents/lb, with glue containing 22% moisture, selling at 14 cents/lb, so that the mixture contains 16% moisture. What should be the selling price per pound of the mixed glue?

2.36. A paper manufacturer contracts for rosin size containing not more than 20% water at 12 cents/lb f.o.b. the rosin-size plant, a deduction to be made for water above this amount, and the excess freight on the water is to be charged back to the manufacturer at 80 cents/100 lb. A shipment of 2400 lb is received which analyzes 26.3% water. What should the paper manufacturer pay for the shipment?

2.37. A laundry can purchase soap containing 30% water at a price of $7.00/100 lb f.o.b. the factory. The same manufacturer offers a soap containing 5% water. If the freight rate is 60 cents/100 lb, what is the maximum price that the laundry should pay the manufacturer for the soap containing 5% water?

2.38. Pure carbon dioxide may be prepared by treating limestone with aqueous sulfuric acid. The limestone used in such a process contained calcium carbonate and magnesium carbonate, the remainder being inert, insoluble materials. The acid used contained 12% H_2SO_4 by weight. The residue from the process had the following composition: $CaSO_4$, 8.56%; $MgSO_4$, 5.23%; H_2SO_4, 1.05%; inerts, 0.53%; CO_2, 0.12%; water, 84.51%. During the process the mass was warmed and carbon dioxide and water vapor removed. Calculate the:

(a) Analysis of the limestone used

(b) Percentage of excess aicd used

(c) Weight and analysis of the material distilled from the reaction mass per 1000 lb of limestone treated

2.39. A natural gas which is entirely methane, CH_4, is burned with an oxygen-enriched air so that a higher flame temperature may be obtained. The flue gas analyzes CO_2, 22.2%; O_2, 4.4%; N_2, 73.4%. Calculate the per cent of O_2 and N_2 in the oxygen-enriched air.

2.40. As superintendent of a lacquer plant, your foreman brings you the following problem: He has to make up 1000 lb of an 8% nitrocellulose solution. He has available a tank of a 5.5% solution. How much dry nitrocellulose must he add to how much of the 5.5% solution in order to fill the order?

2.41. Your boss asks you to calculate the flow through a natural-gas pipe line. Since it is 26 in. in diameter, it is impossible to run the gas through any kind of meter or measuring device. You decide to add 100 lb of CO_2 per minute to the gas through a small $\frac{1}{2}$-in. piece of pipe, collect samples of the gas downstream, and analyze them for CO_2. Several consecutive samples after 1 hr are:

time	% CO_2
1 hr, 0 min	2.0
10 min	2.2
20 min	1.9
30 min	2.1
40 min	2.0

(a) Calculate the flow of gas in pounds per minute at the point of injection.

(b) Unfortunately for you, the gas at the point of injection of CO_2 already contained 1.0% CO_2. How much was your original flow estimate in error (in per cent)?

Note: In (a) the natural gas is all methane, CH_4.

2.42. Chlorine gas containing 2.4% O_2 is flowing through an earthenware pipe. The gas flow is measured by introducing air into it at the rate of 115 ft³/min and further down the line, after mixing is complete, removing a sample of gas for analysis. The gas is now found to contain 10.85% O_2. How many cubic feet of the initial gas were flowing per minute through the pipe?

2.43. It is desired to measure the rate at which waste gases are passing up a stack. The gases entering contain 2.1% carbon dioxide by weight. Pure carbon dioxide is introduced into the bottom of the stack at a measured rate of 4.0 lb/min. It is found that the gases leaving the stack contain 3.2% carbon dioxide by weight. Calculate the rate of flow, in pounds per minute, of the entering waste gases.

2.44. Seidell, *Solubilities of Inorganic Compounds*, p. 1210, gives the following data for the solubility in the ternary system Na_2CO_3—Na_2SO_4—H_2O. Below about 30°C the stable form of each salt is the decahydrate and no double salts are formed.

temp.	grams salt/100 g sat. soln.		
°C	Na_2CO_3	Na_2SO_4	solid phases
15	14.1	0.0	C-10*
	12.3	8.0	C-10 + S-10**
	0.0	11.8	S-10
20	17.75	0.0	C-10
	14.95	11.2	C-10 + S-10
	0.0	16.25	S-10
25	22.6	0.0	C-10
	17.9	16.2	C-10 + S-10
	0.0	21.9	S-10

    * C-10 = $Na_2CO_3 \cdot 10\ H_2O$
 ** S-10 = $Na_2SO_4 \cdot 10\ H_2O$

One thousand pounds of a solution containing 3.0% Na_2SO_4 and 18.0% Na_2CO_3 has 100 lb of water removed by flash vaporization, which cools the solution to 15°C. How much of what crystallizes from the solution?

2.45. A low-grade pyrites containing 32% S is mixed with 10 lb of pure sulfur per 100 lb pyrites so the mixture will burn readily, forming a burner gas that analyzes (Orsat) SO_2, 13.4%; O_2, 2.7%; N_2, 83.9%. No sulfur is left in the cinder. Calculate the percentage of the sulfur fired that burned to SO_3. (The SO_3 is not detected by the Orsat analysis.)

2.46. Reclaimed rubber containing 3.0% S is milled with crude rubber until the mix contains 0.80% S. How many pounds of reclaimed rubber are used per ton of crude?

2.47. Because of the shortage of sulfur, many plants use the combustion of pyrites (the pure mineral is FeS_2, the commercial mineral always contains gangue) as a source of SO_2 for the production of sulfuric acid and sulfite pulping liquor. Pyrites containing 48.0% sulfur is burned by flash combustion, in which apparatus all iron forms Fe_3O_4 in the cinder and a negligible amount of SO_3 is formed in either the cinder or the burner gas. The gas from such a furnace is passed through milk-of-lime absorbers to produce bisulfite pulping liquor. The exit gas analyzes SO_2, 0.7%; O_2, 2.9%; N_2, 96.4%. Calculate the pounds of air supplied to the burner per pound of pyrites.

2.48. An SO_2 absorption column is designed to reduce the SO_2 content of air. If the entering water contains 5% SO_2 and the exit water contains 20% SO_2, how much 5% solution is needed to make 100 lb of 20% SO_2 solution?

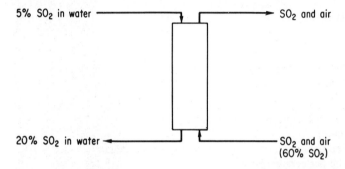

2.49. Pure barytes, $BaSO_4$, is fused with soda ash, Na_2CO_3, and the fusion mass is then leached with water. The solid residue from the leaching analyzes 33.6% $BaSO_4$ and 66.4% $BaCO_3$. The soluble salts in solution analyze 41.9% Na_2SO_4 and 58.1% Na_2CO_3. Calculate the composition of the mixture before fusion.

2.50. A power company operates one of its boilers on natural gas and another on oil (for peak period operation). The analysis of the fuels are as follows:

natural gas	*oil*
96% CH_4	$(CH_{1.8})_n$
4% CO_2	

When both boilers are on the line, the flue gas shows (Orsat analysis) 10.0% CO_2, 4.5% O_2, and the remainder N_2. What percentage of the total carbon burned comes from the oil?

Hint: Do not forget the H_2O in the stack gas.

2.51. A power company operates one of its boilers on natural gas and another on oil. The analyses of the fuels show 96% CH_4, 2% C_2H_2, and 2% CO_2 for the natural gas and $C_nH_{1.8n}$ for the oil. The flue gases from both groups enter the same stack, and an Orsat analysis of this combined flue gas shows 10.0% CO_2, 0.63% CO, and 4.55% O_2. What percentage of the total carbon burned comes from the oil?

2.52. An automobile engine burning a fuel consisting of a mixture of hydrocarbons is found to give an exhaust gas analyzing 10.0% CO_2 by the Orsat method. It is known that the exhaust gas contains no oxygen or hydrogen. Careful metering of the air entering the engine and the fuel used shows that 12.4 lb of dry air enter the engine for every pound of fuel used.

(a) Calculate the complete Orsat gas analysis.

(b) What is the weight ratio of hydrogen to carbon in the fuel?

2.53. A fuel oil and a sludge are burned together in a furnace with dry air. Assume the fuel oil contains only C and H.

fuel oil	sludge		flue gas
	wet	*dry*	
C = ?%	water = 50%	S = 32%	SO_2 = 1.52%
	solids = 50	C = 40	CO_2 = 10.14
H = ?%		H_2 = 4	CO = 2.02
		O_2 = 24	O_2 = 4.65
			N_2 = 81.67

(a) Determine the weight per cent composition of the fuel oil.

(b) Determine the ratio of pounds of sludge to pounds of fuel oil.

2.54. A coal analyzes 74% C and 12% ash (inert). The flue gas from the combustion of the coal analyzes CO_2, 12.4%; CO, 1.2%; O_2, 5.7%; and N_2, 80.7%. Calculate:

(a) The pounds of coal fired per 100 mole of flue gas

(b) The per cent excess air

(c) The pounds of air used per pound of coal

2.55. A solvent dewaxing unit in an oil refinery is separating 3000 bbl per day of a lubricating distillate into 23 vol. % of slack wax and 77 vol. % of dewaxed oil. The charge is mixed with solvent, chilled, and filtered into wax and oil solution streams. The solvent is then removed from the two streams by two banks of stripping columns, the bottoms from each column in a bank being charged to the next column in the bank. The oil bank consists of four columns, and the wax bank of three. A test on the charge and bottoms from each column gave the following results:

	per cent solvent by volume				
	to 1st column	*no. 1 bottoms*	*no. 2 bottoms*	*no. 3 bottoms*	*no. 4 bottoms*
pressed oil	83	70	27	4.0	0.8
wax	83	71	23	0.5	—

Calculate:

(a) Total solution per day charged to the whole unit

(b) Per cent of total solvent in oil solution removed by each column in oil bank

(c) Per cent of total solvent in wax solution removed by each column in wax bank

(d) Barrels of solvent lost per day (in bottoms from last column of each bank)

2.56. HCl gas is absorbed from air in a countercurrent system consisting of three packed towers. The gas is drawn through the towers by an exhauster attached to the gas discharge of the third tower, the whole system being under slight suction. The HCl solution is pumped from the bottom of each tower to the top of the next preceding one in the series. The production is 2640 lb/hr of 36.2% HCl, 1.18 sp gr. The tower temperatures average 28°C; the barometer is 29.1 in.

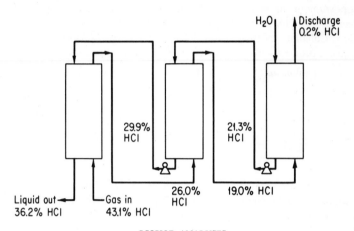

LIQUOR ANALYSES
samples taken at liquor exit from each tower

	tower 1	tower 2	tower 3
per cent HCl	36.2%	29.9%	21.3%

GAS ANALYSES
first three samples taken at bottom of each tower

	tower 1	tower 2	tower 3	leaving tower 3
per cent HCl	43.1%	26.0%	19.0%	0.2%

Calculate the per cent of the total acid absorbed which is dissolved in the second tower. What can you conclude from a complete material balance on this system?

2.57. The price of crude oil is based on its API gravity; the highest gravities command the best prices. It is often possible to blend two crudes advantageously so that the price obtained for the mixture is greater than the price of the separate crudes. This is possible because the price vs. API function is discontinuous (like income tax rates). A crude oil with a 34.4° API gravity is to be mixed with 50,000 bbl of a 30.0° API gravity crude to give a mixture which has a gravity of 31.0° API. What is the increased selling price of the mixed crude over that of the separate components?

Data: (1) Crude prices:

API	$/bbl
29.0–30.9	$2.60
31.0–32.9	2.65
33.0–34.9	2.70

(2) API gravities are not additive on any basis.

(3) Sp gr at 60°F = 141.5/(131.5 + API).

2.58. It is desired to mix three L.P.G. (Liquified Petroleum Gas) products in certain proportions in order that the final mixture will meet certain vapor pressure specifications. These specifications will be met by a stream of composition D below. Calculate the proportions in which streams A, B, and C must be mixed to give a product with a composition of D. The values are liquid volume %.

component	stream A	B	C	D
C_2	5.0			1.4
C_3	90.0	10.0		31.2
iso-C_4	5.0	85.0	8.0	53.4
n-C_4		5.0	80.0	12.6
iso-C_5^+			12.0	1.4
	100.0	100.0	100.0	100.0

2.59. A plant is to produce 50 tons per day of the solid product shown. A solution of sodium carbonate in water is pumped to the first neutralization tank where it is reacted with 10% excess phosphoric acid.

$$Na_2CO_3 + H_3PO_4 \longrightarrow Na_2HPO_4 + CO_2 + H_2O$$

The phosphoric acid is fed as an 85% solution of H_3PO_4 in water. The carbon dioxide produced leaves as a gas. The disodium phosphate solution produced is pumped to a second neutralizer where the excess phosphoric acid and the disodium phosphate are converted to trisodium phosphate by the addition of a 50% NaOH solution. The solution leaving the second neutralizer contains

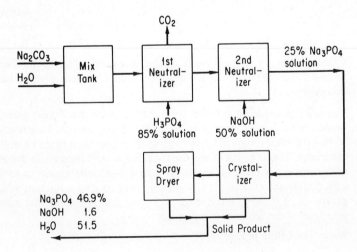

25% by weight trisodium phosphate, Na_3PO_4. All of the phosphate is converted to trisodium phosphate in the second neutralizer. The trisodium phosphate solution is cooled and some solid product crystallizes out. The solution remaining is spray dried, and the solid products of the crystallizer and the spray drier are combined. Compute:

(a) The composition of the Na_2CO_3 solution pumped to the first neutralizer in weight per cent

(b) The pounds of 85% phosphoric acid, Na_2CO_3, and 50% NaOH required per hour

2.60. Ethylene oxide, C_2H_4O, is made by the catalytic reaction between ethylene (C_2H_4) and oxygen. Fresh C_2H_4, O_2, and recycled ethylene are mixed to give a reactor feed containing 40 mole % C_2H_4. This reacts at 1 atm and 260°C. A test shows 40% of the ethylene entering the reactor is consumed per pass, and, of this, 60% goes to ethylene oxide by the reaction:

$$C_2H_4 + \tfrac{1}{2}O_2 \longrightarrow C_2H_4O$$

The rest decomposes to CO_2 and H_2O. The unreacted ethylene is separated from the reactor products and is recycled. The CO_2, H_2O, and O_2 are vented. For each 100,000 ft³ of ethylene introduced to the process at 60°F and 1 atm, calculate the moles of ethylene oxide recycled per mole of ethylene introduced.

2.61. If machine parts are degreased by means of kerosene as shown in the diagram, how much kerosene make-up is needed per day? How much kerosene has to enter the degreasing vat per day? There are about 3 lb of grease per 100 lb of machine parts, and 60 tons of machine parts are processed each day. Five thousand pounds of kerosene (the 10% solution) are carried away by the

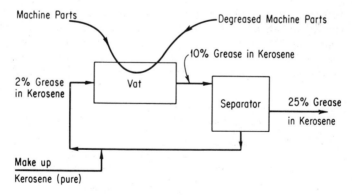

machine parts each day but drip off and are caught and put back into the degreasing vat. Two hundred pounds of the 10% solution are lost each day from the vat by evaporation, spillage, or by being carried away.

2.62. Butane is being dehydrogenated to butene in a catalytic reactor. A flow diagram of the process is shown. If the per cent conversion is 5% and the per cent selectivity is 50%, calculate the moles of butene, off gas, and coke produced per mole of *fresh* butane feed.

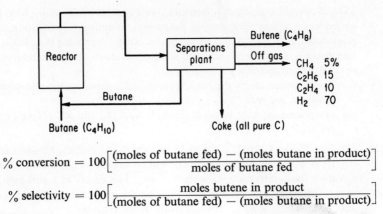

$$\% \text{ conversion} = 100 \left[\frac{(\text{moles of butane fed}) - (\text{moles butane in product})}{\text{moles of butane fed}} \right]$$

$$\% \text{ selectivity} = 100 \left[\frac{\text{moles butene in product}}{(\text{moles of butane fed}) - (\text{moles butane in product})} \right]$$

2.63. What is the pound recycle per pound feed if the amount of A waste is . . . lb?

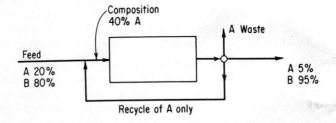

2.64. Benzene, toluene, and other aromatic compounds can be recovered by solvent extraction with sulfur dioxide. As an example, a catalytic reformate stream containing 70% by weight benzene and 30% nonbenzene material is passed through the countercurrent extractive recovery scheme shown in the diagram. One thousand pounds of the reformate stream and 3000 lb of sulfur dioxide

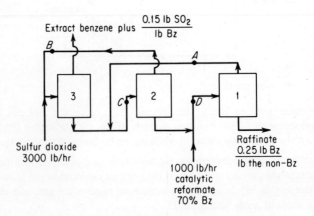

are fed to the system per hour. The benzene product stream contains 0.15 lb of sulfur dioxide per pound of benzene. The raffinate stream contains all the initially charged nonbenzene material as well as 0.25 lb of benzene per pound of nonbenzene material. The remaining component in the raffinate stream is the sulfur dioxide.

(a) How many pounds of benzene are extracted per hour? What are the lb of extract and raffinate per hour?

(b) If 800 lb of benzene containing 0.25 lb of nonbenzene material per pound of benzene are flowing per hour at point A and 700 lb of benzene containing 0.07 lb of nonbenzene material per pound of benzene are flowing at point B, how many pounds (exclusive of the sulfur dioxide) are flowing at points C and D?

2.65. A contact sulfuric acid plant produces 98.0% sulfuric acid. A gas containing 8.00% SO_3 (remainder inerts) enters the SO_3 absorption tower at the rate of 28 lb mole/hr. Of the SO_3, 98.5% is absorbed in this tower; 97.3% (wt) H_2SO_4 is introduced into the top of the tower; and 95.9% (wt) H_2SO_4 from the air-drying tower is used as make-up acid. The flow sheet is given below.

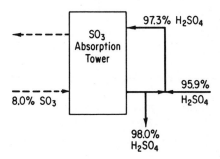

Compute:

(a) Tons/day of 95.9% H_2SO_4 make-up acid solution required

(b) Tons/day of 97.3% H_2SO_4 solution introduced into the top of the tower

(c) Tons/day of 98.0% H_2SO_4 solution produced

2.66. In the production of NH_3, the mole ratio of the N_2 to the H_2 in the feed to the whole process is 1 N_2 to 3 H_2. Of the feed *to the reactor*, 25% is converted to NH_3. The NH_3 formed is condensed to a liquid and completely removed from the reactor, while the unreacted N_2 and H_2 are recycled back to mix with the feed to the process. What is the ratio of recycle to feed in pound recycle per pound feed? The feed is at 100°F and 10 atm, while the product is at 40°F and 8 atm.

2.67. An isomerizer is a catalytic reactor which simply tends to rearrange isomers. The number of moles entering an isomerizer is equal to the number of moles leaving. A process, as shown in the figure, has been designed to produce a *p*-xylene-rich product from an aromatic feed charge. All compositions on the flow sheet are in mole per cent. The components are indicated as follows:

A	ethyl benzene
B	o-xylene
C	m-xylene
D	p-xylene

Eighty per cent of the ethyl benzene entering the distillation tower is removed in the top stream from the tower. The ratio of the moles of feed per mole of product from the crystallizer is 1.63. Find the:

(a) Reflux ratio (ratio of moles of stream from the bottom of the distillation tower per mole of feed to the tower)
(b) Composition (in mole per cent) of the product from the crystallizer
(c) Moles leaving the isomerizer per mole of feed

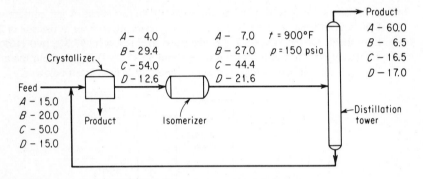

2.68. In a process for the preparation of methyl iodide, 2000 lb per day of hydro-iodic acid are added to an excess of methanol.

$$HI + CH_3OH \longrightarrow CH_3I + H_2O$$

If the product contains 81.6% CH_3I along with the unreacted methanol, and the waste contains 82.6% hydro-iodic acid and 17.4% H_2O, calculate, assuming the reaction is 50% complete:

(a) The weight of methanol added per day
(b) The amount of HI recycled

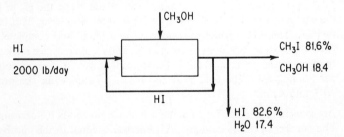

2.69. Raw water for use in a boiler has the following analysis in ppm (pounds per million pounds of pure water):

Ca^{++}	90
Mg^{++}	60
Na$^+$ and K$^+$	40
HCO$_3^-$	270
SO$_4^{--}$ and Cl$^-$	160
total solids	620 ppm

Na$_3$PO$_4$ is added in 10% excess above that required to form insoluble Ca$_3$(PO$_4$)$_2$ and Mg$_3$(PO$_4$)$_2$, which are allowed to settle out before the treated water is fed to the boiler. The reactions are complete, and no other reactions

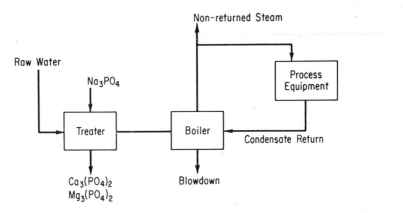

occur. The steam produced entrains 4 lb of liquid per 100 lb of dry steam. Sixty per cent of this wet steam returns to the boiler as condensate after picking up an additional 40 ppm of dissolved solids during passage through the equipment and return lines. The total solids concentration in the boiler must not exceed 3000 ppm. Therefore, water of this concentration is continuously withdrawn, or "blown down." The solids content of the liquid in the steam is the same as that of the liquid in the boiler. Compute the ratio of blowdown to treated-water feed required.

2.70. A 50% NaCl solution is to be concentrated in a triple-effect evaporator as shown in the diagram. (Each individual evaporator is termed an "effect.")

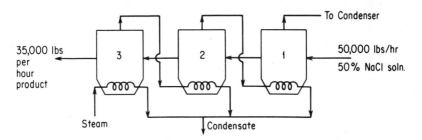

An equal amount of water is evaporated in each effect. Determine the composition of the outlet stream from effect no. 2 if the internal contents of effect no. 2 are uniformly mixed so that the outlet stream has the same composition as the internal contents of effect no. 2. The steam lines in each effect are completely separate from the evaporator contents so that no mixing of the steam with the contents occurs.

Chapter 3

GASES, VAPORS, LIQUIDS,

AND SOLIDS

The investigators who originally developed correlating relations for gas temperature, pressure, and volume worked at temperatures and pressures such that the average distance between the molecules was great enough to neglect the effect of the intermolecular forces and the volume of the molecules themselves. This convenient situation led to the laws of Boyle, Gay-Lussac, and Charles and to the "perfect" ("ideal") gas law. For many engineering purposes, the ideal gas laws, if properly applied, will give answers correct within a few per cent, or less. In the liquid and solid states with the molecules compacted relatively close together, we do not have such general laws. In this section we are going to discuss real gas relationships as well as some of the gas laws for pure components and mixtures of ideal gases. You will learn about methods of expressing the p-V-T properties of real gases by means of equations of state and, alternatively, by compressibility factors. Finally, you will be introduced to the concept of vaporization, condensation, and vapor pressure for pure components.

3.1 Ideal gas laws

An ideal gas is an imaginary gas which obeys exactly certain simple laws such as the laws of Boyle, Charles, Dalton, and Amagat. Such a gas has mass, but the gas molecules themselves occupy no volume and do not exert forces on one another. No real gas obeys these laws exactly over all ranges of temperature and pressure, although the lighter gases (hydrogen, oxygen, air, etc.) under ordinary circumstances obey the ideal gas laws with but negligible deviations. The heavier gases such as sulfur dioxide and hydrocarbons, particularly at high pressures and low temperatures, deviate considerably from the ideal gas laws. Vapors, under conditions near the boiling point, deviate markedly from the ideal gas laws. However, at low pressures and high temperatures the behavior of a vapor approaches that of an ideal gas.

In order that the volumetric properties of various gases may be compared, several arbitrarily specified standard states (usually known as *standard conditions*, or S.C.) of temperature and pressure have been selected by custom. The most common standard conditions of temperature and pressure are:

Universal Scientific   32°F and 760 mm Hg (and their equivalents)

Natural Gas Industry   60°F and 14.7 psia

The first set of standard conditions, the Universal Scientific, is the one you have previously encountered and is by far the most common in use. Under these conditions the following volumetric data are true for any *ideal gas:*

$$1 \text{ g mole} = 22.4 \text{ liters at S.C.}$$

$$1 \text{ lb mole} = 359 \text{ cubic feet at S.C.}$$

$$1 \text{ kg mole} = 22.4 \text{ cubic meters at S.C.}$$

The fact that a substance cannot exist as a gas at 32°F and 29.92 in. Hg is immaterial. Thus, as we shall see later on, water vapor at 32°F cannot exist at a pressure greater than its saturation pressure of 0.18 in. Hg without condensation occurring. However, the imaginary volume at standard conditions can be calculated and is just as useful a quantity in the calculation of volume-mole relationships as though it could exist. In the following, the symbol V will stand for total volume, and the symbol $\hat{V}$ for volume per mole, or per unit mass.

Example 3.1   Use of Standard Conditions

Calculate the volume, in cubic feet, occupied by 88 lb of CO_2 at standard conditions.

Solution:

Basis: 88 lb CO_2

$$\frac{88 \text{ lb } CO_2}{} \left| \frac{1 \text{ lb mole } CO_2}{44 \text{ lb } CO_2} \right| \frac{359 \text{ ft}^3 \text{ } CO_2}{1 \text{ lb mole } CO_2} = 718 \text{ ft}^3 \text{ } CO_2 \text{ at S.C.}$$

Notice how in this problem the information that 359 ft³ at S.C. = 1 lb mole is applied to transform a known number of moles into an equivalent number of cubic feet. Incidentally, whenever you use cubic feet, you must establish the conditions of temperature and pressure at which the cubic feet are measured, since the term "ft³," standing alone, is really not any particular *quantity* of material.

3.1-1 Perfect Gas Law. Boyle found that the volume of a gas is inversely proportional to the absolute pressure at constant temperature. Charles showed that, at constant pressure, the volume of a given mass of gas varies directly with the absolute temperature. From the work of Boyle and Charles scientists developed the relationship now called the "perfect gas law" (or sometimes "the ideal gas law"):

$$pV = nRT \tag{3.1}$$

In applying this equation to a process going from an initial set of conditions to a final set of conditions, you can set up ratios of similar terms which are dimensionless as follows:

$$\left(\frac{p_1}{p_2}\right)\left(\frac{V_1}{V_2}\right) = \left(\frac{n_1}{n_2}\right)\left(\frac{T_1}{T_2}\right) \tag{3.2}$$

in which the subscripts 1 and 2 refer to the initial and final conditions. This arrangement of the perfect gas law has the convenient feature that the pressures may be expressed in any system of units you choose, such as in. Hg, mm Hg, kg/cm², atm., etc., so long as the same units are used for both conditions of pressure (of course the pressure must be *absolute* pressure in both cases). Similarly, the grouping together of the *absolute* temperature and the volume terms gives ratios that are dimensionless.

Let us see how we can use the perfect gas law.

Example 3.2   Perfect Gas Law

An oxygen cylinder contains 1.000 ft³ of O_2 at 70°F and 2000 psig. What will be the volume of this O_2 in a dry-gas holder at 90°F and 4.0 in. H_2O above atmospheric? The barometer reads 29.92 in. Hg.

Solution:
You must first convert the temperatures and pressures into absolute units.

$$°R_1 = 460 + 70 = 530°R$$
$$°R_2 = 460 + 90 = 550°R$$

atmospheric pressure $= 29.92$ in. Hg $=$ std atm $= 14.7$ psia

$$\text{initial pressure} = \frac{2000 \text{ psig} + 14.7 \text{ psia}}{} \bigg| \frac{29.92 \text{ in. Hg}}{14.7 \text{ psia}} = 4100 \text{ in. Hg}$$

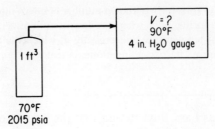

$$\text{final pressure} = 29.92 \text{ in. Hg} + \frac{4 \text{ in. } H_2O}{12 \text{ in. } H_2O} \left| \frac{29.92 \text{ in. Hg}}{33.91 \text{ ft } H_2O} \right.$$

$$= 29.92 + 0.29 = 30.21 \text{ in. Hg}$$

The simplest way to proceed, now that the data are in good order, is to apply the laws of Charles and Boyle, and, in effect, to apply the perfect gas law.

From Charles' law, since the temperature *increases*, the volume *increases;* hence the ratio of the temperatures *must* be greater than 1. The pressure *decreases*; therefore from Boyle's law, the volume will *increase*; hence the ratio of pressures will be *greater* than 1.

Basis: 1 ft³ of oxygen at 70°F and 2000 psig

$$\text{final volume} = \frac{1.00 \text{ ft}^3}{} \left| \frac{550°R}{530°R} \right| \frac{4100 \text{ in. Hg}}{30.21 \text{ in. Hg}}$$

$$= 141 \text{ ft}^3 \text{ at } 90°F \text{ and } 4 \text{ in. } H_2O \text{ gauge}$$

Formally, the same calculation can be made using Eq. (3.2),

$$V_2 = V_1\left(\frac{p_1}{p_2}\right)\left(\frac{T_2}{T_1}\right) \qquad \text{since } n_1 = n_2$$

Example 3.3   Perfect Gas Law

Calculate the weight of 100 ft³ of water vapor at 15.5 mm Hg and 23°C. Assume water vapor is an ideal gas under these conditions.

Solution:

First visualize the information available to you, and then decide how to convert it into the desired weight. If you can convert the original amount of water vapor to S.C. by use of the ideal gas law and then make use of the fact that 359 ft³ = 1 lb mole, you can easily get the desired weight of water vapor.

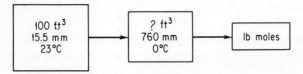

Basis: 100 ft³ H_2O vapor at 15.5 mm Hg and 23°C

$$\frac{100 \text{ ft}^3}{} \left| \frac{15.5 \text{ mm}}{760 \text{ mm}} \right| \frac{(273 + 0)°K}{(273 + 23)°K} \left| \frac{1 \text{ lb mole}}{359 \text{ ft}^3} \right| \frac{18 \text{ lb } H_2O}{1 \text{ lb mole}} = 0.0942 \text{ lb } H_2O$$

Notice how the entire calculation can be carried out in a single dimensional equation.

Example 3.4   Perfect Gas Law

You have 10 lb of CO_2 in a 20-ft³ tank at 30°C. Assuming the ideal gas laws hold, what will the pressure gauge on the tank read?

Solution:

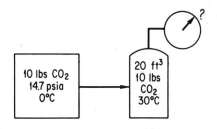

Basis: 10 lb CO_2

Employing Eq. (3.2) we can write (the subscript 1 stands for standard conditions, 2 for the conditions in the tank)

$$p_2 = p_1 \left(\frac{V_1}{V_2} \right) \left(\frac{T_2}{T_1} \right)$$

$$\overset{p_1}{\overbrace{14.7 \text{ psia}}} \left| \frac{10 \text{ lb } CO_2}{} \right| \frac{1 \text{ lb mole } CO_2}{44 \text{ lb } CO_2} \left| \frac{359 \text{ ft}^3}{1 \text{ lb mole}} \right| \underset{V_2}{\overset{}{\underbrace{}}} \frac{}{20 \text{ ft}^3} \left| \overset{\overbrace{}}{\underset{\frac{T_2}{T_1}}{}} \frac{303°K}{273°K} \right.$$

$$\underbrace{\hspace{6cm}}_{V_1}$$

$$= p_2 = 66 \text{ psia}$$

Hence the gauge on the tank will read (assuming it reads gauge pressure and the barometer reads 14.7 psia) 66 − 14.7 = 51.3 psig.

We have not used the gas constant R in the solution of any of the example problems so far, but you can use Eq. (3.1) to solve for one unknown as long as all the other factors in the equation are known. However, such a calculation requires that the units of R be expressed in units corresponding to those used in expressing the variable quantities p-V-T. There are so many possible units you can use to express each variable quantity that a very large table of R values will be required. If, however, you want to use R, you can always determine R from the p-V-T data at standard conditions which you have already memorized and used; R merely represents a pV/T relation at some fixed condition of temperature and pressure.

Example 3.5   Calculation of R

Find the value for the universal gas constant R under the following circumstances:

(a) For 1 lb mole of ideal gas when the pressure is expressed in psia, the volume is in ft³/lb mole, and the temperature is in °R

(b) For 1 g mole of ideal gas when the pressure is in atm, the volume in cm³, and the temperature in °K

Solution:

(a) At standard conditions:

$$p = 14.7 \text{ psia}$$
$$\hat{V} = 359 \text{ ft}^3/\text{lb mole}$$
$$T = 492°\text{R}$$

Then

$$R = \frac{p\hat{V}}{T} = \frac{14.7 \text{ psia}}{492°\text{R}} \left| \frac{359 \text{ ft}^3}{1 \text{ lb mole}} \right. = 10.73 \frac{(\text{psia})(\text{ft}^3)}{(°\text{R})(\text{lb mole})}$$

(b) Similarly at standard conditions:

$$p = 1 \text{ atm}$$
$$\hat{V} = 22,400 \text{ cm}^3/\text{g mole}$$
$$T = 273°\text{K}$$

$$R = \frac{p\hat{V}}{T} = \frac{1 \text{ atm}}{273°\text{K}} \left| \frac{22,400 \text{ cm}^3}{1 \text{ g mole}} \right. = 82.06 \frac{(\text{cm}^3)(\text{atm})}{(°\text{K})(\text{g mole})}$$

We would like to emphasize that R does not have a universal value even though it is called the "universal gas constant." The value of R depends upon the units of p, $\hat{V}$, and T. Similarly, you should realize that R is not a dimensionless quantity; i.e., there is no value of $R = 23.38$, but there is a very important value of

$$R = 21.9 \frac{(\text{in. Hg})(\text{ft}^3)}{(\text{lb mole})(°\text{R})}$$

Example 3.6   Perfect Gas Law

Calculate the volume occupied by 88 lb of CO_2 at a pressure of 32.2 ft of water and at 15°C.

Solution:

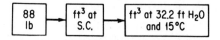

Solution No. 1 (using Boyle's and Charles' laws):
At S.C.:

$$p = 33.91 \text{ ft } H_2O$$

$$\hat{V} = 359 \frac{ft^3}{lb \text{ mole}}$$

$$T = 273°K$$

Basis: 88 lb of CO_2

$$\frac{88 \text{ lb } CO_2}{} \left| \frac{1 \text{ lb mole } CO_2}{44 \text{ lb } CO_2} \right| \frac{359 \text{ ft}^3}{1 \text{ lb mole}} \left| \frac{288}{273} \right| \frac{33.91}{32.2} = \frac{798 \text{ ft}^3 CO_2}{\text{at } 32.2 \text{ ft } H_2O \text{ and } 15°C}$$

Solution No. 2 (using gas constant *R*):
First, the value of *R* must be obtained in the same units as the variables
p, $\hat{V}$, and T. For 1 lb mole,

$$R = \frac{p\hat{V}}{T}$$

and at S.C.,

$$p = 33.91 \text{ ft } H_2O$$

$$V = 359 \text{ ft}^3/\text{lb mole}$$

$$T = 273°K$$

$$R = \frac{33.91}{} \left| \frac{359}{273} \right. = 44.6 \frac{(\text{ft } H_2O)(ft^3)}{(\text{lb mole})(°K)}$$

Now, using Eq. (3.1), inserting the given values and performing the necessary
calculations, we get

Basis: 88 lb CO_2

$$V = \frac{nRT}{p} = \frac{88 \text{ lb } CO_2}{\frac{44 \text{ lb } CO_2}{\text{lb mole } CO_2}} \left| \frac{(44.6 \text{ ft } H_2O)(ft^3)}{(\text{lb mole})(°K)} \right| \frac{288°K}{32.2 \text{ ft } H_2O}$$

$$= 798 \text{ ft}^3 \ CO_2 \text{ at } 32.2 \text{ ft } H_2O \text{ and } 15°C$$

If you will inspect both solutions closely, you will observe that in both
cases the same numbers appear, and both are identical except that in the second
solution (gas-constant method) two steps are required to obtain the solution.

Example 3.7   Perfect Gas Law

Nitrogen tetroxide dissociates as follows:

$$N_2O_4 \longrightarrow 2 \ NO_2$$

If a 100-ml flask contains 1.00 g of N_2O_4 that is 30% dissociated at 40°C, what is the pressure inside the flask in atmospheres?

Solution:

The moles inside the flask are composed partly of N_2O_4 and partly of NO_2. Since the molecular weight of N_2O_4 is 92 ($NO_2 = 46$), we can calculate the

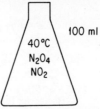

100 ml

40°C
N_2O_4
NO_2

number of moles inside the flask by use of the principles of stoichiometry. Examining the ideal gas law for known and unknown factors,

	p	V	$=$	n	R	T
known		x		x	x	x
unknown	x					

it is apparent that only the pressure is unknown.

Basis: 1.00 g N_2O_4

Seventy per cent of the N_2O_4 is not dissociated.

$$\text{number of moles } N_2O_4 = \frac{1.00 \text{ g } N_2O_4}{} \left| \frac{1 \text{ g mole } N_2O_4}{92 \text{ g } N_2O_4} \right| \frac{0.70}{} = 0.00761$$

Since 2 moles of NO_2 are formed for each mole of N_2O_4 which dissociates the number of moles of NO_2 is

$$= \frac{1.00 \text{ g } N_2O_4}{} \left| \frac{1 \text{ g mole } N_2O_4}{92 \text{ g } N_2O_4} \right| \frac{2 \text{ g mole } NO_2}{1 \text{ g mole } N_2O_4} \left| \frac{0.30}{} \right. = 0.00652$$

total number of moles $= 0.00761 + 0.00652 = 0.01413$

$$p = \frac{nRT}{V}$$

$$= \frac{0.01413 \text{ g mole}}{} \left| \frac{0.08205 \text{ (liter)(atm)}}{\text{(g mole)(°K)}} \right| \frac{(273 + 40)°K}{} \left| \frac{}{0.100 \text{ liter}} \right.$$

$$= 3.63 \text{ atm}$$

If everything but the per cent dissociation is known, i.e., the number of moles after dissociation is known or can be calculated, then you can calculate the per cent dissociation. This is the reverse of the above problem. If the total number of moles is 0.01413, let $x =$ the fraction dissociation of N_2O_4. The quantity $(1 - x)$ represents the fraction of N_2O_4 not dissociated.

N_2O_4 left

$$\frac{1.00 \text{ g } N_2O_4}{} \left| \frac{1 \text{ g mole } N_2O_4}{92 \text{ g } N_2O_4} \right| \frac{(1 - x)}{}$$

$$\text{NO}_2 \text{ formed}$$

$$+\; \frac{1.00 \text{ g N}_2\text{O}_4 \;\bigg|\; 1 \text{ g mole N}_2\text{O}_4 \;\bigg|\; x \;\bigg|\; 2 \text{ g mole NO}_2}{\bigg|\; 92 \text{ g N}_2\text{O}_4 \;\bigg|\; \bigg|\; 1 \text{ g mole N}_2\text{O}_4} = 0.01413$$

Solving, $x = 0.30$.

3.1-2 Gas Density and Specific Gravity. The density of a gas is defined as the mass per unit volume, such as pounds per cubic foot, or grams per liter. Inasmuch as the mass contained in a unit volume varies with the temperature and pressure, as we have previously mentioned, you should always be careful to specify these two conditions. Unless otherwise specified the volumes are presumed to be at S.C. Density can be calculated by selecting a unit volume as the basis and calculating the mass of the contained gas.

Example 3.8   Gas Density

What is the density of N_2 at 80°F and 745 mm Hg expressed in:

(a) American engineering and
(b) cgs units?

Solution:
(a)

Basis: 1 ft³ N_2 at 80°F and 745 mm Hg

$$\frac{1 \text{ ft}^3 \;\bigg|\; 492°\text{R} \;\bigg|\; 745 \text{ mm Hg} \;\bigg|\; 1 \text{ lb mole} \;\bigg|\; 28 \text{ lb}}{\bigg|\; 540°\text{R} \;\bigg|\; 760 \text{ mm Hg} \;\bigg|\; 359 \text{ ft}^3 \;\bigg|\; 1 \text{ lb mole}} = 0.0696 \text{ lb}$$

density = 0.0696 lb/ft³ of N_2 at 80°F and 745 mm Hg

(b)

Basis: 1 l N_2 at 80°F and 745 mm Hg

$$\frac{1 \; l \;\bigg|\; 492°\text{R} \;\bigg|\; 745 \text{ mm Hg} \;\bigg|\; 1 \text{ g mole} \;\bigg|\; 28 \text{ g}}{\bigg|\; 540°\text{R} \;\bigg|\; 760 \text{ mm Hg} \;\bigg|\; 22.4 \; l \;\bigg|\; 1 \text{ g mole}} = 1.115 \text{ g}$$

density = 1.115 g/l of N_2 at 80°F and 745 mm Hg

The *specific gravity* of a gas is usually defined as the ratio of the density of the gas at a desired temperature and pressure to that of air (or any specified reference gas) at a certain temperature and pressure. The use of specific gravity occasionally may be confusing because of the manner in which the values of specific gravity are reported in the literature. You must be very careful in using literature values of specific gravity, and you must be especially careful to ascertain that the conditions of temperature and pressure are known both for the gas in question and for the reference gas. Among the examples below, several represent inadequate methods of expressing specific gravity.

1. *What is the specific gravity of methane?* Actually this question may have the same answer as the question "How many grapes are in a bunch?" Unfortunately, occasionally one may see this question and the best possible answer is

$$\text{sp gr} = \frac{\text{density of methane at S.C.}}{\text{density of air at S.C.}}$$

2. *What is the specific gravity of methane* $(H_2 = 1.00)$? Again a poor question, and care must be exercised in using these data. The notation of $(H_2 = 1.00)$ means that H_2 at S.C. is used as the reference gas, but the original question does not even give a hint regarding the conditions of temperature and pressure of the methane. Therefore the best interpretation is

$$\text{sp gr} = \frac{\text{density of methane at S.C.}}{\text{density of } H_2 \text{ at S.C.}}$$

3. *What is the specific gravity of ethane* $(air = 1.00)$? Same as number 2 except that in the petroleum industry the following is used:

$$\text{sp gr} = \frac{\text{density of ethane at } 60°F \text{ and } 760 \text{ mm Hg}}{\text{density of air at S.C. } (60°F, 760 \text{ mm Hg})}$$

4. *What is the specific gravity of butane at* 80°F *and* 740 *mm* Hg? No reference gas nor state of reference gas is mentioned. However, when no reference gas is mentioned, it is taken for granted that air is the reference gas. In the case at hand it may be assumed that the reference gas and the desired gas are under the same conditions of temperature and pressure.

$$\text{sp gr} = \frac{\text{density of butane at } 80°F \text{ and } 740 \text{ mm Hg}}{\text{density of air at } 80°F \text{ and } 740 \text{ mm Hg}}$$

5. *What is the specific gravity of* CO_2 *at* 60°F *and* 740 mm Hg *(air =* 1.00)?

$$\text{sp gr} = \frac{\text{density of } CO_2 \text{ at } 60°F \text{ and } 740 \text{ mm Hg}}{\text{density of air at S.C.}}$$

6. *What is the specific gravity of* CO_2 *at* 60°F *and* 740 mm Hg *(ref. air at S.C.)?*

$$\text{sp gr} = \text{same as number 5}$$

Example 3.9 Specific Gravity of a Gas

What is the specific gravity of N_2 at 80°F and 745 mm Hg compared to:
(a) Air at S.C. (32°F and 760 mm Hg)?
(b) Air at 80°F and 745 mm Hg?

Solution:
First you must obtain the density of the N_2 and the air at their respective conditions of temperature and pressure, and then calculate the specific gravity by taking a ratio of their densities. Example 3.8 covers the calculation of the density of a gas, and therefore no units will appear in the following calculations:

(a)   Basis: 1 ft³ N_2 at 80°F and 745 mm Hg

$$\frac{1}{}\left|\frac{492}{540}\right|\frac{745}{760}\left|\frac{}{359}\right|\frac{28}{} = 0.0696 \text{ lb } N_2/\text{ft}^3 \text{ at } 80°F, 745 \text{ mm Hg}$$

Basis: 1 ft³ of air at 32°F and 760 mm Hg

$$\frac{1}{}\left|\frac{492}{492}\right|\frac{760}{760}\left|\frac{}{359}\right|\frac{29}{} = 0.0808 \text{ lb air/ft}^3 \text{ at } 32°F, 760 \text{ mm Hg}$$

therefore

$$\text{sp gr} = \frac{0.0696}{0.0808} = 0.863 \frac{\text{lb } N_2/\text{ft}^3 \text{ } N_2 \text{ at } 80°F, 745 \text{ mm Hg}}{\text{lb air/ft}^3 \text{ air at S.C.}}$$

Note: Specific gravity is not a dimensionless number.

(b)   Basis: 1 ft³ air at 80°F and 745 mm Hg

$$\frac{1}{}\left|\frac{492}{540}\right|\frac{745}{760}\left|\frac{}{359}\right|\frac{29}{} = 0.0721 \text{ lb/ft}^3 \text{ at } 80°F \text{ and } 745 \text{ mm Hg}$$

$$(\text{sp gr})_{N_2} = \frac{0.0696}{0.721} = 0.965 \frac{\text{lb } N_2/\text{ft}^3 \text{ } N_2 \text{ at } 80°F, 745 \text{ mm Hg}}{\text{lb air/ft}^3 \text{ air at } 80°F, 745 \text{ mm Hg}}$$

$$= 0.965 \text{ lb } N_2/\text{lb air}$$

Note: You can work part (b) by dividing the unit equations instead of dividing the resulting densities:

$$\text{sp gr} = \frac{d_{N_2}}{d_{\text{air}}} = \frac{\dfrac{1}{}\left|\dfrac{492}{540}\right|\dfrac{745}{760}\left|\dfrac{}{359}\right|\dfrac{28}{}}{\dfrac{1}{}\left|\dfrac{492}{540}\right|\dfrac{745}{760}\left|\dfrac{}{359}\right|\dfrac{29}{}} = \frac{28}{29} = 0.965 \text{ lb } N_2/\text{lb air}$$

This latter calculation shows that the specific gravity is equal to the ratio of the molecular weights of the gases when the densities of both the desired gas and the reference gas are at the same temperature and pressure. This, of course, is true only for ideal gases and should be no surprise to you, since Avogadro's law in effect states that at the same temperature and pressure 1 mole of any ideal gas is contained in identical volumes. Then, the specific gravity of gases at the same temperature and pressure (for *both* the desired gas and the reference gas) is merely the ratio of the molecular weights.

3.1-3 Ideal Gaseous Mixtures. In the majority of cases as an engineer you will deal with mixtures of gases instead of individual gases. There are three ideal gas laws which can be applied successfully to gaseous mixtures. These are:

(a) Dalton's law of partial pressures
(b) Amagat's law of partial volumes
(c) Dalton's law of the summation of partial pressures

(a) *Dalton's laws.* Dalton postulated that the total pressure of a gas is equal to the sum of the pressures exerted by the individual molecules of each component gas. He went one step further to state that each individual gas of a gaseous mixture can hypothetically be considered to exert a "partial pressure," which pressure would be the same pressure obtained if this *same mass* of individual gas were alone in the *same total volume* at the *same temperature*. The sum of these partial pressures for each component in the gaseous mixture would be equal to the total pressure, or

$$p_1 + p_2 + p_3 + \ldots + p_n = p_t \tag{3.3}$$

Equation (3.3) is Dalton's law of the summation of the partial pressures.

To illustrate the significance of Eq. (3.3) and the meaning of partial pressure, suppose you carried out the following experiment with ideal gases. Two tanks of 150 ft³ volume, one containing gas A at 300 mm Hg and the other gas B at 400 mm of Hg (both gases being at the same temperature of 70°F), are connected together. All the gas in B is forced into tank A isothermally. Now you have a 150-ft³ tank of A + B at 700 mm of Hg. For this mixture (in the 150-ft³ tank at 70°F and a total pressure of 700 mm Hg) you could say that gas A exerts a partial pressure of 300 mm and gas B exerts a partial pressure of 400 mm. Of course you cannot put a pressure gauge on the tank and check this conclusion because the pressure gauge will read only the total pressure. These partial pressures are hypothetical pressures that the individual gases would exert and are equivalent to the pressures they actually would have if they were put into the same volume at the same temperature all by themselves.

You can surmise that, at constant volume and at constant temperature, the pressure is a function only of the number of molecules of gas present.

If you divide the perfect gas law for component 1, $p_1 V_1 = n_1 R T_1$, by that for component 2, $p_2 V_2 = n_2 R T_2$, at *constant temperature and volume,* you can obtain

$$\frac{p_1}{p_2} = \frac{n_1}{n_2} \tag{3.4}$$

which shows that the ratio of the partial pressures is exactly the same numerically as the ratio of the moles of components 1 and 2. Similarly, dividing by the gas law for all the moles, $p_t V_t = n_t R T_t$, you will get Dalton's law of partial pressures,

$$\frac{p_1}{p_t} = \frac{n_1}{n_t} = \text{mole fraction} = y_1 \tag{3.5}$$

which shows that the ratio of the partial pressure of an individual component to the total pressure is exactly the same numerically as the ratio of the moles of the individual component to the total moles. With this principle under your belt, if the mole fraction of an individual gaseous component in a gaseous mixture is known and the total pressure is known, then you are able to calculate the partial pressure of this component gas by generalizing Eq. (3.5):

$$p_i = y_i p_t \qquad (3.5a)$$

where i stands for any component.

(b) *Amagat's law.* Amagat's law of additive volumes is analogous to Dalton's law of additive pressures. Amagat stated that the total volume of a gaseous mixture is equal to the sum of the volumes of the individual gas components at the same temperature and pressure. The individual volumes of these individual components at the same temperature and pressure are called the *partial volumes* (or sometimes "pure component" volumes) of the individual components, or

$$V_1 + V_2 + V_3 + \ldots + V_n = V_t \qquad (3.6)$$

Reasoning in the same fashion as in our explanation of partial pressures, *at the same temperature and pressure*, the partial volume is a function only of the number of molecules of the individual component gas present in the gaseous mixture, or

$$\frac{V_1}{V_2} = \frac{n_1}{n_2} \qquad (3.7)$$

and

$$\frac{V_1}{V_t} = \frac{n_1}{n_t} = y_1 = \text{mole fraction} \qquad (3.8)$$

which shows that the ratio of the partial volumes is exactly the same, numerically, as the ratio of the moles of components 1 and 2, or the ratio of the moles of component 1 to the total moles. Equation (3.8) states the principle, presented without proof in Chap. 1, that

$$\text{volume fraction} = \text{mole fraction} = y_i \qquad (3.9)$$

for an ideal gas.

Example 3.10 Partial Pressures and Volumes

A gas-tight room has a volume of 10,000 ft³. This room contains air (considered to be 21 % O_2 and 79 % N_2) at 70°F and a total pressure of 760 mm Hg.

(a) What is the partial volume of O_2 in the room?
(b) What is the partial volume of N_2 in the room?

(c) What is the partial pressure of O_2 in the room?

(d) What is the partial pressure of N_2 in the room?

(e) If all of the O_2 were removed from the room by some method, what would be the subsequent total pressure in the room?

Solution:

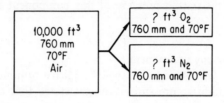

Basis: 10,000 ft³ of air at 70°F and 760 mm Hg

Partial volumes can be calculated by multiplying the total volume by the respective component mole fractions [Eq. (3.8)]:

(a) $V_{O_2} = (0.21)(10,000) =$ 2,100 ft³ O_2 at 70°F, 760 mm

(b) $V_{N_2} = (0.79)(10,000) =$ 7,900 ft³ N_2 at 70°F, 760 mm

               total volume = 10,000 ft³ air at 70°F, 760 mm

Note how the temperature and pressure have to be specified for the partial volumes to make them meaningful.

Partial pressures can be calculated by multiplying the total pressure by the respective component mole fractions [Eq. (3.5a)]; the basis is still the same:

(c) $p_{O_2} = (0.21)(760) = 160$ mm Hg when $V = 10,000$ ft³ at 70°F

(d) $p_{N_2} = (0.79)(760) = 600$ mm Hg when $V = 10,000$ ft³ at 70°F

            total pressure = 760 mm Hg when $V = 10,000$ ft³ at 70°F

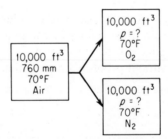

(e) If a tight room held dry air at 760 mm Hg and all the oxygen were removed from the air by a chemical reaction, the pressure reading would fall to 600 mm Hg. This is the partial pressure of the nitrogen and inert gases in the air. Alternatively, if it were possible to remove the nitrogen and inert gases and leave only the oxygen, the pressure reading would fall to 160 mm Hg. In either case, you would have left in the room 10,000 ft³ of gas at 70°F.

For use in our subsequent calculations you should clearly understand now that the original room contained:

1.   7,900 ft³ dry N_2 at 760 mm Hg and 70°F
2.   2,100 ft³ dry O_2 at 760 mm Hg and 70°F
3.   10,000 ft³ dry air at 760 mm Hg and 70°F
                                            (add 1 and 2)

or

1.   10,000 ft³ dry O_2 at 160 mm Hg and 70°F
2.   10,000 ft³ dry N_2 at 600 mm Hg and 70°F
3.   10,000 ft³ dry air at 760 mm Hg and 70°F
                                            (add 1 and 2)

Example 3.11   Ideal Gas Mixtures

A flue gas analyzes CO_2, 14.0%; O_2, 6.0%; and N_2, 80.0%. It is at 400°F and 765.0 mm Hg pressure. Calculate the partial pressure of each component.

Solution:

Basis: 1.0 lb mole flue gas

comp.	lb moles	p (mm Hg)
CO_2	0.140	107.1
O_2	0.060	45.9
N_2	0.800	612.0
	1.000	765.0

On the basis of 1.0 lb mole of flue gas, the mole fraction y of each component, when multiplied by the total pressure, gives the partial pressure of that component. Thus, V ft³ of flue gas represents four different things:

V ft³ flue gas	at 765.0 mm Hg and 400°F
V ft³ carbon dioxide	at 107.1 mm Hg and 400°F
V ft³ oxygen	at 45.9 mm Hg and 400°F
V ft³ nitrogen	at 612.0 mm Hg and 400°F

3.2   Real gas relationships

We have said that at room temperature and pressure many gases can be assumed to act as ideal gases. However, for some gases under normal conditions, and for most gases under conditions of high pressure, such calculations as you might make using the ideal gas law would be at wide variance with the experimental evidence. With so much emphasis placed on ideal gases, as an engineer you might wonder exactly how the behavior of real gases does compare with that calculated from the ideal gas laws. In Fig. 3.1 you can see how the $p\hat{V}$ product of several gases deviates from that predicted by the ideal gas laws as the pressure increases substantially.

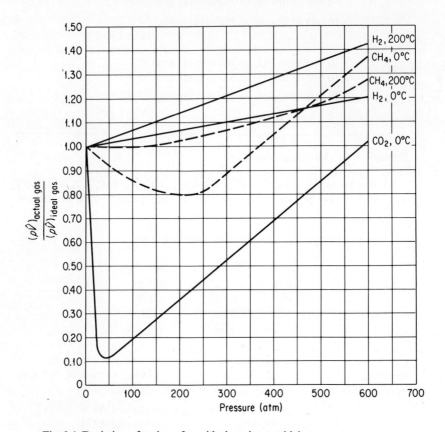

Fig. 3.1. Deviation of real gas from ideal gas laws at high pressures.

Essentially there are four methods of handling real gas calculations. You may use:

1. Equations of state
2. Compressibility charts
3. Estimated properties[1]
4. Actual experimental data

Even if this latter information is available, the other three techniques still may be quite useful for certain types of calculations. Of course, under con-

---

[1] Computer programs are available to estimate physical properties of compounds and mixtures based on structural group contributions and other basic parameters; refer to E. L. Meadows, *Chem. Eng. Progr.*, vol. 61, p. 93 (1965).

ditions such that part of the gas liquefies, the gas laws apply only to the gas phase portion of the system—you cannot extend these real gas laws into the liquid region any more than you can apply the ideal gas laws to a liquid.

3.2-1 Equations of State. Equations of state relate the p-V-T properties of a pure substance (or mixtures) by semitheoretical or empirical relations. By *property* we will mean any measurable characteristic of a substance, such as pressure, volume, or temperature, or a characteristic that can be calculated or deduced, such as internal energy, to be discussed in Chap. 4. The actual data for a gas are illustrated in Fig. 3.2 which is a plot of pressure

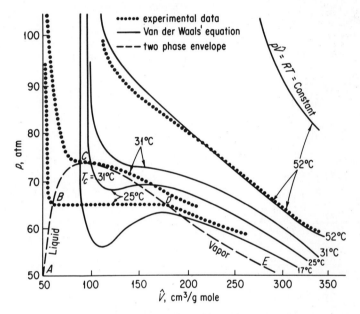

Fig. 3.2. p-V-T properties of CO_2.

versus molal volume with absolute temperature as the third parameter. The perfect gas law, $p\hat{V} = RT$ (for 1 mole), is, on this plot for a constant temperature, a rectangular hyperbola because $p\hat{V}$ = constant. The actual data at high temperatures and low pressures closely approximate this equation of state. However, as we approach the point C, called the critical point (discussed in Sec. 3.2-2), we see the actual lines for the experimental data are quite different from the lines which would represent the relation $p\hat{V}$ = constant.

The problem, then, is to predict these experimental points by means of some equation which can, with reasonable accuracy, represent the experimental data throughout the gas phase. A number of equations of state which have been proposed to accomplish this task are shown in Table 3.1. We would not, of course, expect the function to follow the experimental data within the two-phase region outlined by the area inside the envelope A, B, C, D, and E.

TABLE 3.1 EQUATIONS OF STATE
(for 1 mole)

Van der Waals:

$$\left(p + \frac{a}{\hat{V}^2}\right)(\hat{V} - b) = RT$$

Macleod:

$$n(\hat{V} - b') = RT$$

$$\pi = p + \frac{a}{\hat{V}^2}$$

$$b' = b_0(1 - B\pi + C\pi^2)$$

Clausius:

$$p = \frac{RT}{(\hat{V} - b)} - \frac{a}{T(\hat{V} + c)^2}$$

Lorentz:

$$p = \frac{RT}{\hat{V}^2}(\hat{V} + b) - \frac{a}{\hat{V}^2}$$

Dieterici:

$$p = \frac{RT}{(\hat{V} - b)}e^{-a/\hat{V}RT}$$

Berthelot:

$$p = \frac{RT}{(\hat{V} - b)} - \frac{a}{T\hat{V}^2}$$

Wohl:

$$p = \frac{RT}{(\hat{V} - b)} - \frac{a}{\hat{V}(\hat{V} - b)} + \frac{c}{T\hat{V}^3}$$

Keyes:

$$p = \frac{RT}{(\hat{V} - \delta)} - \frac{A}{(\hat{V} - l)^2}$$

$$\delta = \beta e^{-\alpha/\hat{V}}$$

Redlich-Kwong:

$$\left[p + \frac{a}{T^{1/2}\hat{V}(\hat{V} + b)}\right](\hat{V} - b) = RT$$

$$a = 0.4278\frac{R^2T_c^{2.5}}{p_c}$$

$$b = 0.0867\frac{RT_c}{p_c}$$

Kammerlingh-Onnes:

$$p\hat{V} = RT\left[1 + \frac{B}{\hat{V}} + \frac{C}{\hat{V}^2} + \cdots\right]$$

Holborn:

$$p\hat{V} = RT[1 + B'p + C'p^2 + \cdots]$$

Beattie-Bridgeman:

$$p\hat{V} = RT + \frac{\beta}{\hat{V}} + \frac{\gamma}{\hat{V}^2} + \frac{\delta}{\hat{V}^3}$$

$$\beta = RTB_0 - A_0 - \frac{Rc}{T^2}$$

$$\gamma = -RTB_0b + aA_0 - \frac{RB_0c}{T^2}$$

$$\delta = \frac{RB_0bc}{T^2}$$

Benedict-Webb-Rubin:

$$p\hat{V} = RT + \frac{\beta}{\hat{V}} + \frac{\sigma}{\hat{V}^2} + \frac{\eta}{\hat{V}^4} + \frac{w}{\hat{V}^5}$$

$$\beta = RTB_0 - A_0 - \frac{C_0}{T^2}$$

$$\sigma = bRT - a + \frac{c}{T^2}\exp-\frac{\gamma}{\hat{V}^2}$$

$$\eta = c\gamma \exp -\frac{\gamma}{\hat{V}^2}$$

$$w = a\alpha$$

(a) *Van der Waals' equation.* Of historical interest as one of the earliest equations of state is van der Waals' equation, first proposed in 1873. Not universally accurate, although an improvement over the ideal gas law, it is one of the simpler equations of state and illustrates some of the theoretical concepts used to develop equations of state. Many of these equations are actually semiempirical in the sense that although they were developed as theoretical concepts, the constants in the equation or portions of the equation are determined by empirical methods.

Van der Waals tried to include in the ideal gas law the effect of the attractive forces among the molecules by adding to the pressure term the term

$$\frac{n^2 a}{V^2} \tag{3.10}$$

where n = number of moles

V = volume

a = a constant, different for each gas

He also tried to take into account the effect of the volume occupied by the molecules themselves by subtracting a term from the volume in the ideal gas law. These corrections led to the following equation:

$$\left(p + \frac{n^2 a}{V^2}\right)(V - nb) = nRT \tag{3.11}$$

where a and b, the constants, have the units of

$$a = \text{atm}\left(\frac{\text{cm}^3}{\text{g mole}}\right)^2$$

$$b = \left(\frac{\text{cm}^2}{\text{g mole}}\right)$$

in the cgs system. You should be able to say by inspection of Eq. (3.11) what the units would be in any other system, and be able to convert such values of a and b as you would find in a handbook to another system of units. The constants a and b are determined by fitting van der Waals' equation to experimental p-V-T data, particularly the values at the critical point. Values of the van der Waals'constants for a few gases can be found in Table 3.2. A comparison of predicted p-V-T relations from the ideal gas law and from van der Waals' equation with the actual experimental data is shown in Fig. 3.2.

Van der Waals' equation can be explicitly solved for p as follows:

$$p = \frac{nRT}{(V - nb)} - \frac{n^2 a}{V^2} \tag{3.12}$$

However, if you want to solve for V (or n), you can see that the equation becomes cubic in V (or n), or

$$V^3 - \left(nb + \frac{nRT}{p}\right)V^2 + \frac{n^2 a}{p}V - \frac{n^3 ab}{p} = 0 \tag{3.13}$$

To solve for V (or n) then, you would have to:

(a) Resort to a trial-and-error method.

(b) Plot the equation assuming various values of V (or n), and see at what value of V (or n) the curve you plot intersects the abscissa, or

(c) Use Newton's method.

TABLE 3.2 VAN DER WAALS' CONSTANTS FOR GASES
(From the data of the International Critical Tables)

	$a*$ $\text{atm}\left(\dfrac{\text{cm}^3}{\text{g mole}}\right)^2$	$b\dagger$ $\left(\dfrac{\text{cm}^3}{\text{g mole}}\right)$
Air	1.33×10^6	36.6
Ammonia	4.19×10^6	37.3
Carbon dioxide	3.60×10^6	42.8
Ethylene	4.48×10^6	57.2
Hydrogen	0.245×10^6	26.6
Methane	2.25×10^6	42.8
Nitrogen	1.347×10^6	38.6
Oxygen	1.36×10^6	31.9
Water vapor	5.48×10^6	30.6

*To convert to psia $\left(\dfrac{\text{ft}^3}{\text{lb mole}}\right)^2$, multiply table value by 3.776×10^{-3}.

†To convert to $\dfrac{\text{ft}^3}{\text{lb mole}}$, multiply table value by 1.60×10^{-2}.

You can obtain a close approximation to V (or n) in many cases from the ideal gas law, useful at least for the first trial, and then you can calculate a more exact value of V (or n) by using van der Waals' equation.

Example 3.12   Van der Waals' Equation

A 5.0-ft³ cylinder containing 50.0 lb of propane (C_3H_8) stands in the hot sun. A pressure gauge shows that the pressure is 665 psig. What is the temperature of the propane in the cylinder? Use van der Waals' equation.

Solution:

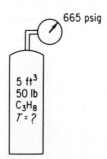

665 psig

5 ft³
50 lb
C_3H_8
$T = ?$

Basis: 50 lb of propane

The van der Waals' constants obtained from any suitable handbook are

$$a = 3.27 \times 10^4 \text{ psia} \left(\frac{\text{ft}^3}{\text{lb mole}}\right)^2$$

$$b = 1.35 \frac{ft^3}{lb \text{ mole}}$$

$$\left(p + \frac{n^2 a}{V^2}\right)(V - nb) = nRT$$

All the additional information you need is as follows:

$$p = 665 \text{ psig} + 14.7 = 679.7 \text{ psia}$$

$$R \text{ in proper units is} = 10.73 \frac{(\text{psia})(ft^3)}{(lb \text{ mole})(°R)}$$

$$n = \frac{50 \text{ lb}}{44 \text{ lb/lb mole}} = 1.137 \text{ lb mole propane}$$

$$\left[679.7 + \frac{(1.137)^2(3.27 \times 10^4)}{(5)^2}\right][5 - (1.137)(1.35)] = 1.137(10.73)T$$

$$T = 673°R = 213°F$$

Example 3.13   Van der Waals' Equation

An oxygen tank contains 100 ft³ of dry oxygen (measured at 25°C and 720 mm Hg). You are asked to put this oxygen into a tank of 1-ft³ size at −25°C. What will the pressure be in the tank? Use van der Waals' equation.

Solution:

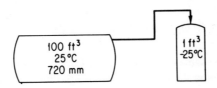

100 ft³
25 °C
720 mm

1 ft³
-25°C

Inspection of what is immediately known and unknown about this problem shows:

known	unknown
Van der Waals'	n_1
constants a and b	n_2
p_1	p_2
V_1, V_2	
T_1, T_2	

Van der Waals' equation applied to the initial conditions

$$\left(p_1 + \frac{n_1^2 a}{V_1^2}\right)(V_1 - n_1 b) = n_1 R T_1 \tag{a}$$

indicates that n_1 can be calculated since all the other factors in the equation are known. Furthermore, $n_1 = n_2$, so that all the factors in van der Waals' equation as applied to the final situation are known except p_2:

$$\left(p_2 + \frac{n_2^2 a}{V_2^2}\right)(V_2 - n_2 b) = n_2 R T_2 \tag{b}$$

Basis: 100 ft³ O_2 at 25°C and 720 mm Hg

From Table 3.2 (or any suitable handbook),

$$a = 1.36 \times 10^6$$
$$b = 31.9$$

Converting to more appropriate units,

$$a = \frac{1.36 \times 10^6 \text{ atm} \left(\dfrac{cm^3}{g \text{ mole}}\right)^2 \left| 3.776 \times 10^{-3} \text{ psia} \left(\dfrac{ft^3}{lb \text{ mole}}\right)^2 \right.}{1 \text{ (atm)} \left(\dfrac{cm^3}{g \text{ mole}}\right)^2}$$

$$= 5140 \text{ psia} \left(\frac{ft^3}{lb \text{ mole}}\right)^2$$

$$b = \frac{31.9 \dfrac{cm^3}{g \text{ mole}} \left| 1.6 \times 10^{-2} \dfrac{ft^3}{lb \text{ mole}} \right.}{1 \dfrac{cm^3}{g \text{ mole}}} = 0.510 \frac{ft^3}{lb \text{ mole}}$$

Rather than solve Eq. (a) for n_1 (which would involve the solution of a cubic equation), let us assume O_2 behaves enough like an ideal gas that at the initial conditions of 25°C and 720 mm Hg we can compute n_1 as follows:

$$n_1 = \frac{p_1 V_1}{RT} \tag{c}$$

or, in effect,

$$n_1 = \frac{100 \text{ ft}^3 O_2 \left| 720 \text{ mm} \right| 273°K \left| 1 \text{ lb mole} \right.}{760 \text{ mm} \left| 298°K \right| 359 \text{ ft}^3} = 0.242 \text{ lb mole}$$

If you make the same calculation using Eq. (a), you will find the error introduced by assuming the initial conditions are ideal is negligible, certainly well within the error inherent in van der Waals' equation itself.

Now we will solve Eq. (b) for p_2, or

$$p_2 = \left(\frac{n_2 T R_2}{V_2 - n_2 b}\right) - \left(\frac{n_2^2 a}{V_2^2}\right)$$

R in the units needed here is 19.3 $\dfrac{(psia)(ft^3)}{(°K)(lb \text{ mole})}$

$$p_2 = \frac{0.242 \text{ lb mole} \left| (19.3 \text{ psia})(ft^3) \right| 248°K \left| \right.}{(°K)(lb \text{ mole}) \left| \right| 1 \text{ ft}^3 - (0.242 \text{ lb mole})\left(0.510 \dfrac{ft^3}{lb \text{ mole}}\right)}$$

$$- \frac{(0.242 \text{ lb mole})^2 \left| (5140 \text{ psia})(ft^3)^2 \right|}{(lb \text{ mole})^2 \left| (1 \text{ ft}^3)^2 \right.} = 1025 \text{ psia}$$

Example 3.14   Van der Waals' Equation

You have just received a reactor for NH_3 gas, and decide to fill it with a net weight of 8.0 lb of NH_3. The pressure in the reactor is 150 psia and the temperature 250°F. Apply van der Waals' equation, and find the volume of the reactor.

Solution:

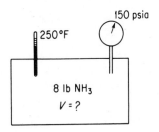

The additional data we need are

$$a = (4.19 \times 10^6)(3.776 \times 10^{-3})$$

$$= 15,810 \frac{(\text{psia})(\text{ft}^3)^2}{(\text{lb mole})^2}$$

$$b = (37.3)(0.016) = 0.597 \frac{\text{ft}^3}{\text{lb mole}}$$

$$\text{mol. wt NH}_3 = \frac{17 \text{ lb}}{\text{lb mole}}$$

$$n = \frac{8}{17} = 0.47 \text{ lb mole}$$

$$R = 10.73 \frac{(\text{psia})(\text{ft}^3)}{(\text{lb mole})(°R)}$$

Checking van der Waals' equation for knowns and unknowns, we find everything is known except V,

$$\left(p + \frac{n^2 a}{V^2}\right)(V - nb) = nRT$$

However to solve for V we have to solve a cubic equation. Some of the ways in which this can be done have been mentioned in the text. Suppose we decide to carry out a trial-and-error solution; with what value of V should we start? The best value is probably the one calculated by using the ideal gas law

$$V = \frac{nRT}{p} = \frac{(0.47)(10.73)(710)}{150}$$

$$= 23.9 \text{ ft}^3 \cong 24 \text{ ft}^3$$

Our trial equation is

$$\phi = \left[150 + \frac{(15,810)(0.47)^2}{V^2}\right][V - (0.47)(0.597)] - (0.47)(10.73)(710) = 0$$

$$= \left[150 + \frac{3510}{V^2}\right][V - 0.281] - 3585$$

$$= [A][B] - [C]$$

Starting with $V = 24 \text{ ft}^3$,

V	$[A]$	$[B]$	$[C]$	$[A][B]$	$\phi =$ $[A][B] - [C]$
24	156.10	23.72	3585	3705	$+120$
23	156.64	22.72	3585	3560	-25
23.2	156.52	22.92	3585	3585	0

Thus $V = 23.2 \text{ ft}^3$, a value not far from that predicted by the ideal gas law. A higher pressure would have caused a greater discrepancy to appear.

After trying the calculations in these examples yourself, you can get a taste of some of the computational intricacies involved in using equations of state.

(b) *Other equations of state.* Among the numerous other equations of state which have been proposed in addition to van der Waals' equation are those shown in Table 3.1. The form of these equations is of interest inasmuch as they are attempts to fit the experimental data with as few constants in the equation as possible. One form of the equation known as the *virial* form is illustrated by the equations of Kammerlingh-Onnes and Holborn. These are essentially power series in $1/\hat{V}$ or in p, and the quantities B, C, D, etc. are known as *virial coefficients*. These equations reduce to $p\hat{V} = RT$ at low pressures. The virial form of an equation of state is the best we have today; however, it is not possible to solve theoretically by statistical thermodynamics for the constants beyond the first two. So fundamentally these equations are semiempirical, the constants being determined by fitting the equation to experimental data. The Beattie-Bridgeman equation, which has five constants (exclusive of R), and the Benedict-Webb-Rubin equation, which has eight constants, are among the best we have at the present time. The two-constant Redlich-Kwong equation also appears to be quite good according to a study of Thodos and Shah.[2] Naturally, the use of these equations involves time-consuming calculations, particularly when carried out by hand rather than on the computer, but the results will frequently be more accurate than those obtained by other methods to be described shortly.

In spite of the complications involved in their use, equations of state are important for several reasons. They permit a concise summary of a large mass of experimental data and also permit accurate interpolation between the experimental data points. They provide a continuous function to facilitate thermodynamic calculations involving differentiation and integration. Finally, they provide a point of departure for the treatment of thermodynamic properties of mixtures. However, for instructional purposes, and for many engineering calculations, the techniques of predicting p-V-T values discussed in the next section are considerably more convenient to use and are usually just as accurate as equations of state.

[2] G. Thodos and K. K. Shah, *Ind. Eng. Chem.*, vol. 57, p. 30 (1965).

3.2-2 Compressibility Factors. In the attempt to devise some truly universal gas law for high pressures, the idea of corresponding states was developed. Early experimenters found that at the critical point all substances are in approximately the same state of molecular dispersion. Consequently, it was felt that their thermodynamic and physical properties should be similar. The *law of corresponding states* expresses the idea that in the critical state all substances should behave alike.

Now that we have mentioned "critical state" several times, let us consider exactly what the term means. You can find many definitions, but the one most suitable for general use with pure component systems as well as with mixtures of gases is this:

The *critical state* is the set of physical conditions at which the density and other properties of the liquid and vapor become identical.

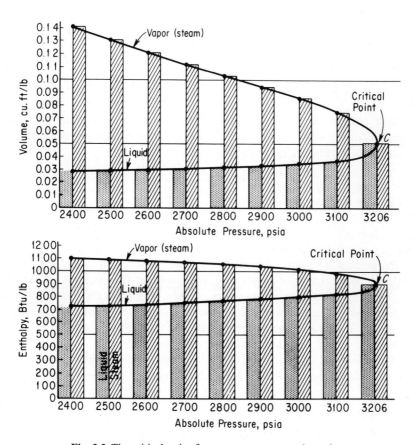

Fig. 3.3. The critical point for a pure component (water).

Referring to Fig. 3.3, the specific volumes of the liquid and gas approach each other and finally become the same at the point C. This point, for a pure component (only), is the highest temperature at which liquid and vapor can exist in equilibrium. Experimental values of the critical temperature (T_c) and the critical pressure (p_c) for various compounds will be found in Appendix D. If you cannot find a desired critical value in this text or in a handbook, you can always consult Reid and Sherwood[3] which describes and evaluates methods of estimating critical constants for various compounds.

Another set of terms with which you should immediately become familiar are the *reduced* conditions. These are "corrected," or "normalized," conditions of temperature, pressure, and volume and are expressed mathematically as

$$T_r = \frac{T}{T_c} \tag{3.14}$$

$$p_r = \frac{p}{p_c} \tag{3.15}$$

$$V_r = \frac{V}{V_c} \tag{3.16}$$

The idea, as suggested by van der Waals, is that all substances behave alike in their reduced, i.e., their "corrected", states. In particular, any substance would have the same *reduced* volume at the same *reduced* temperature and pressure. Mathematically we should say

$$f(p_r, T_r, V_r) = 0 \tag{3.17}$$

or, to take one simple function,

$$p_r V_r = \gamma T_r \tag{3.18}$$

where γ is some constant.

Now, how does this concept work out in practice? If we plot p_r vs. T_r with a third parameter of constant V_r, we should get straight lines for constant V_r. That this is actually what happens can be seen from Fig. 3.4 for various hydrocarbons. Furthermore, this type of correlation works in the region where $pV = nRT$ is in great error. Also, at the critical point ($p_r = 1.0$, $T_r = 1.0$), V_r should be 1.0 as it is in the diagram.

However, the ability of Eq. (3.18) to predict gas properties breaks down for most substances as they approach the perfect gas region (the area of low pressures somewhat below $p_r = 1.0$). If this concept held in the perfect gas region for all gases, then for 1 mole

---

[3] R. C. Reid and T. K. Sherwood, *The Properties of Gases and Liquids*, McGraw-Hill Book Company, 2nd ed, New York, 1965.

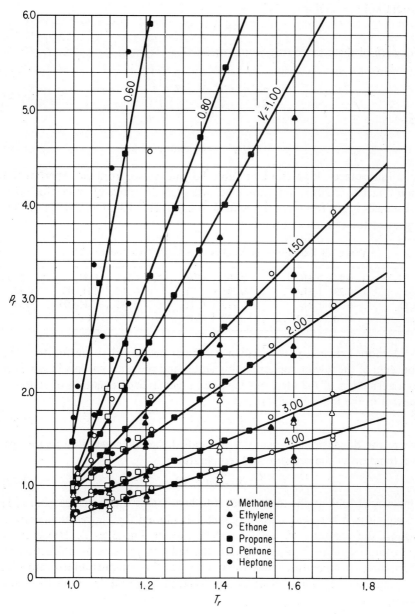

Fig. 3.4. A test of the relation $\dfrac{p_r}{T_r} = \dfrac{\gamma}{V_r}$.

$$p\hat{V} = RT \tag{3.1a}$$

should hold as well as

$$p_r V_r = \gamma T_r \tag{3.18}$$

For *both* of these to be true would mean

$$\frac{p\hat{V}}{RT} = \frac{p_r V_r}{\gamma T_r} = \frac{\left(\dfrac{p}{p_c}\right)\left(\dfrac{\hat{V}}{\hat{V}_c}\right)}{\gamma\left(\dfrac{T}{T_c}\right)} \tag{3.19}$$

or

$$\frac{p_c \hat{V}_c}{RT_c} = \text{constant} \tag{3.20}$$

for all substances. If you look at Table 3.3 you can see from the experimental data that Eq. (3.20) is not quite true, although the range of values for most substances is not too great (from 0.24 to 0.28). He (0.305) and HCN (0.197) represent the extremes of the range.

TABLE 3.3 EXPERIMENTAL VALUES OF $p_c\hat{V}_c/RT_c$ FOR VARIOUS GASES

NH_3	0.243	HCN	0.197	CH_4	0.290	C_2H_4	0.270
Ar	0.291	H_2O	0.233	C_2H_6	0.285	CH_3OH	0.222
CO_2	0.279	N_2	0.292	C_3H_8	0.277	C_2H_5OH	0.248
He	0.305	Toluene	0.270	C_6H_{14}	0.264	CCl_4	0.272

A more convenient way which has been developed to tie together the concepts of the law of corresponding states and the ideal gas law is to revert to a correction of the ideal gas law, i.e., a generalized equation of state expressed in the following manner:

$$pV = znRT \tag{3.21}$$

where the dimensionless quantity z is called the *compressibility factor* and is a function of the pressure and temperature:

$$z = \psi(p, T) \tag{3.22}$$

One way to look at z is to consider it to be a factor which makes Eq. (3.21) an equality. If the compressibility factor is plotted for a given temperature against the pressure, we obtain something like Fig. 3.5 (a). However, if the compressibility is plotted against the reduced pressure as a function of the reduced temperature, then for most gases the compressibility values at the same reduced temperature and reduced pressure fall at about the same point,

$$z = \psi(p_r, T_r) \tag{3.23}$$

as illustrated in Fig. 3.5(b).

This permits the use of what is called a generalized compressibility factor, and Figs. 3.6 through 3.10 are the *generalized compressibility charts* or *z-*

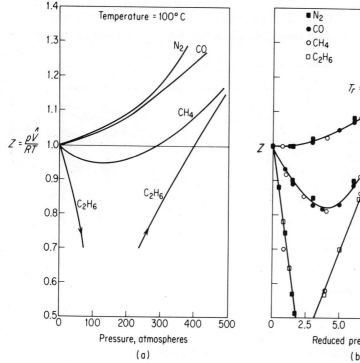

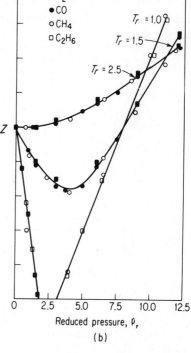

Fig. 3.5.(a) Compressibility factor as a function of temperature and pressure.

Fig. 3.5.(b) Compressibility as a function of reduced temperature and reduced pressure.

factor charts prepared by Nelson and Obert.[4] These charts are based on 30 gases. Figures 3.6(b) and 3.7 represent z for 26 gases (excluding H_2, He, NH_3, H_2O) with a maximum deviation of 1 per cent, and H_2 and H_2O within a deviation of 1.5 per cent. Figure 3.8 is for 26 gases and is accurate to 2.5 per cent, while Fig. 3.9 is for nine gases and errors can be as high as 5 per cent. For H_2 and He only, Newton's corrections to the actual critical constants are used to give pseudocritical constants

$$T'_c = T_c + 8°K \tag{3.24}$$

$$p'_c = p_c + 8 \text{ atm} \tag{3.25}$$

which enable you to use Figs. 3.6 to 3.10 for these two gases with minimum error. These Newton corrections bring the calculated values of p-V-T more closely in line with the experimental ones for H_2 and He. Figure 3.10 is

[4] L. C. Nelson and E. F. Obert, *Chem. Eng.*, vol. 61, no. 7, pp. 203–8 (1954). O. A. Hougen and K. M. Watson, *Chemical Process Principles*, John Wiley & Sons, Inc., New York, 1943, also presents z-factor charts as do many articles in the literature for specialized gases, such as natural gases.

a unique chart which, by having several parameters plotted simultaneously on it, helps you avoid trial-and-error solutions or graphical solutions of real gas problems. One of these helpful factors is the ideal reduced volume defined as

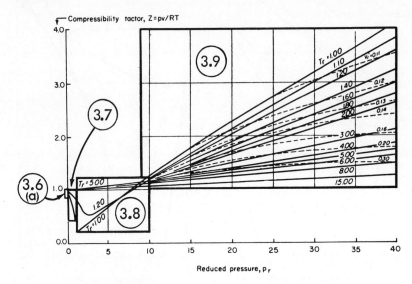

Fig. 3.6.(a) General compressibility chart.

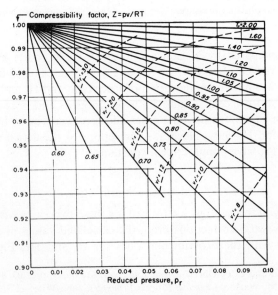

Fig. 3.6.(b) General compressibility chart, very low pressures.

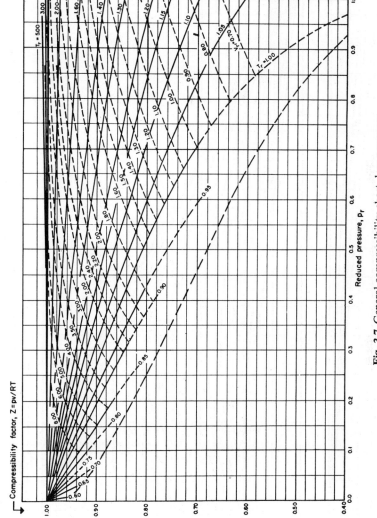

Fig. 3.7. General compressibility chart, low pressures.

155

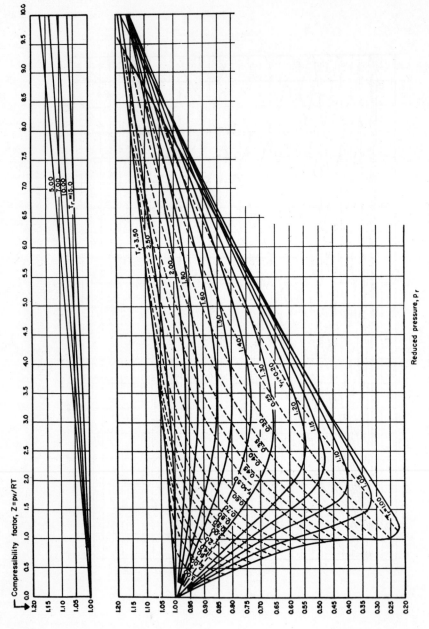

Fig. 3.8. General compressibility chart, medium pressures.

156

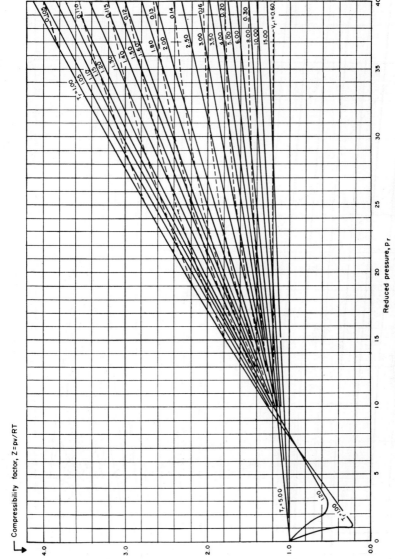

Fig. 3.9. Generalized compressibility chart, high pressures.

157

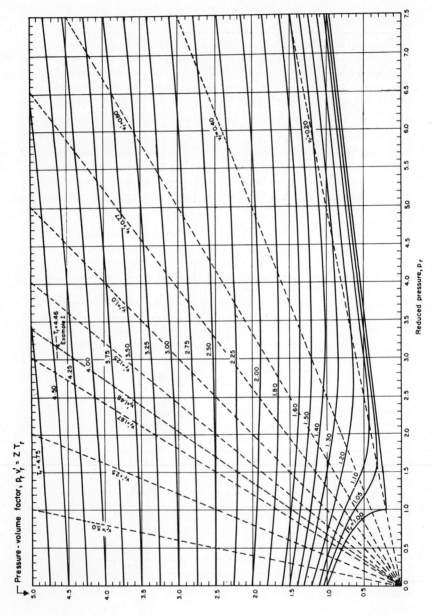

Fig. 3.10. Generalized compressibility chart, with special scales.

158

$$V_{r_i}(\text{ or } V_r' \text{ in the Nelson and Obert charts}) = \frac{\hat{V}}{\hat{V}_{c_i}} \qquad (3.26)$$

$\hat{V}_{c_i}$ is the ideal critical volume, or

$$\hat{V}_{c_i} = \frac{RT_c}{p_c} \qquad (3.27)$$

Both V_{r_i} and $\hat{V}_{c_i}$ are easy to calculate since T_c and p_c are presumed known. The development of the generalized compressibility chart is of considerable practical as well as pedagogical value because it enables engineering calculations to be made with considerable ease, and also permits the development of thermodynamic functions for gases for which no experimental data are available. All you need to know to use these charts are the critical temperature and the critical pressure for a pure substance (or the pseudo values for a mixture, as we shall see later). The value $z = 1$ represents ideality, and the value $z = 0.27$ is the compressibility factor at the critical point.

Lydersen, Greenkorn, and Hougen[5] have developed tables of z which include in addition to p_r and T_r a third parameter, the critical compressibility factor, $z_c = p_c\hat{V}_c/RT_c$. The use of this additional parameter enables gas calculations to be made with somewhat greater accuracy, but the presentation of z values so as to include the third parameter is somewhat more cumbersome and will not be shown here.

Viswanath and Su[6] compared the z factors from the Nelson and Obert charts, the Lydersen-Greenkorn-Hougen charts, and the Su chart for T_r of 1.00 to 15.00 with the following results:

	Su	*N–O*	*L–G–H*
number of points	415	355	339
average deviation (%)	0.61	0.83	1.26

It is seen that all these charts yield quite reasonable values as a general rule.

Example 3.15   Use of Compressibility Factor

Repeat Example 3.14, this time using the compressibility factor instead of van der Waals' equation. "You have a reactor for NH_3 gas and fill it with a net weight of 8 lb of NH_3. The pressure in the reactor is 150 psia and the temperature is 250°F. Find the volume of the reactor."

---

[5] A. L. Lydersen, R. A. Greenkorn, and O. A. Hougen, Univ. of Wis. Engr. Expt. Sta. Rept. no. 4, Madison, Wisconsin, 1955.

[6] D. S. Viswanath and G. J. Su, *A. I. Ch. E. J.*, vol. 11, p. 202 (1965).

Solution:

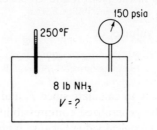

The equation we will be using this time is

$$pV = znRT$$

What is known and unknown in the equation?

$$p = 150 \text{ psia}$$
$$V = ?$$
$$z = ?$$
$$n = \frac{8 \text{ lb}}{17 \text{ lb/lb mole}} = 0.47 \text{ lb mole NH}_3$$
$$T = 250°\text{F} = 250 + 460 = 710°\text{R}$$

Additional information needed (taken from Appendix D) is

$$T_c = 405.4°\text{K} \cong 729°\text{R}$$
$$p_c = 111.3 \text{ atm} \cong 1640 \text{ psia}$$

Then, since z is a function of T_r and p_r,

$$T_r = \frac{T}{T_c} = \frac{710°\text{R}}{729°\text{R}} = 0.975$$

$$p_r = \frac{p}{p_c} = \frac{150 \text{ psia}}{1640 \text{ psia}} = 0.0915$$

From the Nelson and Obert chart, Fig. 3.6,[7] you can read $z \cong 0.963$. Now V can be calculated as

$$\frac{8.0 \text{ lb}}{} \bigg| \frac{1 \text{ lb mole}}{17 \text{ lb}} \bigg| \frac{259 \text{ ft}^3 \text{ ideal}}{1 \text{ lb mole}} \bigg| \frac{14.7 \text{ psia}}{150 \text{ psia}} \bigg| \frac{710°\text{R}}{492°\text{R}} \bigg| 0.963 \frac{\text{ft}^3 \text{ actual}}{\text{ft}^3 \text{ ideal}}$$

$$= 22.9 \text{ ft}^3 \text{ NH}_3 \text{ at 150 psia and 250°F}$$

or as

$$V = \frac{znRT}{p} = \frac{0.963}{} \bigg| \frac{8}{17} \bigg| \frac{1}{150} \bigg| \frac{10.73}{} \bigg| \frac{710}{} = 22.9 \text{ ft}^3$$

Note in the calculation above we have added some hypothetical units to z to make clear the conversion from ideal cubic feet to actual cubic feet.

[7] Figure 3.6 in general is not as accurate for use with NH_3 as with hydrocarbon gases, but is used here for illustrative purposes.

Example 3.16   Use of Compressibility Factor

Re-do Example 3.13, this time employing the compressibility factor. "An oxygen tank contains 100 ft³ of dry oxygen (measured at 25°C and 720 mm Hg). You are asked to put this oxygen into a tank of 1-ft³ size at −25°C. What will the pressure be in the tank?"

Solution:

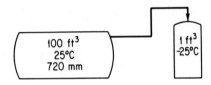

Basis: 100 ft³ O_2 at 25°C and 720 mm Hg

initial conditions	*final conditions*
$V_1 = 100$ ft³	$V_2 = 1.0$ ft³
$T_1 = 298°$K	$T_2 = 248°$K
$p_1 = 720$ mm	$p_2 = ?$
$n_1 = ?$	$n_2 = ?$
$z_1 = ?$	$z_2 = ?$

Since $z = \psi(p_r, T_r)$, and since we know T_1 and p_1, we can calculate z_1 with the aid of Fig. 3.6. From Appendix D, for O_2:

$$p_c = 49.7 \text{ atm} = (49.7 \text{ atm})\left(760 \frac{\text{mm}}{\text{atm}}\right) = 38,000 \text{ mm}$$

$$T_c = -118.8°\text{C} = -118.8 + 273.1 = 154.3°\text{K}$$

Then

$$T_{r_1} = \frac{T_1}{T_c} = \frac{298°\text{K}}{154.3°\text{K}} = 1.94$$

$$p_{r_1} = \frac{p_1}{p_c} = \frac{720 \text{ mm}}{38,000 \text{ mm}} = 0.019$$

and from the Nelson and Obert chart we find

$$z \cong 0.999 \quad \text{(almost ideal behavior)}$$

With z_1 known,

$$n_1 = \frac{100 \text{ ft}^3 \text{ actual gas}}{0.999 \frac{\text{ft}^3 \text{ actual}}{\text{ft}^3 \text{ ideal}}} \left| \frac{720 \text{ mm}}{760 \text{ mm}} \right| \frac{273°\text{K}}{298°\text{K}} \left| \frac{1 \text{ lb mole}}{359 \text{ ft}^3} \right.$$

$$= 0.242 \text{ lb mole } O_2$$

Alternatively we could have used, of course,

$$n_1 = \frac{p_1 V_1}{z_1 R T_1}$$

Now we are faced with a problem in obtaining p_2. Since $z_2 = \psi(p_{r_2}, T_{r_2})$ and p_{r_2} is unknown, we are stymied in obtaining p_2 by this route. However, another parameter, $V_{r_i}(V_r')$, is available on the Nelson and Obert charts, and we can calculate $V_{r_{i_2}}$ from data for $\hat{V}_2$ and $\hat{V}_{c_i}$.

$$\hat{V}_2 \text{ (final } molal \text{ volume)} = \frac{1.0 \text{ ft}^3}{0.242 \text{ lb mole}} = 4.13 \frac{\text{ft}^3}{\text{lb mole}}$$

Note that the molal volume must be used in calculating V_{r_i} since $\hat{V}_{c_i}$ is a volume per mole.

$$\hat{V}_{c_i} = \frac{359 \text{ ft}^3}{1 \text{ lb mole}} \left| \frac{760 \text{ mm}}{38,000 \text{ mm}} \right| \frac{154.3°\text{K}}{273°\text{K}} = 4.06 \frac{\text{ft}^3}{\text{lb mole}}$$

or

$$\hat{V}_{c_i} = \frac{RT_c}{p_c}$$

Then

$$V_{r_{i_2}} = \frac{\hat{V}_2}{\hat{V}_{c_i}} = \frac{4.13}{4.06} = 1.02$$

Now we know two parameters, $V_{r_{i_2}}$ and

$$T_{r_2} = \frac{T_2}{T_c} = \frac{248°\text{K}}{154.3°\text{K}} = 1.61$$

From the Nelson and Obert chart, Fig. 3.8 or 3.10,

$$p_{r_2} = 1.43, \qquad p = p_r p_c$$

$$p_2 = p_{r_2} p_c$$
$$= 1.43(38,000 \text{ mm}) = 54,000 \text{ mm Hg}$$
$$= 1.43(49.7)(14.7) = 1040 \text{ psia}$$

Example 3.17   Use of Compressibility Factor

Repeat Example 3.12, this time using the compressibility factor, i.e., the equation of state $pV = znRT$. "A 5-ft³ cylinder containing 50.0 lb of propane (C_3H_8) stands in the hot sun. A pressure gauge shows that the pressure is 665 psig. What is the temperature of the propane in the cylinder?"

Solution:

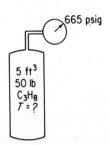

665 psig

5 ft³
50 lb
C_3H_8
$T = ?$

In the equation $pV = znRT$, we know

$$V = 5 \text{ ft}^3$$

$$n = \frac{50 \text{ lb}}{44 \text{ lb/lb mole}} = 1.135 \text{ lb mole } C_3H_8$$

$$p = 665 \text{ psig} + 14.7 \cong 680 \text{ psia}$$

However, z as well as T is unknown. Since z is a function of T_r and p_r, we should first calculate these latter two quantities ($T_c = 370°K$, or $666°R$; $p_c = 42.1$ atm, or 617 psia, from Appendix D) but are stopped by the fact that T is unknown. Another parameter available for use, to avoid a trial-and-error or graphical solution, is the factor zT_r (or V'_r could be used, as in the last example)

$$zT = \frac{pV}{nR} \quad \text{or} \quad zT_r = \frac{pV}{nRT_c}$$

$$zT_r = \frac{680 \text{ psia} \mid 5 \text{ ft}^3 \mid}{\mid 1.135 \text{ lb mole} \mid 10.73 \dfrac{(\text{psia})(\text{ft}^3)}{(\text{lb mole})(°R)} \mid 666°R}$$

$$= 0.42$$

From the Nelson and Obert chart, Fig. 3.10, at

$$\left. \begin{aligned} zT_r &= 0.42 \\ p_r &= \frac{680}{617} = 1.10 \end{aligned} \right\}$$

you can find $T_r = 1.02$ and

$$T = T_r T_c = (370)(1.02) = 378°K$$
$$= (666)(1.02) = 680°R$$

3.2-3 Gaseous Mixtures. So far we have only discussed pure components and their p-V-T relations. Many practical problems involve gaseous mixtures —the question is how should we treat gaseous mixtures? The most desirable technique would be to develop methods of calculating p-V-T data for mixtures based solely on the properties of the pure components. Possible ways of doing this for real gases are discussed below. We treated ideal gas mixtures in Sec. 3.1-3. We will see later (Chap. 4) that for ideal mixtures the thermodynamic properties of the individual components can be added together to give the desired property of the mixture.

(a) *Van der Waals' equation.* The laws of Dalton and Amagat can be combined with van der Waals' equation as follows:

(1) *Dalton's laws.* You can compute the partial pressure of each component by van der Waals' equation and then add the individual partial pressures together to give the total pressure of the system,

for component A,

$$p_A = \frac{n_A RT}{V - n_A b_A} - \frac{n_A^2 a_A}{V^2} \tag{3.28}$$

for component B,

$$p_B = \frac{n_B RT}{V - n_B b_B} - \frac{n_B^2 a_B}{V^2} \tag{3.29}$$

etc.,

in total,

$$v_T = RT\left[\frac{n_A}{V - n_A b_A} + \frac{n_B}{V - n_B b_B} + \cdots\right]$$
$$- \frac{1}{V^2}[n_A^2 a_A + n_B^2 a_B + \cdots] \tag{3.30}$$

This technique provides a direct solution for p_T if everything else is known; however, the solution for V or n_A from Eq. (3.30) is quite cumbersome.

(2) *Amagat's laws.* You add the partial volume for each component, and the sum of these partial volumes is the total volume

$$V_A + V_B + V_C + \cdots = V_T$$

The difficulty here is that each V is itself obtained from the solution of a cubic equation, Eq. (3.11), and you can see that the solution of a gas mixture problem in this manner is quite lengthy and complex.

(3) *Average constants.* A simpler and usually equally effective way to solve gas mixture problems is to use average constants in the equation of state. The problem resolves itself into this question: How should the constants be averaged to give the least error on the whole? For van der Waals' equation, you should proceed as follows:

b (Use linear mole fraction weight):

$$b_{\text{mixture}} = b_A y_A + b_B y_B + \cdots \tag{3.31}$$

a (Use linear square root average weight):

$$a_{\text{mixture}}^{1/2} = a_A^{1/2} y_A + a_B^{1/2} y_B + \cdots \tag{3.32}$$

If you are puzzled as to the reasoning behind the use of the square root type of weighting for a, remember that the term in van der Waals' equation involving a is

$$\frac{n^2 a}{V^2}$$

in which the number of moles is squared. The method of average constants can be successfully applied to most of the other equations of state listed in Table 3.1.

(b) *Mean compressibility factor.* Another approach toward the treatment of gaseous mixtures is to say that $pV = z_m nRT$, where z_m can be called the *mean compressibility factor.* With such a relationship the only problem is how to evaluate the mean compressibility factor in order to have this expression correctly predict *p-V-T* relationships. One obvious technique that might occur to you is to make z_m a mole average as follows:

$$z_m = z_A y_A + z_B y_B + \cdots \tag{3.33}$$

Since z is a function of both the reduced temperature and the reduced pressure, it is necessary to decide what pressure will be used to evaluate p_r.

(1) *Assume Dalton's law of partial pressures.* For each component z is evaluated at T_r and the reduced *partial pressure* for each gaseous component. The reduced partial pressure is defined as

$$p_{r_A} = \frac{p_A}{p_{c_A}} = \frac{(p_T) y_A}{p_{c_A}} \tag{3.34}$$

(2) *Assume Amagat's law of pure component volumes.* For each component z is evaluated at T_r and the reduced *total pressure* on the system.

(3) *Pseudocritical properties (Kay's method).* Kay's method is to use the generalized compressibility charts but to employ *pseudo* properties for the critical temperature and critical pressure[8] of the mixture. In instances where you know nothing about the gas mixture this technique is preferable to any of those discussed previously. Pseudocritical values for mixtures of gases are calculated on the assumption that each component in the mixture contributes to the pseudocritical value in the same proportion as the number of moles of that component. Thus, the pseudocritical values are computed as follows:

$$p'_c = p_{c_A} y_A + p_{c_B} y_B + \cdots \tag{3.35}$$

$$T'_c = T_{c_A} y_A + T_{c_B} y_B + \cdots \tag{3.36}$$

where p'_c = pseudocritical pressure, T'_c = pseudocritical temperature. (It has also been found convenient in some problems to calculate similarly a weighted pseudo-ideal-critical volume V'_{c_i}.) You can see that these are linearly weighted mole average pseudocritical properties. Then the respective pseudoreduced values are

$$p'_r = \frac{p}{p'_c} \tag{3.37}$$

$$T'_r = \frac{T}{T'_c} \tag{3.38}$$

(A like reduced value may be calculated for the pseudoreduced ideal critical volume.) In Sec. 3.8 we will compare the true critical point of a gaseous mixture with the pseudocritical point. If you are faced with a complicated

---

[8] You should still add Newton's corrections for H_2 and He.

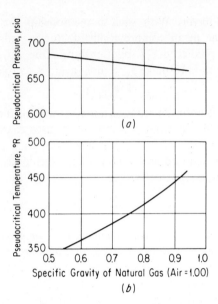

Fig. 3.11. Estimation of critical properties of natural gases.

mixture of gases whose composition is not well known, you still can estimate the pseudocritical constants from charts[9] such as shown in Figs. 3.11(a) and 3.11(b) if you know the gas specific gravity. Figure 3.11 is good only for natural gases composed mainly of methane which contain less than 5 per cent impurities (CO_2, N_2, H_2S, etc.).

Kay's method is known as a two-parameter rule since only p_c and T_c for each component are involved in the calculation of z_m. If a third parameter such as z_c or $\hat{V}_{c_i}$ is included in the determination of the mean compressibility factor, then we would have a three-parameter rule. Stewart[10] has reviewed 21 different methods of determining the mean compressibility factor by three-parameter rules (see Table 3.4). Although Kay's method is not the most accurate, it is easy to use and not considerably poorer than some of the more complex techniques of averaging critical properties.

In summary, to evaluate all the various methods which have been presented for treating p-V-T relationships of gaseous mixtures, we would have to state that no one method will consistently give the best results. Kay's pseudocritical method, on the average, will prove reliable, although other methods of greater accuracy (and of greater complexity) are available in

---

[9] Natural Gasoline Supply Men's Association, *Engineering Data Book*, Tulsa, Okla., 1957, p. 103.

[10] W. E. Stewart, S. F. Burkhart, and David Voo, Paper given at the *A.I.Ch.E.* meeting in Kansas City, Mo., May 18, 1959. Also refer to A. Satter and J. M. Campbell, *Soc. Petrol. Engrs. J.*, Dec., 1963, p. 333.

TABLE 3.4 PREDICTION OF p-V-T VALUES OF GAS DENSITY
BY PSEUDOCRITICAL METHODS

Method	% Root-mean-square deviation of density, 35 systems	% Root-mean-square deviation of density, CO_2 and H_2S free systems
(1) *Three-parameter Kay's rule:* $T'_c = \sum T_{c_i} y_i$ $p'_c = \sum p_{c_i} y_i$ $z'_c = \sum z_{c_i} y_i$	10.74	6.82
(2) *Empirical:* $T'_c = \sum T_{c_i} y_i$ $\dfrac{T'_c}{p'_c} = \sum \dfrac{T'_{c_i} y_i}{p'_{c_i}}$ $\hat{V}'_c = \sum \hat{V}_{c_i} y_i$	6.06	5.85
(3) *Virial approach (Joffe's method III):* $\dfrac{T'_c}{p'_c} = \dfrac{1}{8} \sum_i \sum_j y_i y_j \left[\left(\dfrac{T_{c_i}}{p_{c_i}} \right)^{1/3} + \left(\dfrac{T_{c_j}}{p_{c_j}} \right)^{1/3} \right]^3$ $\dfrac{T'_c}{\sqrt{p'_c}} = \sum y_i \dfrac{T_{c_i}}{\sqrt{p_{c_i}}}$ $\hat{V}'_c = \sum \hat{V}_{c_i} y_i$	4.98	4.24
(4) *"Recommended" method:* $\dfrac{T'_c}{p'_c} = \dfrac{1}{3} \sum y_i \dfrac{T_{c_i}}{p_{c_i}} + \dfrac{2}{3} \left[\sum y_i \left(\dfrac{T_{c_i}}{p_{c_i}} \right)^{1/3} \right]^2$ $\dfrac{T'_c}{\sqrt{p'_c}} = \sum y_i \dfrac{T_{c_i}}{p_{c_i}}$ $z'_c = \sum z_{c_i} y_i$	4.32	3.26

the literature as brought out in Table 3.4. Some of the longer equations of state, with average constants, are quite accurate. All these methods begin to break down near the true critical point for the mixture.

Example 3.18 p-V-T Relations for Gas Mixtures

A gaseous mixture has the following composition (in mole per cent):

methane	CH_4	20
ethylene	C_2H_4	30
nitrogen	N_2	50

at 90 atm pressure and 100°C. Compare the molal volume as computed by the methods of:

(1) Van der Waals' equation plus Dalton's law
(2) Van der Waals' equation using averaged constants
(3) Mean compressibility factor and Dalton's law
(4) Mean compressibility factor and Amagat's law
(5) Perfect gas law
(6) Pseudoreduced technique (Kay's method)

Solution:

Basis: 1 g mole of gas mixture

Additional data needed are:

	$a(atm)\left(\dfrac{cm^3}{g\ mole}\right)^2$	$b\left(\dfrac{cm^3}{g\ mole}\right)$	$T_c(°K)$	$p_c(atm)$
CH_4	2.25×10^6	42.8	191	45.8
C_2H_4	4.48×10^6	57.2	283	50.9
N_2	1.35×10^6	38.6	126	33.5

$$R = 82.06 \frac{(cm^3)(atm)}{(g\ mole)(°K)}$$

(1) Combine van der Waals' equation and Dalton's law according to Eq. (3.30):

$$p_T = RT\left[\frac{n_{CH_4}}{V - n_{CH_4}b_{CH_4}} + \frac{n_{C_2H_4}}{V - n_{C_2H_4}b_{C_2H_4}} + \frac{n_{N_2}}{V - n_{N_2}b_{N_2}}\right]$$

$$- \frac{1}{V^2}[n_{CH_4}^2 a_{CH_4} + n_{C_2H_4}^2 a_{C_2H_4} + n_{N_2}^2 a_{N_2}]$$

Substitute the numerical values (in the proper units):

$$90 = 82.06(373)\left[\frac{0.2}{V - 8.56} + \frac{0.3}{V - 17.1} + \frac{0.5}{V - 19.3}\right]$$

$$- \frac{1}{V^2}[9 \times 10^4 + 40.5 \times 10^4 + 33.8 \times 10^4] \quad (a)$$

The solution to this equation can be obtained by trial and error or graphical means. For the first trial assume ideal conditions so that

$$V = \frac{nRT}{p} = \frac{1(82.06)(373)}{90} = 340 \text{ cm}^3 \text{ at 90 atm and } 373°K \qquad ⑤$$

By plotting the right-hand side of Eq. (a) against V until the total is 90, we find the equation converges at about $V = 332$ cm^3 at 90 atm and 373°K.

(2) To use average constants in van der Waals' equation, write it in the following fashion:

$$V^3 - \left(\bar{b} + \frac{RT}{p}\right)nV^2 + \left(\frac{\bar{a}}{p}\right)n^2V - \frac{\bar{a}\bar{b}}{p}n^3 = 0$$

where $\bar{a}$ and $\bar{b}$ are the average constants.

$$(\bar{a})^{1/2} = 0.2a_{CH_4}^{1/2} + 0.3a_{C_2H_4}^{1/2} + 0.5a_{N_2}^{1/2}$$

$$\bar{a} = 2.30 \times 10^6 \text{ atm}\left(\frac{cm^3}{g \text{ mole}}\right)^2$$

$$\bar{b} = 0.2b_{CH_4} + 0.3b_{C_2H_4} + 0.5b_{N_2} = 45.0 \frac{cm^3}{g \text{ mole}}$$

$$n = 1 \text{ g mole (the basis)}$$

$$V^3 - \left[45.0 + \frac{(82.06)(373)}{90}\right]V^2 + \left[\frac{2.30 \times 10^6}{90}\right]V$$

$$- \left[\frac{(2.30 \times 10^6)(45.0)}{90}\right] = 0 \quad (b)$$

Let us work out a method of solving Eq. (b) for V different from the method used in part (1).

$$f(V) = V^3 - 385V^2 + 2.56 \times 10^4V - 1.15 \times 10^6 = 0$$
$$- V^3 + 385V^2 = 2.56 \times 10^4V - 1.15 \times 10^6 \quad (c)$$

Splitting this equation into two parts,

$$f_1(V) = 2.56 \times 10^4V - 1.15 \times 10^6 \quad (d)$$
$$f_2(V) = -V^3 + 385V^2 = V^2(385 - V) \quad (e)$$

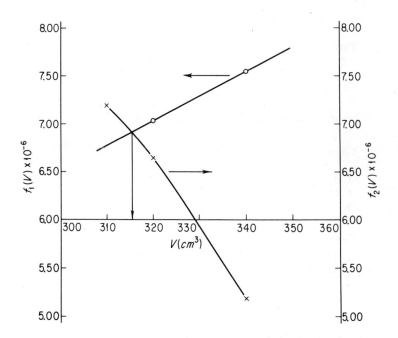

and plotting these parts to see where they cross is one method of obtaining the real root of the equation. You know V is in the vicinity of 340 cm³.

$V(cm^3)$	$f_1(V)$	$f_2(V)$
340	7.55×10^6	5.20×10^6
320	7.04×10^6	6.65×10^6
310	(only 2 points required for straight line)	7.20×10^6

From the graph $V \cong 316$ cm³ at 90 atm and 373°K.

(3) The table below shows how Dalton's law can be used to estimate a mean compressibility factor.

Comp.	$p_c(atm)$	$T_c(°K)$	y	$(90)y = p$	$p_r = \dfrac{p}{p_c}$	$T_r = \dfrac{373}{T_c}$
CH_4	45.8	191	0.2	18	0.394	1.95
C_2H_4	50.9	283	0.3	27	0.535	1.32
N_2	33.5	126	0.5	45	1.340	2.95

Comp.	z	$(z)(y)$
CH_4	0.99	0.198
C_2H_4	0.93	0.279
N_2	1.00	0.500
z mean $=$		0.977

Then

$$V = \frac{z_{mean} RT}{p} = \frac{(0.977)(82.06)(373)}{90}$$
$$= 332 \text{ cm}^3 \text{ at 90 atm and 373°K}$$

(4) Combining Amagat's law and the z factor:

Comp.	$p_c(atm)$	$T_c(°K)$	y	$p_r = \dfrac{90}{p_c}$	$T_r = \dfrac{373}{T_c}$
CH_4	45.8	191	0.2	1.97	1.95
C_2H_4	50.9	283	0.3	1.78	1.32
N_2	33.5	126	0.5	2.68	2.95

Comp.	z	$(z)(y)$
CH_4	0.97	0.194
C_2H_4	0.75	0.225
N_2	1.01	0.505
$z_{mean} =$		0.924

$$V = \frac{0.924(82.06)(373)}{90} = 313 \text{ cm}^3 \text{ at 90 atm and } 373°K$$

(5) According to Kay's method, we first calculate the pseudocritical values for the mixture by Eqs. (3.35) and (3.36).

$$\begin{array}{ccc} & CH_4 & C_2H_4 & N_2 \end{array}$$

$$p'_c = p_{c_A}y_A + p_{c_B}y_B + p_{c_C}y_C = (45.8)(0.2) + (50.9)(0.3) + (33.5)(0.5)$$
$$= 41.2 \text{ atm}$$

$$T'_c = T_{c_A}y_A + T_{c_B}y_B + T_{c_C}y_C = (191)(0.2) + (283)(0.3) + (126)(0.5)$$
$$= 186°K$$

Then we calculate the pseudoreduced values for the mixture by Eqs. (3.37) and (3.38).

$$p'_r = \frac{p}{p'_c} = \frac{90}{41.2} = 2.18, \qquad T'_r = \frac{T}{T'_c} = \frac{373}{186} = 2.00$$

With the aid of these two parameters we can find from Fig. 3.8 that $z = 0.965$. Thus

$$V = \frac{zRT}{p} = \frac{(0.965)(82.06)(373)}{90} = 328 \text{ cm}^3 \text{ at 90 atm and } 373°K$$

Example 3.19 Use of Pseudoreduced Ideal Molal Volume

In instances where the temperature or pressure of a gas mixture is unknown, it is convenient, in order to avoid a trial-and-error solution using the generalized compressibility charts, to compute a pseudocritical ideal volume and a pseudoreduced ideal volume as illustrated below. Suppose we have given that the molal volume of the gas mixture in the previous problem was 326 cm³ at 90 atm. What was the temperature?

Solution:

Comp.	$\hat{V}_{c_i} = RT_c/p_c$	y	$y\hat{V}_{c_i}$
CH_4	$\frac{(82.06)(191)}{45.8} = 342$	0.2	68.4
C_2H_4	$\frac{(82.06)(283)}{50.9} = 456$	0.3	137
N_2	$\frac{(82.06)(126)}{33.5} = 309$	0.5	154
		$\hat{V}'_{c_i} =$	$\overline{359.4}$

$$V'_{r_i} = \frac{\hat{V}}{\hat{V}'_{c_i}} = \frac{326}{359.4} = 0.907$$

Using the data obtained in the previous example, we know that p'_r is 2.18. From either Fig. 3.8 or 3.10, at the intersection of V'_{r_i} of 0.907 and p'_r of 2.18 we can read that T'_r is about 2.04. Consequently, with $T'_c = 186°K$,

$$T = T'_c T'_r = (186)(2.04) = 379°K$$

3.3 Vapor pressure

The terms *vapor* and *gas* are used very loosely. A gas which exists below its critical temperature is usually called a vapor because it can condense. If you continually compress a pure gas at constant temperature, provided the temperature is below the critical temperature, some pressure is eventually reached at which the gas starts to condense into a liquid. Further compression does not increase the pressure but merely increases the fraction of gas that condenses. A reversal of the procedure just described will cause the liquid to be transformed into the gaseous state again. From now on, the word "vapor" will be reserved to describe a gas below its critical point in a process in which the phase change is of primary interest, while the word "gas" or "noncondensable gas" will be used to describe a gas above the critical point or a gas in a process in which it cannot condense.

Vaporization and condensation at constant temperature and pressure are *equilibrium* processes, and the equilibrium pressure is called the *vapor pressure*. At a given temperature there is only one pressure at which the liquid and vapor phases of a pure substance may exist in equilibrium. Either phase alone may exist, of course, over a wide range of conditions. By equilibrium we mean a state in which there is no tendency toward spontaneous

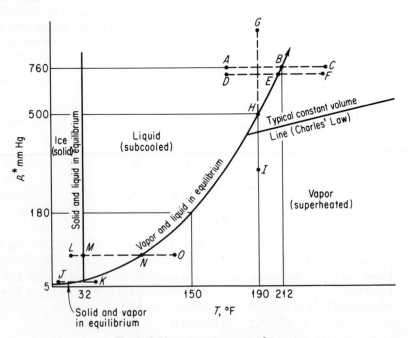

Fig. 3.12. Vapor pressure curve for water.

change. Another way to say the same thing is to say equilibrium is a state in which all the rates of attaining and departing from the state are balanced.

You can visualize vapor pressure, vaporization, and condensation more easily with the aid of Fig. 3.12. Figure 3.12 is an expanded p-T diagram for pure water. For each temperature you can read the corresponding pressure at which water vapor and water liquid exist in equilibrium. You have encountered this condition of equilibrium many times—for example, in boiling. Any substance has an infinite number of boiling points, but by custom we say the "normal" boiling point is the temperature at which boiling takes place under a pressure of 1 atm (760 mm). Unless another pressure is specified, 1 atm is assumed, and the term "boiling point" is taken to mean the "normal boiling point." The normal boiling point for water occurs when the vapor pressure of the water equals the pressure of the atmosphere on top of the water. A piston with a force of 14.7 psia could just as well take the place of the atmosphere as shown in Fig. 3.13. For example, you know

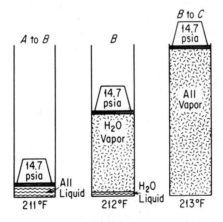

Fig. 3.13. Transformation of liquid water into water vapor at constant pressure.

that at 212°F water will boil (vaporize) and the pressure will be 760 mm Hg, or 1 atm (point B). Suppose you heat water starting at 170°F (point A) in an open pan—what happens? We assume that the water vapor above the pan is at all times in equilibrium with the liquid water. This is a constant-pressure process since the air around the water in the pan acts similarly to a piston in a cylinder to keep the pressure at atmospheric pressure. As the temperature rises and the confining pressure stays constant, nothing particularly noticeable occurs until 212°F is reached, at which time the water begins to boil, i.e., evaporate. It pushes back the atmosphere and will completely change from liquid into vapor. If you heated the water in an enclosed cylinder, and if after it had all evaporated at point *B* you continued heating the water vapor formed at constant pressure, you could apply the gas laws in the region *B-C* (and higher temperatures). A reversal of this process would cause the vapor to condense at *B* to form a liquid. The temperature at point *B* would in these circumstances represent the *dew point*.

Suppose you went to the top of Pikes Peak and repeated the experiment —what would happen then? Everything would be the same (points *D-E-F*) with the exception of the temperature at which the water would begin to boil, or condense. Since the pressure of the atmosphere at the top of Pikes Peak would presumably be lower than 760 mm Hg, the water would start to displace the air, or boil, at a lower temperature. However, water still exerts a vapor pressure of 760 mm Hg at 212°F. You can see that (a) at any given temperature water exerts its vapor pressure (at equilibrium), (b) as the temperature goes up, the vapor pressure goes up, and (c) it makes no difference whether water vaporizes into air, into a cylinder closed by a piston, or into an evacuated cylinder—at any temperature it still exerts the same vapor pressure as long as the water is in equilibrium with its vapor.

A process of vaporization or condensation at constant temperature is illustrated by the lines *G-H-I* or *I-H-G*, respectively, in Fig. 3.12. Water would vaporize or condense at constant temperature as the pressure reached point *H* on the vapor-pressure curve (also look at Fig. 3.14).

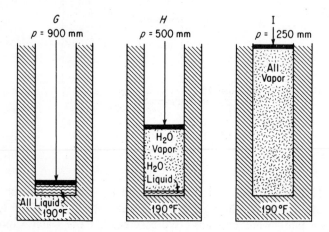

Fig. 3.14. Transformation of liquid water into water vapor at constant temperature.

The *p-T* conditions at which ice (in its common form) and water vapor are in equilibrium are also seen in Fig. 3.12. When the solid passes directly into the vapor phase without first becoming a liquid (line *J-K* as opposed to line *L-M-N-O*), it is said to *sublime*. Iodine crystals do this at room temperature; water sublimes only below 32°F, as when the frost disappears in the winter when the thermometer reads 20°F.

The vapor-pressure line indicates the separation of both solid and liquid regions from the vapor region and extends well past the conditions shown in Fig. 3.12 all the way to the critical temperature and pressure (not shown). Above the critical temperature, water can exist only as a gas. A term commonly applied to the vapor-liquid portion of the vapor-pressure curve is the word *saturated*. It means the same thing as vapor and liquid in equilibrium with each other. If a gas is just ready to start to condense the first drop of liquid, it is a saturated gas; if a liquid is just about to vaporize, it is a saturated liquid. These two conditions are also known as the *dew point* and *bubble point*, respectively.

If you have a mixture of liquid and vapor at equilibrium (called a "wet gas"), both the liquid and vapor are said to be saturated at these conditions. The vapor-pressure line in Fig. 3.12 thus represents the state of a pure component designated by a number of special terms depending on what aspect of the state is of primary importance:

(a) The saturated liquid
(b) The saturated vapor
(c) The bubble point
(d) The dew point

The region to the right of the vapor-pressure curve in Fig. 3.12 is called the *superheated* region and the one to the left of the vapor-pressure curve is called the *subcooled* region. The temperatures in the superheated region, if measured as the difference $(O - N)$ between the actual temperature of the superheated vapor and the saturation temperature for the same pressure, are called *degrees of superheat*. For example, steam at 500°F and 100 psia (saturation temperature for 100 psia is 327.8°F) has $(500 - 327.8) = 172.2°$ of superheat. Another new term you will find used frequently is the word *quality*. A "wet" vapor consists of saturated vapor and saturated liquid in equilibrium. The weight fraction of vapor is known as the quality.

Example 3.20   Properties of "Wet" Vapors

The properties of a mixture of vapor and liquid in equilibrium (for a single component) can be computed from the individual properties of the saturated vapor and saturated liquid. The Steam Tables (Appendix C) are a good source of data to illustrate such computations. At 400°F and 247.3 psia the specific volume of a wet steam mixture is 1.05 ft³ per pound. What is the quality of the steam?

Solution:

From the Steam Tables the specific volumes of the saturated vapor and liquid are

$$V_l = 0.0186 \text{ ft}^3/\text{lb}, \qquad V_g = 1.8633 \text{ ft}^3/\text{lb}$$

Basis: 1 lb wet steam mixture

Let x = weight fraction vapor.

$$\frac{0.0186 \text{ ft}^3}{1 \text{ lb liquid}} \left| \frac{(1-x) \text{ lb liquid}}{} + \frac{1.8633 \text{ ft}^3}{1 \text{ lb vapor}} \right| \frac{x \text{ lb vapor}}{} = 1.05 \text{ ft}^3$$

$$0.0186 - 0.0186x + 1.8633x = 1.05$$

$$1.845x = 1.03$$

$$x = 0.56$$

Other properties of wet mixtures can be treated in the same manner.

3.3-1 Change of Vapor Pressure with Temperature. A large number of experiments on many substances have shown that a plot of the vapor pressure (p^*) of a compound against temperature does not yield a straight line but a curve, as you saw in Fig. 3.12. To reduce this curve to a linear form ($y = mx + b$), many types of correlations have been proposed; a plot of log (p^*) vs. ($1/T$), for moderate temperature intervals, is reasonably linear:

$$\underbrace{\log (p^*)}_{y} = \underbrace{m\left(\frac{1}{T}\right) + b}_{= mx + b} \tag{3.39}$$

Equation 3.39 is derived from the Clausius-Clapeyron equation (see Chap. 4). Empirical correlations of vapor pressure are frequently given in the following form (refer to Appendix G for values of the constants):

$$\log (p^*) = -\frac{A}{t + C} + B \tag{3.40}$$

where A, B, C = constants different for each substance

t = temperature in °F

Over wide temperature intervals the experimental data are not exactly linear as indicated by Eq. (3.39), but have a slight tendency to curve. This curvature can be straightened out by using a special plot known as a Cox chart.[11] The log of the vapor pressure of a compound is plotted against a special nonlinear temperature scale constructed from the vapor-pressure data for water (called a *reference substance*).

---

[11] E. R. Cox, *Ind. Eng. Chem.*, vol. 15, p. 592 (1923).

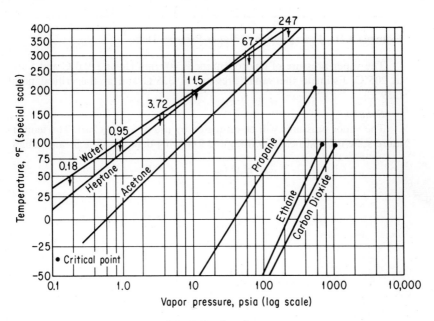

Fig. 3.15. Cox chart.

As illustrated in Fig. 3.15, the temperature scale is established by record-ing the temperature at a given vapor pressure of water for a number of vapor pressures. The vapor pressures of other substances plotted on this same graph will yield straight lines over extensive temperature ranges, and thus facilitate the extrapolation and interpolation of vapor-pressure data. It has been found that lines so constructed for closely related compounds, such as hydrocarbons, all meet at a common point. Since straight lines can be obtained on such a plot, only two sets of vapor-pressure data are needed to provide complete information about the vapor pressure of a substance over a considerable temperature range. We will discuss in Chap. 4 under the topic of the Clausius-Clapeyron equation other information that can be obtained from vapor-pressure plots.

3.3-2 Change of Vapor Pressure with Pressure. The equation for the change of vapor pressure with total pressure at constant temperature in a system is

$$\left(\frac{\partial(p^*)}{\partial p_T}\right)_T = \frac{\hat{V}_i}{\hat{V}_g} \tag{3.41}$$

where $\hat{V}$ = molal volume of saturated liquid or gas

$\quad p_T$ = total pressure on the system

Under normal conditions the effect is negligible.

178 GASES, VAPORS, LIQUIDS, AND SOLIDS Sec. 3.3

Example 3.21 Extrapolation of Vapor-Pressure Data

The vapor pressure of chlorobenzene is 400 mm Hg at 110.0°C and 5 atm at 205°C. Estimate the vapor pressure at 325°C and at the critical point (359°C).

Solution:

The vapor pressures will be estimated by use of a Cox chart. The temperature scale is constructed by using the following data from the Steam Tables:

p^* H$_2$O (*psia*)	t(°F)
0.95	100
3.72	150
11.5	200
29.8	250
67.0	300
247	400
680	500
1543	600
3094	700

The range of vapor pressures from 1 to 3100 psia is laid on the horizontal logarithmic scale. Next, draw a line representing the vapor pressure of water at any suitable angle on the graph so as to stretch the desired temperature range from the bottom to the top of the vertical axis. For each vapor pressure, the temperature is marked and a horizontal line drawn to the ordinate. This establishes the temperature scale (which looks almost logarithmic in nature).

Now convert the two vapor pressures of chlorobenzene into psia,

$$\frac{400 \text{ mm} \mid 14.7 \text{ psia}}{760 \text{ mm}} = 7.74 \text{ psia} \mid 110°C = 230°F$$

$$\frac{5 \text{ atm} \mid 14.7 \text{ psia}}{1 \text{ atm}} = 73.5 \text{ psia} \mid 205°C = 401°F$$

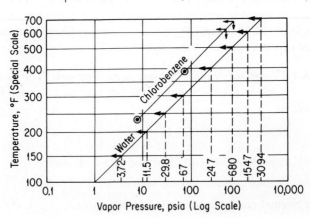

and plot these two points on the graph paper. Next draw a straight line between them, and extrapolate to 617°F(325°C) and 678°F(359°C). At these two temperatures read off the estimated vapor pressures:

	617°F(325°C)	678°F(359°C)
estimated	450 psia	700 psia
experimental	441 psia	666 psia

Experimental values are given for comparison.

3.3-3 Estimating Vapor Pressures. Miller[12] recommends the following equation to estimate vapor pressures based on the normal boiling-point temperature (T_b) and the critical temperature and pressure:

$$\log p_r = -\frac{G}{T_r}[1 - T_r^2 + k(3 + T_r)(1 - T_r)^3]$$

where
$$G = 0.210 + 0.200\,a$$

$$a = \frac{T_{rb}\ln p_c}{1 - T_{rb}}$$

$$k = \frac{(a/2.306\,G) - (1 + T_{rb})}{(3 + T_{rb})(1 - T_{rb})^2}$$

$$T_{rb} = \frac{T_b}{T_c}$$

Other methods of estimating vapor pressures are given by McGowan[13] or see the footnote on page 237 and the Othmer plot on page 259.

3.4. Saturation

How can you predict the properties of a pure vapor (which can condense) mixed with a noncondensable gas? This situation is somewhat different than the case of a pure component alone. A typical example with which you are quite familiar is that of water vapor in air.

Water vapor is a gas, and like all gases its molecules are free to migrate in any direction. They will do so as long as they are not stopped by the walls of a container. Furthermore, the molecules will evenly distribute themselves throughout the entire volume of the container.

When any pure gas (or a gaseous mixture) comes in contact with a liquid, the gas will acquire vapor from the liquid. If this contact is maintained

[12] D. G. Miller, *J. Phys. Chem.*, v. 69, p. 3209 (1965).
[13] J. C. McGowan, *Rec. Trav. Chim.*, v. 84, p. 99 (1965).

for a considerable length of time, equilibrium is attained, at which time the *partial pressure of the vapor* (vaporized liquid) *will equal the vapor pressure* of the liquid at the temperature of the system. Regardless of the duration of contact between the liquid and gas, after equilibrium is reached no more liquid will vaporize into the gas phase. The gas is then said to be *saturated* with the particular vapor at the given temperature. We can also say the gas is at its dew point.

As an illustration, assume you put dry air at 150°F into a container in which liquid water is present. The initial total pressure on the air and water is to be 760 mm Hg. If you keep the total pressure on the container constant at 760 mm Hg (Figs. 3.16 and 3.17), eventually the water will vaporize, and

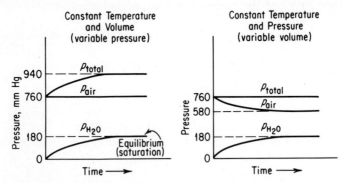

Fig. 3.16. Change of partial and total pressures on vaporization of water into air at constant temperature.

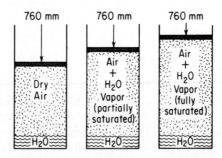

Fig. 3.17. Evaporation of water at constant pressure and temperature.

water vapor will enter and mix with the air until the partial pressure of the water in the air reaches 180 mm Hg (the vapor pressure of water at 150°F). Regardless of the duration of contact between the water and the air (after this partial pressure of water vapor is reached), no more water vapor can enter the air. The air is saturated with respect to water vapor and cannot contain additional water. Of course the volume of the system will change if the total pressure is maintained at 760 mm Hg, or else some air will have to leave the system if the volume and pressure are to stay constant. If the volume of the system is fixed, the total pressure will rise to $760 + 180 = 940$ mm Hg.

Assuming the ideal gas laws apply to both air and water vapor, as they do with excellent precision, you can calculate the partial pressure of the air as follows *at saturation:*

Dalton's law of additive pressures:

$$p_{air} + p_{H_2O} = p_{total}, \qquad p_{air} + 180 \text{ mm} = 760 \text{ mm}$$
$$p_{air} = 760 - 180 = 580 \text{ mm Hg}$$

From Eq. (3.4), we know

$$\frac{p_{air}}{p_{H_2O}} = \frac{n_{air}}{n_{H_2O}} \qquad \text{at constant temperature}$$

or, from Eq. (3.7),

$$\frac{V_{air}}{V_{H_2O}} = \frac{n_{air}}{n_{H_2O}} \qquad \text{at constant temperature}$$

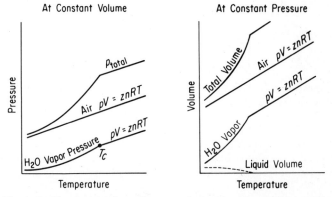

Fig. 3.18. The change of total pressure (volume) and partial pressures (volumes) of air and water in a saturated mixture with increasing temperature.

Then

$$\frac{p_{air}}{p_{H_2O}} = \frac{p_{air}}{p_{total} - p_{air}} = \frac{V_{air}}{V_{total} - V_{air}} \qquad (3.42)$$

We can generalize these expressions for any two components as follows:

$$\frac{p_1}{p_2} = \frac{p_1}{p_t - p_1} = \frac{n_1}{n_2} = \frac{V_1}{V_t - V_1} = \frac{V_1}{V_2} \qquad (3.43)$$

and

$$p_1 = \frac{V_1}{V_2} p_2 \quad \text{or} \quad V_1 = \frac{p_1}{p_2} V_2 \qquad (3.44)$$

where the subscripts indicate component 1, component 2, and total.

If the temperature rises in an air-water mixture and the vapor phase is always saturated with water vapor, the change in the partial pressure of the water and the air, and in the total pressure, as a function of temperature can be graphically shown as in Fig. 3.18.

Example 3.22   Saturation

What is the minimum number of cubic feet of dry air at 20°C and 738 mm Hg that are necessary to evaporate 13.1 lb of alcohol, if the total pressure remains constant at 738 mm Hg? Assume that the air is blown over the alcohol to evaporate it in such a way that the exit pressure of the air-alcohol mixture is at 738 mm Hg.

Solution:

Assume the process is isothermal. The additional data needed are:

$$p^*_{\text{alcohol}} \text{ at } 20°C \ (68°F) = 44.5 \text{ mm Hg}$$

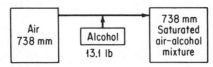

The most alcohol the air can pick up is a saturated mixture; any condition less than saturated would require more air.

Basis: 13.1 lb alcohol

The ratio of moles of alcohol to moles of air in the final gaseous mixture is the same as the ratio of the partial pressures of these two substances. Since we know the moles of alcohol, we can find the number of moles of air.

$$\frac{p_{\text{alcohol}}}{p_{\text{air}}} = \frac{n_{\text{alcohol}}}{n_{\text{air}}}$$

From Dalton's law,

$$p_{\text{air}} = p_{\text{total}} - p_{\text{alcohol}}$$

$$p_{\text{alcohol}} = 44.5 \text{ mm}$$

$$p_{\text{air}} = (738 - 44.5) \text{ mm}$$

$$\frac{13.1 \text{ lb alcohol}}{} \left| \frac{1 \text{ lb mole alcohol}}{46 \text{ lb alcohol}} \right| \frac{(738 - 44.5) \text{ lb mole air}}{44.5 \text{ lb mole alcohol}}$$

$$\frac{359 \text{ ft}^3}{1 \text{ lb mole}} \left| \frac{293°K}{273°K} \right| \frac{760 \text{ mm}}{738 \text{ mm}} = 1800 \text{ ft}^3 \text{ air}$$

at 20°C and 738 mm Hg

Example 3.23   Saturation

If 1250 cm³ of wet H_2 are saturated with water at 30°C and 742 mm Hg, what is the volume of dry gas at standard conditions? The vapor pressure of water at 30°C is 32 mm Hg.

Solution:

(a) *Long Solution:*

Your first impulse in selecting a basis is probably to ask yourself the question,

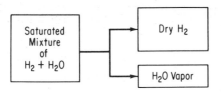

"What do I have or what do I want?" The answer might be that you have 1250 cm³ of saturated H_2 at 30°C and 742 mm Hg.

Basis: 1250 cm³ H_2 saturated with water at 30°C and 742 mm Hg

$$\frac{1250 \text{ cm}^3 \text{ wet gas}}{} \left| \frac{(742 - 32) \text{ cm}^3 \text{ dry } H_2}{742 \text{ cm}^3 \text{ wet gas}} \right| \frac{273°K}{303°K} \left| \frac{742 \text{ mm}}{760 \text{ mm}} \right.$$

$$= 1051 \text{ cm}^3 \text{ dry } H_2 \text{ at S.C.}$$

(b) *Shorter Solution:*

You can save a little time by recalling that

$$p_{\text{total}} = p_{H_2O} + p_{H_2}$$
$$742 = 32 + 710$$

In the given gas mixture you have *any* of the following:

  (a) 1250 cm³ wet H_2 at 30°C and 742 mm Hg
  (b) 1250 cm³ dry H_2 at 30°C and 710 mm Hg
  (c) 1250 cm³ water vapor at 30°C and 32 mm Hg

Therefore, since the problem asks for the volume of dry H_2, you should take as a basis (b) dry H_2, and then apply the ideal gas laws to the dry H_2.

Basis: 1250 cm³ dry H_2 at 30°C and 710 mm Hg

$$\frac{1250 \text{ cm}^3 \text{ dry } H_2}{} \left| \frac{273°K}{303°K} \right| \frac{710 \text{ mm}}{760 \text{ mm}} = 1051 \text{ cm}^3 \text{ dry } H_2 \text{ at S.C.}$$

You can see that by choosing this basis you can eliminate the two values which cancel in solution (a), the 742 mm Hg.

Example 3.24   Saturation

A telescopic gas holder contains 10,000 ft³ of saturated gas at 80°F and a pressure of 6.0 in. H_2O above atmospheric. The barometer reads 28.46 in. Hg. Calculate the weight of water vapor in the gas.

Solution:

The total pressure of the saturated gas must be calculated first in in. Hg.

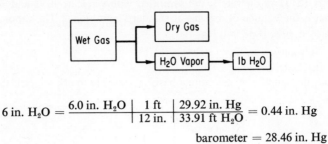

$$6 \text{ in. } H_2O = \frac{6.0 \text{ in. } H_2O}{} \Big| \frac{1 \text{ ft}}{12 \text{ in.}} \Big| \frac{29.92 \text{ in. Hg}}{33.91 \text{ ft } H_2O} = 0.44 \text{ in. Hg}$$

$$\text{barometer} = \underline{28.46 \text{ in. Hg}}$$

$$p_{total} = 28.90 \text{ in. Hg}$$

$$p_w = \text{vapor pressure of } H_2O \text{ at } 80°F = 1.03 \text{ in. Hg}$$

$$p_t = p_g + p_w$$

$$28.90 = 27.87 + 1.03$$

There exists

10,000 ft³	wet gas	at 28.90 in. Hg and	80°F
10,000	dry gas	27.87	80°F
10,000	water vapor	1.03	80°F

$$°R = 80 + 460 = 540°R$$

From the volume of water vapor present at known conditions, you can calculate the volume at S.C. and hence the lb moles and lbs of water.

Basis: 10,000 ft³ water vapor at 1.03 in. Hg and 80°F

$$\frac{10,000 \text{ ft}^3 \text{ H}_2\text{O vapor} \Big| 492°R \Big| 1.03 \text{ in. Hg} \Big| 1 \text{ lb mole} \Big| 18 \text{ lb H}_2\text{O}}{\Big| 540°R \Big| 29.92 \text{ in. Hg} \Big| 359 \text{ ft}^3 \Big| 1 \text{ lb mole H}_2\text{O}}$$

$$= 15.7 \text{ lb H}_2\text{O}$$

3.5. Partial saturation and humidity

In the foregoing section we dealt with mixtures of gas and vapor in which the gas was saturated with the vapor. More often, the contact time required between the gas and liquid for equilibrium (or saturation) to be attained is too long, and the gas is not completely saturated with the vapor. Then the vapor is not in equilibrium with a liquid phase, and the partial pressure of the vapor is less than the vapor pressure of the liquid at the given temperature. This situation is called *partial saturation*. What we have is simply a mixture of two or more gases which obey the real gas laws. What distinguishes this situation from the previous examples for gas mixtures is that under suitable conditions it is possible to condense part of one of the gaseous components. In Fig. 3.19 you can see how the partial pressure of the water vapor in a gaseous mixture at constant volume obeys the ideal gas laws as the temperature drops until saturation is reached, at which time the water vapor starts to condense. Until these conditions are achieved, you can confidently apply the gas laws to the mixture.

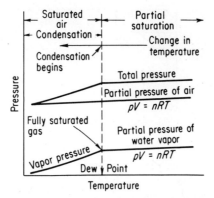

Fig. 3.19. Transformation of a partially saturated water vapor-air mixture into a saturated mixture as the temperature is lowered (volume = constant).

Several ways exist to express the concentration of a vapor in a gas mixture. You sometimes encounter weight or mole fraction (or per cent), but more frequently one of the following:

(1) Relative saturation (relative humidity)
(2) Molal saturation (molal humidity)
(3) "Absolute" saturation ("absolute" humidity)

When the vapor is water vapor and the gas is air, the special term *humidity* applies. For other gases or vapors, the term saturation is used.

3.5-1 Relative Saturation. Relative saturation is defined as

$$\frac{p_{\text{vapor}}}{p_{\text{satd}}} = \text{relative saturation} \tag{3.45}$$

where p_{vapor} = partial pressure of the vapor in the gas mixture
  p_{satd} = partial pressure of the vapor in the gas mixture *if* the gas were saturated at the given temperature of the mixture, i.e., the vapor pressure of the condensed vapor

Then, for brevity, if the subscript 1 denotes vapor,

$$\frac{p_1}{p_1^*} = \frac{p_1/p_t}{p_1^*/p_t} = \frac{V_1/V_t}{V_{\text{satd}}/V_t} = \frac{n_1}{n_{\text{satd}}} = \frac{\text{lb}_1}{\text{lb}_{\text{satd}}} \tag{3.46}$$

You can see that relative saturation, in effect, represents the fractional approach to total saturation as shown in Fig. 3.20. If you listen to the radio or TV and hear the announcer say that the temperature is 70°F and the *relative humidity* is 60 per cent, he means

$$\frac{p_{H_2O}}{p^*_{H_2O}}(100) = \% \text{ R.H.} \tag{3.47}$$

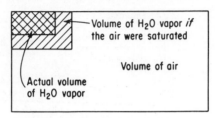

Fig. 3.20. A gas partially saturated with water vapor.

with both the p_{H_2O} and the $p^*_{H_2O}$ being measured at 70°F. Zero per cent relative saturation means no vapor in the gas; 100 per cent relative saturation means the partial pressure of the vapor is the same as the vapor pressure of the condensed vapor.

Example 3.25   Relative Humidity

The weather man on the radio this morning reported that the temperature this afternoon would reach 94°F, the relative humidity would be 43%, the barometer 29.67 in. Hg, partly cloudy to clear, with the wind from SSE at 8 mph. How many pounds of water vapor would be in 1 mile³ of afternoon air? What would be the dew point of this air?

Solution:

The vapor pressure of water at 94°F is 1.61 in. Hg. We can calculate the partial pressure of the water vapor in the air from the given per cent relative humidity; from this point forward, the problem is the same as the examples in the previous section.

$$p_w = (1.61 \text{ in. Hg})(0.43) = 0.69 \text{ in. Hg}$$

$$p_{air} = p_t - p_w = 29.67 - 0.69 = 28.98 \text{ in. Hg}$$

Basis: 1 mile³ water vapor at 94°F and 0.69 in. Hg

$$\frac{1 \text{ mile}^3}{} \left| \left(\frac{5280 \text{ ft}}{1 \text{ mile}}\right)^3 \right| \frac{492°R}{554°R} \left| \frac{0.69 \text{ in. Hg}}{29.92 \text{ in. Hg}} \right| \frac{1 \text{ lb mole}}{359 \text{ ft}^3} \left| \frac{18 \text{ lb } H_2O}{1 \text{ lb mole}} \right.$$

$$= 1.51 \times 10^8 \text{ lb } H_2O$$

Now the dew point is the temperature at which the water vapor in the air will first condense on cooling at *constant total pressure and composition*. As the gas is cooled you can see from Eq. (3.47) that the per cent relative humidity increases since the partial pressure of the water vapor is constant while the vapor pressure of water decreases with temperature. When the per cent relative humidity reaches 100%,

$$100\frac{p_1}{p_1^*} = 100\% \quad \text{or} \quad p_1 = (p_1^*)$$

the water vapor will start to condense. This means that at the dew point the vapor pressure of water will be 0.69 in. Hg. From the Steam Tables you can see this corresponds to a temperature of about 69°F.

3.5-2 Molal Saturation. Another way to express vapor concentration in a gas is to use the ratio of the moles of vapor to the moles of vapor-free gas

$$\frac{n_{\text{vapor}}}{n_{\text{vapor-free gas}}} = \text{molal saturation} \tag{3.48}$$

If subscripts 1 and 2 represent the vapor and the dry gas, respectively, then for a binary system,

$$p_1 + p_2 = p_t \tag{3.49}$$

$$n_1 + n_2 = n_t \tag{3.50}$$

$$\frac{n_1}{n_2} = \frac{p_1}{p_2} = \frac{V_1}{V_2} = \frac{n_1}{n_t - n_1} = \frac{p_1}{p_t - p_1} = \frac{V_1}{V_t - V_1} \tag{3.51}$$

By multiplying by the appropriate molecular weights, you can find the weight of vapor per weight of dry gas

$$\frac{(n_{\text{vapor}})(\text{mol. wt}_{\text{vapor}})}{(n_{\text{dry gas}})(\text{mol. wt}_{\text{dry gas}})} = \frac{\text{wt}_{\text{vapor}}}{\text{wt}_{\text{dry gas}}} \tag{3.52}$$

3.5-3 "Absolute" Saturation; Percentage Saturation. "Absolute" saturation is defined as the ratio of the moles of vapor per mole of *vapor-free* gas to the moles of vapor *which would be present* per mole of *vapor-free* gas if the mixture were completely saturated at the existing temperature and total pressure.

$$\text{"absolute saturation"} = \frac{\left(\dfrac{\text{moles vapor}}{\text{moles vapor-free gas}}\right)_{\text{actual}}}{\left(\dfrac{\text{moles vapor}}{\text{moles vapor-free gas}}\right)_{\text{saturated}}} \tag{3.53}$$

Using the subscripts 1 for vapor and 2 for vapor-free gas,

$$\left.\begin{array}{c}\text{per cent}\\\text{saturation}\end{array}\right\} \frac{\left(\dfrac{n_1}{n_2}\right)_{\text{actual}}}{\left(\dfrac{n_1}{n_2}\right)_{\text{saturated}}}(100) = \frac{\left(\dfrac{p_1}{p_2}\right)_{\text{actual}}}{\left(\dfrac{p_1}{p_2}\right)_{\text{saturated}}}(100) \tag{3.54}$$

Since p_1 saturated $= p_1^*$ and $p_t = p_1 + p_2$, therefore,

$$\left.\begin{array}{c}\text{per cent}\\ \text{saturation}\end{array}\right\} = 100\,\frac{\dfrac{p_1}{p_t - p_1}}{\dfrac{p_1^*}{p_t - p_1^*}} = \frac{p_1^*}{p_1}\left(\frac{p_t - p_1^*}{p_t - p_1}\right)100 \qquad (3.55)$$

Now you will recall that $p_1/p_1^* = $ relative saturation. Therefore,

$$\left.\begin{array}{c}\text{per cent}\\ \text{saturation}\end{array}\right\} = (\text{relative saturation})\left(\frac{p_t - p_1^*}{p_t - p_1}\right)100 \qquad (3.56)$$

Per cent saturation is always less than relative saturation except at saturated conditions (or at zero per cent saturation) when per cent saturation = per cent relative saturation.

Example 3.26 Partial Saturation

Helium contains 12% (volume) of ethyl acetate. Calculate the per cent relative saturation and the per cent saturation of the mixture at a temperature of 30°C and a pressure of 740 mm of Hg.

Solution:

The additional data needed are

p_{EtAc}^* at 30°C $= 119$ mm Hg (from any suitable handbook)

Using Dalton's laws,

$$p_{\text{EtAc}} = p_t y_{\text{EtAc}} = p_t\left(\frac{n_{\text{EtAc}}}{n_t}\right) = p_t\left(\frac{V_{\text{EtAc}}}{V_t}\right)$$

$$= (740)(0.12) = 88.9 \text{ mm Hg}$$

$$p_{\text{He}} = p_t - p_{\text{EtAc}}$$

$$= 740 - 88.9 = 651.1 \text{ mm Hg}$$

At 30°C the:

(a) *Per cent relative saturation* $=$

$$100\,\frac{p_{\text{EtAc}}}{p_{\text{EtAc}}^*} = 100\,\frac{88.9}{119} = 74.6\%$$

(b) *Per cent saturation* $=$

$$100\,\frac{\dfrac{p_{\text{EtAc}}}{p_t - p_{\text{EtAc}}}}{\dfrac{p_{\text{EtAc}}^*}{p_t - p_{\text{EtAc}}^*}} = \frac{\dfrac{88.9}{740 - 88.9}}{\dfrac{119}{740 - 119}}\,100 = \frac{\dfrac{88.9}{651.1}}{\dfrac{119}{621}}\,100$$

$$= 71.1\%$$

Example 3.27 Partial Saturation

A mixture of ethyl acetate vapor and air has a relative saturation of 50% at 30°C and a total pressure of 740 mm Hg. Calculate the analysis of the vapor and the molal saturation.

Solution:

The vapor pressure of ethyl acetate at 30°C from the previous problem is 119 mm Hg.

$$\% \text{ relative saturation} = 50 = \frac{p_{EtAc}}{p^*_{EtAc}} \, 100$$

From the above relation, the p_{EtAc} is

$$p_{EtAc} = 0.50(119) = 59.5 \text{ mm Hg}$$

(a) $$\frac{n_{EtAc}}{n_t} = \frac{p_{EtAc}}{p_t} = \frac{59.5}{740} = 0.0805$$

Hence, the vapor analyzes EtAc, 8.05%; air, 91.95%.

(b) Molal saturation is

$$\frac{n_{EtAc}}{n_{air}} = \frac{p_{EtAc}}{p_{air}} = \frac{p_{EtAc}}{p_t - p_{EtAc}} = \frac{59.5}{740 - 59.5}$$

$$= 0.0876 \, \frac{\text{mole EtAc}}{\text{mole air}}$$

Example 3.28   Partial Saturation

The percentage humidity of air at 86°F and a total pressure of 750 mm of Hg is 20%. Calculate the per cent relative humidity and the partial pressure of the water vapor in the air. What is the dew point of the air?

Solution:

Data from the Steam Tables are

$$p^*_{H_2O} \text{ at } 86°F = 31.8 \text{ mm Hg}$$

To get the relative humidity, $p_{H_2O}/p^*_{H_2O}$, we need to find the partial pressure of the water vapor in the air. This may be obtained from

$$\%\mathscr{H} = 20 = \frac{\dfrac{p_{H_2O}}{p_t - p_{H_2O}}}{\dfrac{p^*_{H_2O}}{p_t - p^*_{H_2O}}} \, 100 = \frac{\dfrac{p_{H_2O}}{750 - p_{H_2O}}}{\dfrac{31.8}{750 - 31.8}} \, 100$$

This equation can be solved for p_{H_2O}

$$0.00885 = \frac{p_{H_2O}}{750 - p_{H_2O}}$$

$$6.65 - 0.00885 \, p_{H_2O} = p_{H_2O}$$

(a) $$p_{H_2O} = 6.6 \text{ mm Hg}$$

(b) $$\% \text{ R.H.} = 100 \, \frac{6.6}{31.8} = 20.7\%$$

(c) The dew point is the temperature at which the water vapor in the air would commence to condense. This would be at the vapor pressure of 6.6 mm, or about 41°F.

3.6. Material balances involving condensation and vaporization

The solution of material balance problems involving partial saturation, condensation, and vaporization will now be illustrated. Remember our drying problems? They included water and some bone-dry material as at the top of Fig. 3.21.

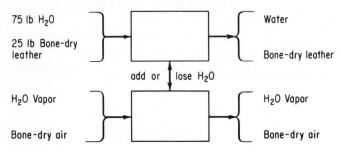

Fig. 3.21. Complete drying schematic.

You can handle material balance problems involving water vapor in air in exactly the same fashion as you handled the material balance problems for the drying of leather (or paper, etc.), depending upon the information provided and sought. (You can find additional humidity and saturation problems which include the use of energy balances and humidity charts in Chap. 5.)

We should again stress in connection with the examples to follow that if you know the dew point of a gas mixture, you automatically know the partial pressure of the water vapor in the gas mixture. When a partially saturated gas is cooled at constant pressure, as in the cooling of air containing some water vapor at atmospheric pressure, the volume of the mixture may change slightly, but the partial pressures of the air and water vapor remain constant until the dew point is reached. At this point water begins to condense; the air remains saturated as the temperature is lowered. All that happens is that more water goes from the vapor into the liquid phase. At the time the cooling is stopped, the air is still saturated, and at its dew point.

Example 3.29   Material Balance with Condensation

If the atmosphere in the afternoon during a humid period is at 90°F and 80% R.H. (barometer reads 738 mm Hg) while at night it is at 68°F (barometer reads 745 mm Hg), what per cent of the water in the afternoon air is deposited as dew?

Solution:
Data:

Temperature	90°F	68°F
$p_{H_2O}^*$ (mm Hg)	36	17.5

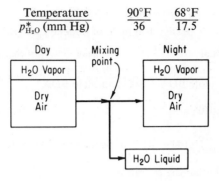

If any dew is deposited at night, the air must be fully saturated at 68°F. You can easily check the dew point of the day air and find it is 83°F. Thus the air first becomes saturated at 83°F. The partial pressures of air and water vapor during the day and night are

$$p_w \text{ day} = 36(0.80) = 28.8 \text{ mm}$$

$$p_w \text{ night} = 17.5(1.00) = 17.5 \text{ mm}$$

$$p_t = p_{air} + p_w$$

day: $\quad p_{air} = 738 - 28.8 = 709.2 \text{ mm}$

night: $\quad p_{air} = 745 - 17.5 = 727.5 \text{ mm}$

This gives us in effect the compositions of all the streams.

As a basis you could select 1 ft³ of wet air, 1 lb mole wet (or dry) air, or many other suitable factors. The simplest basis to take is

Basis: 738 lb mole moist day air

because then the moles = the partial pressures.

	initial mixture (day)		final mixture (night)
	lb moles =		
comp.	partial press.		partial press.
air	709.2	tie element	727.5
H₂O	28.8		17.5
total	738.0		745.0

On the basis of 738 lb mole of moist day air we have the following water in the night air:

$$\frac{17.5 \text{ lb mole } H_2O \text{ in night air}}{727.5 \text{ lb mole air}} \mid 709.2 \text{ lb mole air} = 17.0 \text{ lb mole } H_2O$$

$$28.8 - 17.0 = 11.8 \text{ lb mole } H_2O \text{ deposited as dew}$$

$$100 \frac{11.8}{28.8} = 41\% \text{ of water in day air deposited as dew}$$

This problem could also be solved on the basis of:

Basis: 1 lb mole of bone-dry air (BDA)

initial   —   final   = change

$$\frac{28.8 \text{ lb mole H}_2\text{O}}{709.2 \text{ lb mole BDA}} - \frac{17.5 \text{ lb mole H}_2\text{O}}{727.5 \text{ lb mole BDA}} = \text{change}$$

$$0.0406 \quad - \quad 0.0241 \quad = 0.0165 \frac{\text{lb mole H}_2\text{O}}{\text{lb mole BDA}}$$

$$\frac{0.0165}{0.0406} 100 = 41\% \text{ of water vapor deposited as dew}$$

Note especially that the operation

initial   final

$$\frac{28.8}{738} - \frac{17.5}{745}$$

is meaningless since two different bases are involved—the wet initial air and the wet final air.

Example 3.30   Dehydration

By absorption in silica gel you are able to remove all (0.72 lb) of the H_2O from moist air at 60°F and 29.2 in. Hg. The same air measures 1000 ft³ at 70°F and 32.0 in. Hg when dry. What was the relative humidity of the moist air?

Solution:

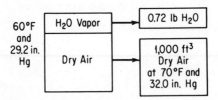

Basis: 1000 ft³ bone-dry air (BDA) at 70°F and 32.0 in. Hg

$$\frac{1000 \text{ ft}^3 \text{ BDA}}{} \left| \frac{492°\text{R}}{530°\text{R}} \right| \frac{32.0 \text{ in. Hg}}{29.92 \text{ in. Hg}} \left| \frac{1 \text{ lb mole}}{359 \text{ ft}^3} \right| = 2.77 \text{ lb mole dry air}$$

The wet air now appears to have the following composition:

BDA	2.77
H₂O	
0.72/18 =	0.040
wet air	2.81 lb mole

The partial pressure of the water in the moist air was the total pressure times the mole fraction water vapor

$$\frac{29.2 \text{ in. Hg} \mid 0.04}{\mid 2.81} = 0.415 \text{ in. Hg}$$

Saturated air at 60°F has a vapor pressure of water of 0.52 in. Hg .Consequently, the relative humidity was

$$\frac{p_{H_2O}}{p_{H_2O}^*} = \frac{0.415}{0.52} \ 100 = 80\%$$

Example 3.31   Humidification

One thousand cubic feet of moist air at 760 mm Hg and 72°F and with a dew point of 53°F enter a process and leave the process at 740 mm Hg with a dew point of 137°F. How many pounds of water vapor are added to each pound of wet air entering the process?

Solution:

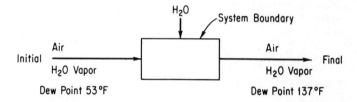

Additional data are:

	dew point	
	t (°F)	$p_{H_2O}^*$ (*mm Hg*)
	53°F	10*
	137°F	140*

*These give the partial pressures of the water vapor in the initial and final gas mixtures.

We know the initial and final compositions of the air-water vapor mixture, since the partial pressure of the water vapor in the moist air is the pressure of water at the dew point for each case.

Basis: 760 moles initial wet air

component	*initial* moles		*final* moles	*pressure (mm)*
vapor	10			140
BDA*	750	tie ←→ element	750	600
total	760			740

*Bone-dry air.

In the final gas we can say there are

> 140 moles vapor/600 moles BDA
> 140 moles vapor/740 moles moist air
> 600 moles BDA/740 moles moist air

Since we have a tie element of 750 moles of bone-dry air and want to know how many moles of vapor are present in the final air on our basis of 760 moles initial wet air,

$$\frac{750 \text{ moles BDA} \mid 140 \text{ moles vapor in final}}{\mid 600 \text{ moles BDA in final}} = 175 \text{ moles vapor in final}$$

175 moles final vapor − 10 moles initial vapor = 165 moles of vapor added

But these calculations were all based on 760 moles of initial wet gas. Therefore, our answer should be

$$\frac{165 \text{ moles vapor added}}{760 \text{ moles wet gas in}} = \frac{0.217 \text{ moles vapor added}}{1 \text{ mole wet gas in}}$$

Now the molecular weight of water is 18; the average molecular weight of the original wet air has to be calculated:

comp.	moles	mol. wt	lb
BDA	750	29	21,750
H_2O	10	18	180
	760		21,930

$$\frac{21,930 \text{ lb}}{760 \text{ lb moles}} = 28.8$$

$$\frac{0.217 \text{ lb mole } H_2O \mid 18 \text{ lb} \mid 1 \text{ lb mole wet gas}}{1 \text{ lb mole wet gas} \mid 1 \text{ lb mole } H_2O \mid 28.8 \text{ lb}} = 1.035 \frac{\text{lb } H_2O}{\text{lb wet gas}}$$

Comments:
   (a) If the original problem had asked for the moles of final wet gas, we could have used the tie element in the following manner:

$$\frac{750 \text{ moles BDA} \mid 740 \text{ moles wet gas out}}{\mid 600 \text{ moles BDA out}} = 925 \text{ moles wet gas out}$$

   (b) If a basis of 1 mole of bone-dry air had been used, the following calculation would apply:

> Basis: 1 mole BDA

in: $\dfrac{\text{moles vapor}}{\text{mole BDA}} = \dfrac{10}{750} = 0.0133$

out: $\dfrac{\text{moles vapor}}{\text{mole BDA}} = \dfrac{140}{600} = 0.2333$

Since there are more moles of vapor in the final air (per mole of bone-dry air), we know that vapor must have been added:

moles vapor added $= 0.2333 - 0.0133 = 0.2200$ moles

The remainder of the calculation would be the same.

We have gone over a number of examples of condensation and vaporization, and you have seen how a given amount of air at atmospheric pressure can hold only a certain maximum amount of water vapor. This amount depends on the temperature of the air, and any decrease in the temperature will lower the water-bearing capacity of the air. An increase in pressure also will accomplish the same effect. If a pound of saturated air at 75°F is isothermally compressed (with a reduction in volume, of course), liquid water will be deposited out of the air just like water being squeezed out of a wet sponge (Fig. 3.22). This process has been previously described in the *p-T* diagram for water (Fig. 3.12), by line *G-H-I*.

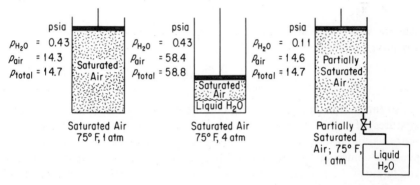

Fig. 3.22. Effect of an increase of pressure on saturated air and a return to the initial pressure.

For example, if a pound of saturated air at 75°F and 1 atm is compressed isothermally to 4 atm (58.8 psia), almost three-quarters of the original content of water vapor now will be in the form of liquid, and the air has a dew point of 75°F at 4 atm. Remove the liquid water, expand the air isothermally back to 1 atm, and you will find the dew point has been lowered to about 36°F. Mathematically (1 = state at 1 atm, 2 = state at 4 atm) with $z = 1.00$ for both components:

for saturated air at 75°F and 4 atm,

$$\left(\frac{n_{\mathrm{H_2O}}}{n_{\mathrm{air}}}\right)_2 = \left(\frac{p^*_{\mathrm{H_2O}}}{p_{\mathrm{air}}}\right)_2 = \frac{0.43}{58.4}$$

for the same air saturated at 75°F and 1 atm,

$$\left(\frac{n_{\mathrm{H_2O}}}{n_{\mathrm{air}}}\right)_1 = \left(\frac{p^*_{\mathrm{H_2O}}}{p_{\mathrm{air}}}\right)_1 = \frac{0.43}{14.3}$$

Since the air is the tie element in the process,

$$\left(\frac{n_2}{n_1}\right)_{\mathrm{H_2O}} = \frac{\dfrac{0.43}{58.4}}{\dfrac{0.43}{14.3}} = \frac{14.3}{58.4} = 0.245$$

24.5 per cent of the original water will remain as vapor. After the air-water vapor mixture is returned to a total pressure of 1 atm, the following two familiar equations now apply:

$$p_{\mathrm{H_2O}} + p_{\mathrm{air}} = 14.7$$

$$\frac{p_{\mathrm{H_2O}}}{p_{\mathrm{air}}} = \frac{n_{\mathrm{H_2O}}}{n_{\mathrm{air}}} = \frac{0.43}{58.4} = 0.00737$$

From these two relations you can find that

$$p_{\mathrm{H_2O}} = 0.108 \text{ psia}$$
$$p_{\mathrm{air}} = 14.6$$
$$p_{\mathrm{total}} = \overline{14.7} \text{ psia}$$

The pressure of the water vapor represents a dew point of about 36°F, and a relative humidity of

$$100 \frac{p_{\mathrm{H_2O}}}{p_{\mathrm{H_2O}}^*} = \frac{0.108}{0.43} 100 = 25\%$$

So far in this chapter we have considered pure gases, pure vapors, and mixtures of noncondensable gases containing one pure vapor (example, water vapor in air). We do not have the space to discuss the many other possible combinations of systems that can exist involving gases, vapors, and liquids for ideal and nonideal systems, but this information can be found in many standard textbooks of a more advanced nature.

3.7. Phase phenomena

3.7-1 The Phase Rule. You will find the phase rule a useful guide in establishing how many properties, such as pressure and temperature, have to be specified to definitely fix all the remaining properties and number of phases that can coexist for any physical system. The rule can be applied only to systems in *equilibrium*. It says

$$F = C - \mathscr{P} + 2 \qquad (3.57)$$

where F = number of degrees of freedom, i.e., the number of independent properties which have to be specified to determine all the intensive properties of each phase of the system of interest.

C = number of components in the system. For circumstances involving chemical reactions, C is *not* identical to the number of chemical compounds in the system but is equal to the number of chemical compounds less the number of independent-reaction and other equilibrium relationships among these compounds.

$\mathscr{P}$ = number of phases that can exist in the system. A phase is a homogeneous region such as a gas, a pure liquid, a solution, or a homogeneous solid.

Variables of the kind with which the phase rule is concerned are called "phase-rule variables," and they are *intensive* properties of the system. By this we mean properties which do not depend on the quantity of material present. If you think about the properties we have employed so far in this text, you have the feeling that pressure and temperature are independent of the amount of material present. So is concentration, but what about volume? The total volume of a system is called an *extensive* property because it does depend on how much material you have; the specific volume, on the other hand, the cubic feet per pound, for example, is an intensive property because it is independent of the amount of material present. In the next chapter we will take up additional properties such as internal energy and enthalpy; you should remember that the specific (per unit mass) values of these quantities are intensive properties; the total quantities are extensive properties.

An example will clarify the use of these terms in the phase rule. You will remember for a pure gas that we had to specify three of the four variables in the ideal gas equation $pV = nRT$ in order to be able to determine the remaining one unknown. For a single phase $\mathscr{P} = 1$, and for a pure gas $C = 1$, so that

$$F = C - \mathscr{P} + 2 = 1 - 1 + 2 = 2 \qquad \text{variables to be specified}$$

How can we reconcile this apparent paradox with our previous statement? Since the phase rule is concerned with intensive properties only, the following are phase-rule variables in the ideal gas law:

$$\left.\begin{array}{l} p \\ \hat{V} \text{ (specific molar volume)} \\ T \end{array}\right\} \quad \text{3 intensive properties}$$

and once two of these quantities are fixed, the third is also automatically fixed.

An *invariant* system is one in which no variation of conditions is possible without one phase disappearing. An example with which you may be familiar is the ice-water-water vapor system which exists at only one temperature (0.01°C):

$$F = C - \mathscr{P} + 2 = 1 - 3 + 2 = 0$$

With the three phases present, none of the physical conditions can be varied without the loss of one phase. As a corollary, if the three phases are present, the temperature, the specific volume, etc., must always be fixed at the same values. This phenomenon is useful in calibrating thermometers and other instruments.

A complete discussion of the significance of the term C and the other terms in the phase rule is beyond the scope of this text; for further information you can read one of the general references on the phase rule listed at the end of this chapter, or consult an advanced book on thermodynamics or physical chemistry. We are now going to consider how phase phenomena can be illustrated by means of diagrams.

3.7-2 Phase Phenomena of Pure Components. We can show the properties of a single-phase pure component, such as a gas, on two-dimensional plots. According to the phase rule,

$$F = C - \mathscr{P} + 2 = 1 - 1 + 2 = 2$$

only two physical variables have to be specified to fix the system definitely, i.e., any point on the two-dimensional diagram will be enough to fix the other properties of the system at that point.

Actually, if we are to clearly understand phase phenomena, the properties of a substance should be shown in three dimensions, particularly if there can be more than one phase in the region for which the p-V-T properties are to be presented. We previously overcame the handicap of using two dimensions to present three-dimensional data by showing, on the two-dimensional graph, lines of constant value for the other properties of the system (see Fig. 3.2, which has p and V as axes, and lines of constant temperature as the third parameter). In this section we are going to present a more elaborate treatment of these same p-V-T properties. Since the data on water, a substance that expands on freezing (to ice I), and carbon dioxide, a substance that contracts on freezing, are so well known, we have illustrated in Figs 3.23 and 3.24 the relationships between three-dimensional presentations of p-V-T data for these two compounds and the conventional two-dimensional diagrams you usually encounter. Be certain that you view Figs. 3.23 and 3.24 as *surfaces* and not as solid figures; only the p-V-T points on the surface exist, and no point exists above or below the surface.

You can see that the two-dimensional diagrams are really projections of the three-dimensional figure onto suitable axes. On the p-V diagram, you will observe lines of constant temperature called *isothermal lines*, and on the p-T diagram you will see lines of constant volume, called *isometric lines* or *isochores*. On the T-$\hat{V}$ diagram, we might have put lines of constant pressure known as *isobaric lines*, but these are not shown since they would obscure the more important features which are shown. The two-phase vapor-liquid

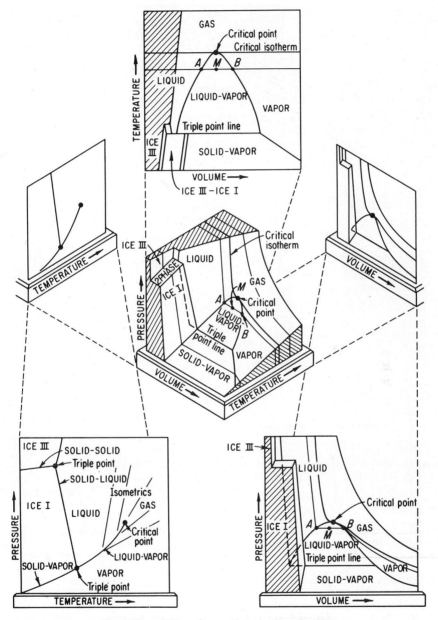

Fig. 3.23. *p-V-T* surface and projections for H_2O.

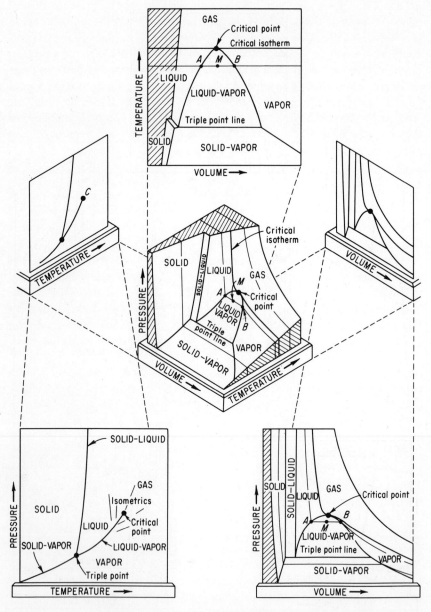

Fig. 3.24. *p-V-T* surface and projections for CO_2.

200

region is represented by the heavy envelope in the p-$\hat{V}$ and the T-$\hat{V}$ diagrams. On the p-T diagram this two-phase region appears only as a single line because you are looking at the three-dimensional diagram from the side. The p-T diagram shows what you have so far called the "vapor-pressure curve," while the associated diagrams show that the "curve" really is an open region in which no material exists as such. The envelope shows merely the over-all composition of one phase in equilibrium with another, as, for example, at point A we have liquid and at point B we have vapor and in between them no single phase exists. If we added the liquid at A to the vapor at B, we would have a two-phase mixture with the gross properties as shown by point M. You will notice that in the p-$\hat{V}$ diagram the lines of constant temperature and pressure become horizontal in the two-phase region, because if you apply the phase rule

$$F = C - \mathscr{P} + 2 = 1 - 2 + 2 = 1$$

only one variable can change, the specific volume. In the two-phase region, where condensation or evaporation takes place, the pressure and temperature remain constant. Think back to our discussion of water boiling in this connection.

Other features illustrated on the diagrams are the critical point; the critical isotherm; the triple point, which becomes a triple-point line actually in the p-$\hat{V}$ and in the T-$\hat{V}$ diagrams; and the existence of two solid phases and a liquid phase in equilibrium, such as (Fig. 3.23) solid ice I, solid ice III, and liquid. The temperature at the freezing point for water, i.e., the point where ice, water, air, and water vapor are in equilibrium, is not quite the same temperature as that at the triple point, which is the point where ice, water, and water vapor are in equilibrium. The presence of air lowers the freezing temperature by about 0.01°C so that the triple point is at 0.00602 atm and 0.01°C. The corresponding values for CO_2 are 5 atm and −57°C, respectively. Another triple point for the water system exists at 2200 atm and 20°C between ice III, ice I, and liquid water.

The critical point can be determined from a p-$\hat{V}$ diagram by plotting constant-temperature lines for the experimental data. As you proceed to higher and higher pressures, the horizontal portion of the isothermal line becomes shorter and shorter until finally the isotherm has only an inflection

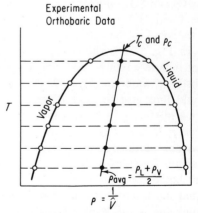

Experimental Orthobaric Data

Fig. 3.25. Law of rectilinear diameters used to find critical temperature and density.

(point of zero slope). Any lines at subsequently higher pressures do not have this inflection. If carefully done, the critical temperature, pressure, and volume can be determined this way. Another way is to use the law of "rectilinear diameters," Fig. 3.25, which says that the arithmetic average of the densities (or specific volumes) of the pure components in the liquid and the vapor state is a linear function of temperature, if the pairs of measurements are made at the same pressure. This is not an exact relationship, but is extremely useful in getting the critical density or critical specific volume since the linear average density relation can be extrapolated until it crosses the two-phase envelope where experimental data are quite difficult to collect.

3.7-3 Phase Phenomena of Mixtures. Presentation of phase phenomena for mixtures which are completely miscible in the liquid state involves some rather complex reduction of three-, four-, and higher-dimensional diagrams into two dimensions. We will restrict ourselves to two-component systems because, although the ideas discussed here are applicable to any number of components, the graphical presentation of more complex systems in an elementary text such as this is probably more confusing than helpful. We will use hydrocarbons for most of our examples of two-component systems since a vast amount of experimental work has been reported for these compounds.

It would be convenient if the critical temperature of a mixture were the mole weight average of the critical temperatures of its pure components, and the critical pressure of a mixture were simply a mole weight average of the critical pressures of the pure components (according to Kay's rule), but these maxims simply are not true, as shown in Fig. 3.26. The pseudo-critical temperature falls on the dashed line between the critical temperatures of CO_2 and SO_2, while the actual critical point for the mixture lies somewhere else. Figure 3.31 illustrates (for another system) the three-dimensional aspects of the locus of the actual critical points.

In Fig. 3.27 is shown a p-T diagram for a 25 per cent methane–75 per cent butane mixture. You can compare this figure with the one for a pure substance, water, in Fig. 3.12; the p-T curve for pure butane or pure methane would look just like the diagram for water (excluding the solid phases). For a mixture of a fixed composition, we have only three variables to consider, p, $\hat{V}$, and T. Lines of constant specific volume are shown outside the envelope of the two-phase region. Inside the envelope are shown lines of constant fractions of liquid, starting at the high pressures, where 100 per cent liquid exists (zero per cent vapor), and ranging down to zero per cent liquid and 100 per cent vapor at the low pressures. The 100 per cent saturated liquid line is the bubble-point line and the 100 per cent saturated vapor line is the dew-point line.

The critical point is shown as point C. You will note that this is not the

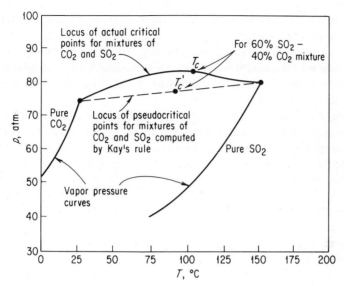

Fig. 3.26. Critical and pseudocritical points for a mixture.

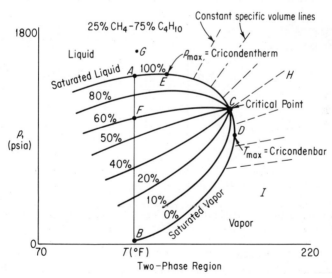

Fig. 3.27. p-T diagram for binary system.

point of maximum temperature at which vapor and liquid can exist in equilibrium; the latter is the maximum cricondentherm, point D. Neither is it the point of maximum pressure at which vapor and liquid can exist in equilibrium; because that point is the maximum cricondenbar (point E).

The maximum temperature at which liquid and vapor can exist in equilibrium for this mixture is about 30 degrees higher than the critical temperature, and the maximum pressure is 60 or 70 psia greater than the critical pressure. You can clearly see, therefore, that the best definition of the critical point was the one which stated that the density and other properties of the liquid and vapor become identical at the critical point. This definition holds for single components as well as mixtures.

Figure 3.27 indicates some of the phenomena that can take place when you change the pressure on the mixture at constant temperature, or change the temperature of a mixture at constant pressure. If you proceed from A in the liquid region to F and then to B in the vapor region by means of an isothermal process of some nature, you can go from 100 per cent liquid to 100 per cent vapor and notice a phase change. A similar type of analysis could have been applied to the p-T water diagram (Fig. 3.12) and the same conclusion reached, although the fraction of vapor and liquid cannot be found from Fig. 3.12. It is only when you cross the two-phase region that a change of phase will be noticed. If you go from A to G to H to B, the liquid will change from 0 to 100 per cent vapor, but there will be no noticeable phase change. Figure 3.28 illustrates this transition for a mixture by a change of shading, and a similar diagram could be drawn for a pure component.

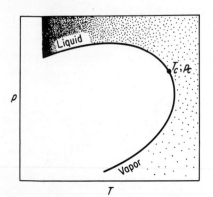

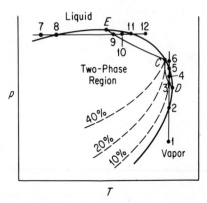

Fig. 3.28. Change in phase characteristics for a mixture of two components.

Fig. 3.29. The two types of retrograde condensation.

A very interesting phenomenon called *retrograde condensation* (or vaporization) can occur in two-phase systems, a phenomenon which initially appears to be quite contrary to your normal expectations. If you start at point 1 in Fig. 3.29 (an enlarged portion of Fig. 3.27 in the vicinity of the critical region) you are in the vapor region. As you proceed to raise the pressure at constant temperature, you will arrive at point 2 where you are on the saturated-vapor line, or the dew-point line. Continuing to increase the pressure will, as you might expect, increase the amount of liquid formed. However, soon you will reach a point where a maximum amount of liquid has formed (3), and increasing the pressure still further to points 4 and 5, will reduce the amount of liquid present, and eventually you will wind up back in the vapor region at 6. This phenomenon of retrograde condensation can happen, of course, only if the critical point, C, is located above and to the left of D as shown on the diagram so that there is a "bulge" in the vicinity of D for the mixture. The interesting thing about this phenomenon is that you would expect, as the pressure increased at constant temperature, to continually increase the amount of liquid formed, whereas the opposite is actually true after point 3 is reached.

Another type of retrograde phenomenon exists in a few systems when you change the temperature at constant pressure. This would be illustrated by the line 7, 8, 9, 10, 11, and 12, where first, as the temperature increases to point 8 on the bubble-point curve, some liquid starts to vaporize. The liquid continues to vaporize until a maximum of vapor is obtained at 9, and then the quantity of vapor starts to decrease until you reach a point where you have all liquid again at 11. Although the points of maximum per cent liquid (or vapor) enveloping the regions of retrograde phenomena are shown in the diagram by solid lines, there are actually no phase boundaries at these points. The solid lines merely represent the locus of the region in which the maximum amount of liquid or vapor can exist (the point of infinite or zero slope on the lines indicating the fraction liquid), exaggerated on the diagram for the purpose of illustration. Formally, retrograde phenomena of these two types are known as (a) isothermal retrograde vaporization (proceeding from 1 to 6) or condensation (proceeding from 6 to 1), or retrograde vaporization or condensation, respectively, of the "first type," and (b) isobaric retrograde vaporization (proceeding from 12 to 7) or condensation (proceeding from 7 to 12), or retrograde vaporization (condensation) of the "second type." Figure 3.30 shows the same phenomena on a $p\text{-}\hat{V}$ diagram.

Figure 3.30 like Fig. 3.29 is for a mixture of fixed composition. The constant-temperature lines illustrated are T_c, the critical temperature, and $T_{\max}$, the cricondentherm. The middle line, 6 to 1, shows a process of retro-

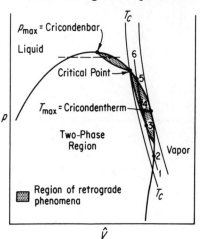

Fig. 3.30. Retrograde condensation on a $p\text{-}V$ diagram.

grade condensation of the first kind. The shadowed areas represent the regions in which retrograde phenomena take place. A $T\text{-}\hat{V}$ diagram is not illustrated since it is not particularly enlightening.

The diagrams shown so far represent two-component systems with a fixed over-all composition. You might wonder what a diagram would look like if we were to try to show systems of several compositions on one page. This has been done in Fig. 3.31. Here we have a composite $p\text{-}T$ diagram, which is somewhat awkward to visualize but represents the bubble-point and dew-point curves for various mixtures of ethane and heptane. These curves in essence are intersections of planes in the composition direction sliced out of a three-dimensional system and are stacked one in front of the other, although in two dimensions it appears that they overlie one another. The vapor-pressure curves for the two pure components are at the extreme sides of the diagrams as single lines (as you might expect). Each of the loops represents the two-phase area for a system of any specific composition. An infinite number of these slices are possible, of course. The dotted line indicates the envelope of the critical points for each possible composition. Although this line appears to be two-dimensional in Fig. 3.31, it actually is a three-dimensional line of which only the projection is shown in the figure.

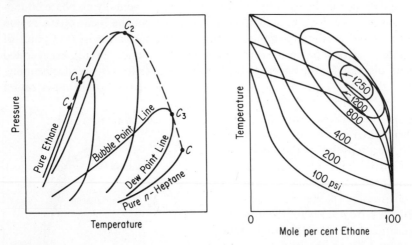

Fig. 3.31. $p\text{-}T$ and $T\text{-}x$ diagrams for ethane-heptane mixtures of different compositions.

Another way to handle and illustrate these phase phenomena for the two-component systems we have been discussing is to use pressure-composition diagrams at constant temperature or, alternatively, to use temperature-composition diagrams at constant pressure. A temperature-composition diagram with pressure as the third parameter is illustrated in Fig. 3.31 for the ethane-heptane system.

Discussion of the phase diagrams for multicomponent systems (ternary and higher) is beyond our scope here.

WHAT YOU SHOULD HAVE LEARNED FROM THIS CHAPTER

1. You should be familiar with the ideal gas laws and know how to apply them in problems.

2. You should be able to distinguish under which circumstances a gas acts as an ideal gas and under which circumstances it acts as a real gas, and be able to use, as appropriate, (a) the ideal gas equation, $pV = nRT$, (b) the compressibility factor together with $pV = znRT$, or (c) an equation of state, specifically van der Waals' equation.

3. You should know how to treat ideal and real gas mixtures, and in particular be able to apply Kay's rule.

4. You should be able to use the generalized compressibility chart with ease, and be able to calculate the parameters required for its use.

5. You should know what the following terms mean:

vapor	saturated vapor
gas	bubble point
vapor pressure	dew point
critical point	superheat
critical temperature	subcooled
critical pressure	quality
pseudocritical temperature	saturated air
pseudocritical pressure	relative humidity
condensation	absolute humidity
vaporization	isometric
sublimation	isobaric
equilibrium	isothermal
normal boiling point	retrograde condensation
saturated liquid	

6. You should be able to estimate vapor pressures as a function of temperature.

7. You should know how to solve material balance problems involving vaporization, condensation, saturation, drying, and humidification.

8. You should be able to apply the phase rule to simple systems.

9. You should be familiar with the qualitative phase behavior of pure components and mixtures, and also be able to draw typical diagrams illustrating this behavior.

NOMENCLATURE

(Units are discussed in the text)

a = constant in van der Waals' equation, Eq. 3.11
A = constant in Eq. (3.40)
b = constant in van der Waals' equation, Eq. 3.11
B = constant in Eq. 3.40
C = number of chemical components in the phase rule
F = number of degrees of freedom in the phase rule
M = molecular weight
n = number of moles
p = pressure
p = partial pressure (with a suitable subscript for the p)
p^* = vapor pressure
$\mathscr{P}$ = number of phases in the phase rule
p_c = critical pressure
p_c' = pseudocritical pressure
p_r = reduced pressure = p/p_c
p_r' = pseudoreduced pressure
p_t = total pressure in a system
R = universal gas constant
R.H. = relative humidity
T = absolute temperature
T_c = critical temperature (absolute)
T_c' = pseudocritical temperature
T_r = reduced temperature = T/T_c
T_r' = pseudoreduced temperature
V_g = specific volume of gas
V_l = specific volume of liquid
V = volume
V_c = critical volume
$\hat{V}_{c_i}$ = ideal critical volume = RT_c/p_c
$\hat{V}_{c_i}'$ = pseudocritical ideal volume
V_r = reduced volume = V/V_c
$V_{r_i} = V_r' $ = ideal reduced volume = $\hat{V}/\hat{V}_{c_i}$
V_r' = pseudoreduced ideal volume = $\hat{V}/\hat{V}_{c_i}'$
y = mole fraction of a component in the gas phase
z = compressibility factor
z_c = critical compressibility factor
z_c' = pseudocritical compressibility factor
z_m = mean compressibility factor

Greek Letters:

γ = constant in Eq. (3.18)
ρ_L = liquid density

ρ_V = vapor density

Subscripts:

A, B = components in a mixture
  c = critical
  i = any component
  i = ideal state
  t = at constant temperature
  t = total
  r = reduced state

Superscript

  $\wedge$ = per unit mass or per mole

SUPPLEMENTARY REFERENCES

1. Daniels, F., and R. A. Alberty, *Physical Chemistry*, John Wiley & Sons, Inc., New York, 1955.

2. Henley, E. J., and H. Bieber, *Chemical Engineering Calculations*, McGraw-Hill Book Company, New York, 1959.

3. Hougen, O. A., K. M. Watson, and R. A. Ragatz, *Chemical Process Principles*, Part I, 2nd ed., John Wiley & Sons, Inc., New York, 1956.

4. Littlejohn, C. E., and G. F. Meenaghan, *An Introduction to Chemical Engineering*, Reinhold Publishing Corp., New York, 1959.

5. Reid, R. C., and T. K. Sherwood, *The Properties of Gases and Liquids*, McGraw-Hill Book Company, New York, 1958.

6. Wexler, A., *Humidity and Moisture*, 4 vols., Reinhold Publishing Corp., New York, 1965.

7. Williams, E. T., and R. C. Johnson, *Stoichiometry for Chemical Engineers*, McGraw-Hill Book Company, New York, 1958.

References on the Phase Rule

8. Wetmore, F. E. W., and D. J. LeRoy, *Principles of Phase Equilibria*, McGraw-Hill Book Company, New York, 1951.

9. Ricci, J. E., *The Phase Rule and Heterogeneous Equilibrium*, D. Van Nostrand Company, New York, 1951.

PROBLEMS

3.1. Five cubic feet of an ideal gas are under a pressure of 27.3 psia of Hg. What is the volume of the gas at 29.92 in. Hg if there is no change in temperature?

3.2. A gas occupies a volume of 450 cc under a pressure of 780 mm of Hg. The temperature remaining constant, what pressure must be applied to reduce the volume to 400 cc?

3.3. A given amount of N_2 has a volume of 300 cm³ at 15.7°C. Find its volume at 0°C, the pressure remaining constant.

3.4. A gas measured 150 cm³ at 17.5°C, and because of a change in temperature, the pressure remaining constant, the volume decreased to 125 cm³. What was the new temperature?

3.5. Under standard conditions, a gas measures 1 liter in volume. What is its volume at 62°F and 29.4 in. Hg?

3.6. The pressure on a confined gas, at 160°F, was 792 mm Hg. If the pressure later registered 820 mm Hg, what was the temperature then, the volume remaining unchanged?

3.7. A cubic foot of gas at standard conditions has its temperature raised to 100°F. What must be the pressure on the gas if the volume of gas is unaltered?

3.8. An oxygen cylinder contains 2 ft³ O_2 at 70°F and 2000 psig. What will the volume be in a dry gas holder at 90°F and 4.0 in. H_2O above atmospheric? (Assume barometer to be normal, 29.92 in. Hg, if no definite statement is made, and that O_2 is an ideal gas.) What volume was in the oxygen cylinder if measured at standard conditions?

3.9. Two hundred and fifty cubic centimeters of gas are at 780 mm Hg and 45°C. What is the volume at standard conditions?

3.10. A gas of 275 in.³ changes its volume to 300 in.³ when it goes from standard conditions to a pressure of 29.8 in. Hg. What is its final temperature in °F?

3.11. A steel tank having a capacity of 100 ft³ contains carbon dioxide at 30°C and 1.6 atm. Calculate the weight, in grams, of the carbon dioxide.

3.12. A certain barometer gives erroneous readings owing to the presence of a small amount of air above the mercury column. At a pressure of 755 mm Hg the barometer reads 748 Hg, and at 740 the reading is 736. What will the barometer read when the actual pressure is 760 mm Hg?

3.13. Nitrogen fills a steel container of volume 40 ft³ at 22°C and atmospheric pressure. If the container valve is opened and the container heated to 200°C, calculate the fraction of the nitrogen which leaves the container.

3.14. It is desired to market oxygen in small cylinders having volumes of 0.5 ft³ and each containing 1.0 lb of oxygen. If the cylinders may be subjected to a maximum temperature of 120°F, calculate the pressure for which they must be designed, assuming the applicability of the ideal gas law.

3.15. A laboratory accident recently occurred in a refinery when a sample container of butane ruptured and flashed. The container was an Air Force surplus O_2 container (completely flushed with N_2 to avoid explosion) of a design pressure of 500 psia and a working pressure of 400 psia. It had been filled in the field at 26°F and a line pressure of 220 psig and was brought into the laboratory which was at 75°F. Explain the cause of the rupture; show calculations.

3.16. Explain whether or not the statement is correct, and, if not, modify the statement to make it correct:

(a) Pressure is how much a fluid weighs.

(b) If more of a gas is pumped into a closed drum, the volume of gas in the drum increases.

(c) If more of a gas is pumped into a closed drum, the weight of gas in the drum decreases.

(d) A pump has a maximum discharge pressure of 43.3 psi. The maximum height that water can be pumped with this pump for 0 psig suction is equivalent to 43.3 psia.

3.17. Hyperbaric oxygen therapy means placing a patient in a pressure chamber and subjecting him to two or more times normal air pressure. The patient is then given pure oxygen to breathe by means of a regular face mask. Under such circumstances the patient's blood carries about 15 times its normal quota of oxygen, enabling his system to be "drenched" with oxygen at a time when oxygen deficiency may be critical. Such critical situations may occur for patients suffering from gas gangrene, or carbon monoxide poisoning. It may be valuable for "blue" babies, shock, strokes, etc. For a cylindrical chamber $41\frac{1}{2}$ ft long and 7 ft in diameter, the air must be changed and filtered eight times per hour. If the chamber operates at 2.5 atm and 70°F, how many cubic feet of air at STP (standard temperature and pressure) must be compressed by the air compressor?

3.18. A boiler of unknown volume contains air at 70°F and atmospheric pressure. One hundred pounds of dry ice (solid CO_2) are thrown into the tank and the manhole is closed. The pressure in the boiler becomes 25.4 psig. What is the volume of the boiler?

3.19. Georgian[14] has suggested that the gas constant arises from an incorrect selection of the temperature scale. Starting with $p\hat{V} = \tilde{R}T$, he proposes to select the temperature scale so that $\tilde{R} = 1.0$ and the gas law becomes $p\hat{V} = T$. In the mks system of units, temperature will have the units of joule/kilomole and the dimensions of length²/time². The scale of temperature can be established from the fundamental constant $p_0\hat{V}_0 = T_0 = 2,271,160$ for an ideal gas at 0°C and $p_0 \longrightarrow 0$. The Boltzmann constant becomes the reciprocal of Avogadro's number. Comment on the usefulness of such a temperature scale. What is the conversion factor from °R to joule/kilomole?

3.20. Fill in the blanks for the following statements:

(a) As oil in the tank is pumped out of a tank 100 ft in diameter, the air vent plugs and the pressure inside the tank drops to 1 psia less than atmospheric pressure. This difference of pressure will cause an external force on the roof of_____lb$_f$.

(b) The two tanks, 10 ft in diameter and 20 ft in diameter, respectively, are

[14] J. C. Georgian, *Nature*, v. 201, p. 695 (1964).

both the same height and full of water. Which one exerts the greater weight against its foundation?_____

(c) For the same tanks of (b), which one exerts the greater pressure against its foundation?_____

3.21. *Chem. Eng.*[15]—The problem all sulfuric acid and oleum plant operators face is that, if there is any water present after SO_2 has been oxidized, the trioxide will combine to form extremely small droplets of mist. The particles, most of which are below 3 microns, pass right through the rest of the plant and produce the familiar bluish plume on the stack outlet.

Such a plume, points out York, is at once a health hazard, an equipment destroyer, and an economic loss.

Stack losses can be estimated from the following typical data:

Acid tonnage	1,000 tons/day
Stack gas flow rate	73,000 ft³/min
Entrainment	100 mg/ft³

These figures, admittedly from a poorly operating plant, mean that 11.56 tons of sulfuric acid are sent up the stack each day. Catching it would save between $52,000 and $86,000/yr.[15]

Verify the stack loss based on the given figure of 11.56 tons of H_2SO_4.

3.22. Two tanks are initially sealed off from one another by means of valve *A*. Tank I initially contains 1.00 ft³ of air at 100 psia and 150°F. Tank II initially contains a nitrogen-oxygen mixture containing. 95 mole % nitrogen at 200 psia and 200°F. Valve *A* is then opened allowing the contents of the two tanks to mix. After complete mixing has been effected, the gas was found to contain 85 mole % nitrogen. Calculate the volume of tank II.

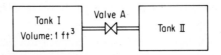

3.23. Calculate the molal gas constant *R* in:

(a) (atm)(cm³)/(g mole)(°K)

(b) (psia)(ft³)/(lb mole)(°R)

(c) (atm)(ft³)/(lb mole)(°K)

(d) kilowatt-hr/(lb mole)(°R)

(e) horsepower-hr/(lb mole)(°R)

3.24. A gas-fired furnace uses 3000 ft³/hr of gas at a pressure of 30.0 in. Hg and a temperature of 100°F. The gas is purchased on a metered basis referred to 30.0 in. Hg and 60°F. Your accounting department wants to know if there is any difference between these two measurements. What per cent increase or decrease, if any, in volume is there? Base your percentage on the metered conditions.

---

[15] *Chem. Eng.*, Oct. 25, 1965, p. 112.

3.25. How much mercuric oxide must be heated to liberate a liter of oxygen measured at 25°C and 765 mm Hg pressure?

3.26. A producer gas has the following composition: CO_2, 7.2%; CO, 24.3%; H_2, 14.1%; CH_4, 3.5%; N_2, 50.9%.
   (a) Calculate the cubic feet of air necessary for complete combustion per cubic foot of producer gas at the same conditions.
   (b) If 38% excess air were used, what volume of flue gas at 750°F and 738 mm would be produced per cubic foot of producer gas at standard conditions?
   (c) Calculate the flue-gas analysis for (a) and (b).

3.27. Pine wood has the following composition: C, 50.31%; H_2, 6.20%; O_2, 43.08%; ash, 0.41%.
   (a) Calculate the cubic feet of air at 76°F and 29.4 in. necessary for complete combustion per pound of wood.
   (b) If 30% excess air were used, calculate the cubic feet of flue gas at 600°F and 29.4 in. produced per pound of wood.
   (c) Calculate the analysis of the flue gas for (a) and (b).

3.28. A hydrogen-free coke analyzes moisture, 4.2%; ash, 10.3%; carbon, 85.5%. It is burned giving a flue gas which analyzes CO_2, 13.6%; CO, 1.5%; O_2, 6.5%; N_2, 78.4%. Calculate:
   (a) Per cent excess air used
   (b) Cubic feet air at 80°F and 740 mm entering per pound carbon burned
   (c) Same as (b) per pound coke burned
   (d) Cubic feet of flue gas at 690°F per pound coke
   (e) Cubic feet stack gas at S.C. per pound coke

3.29. In a test on an oil-fired boiler, it is not possible to measure the amount of oil burned, but the air used is determined by inserting a verturi meter in the air line. It is found that 5000 ft³/min of air at 80°F and 10 psig is used. The flue gas analyzes CO_2, 10.7%; CO, 0.55%; O_2, 4.75%; N_2, 84.0%. If the oil is assumed to be all hydrocarbon, calculate the gallons per hour of oil burned. The specific gravity of the oil is 0.94.

3.30. A hydrocarbon oil is burned in a furnace with 11.7% excess air, yielding a flue gas containing: CO_2, 11.8%; CO, 2.0%; H_2, 1.5%; O_2, 4.0%. Calculate the analysis of the fuel oil.

3.31. A gas analyzes CO_2, 5%; CO, 40%; H_2, 36%; CH_4, 4%; and N_2, 15%. It is burned with 60% excess air; combustion is complete. Gas and air enter at 60°F, and the stack gas leaves at 500°F. Calculate:
   (a) The flue gas analysis
   (b) The ft³ of air per ft³ of gas
   (c) The ft³ of stack gas per ft³ of gas

3.32. An automobile engine is supplied with a gasoline which is found by analysis to contain 88% carbon and 12% hydrogen. It is operated at normal barometer. Calculate the Orsat analysis of the exhaust pipe gases, the pounds of dry air required per pound of fuel, the volume of this air at 60°F, and the volume of the combustion gases at 1000°F:

(a) Granting complete combustion with theoretical dry air

(b) Granting combustion with 90% of the theoretical air under conditions such that the oxygen will be completely eliminated and the ratio of CO to H_2 in the combustion gases will be 2: 1

3.33. For the manufacture of dry ice a furnace produces a flue gas that contains 16.8% CO_2. It is drawn through a waste heat boiler to the absorbers, entering which it contains 15.2% CO_2. Calculate the ft^3 of air that have leaked into the system per ft^3 of flue gas.

3.34. A limestone contains 70% $CaCO_3$ and the remainder SiO_2. To form 500 ft^3 CO_2 at S.C., how much limestone would be required, and how many pounds of commercial HCl (35% HCl)?

$$CaCO_3 + 2\,HCl \longrightarrow CaCl_2 + H_2O + CO_2$$

3.35. In the oxidation of ammonia to oxides of nitrogen, the reaction is

$$4\,NH_3 + 5\,O_2 \longrightarrow 4\,NO + 6\,H_2O$$

What air-ammonia ratio (ft^3 air/ft^3 ammonia) should be used to secure 18% excess air? If the reaction is 93% complete, calculate the composition of the products.

3.36. In the reaction:

$$CaCO_3 + 2\,HCl \longrightarrow CaCl_2 + CO_2 + H_2O$$

(a) How many grams of calcium carbonate are required to produce 1700 cm^3 of carbon dioxide at 780 mm and 17°C?

(b) If 360 cm^3 of carbon dioxide were liberated at 754 mm and 20°C, how many grams of calcium carbonate reacted?

3.37. A rigid closed vessel having a volume of 1 ft^3 contains NH_3 gas at 300°F and 30 psia. Into the closed vessel is pumped 0.35 ft^3 of HCl gas measured at 200°F and 20 psia. NH_4Cl is formed according to the reaction

$$NH_3 + HCl \longrightarrow NH_4Cl$$

Assume that the reaction goes to completion and that the vapor pressure of NH_4Cl at 250°C is 15 psia.

(a) How much NH_4Cl will be formed?

(b) Assuming that NH_4Cl is a solid, what will be the final pressure in the closed vessel if the final temperature is 250°C?

3.38. Gas at 60°F and 31.2 in. Hg is flowing through an irregular duct. In order to determine the rate of flow of the gas, CO_2 is passed into the gas stream. The gas analyzes 1.2% CO_2 (by vol.) before, and 3.4% CO_2 after, addition. The CO_2 tank is placed on a scale and found to lose 15 lb in 30 min. What is the rate of flow of the gas in ft^3/min?

3.39. Methane containing 4% oxygen is flowing through a pipe and it is necessary to calculate the amount of gas flowing. So 100 ft^3 of air per minute at 70°F and 760 mm are introduced into the pipe, and several hundred feet further down the pipe a sample is taken and found to contain 11% (oxygen +

nitrogen). How many cubic feet of the initial gas at 70°F and 740 mm are flowing through the pipe? *Note:* $O_2 + N_2$ together $= 11\%$.

3.40. Chlorine gas containing 2.4% oxygen is flowing through an earthenware pipe. The gas is measured by introducing into it air at the rate of 115 ft³/min at 70°F and 760 mm Hg and further down the line, after mixing is complete, removing a second sample of the gas for analysis. The gas is now found to contain 10.85% (oxygen + N_2). How many cubic feet of the initial gas were flowing per minute (60°F and 740 mm Hg) through the pipe? *Note:* $O_2 + N_2$ together $= 10.85\%$.

3.41. A mixture of NH_3 and air at a pressure of 750 mm and a temperature of 40°C contains 6.5% NH_3 by volume. The gas is passed at a rate of 150 ft³/min through an absorption tower in which only NH_3 is absorbed. The gas leaves the tower at a pressure of 740 mm and a temperature of 20°C and contains 0.09% NH_3 by volume. Calculate the weight of NH_3 absorbed in the tower.

3.42. A mixture of bromine vapor in air contains 1% bromine by volume.
   (a) What weight per cent bromine is present?
   (b) What is the average molecular weight of the mixture?
   (c) What is its specific gravity?
   (d) What is its specific gravity compared to bromine?
   (e) What is its specific gravity at 100°F and 100 psig compared to air at 60°F and 30 in. Hg?

3.43. What is the weight of 1 ft³ of H_2 at 0°F and 29.6 in. Hg? What is the specific gravity of this H_2 compared to air at 0°F and 29.6 in. Hg?

3.44. A glass weighing cell is used to determine the density of a gas. For a certain determination, the data are as follows:
   Weight of the cell full of air in air = 18.602 g.
   Weight of the evacuated cell in air = 18.294 g.
   Weight of the cell filled with sample gas in air = 18.345 g.
   The density of the air is 0.0750 lb/ft³. Calculate the density of the sample gas in lb/ft³.

3.45. A natural gas analyzes CO_2, 4.0%; CH_4, 72.0%; C_2H_6, 12.0%; N_2, 12.0%. What is its composition by weight? Its average molecular weight? Its density at 60°F and 30.0 in. Hg? Its specific gravity compared to methane?

3.46. A natural gas from a gas well has the following composition:

component	%	mol. wt
CH_4	60	16
C_2H_6	16	30
C_3H_8	10	44
C_4H_{10}	14	58

   (a) What is the composition in weight per cent?
   (b) What is the composition in mole per cent?

(c) How many cubic feet will be occupied by 100 lb of the gas at 70°F and 74 cm Hg?

(d) What is the density of the gas in lb/ft³ at 70°F and 740 mm Hg?

(e) What is the specific gravity of the gas?

3.47. In the manufacture of dry ice, a fuel is burned to a flue gas which contains 16.2% CO_2, 4.8% O_2, and the remainder N_2. This flue gas passes through a heat exchanger and then goes to an absorber. The data show the analysis of the flue gas entering the absorber is 13.1% CO_2 with the remainder O_2 and N_2. Apparently something has happened. To check your initial assumption that an air leak has developed in the heat exchanger, you collect the following data with a wet-test meter on the heat exchanger:

Entering flue gas in a 2-min period   47,800 ft³ at 600°F and 740 mm of Hg
Exit flue gas in a 2-min period   30,000 ft³ at   60°F and 720 mm of Hg

Was your assumption about an air leak a good one, or was perhaps the analysis of the gas in error? Or both?

3.48. A gaseous mixture consisting of 50 mole % hydrogen and 50 mole % acetaldehyde (C_2H_4O) is initially contained in a rigid vessel at a total pressure of 760 mm Hg abs. The formation of ethanol (C_2H_6O) occurs according to

$$C_2H_4O + H_2 \longrightarrow C_2H_6O$$

After a time it was noted that the total pressure in the rigid vessel had dropped to 700 mm Hg abs. Calculate the degree of completion of the reaction using the following assumptions:

All reactants and products are in the gaseous state.

The vessel and its contents were at the same temperature when the two pressures were measured.

3.49. The gaseous products from a catalytic cracker amount to 27,400,000 std ft³ per day (27.4 M²SCFD). The composition is as follows:

CH_4	72.5%	$n\text{-}C_4H_{10}$	1.6
C_2H_4	4.0	$n\text{-}C_4H_8$	2.3
C_2H_6	8.8	iso-C_5H_{12}	0.5
C_3H_6	3.1	C_5H_{10}	0.4
C_3H_8	4.0	$n\text{-}C_5H_{12}$	0.7
iso-C_4H_{10}	1.8	iso-C_6^+	0.3
			100.0%

The average molecular weight of the iso-C_6^+ is 96, and its specific gravity in the liquid state at 60°F is 0.89.

(a) Calculate the gallons of each condensable constituent present per 1000 SCF of gas (G/M). Condensables are those hydrocarbons which can be liquified at 100°F at any pressure.

(b) Express the composition of the condensable portion as volume per cent and weight per cent.

(c) Using the formation determined in (a), calculate:
   1) The total G/M of condensables present
   2) The total B/D (bbl/day) of condensables available
   3) The B/D of the material available for alkylation-plant feed stock (Alkylation plants use isobutane (iso-C_4) and condensable unsaturants for feed.)

3.50. Butane heating fuel contains 50% propane (C_3H_8), 48% normal butane (n-C_4H_{10}), and 2% isobutane (iso-C_4H_{10}) by liquid volume.
   (a) If 10 gal of this mixture is vaporized, how many cubic feet are produced at the standard conditions of the Petroleum Industry (60°F and 14.7 psia, dry gas)?
   (b) What is the API gravity of the fuel?

3.51. A natural gas has the following composition by volume:

CH_4	94.1%
N_2	3.0
H_2	1.9
O_2	1.0
	100.0%

This gas is piped from the well at a temperature of 20°C and a pressure of 30 psig. It may be assumed that the ideal gas law is applicable.
   (a) Calculate the partial pressure of the oxygen.
   (b) Calculate the partial volume of the nitrogen per 100 ft^3 of gas.
   (c) Calculate the density of the mixture in lb/ft^3 at the existing conditions.

3.52. A liter of oxygen at 760 mm is forced into a vessel containing a liter of nitrogen at 760 mm. What will be the resulting pressure? What assumptions are necessary for your answer?

3.53. The following mixture of gases is at 40 psig:

	CO_2	CO	N_2	H_2	*total*
lb:	100	50	50	10	210

What is the partial pressure of each component expressed in in. Hg?

3.54. A mixture of 15 lb N_2 and 20 lb H_2 is at a pressure of 50 psig and a temperature of 60°F. Determine:
   (a) The partial pressure of each component
   (b) The partial (or pure component) volumes
   (c) The specific volume of the mixture

3.55. If you mix together 20 ft^3 of N_2 at 300 psig and 100°F, and 30 ft^3 of O_2 at 200 psig and 340°F, and the final volume of the mixture is 15 ft^3 measured at 70°F, what is the final partial pressure of each component? Assume the perfect gas law holds.

3.56. Lead nitrate decomposes on heating according to the following reaction:

$$Pb(NO_3)_2(s) \longrightarrow PbO(s) + N_2O_4 + \tfrac{1}{2}O_2$$

When the gaseous products are cooled to 50°C, 45% of the nitrogen tetroxide (N_2O_4) is dissociated into nitrogen dioxide (NO_2) and the partial
pressure of the oxygen is 0.184 atm. Calculate:

(a) The partial pressures of the NO_2 and N_2O_4

(b) The density of the gaseous mixture at 50°C

3.57. Using data from the Steam Tables for the specific volume of water vapor,
plot percentage deviation curves for the actual specific volume of water
vapor from that calculated by the ideal gas laws:

$$\text{per cent deviation} = 100\,\frac{V_{\text{ideal}} - V_{\text{actual}}}{V_{\text{ideal}}}$$

where V_{ideal} is calculated from the ideal gas law. For the abscissa use
temperatures from 32°F to 1200°F.

(a) Show the deviations for the saturated vapor, i.e., the saturated steam
up to the critical point.

(b) Show also how the deviations would change at constant pressure for
14.7 psia, 1000 psia, and 2000 psia, from the saturated steam curve to
1200°F.

3.58. What pressure would be developed if 100 ft³ of ammonia at 20 atm and
400°F were compressed into a volume of 5.0 ft³, the final temperature being
350°F?

3.59. You desire to compress 100 ft³ of natural gas (100% CH_4) at 25°C and
740 mm Hg to occupy 1.0 ft³ at -40°C. What pressure must you use?

3.60. A block of dry ice weighing 50 lb is dropped into an empty steel bomb,
the volume of which is 5.0 ft³. The bomb is heated until the pressure gauge
reads 1600 psig. What was the temperature of the gas?

3.61. A cylinder of ethylene is standing in the sun so that its temperature becomes
38°C (100°F). The cylinder has a volume of 1.2 ft³ and contains 2.3 lb
ethylene. What is the pressure in the cylinder?

3.62. Ethylene at 500 atm pressure and a temperature of 100°C is contained in
a cylinder of internal volume of 1.0 ft³. How many pounds of C_2H_4 are in
the cylinder?

3.63. Calculate the specific volume of CO_2 at 600 atm and 40°C.

3.64. Calculate the volume occupied by 2.0 lb air at 735 psia and 392°F.

3.65. A high-pressure line carries natural gas (all methane) at 1500 psia and 110°F.
What volume under these conditions is equivalent to M ft³ at S.C. (S.C.
natural gas industry = 14.7 psia, 60°F, and dry).

3.66. What weight of ethane is contained in a gas cylinder of 1.0-ft³ volume if
the gas is at 100°F and 2000 psig?

3.67. Methyl chloride is sold in small cylinders for medical purposes and as a
refrigerant. The volume of a cylinder is 0.15 ft³. What weight of CH_3Cl is
contained in a cylinder if the pressure is 68.0 psia at 20°C?

3.68. A gas mixture of 30% CH_4 and 70% N_2 is at 200°F and 20 atm. What is its volume per mole?

3.69. The fire department is inspecting the fire extinguishers in the Chemical Engineering Building. A no. 2 gas cylinder, weighing 52.27 lb when completely evacuated, is placed on an accurate scales and filled with compressed carbon dioxide gas. When the gas in the cylinder has reached room temperature (54.5°F), the pressure in the cylinder is measured and found to be 338 psig. The capacity of the cylinder is 2.04 ft³. Estimate what the *scales* will read in pounds.

3.70. Perry's *Chemical Engineers Handbook* shows that the "compressibility" of carbon dioxide is 1.1585 at 137°C and 150 atm. However, a careful inspection of the table indicates by "compressibility" is meant the product pV. At 0°C and 1 atm the reference "compressibility" is 1.00000, i.e., $(pV)_{0°C \text{ and } 1 \text{ atm}}$ = 1.00000. Using the Nelson and Obert charts, calculate z at 137°C and 150 atm. Calculate z from Perry's data, and compare with the Nelson and Obert z.

3.71. Gauges used on cylinders containing compressed gases frequently are calibrated to show both the pressure in the cylinder and the volumetric contents of the cylinder. You have a Matheson Co. size 1A cylinder containing methane gas. You have a gauge for a 1A hydrogen cylinder, but not a gauge for methane. When you put the hydrogen gauge on the methane cylinder, it registers 2000 psig at 77°F and a capacity of 200 ft³ (as hydrogen at 77°F and 1 atm pressure). Prepare a calibration so the ft³ as hydrogen can be converted to ft³ as methane.

3.72. Calculate the density of the following gas mixture at 500 psig and 250°F:

component	lb
methane (CH_4)	100
ethane (C_2H_6)	240
propane (C_3H_8)	150
nitrogen (N_2)	50
total	540

3.73. A gaseous mixture has the following composition (in moles %):

C_2H_4	57
Ar	40
He	3

at 120 atm pressure and 25°C. Compare the experimental volume of 0.14 liter per g mole with that computed by:
(a) Van der Waals' equation plus Dalton's law
(b) Van der Waals' equation using averaged constants
(c) Mean compressibility factor and Dalton's law
(d) Mean compressibility factor and Amagat's law
(e) Compressibility factor using pseudoreduced conditions (Kay's method)
(f) Perfect gas law

3.74. A gas analyzes 60% methane and 40% ethylene by volume at 1 atm. It is desired to store 28 lb of this gas mixture in a cylinder having a capacity of 1.82 ft³ at a maximum temperature of 112°F. Calculate the pressure inside the cylinder:
   (a) Assuming that the mixture obeys the ideal gas laws
   (b) Using the compressibility factor determined from the pseudocritical point of the mixture
   How many pounds of this mixture can be stored in the cylinder at 112°F if the maximum allowable pressure is 1250 psig?

3.75. You are in charge of a pilot plant using an inert atmosphere composed of 60% ethylene (C_2H_4) and 40% argon (A). How big a cylinder (or how many) must be purchased if you are to use 300 ft³ of gas measured at the pilot plant conditions of 100 atm and 300°F?

cylinder type	cost	pressure (psig)	lb gas
1A	$40.25	2000	62
2	32.60	1500	47
3	25.50	1500	35

State any additional assumptions. You can buy only one type of cylinder.

3.76. A gas has the following composition by volume:

$$CO_2 \quad 10\%$$
$$CH_4 \quad 40$$
$$C_2H_4 \quad 50$$

It is desired to distribute 33.6 lb of this gas per cylinder. Cylinders are to be designed so that the maximum pressure will not exceed 2400 psig when the temperature is 180°F. Calculate the volume of the cylinder required:
   (a) Assuming the mixture to be an ideal gas
   (b) Using the pseudocritical point of the mixture and the compressibility factor
   What pressure would exist in the cylinder if a cylinder designed from data in part (b) and charged with 33.6 lb of this gas mixture were stored at 57°F? (Use pseudocritical method.)

3.77. Prepare a Cox chart for:
   (a) Acetic acid vapor
   (b) Heptane
   (c) Ammonia
   (d) Methanol
   from 32°F to the critical point (for each substance). Compare the estimated vapor pressure at the critical point with the critical pressure.

3.78. Estimate the vapor pressure of ethyl bromide at 180°F.

3.79. From the following data estimate the vapor pressure of sulfur dioxide at 100°C; the actual vapor pressure is about 29 atm:

t (°C)	-10	6.3	32.1	55.5
p^* (atm)	1	2	5	10

3.80. If air at 750 mm Hg and 75°F is saturated with benzene, compute the mole and weight per cent benzene in the mixture. Also calculate:
(a) The pounds of benzene per pound of gas mixture
(b) The pounds of benzene per pound of air
(c) The pound moles of benzene per mole of air
(d) The grains of benzene per cubic foot of air at S.C.
(e) The grains of benzene per cubic foot of mixture

3.81. If sufficient water is placed in a dry gas at 15°C and 754 mm to saturate it thoroughly, what will be the pressure after saturation, the temperature and volume remaining constant?

3.82. A gas, saturated with water vapor, has a volume of 4 liters at 17.5°C under a pressure of 759 mm. What is its volume, dry, under standard conditions?

3.83. One hundred cubic centimeters of He are measured saturated over water at 15°C and under a total pressure of 765 mm. What would be its volume, dry, at this temperature and pressure? What would be its volume, dry, under standard conditions?

3.84. A sample of oxygen, when collected over water, has a volume of 18.5 ml at 20°C and 700 mm. At what centigrade temperature would the *dry* oxygen occupy a volume of 100 ml under a pressure of 540 mm?

3.85. Four hundred cubic feet of air saturated with water vapor at 25°C and 760 mm are dehydrated. What is the volume of the dry air? Show units at each step.

3.86. The vapor pressure of hexane (C_6H_{14}) at -20°C is 14.1 mm. Dry air at this temperature is saturated with the vapor under a total pressure of 760 mm Hg.
(a) What is the per cent excess air for combustion?
(b) What is the flue-gas analysis if complete combustion occurs?

3.87. A gas bubble of methane 1 mm in diameter is released by decaying vegetation at a depth of 20 ft below the surface of a lake, water temperature 65°F. What will be the diameter of the bubble (assumed spherical) as it breaks at the surface of the lake?

3.88. Fifty pounds of propane from a cylinder is gasified and collected over water in a gas holder at 25°C and a pressure of 6.0 in. H_2O above the normal barometer. What volume of gas is collected?

3.89. A mixture of acetylene (C_2H_2) with an excess of oxygen measured 350 ft³ at 25°C and 745 mm pressure. After explosion the volume of the dry gaseous product was 300 ft³ at 60°C and its partial pressure of 745 mm. Calculate the volume of acetylene and of oxygen in the original mixture. Assume final gas is saturated and only enough water is formed to saturate the gas.

3.90. Dry combustion gases having the following molal composition are passed into an evaporator at a temperature of 200°C and a pressure of 743 mm Hg:

nitrogen	79.2	Remember the water
oxygen	7.2	is being picked up
carbon dioxide	13.6	by the dry gases.
	100.0%	

Water is evaporated, the gases leaving at a temperature of 85°C and a pressure of 740 mm Hg with the following molal composition:

nitrogen	48.3
oxygen	4.4
carbon dioxide	8.3
water	39.0
	100.0%

(a) Calculate the volume of gases leaving the evaporator per 100 ft³ entering.

(b) Calculate the weight of water evaporated per 100 ft³ of gas entering.

3.91. Oxalic acid ($H_2C_2O_2$) is burned with 248% excess air, 65% of the carbon burning to CO. Calculate:

(a) The flue gas analysis

(b) The volume of air at 90°F and 785 mm Hg used per pound of oxalic acid burned

(c) The volume of stack gases at 725°F and 785 mm Hg per pound of oxalic acid burned

(d) The dew point of the stack gas

3.92. Uranium dioxide (UO_2) powder suitable for forming and sintering into high-density ceramic fuel may be prepared by the hydrogen reduction of ammonium diuranate. What size of the commercial hydrogen cylinder is needed to provide 205 ft³ of H_2 saturated with water vapor at a total pressure of 29.8 in. Hg and at 70°F? A commercial hydrogen cylinder contains dry hydrogen at 60°F and a pressure of 2000 psig.

3.93. Benzene vapor (mole weight = 78) is mixed with N_2 at 50°C in such proportions that the partial pressure of the vapor is 137 mm Hg. The total pressure is 700 mm Hg. Calculate the following:

(a) Relative saturation

(b) Moles benzene per mole of vapor-free gas

(c) Weight of benzene per unit weight of vapor-free gas

(d) Percentage of benzene by volume

(e) Percentage of saturation

(f) Grains benzene per cubic foot of mixture

3.94. Ethyl ether (mole weight = 74) is mixed with H_2 at 10°C in such proportions that the partial pressure of the vapor is 150 mm Hg. The total pressure is 715 mm Hg. Calculate the following:

(a) Relative saturation

(b) Moles ether per mole of vapor-free gas

(c) Weight of ether per unit weight of vapor-free gas

(d) Percentage saturation

(e) Per cent ether by volume

(f) Grains ether per cubic foot of mixture

3.95. If a gas at 140°F and 30 in. Hg abs has a molal humidity of 0.03, calculate:

(a) The percentage humidity

(b) The relative humidity

(c) The dew point of the gas (°F)

3.96. A rigid vessel which is 1 ft³ in volume contains 1 lb of N_2 and 1 lb of H_2O at 100°F.

(a) What is the pressure (psia) in the vessel?

(b) What is the molal humidity in the vapor phase?

(c) What mass fraction of the water is liquid?

3.97. Leather containing 100% of its own weight of water (i.e., if the dry leather is 1 lb, the water is 1 lb) is dried by means of air. The dew point of the entering air is 40°F, and in the exit air it is 55°F. If 200 lb of the entering wet air are forced through the dryer per hour, how many pounds of water are removed per hour? The barometer reads 750 mm Hg.

3.98. Under what circumstances can the relative humidity and per cent humidity be equal?

3.99. The temperature on Sunday was 92°F, and the relative humidity was 45%. The barometer read 29.43 in. Hg. Calculate the dew point of this air and its percentage of "absolute" humidity.

3.100. A room is 20 by 20 by 12 ft. The air in it is at 80°F, the barometer reads 29.64 in. Hg, and the dew point is 50°F. How many pounds H_2O vapor are in the room? What is the relative humidity of the air?

3.101. In a gas mixture there is 0.0083 lb mole of water vapor per pound mole of dry CH_4 at a temperature of 80°F and a total pressure of 2 atm. Calculate:

(a) The per cent relative saturation of this mixture

(b) The percentage saturation of the mixture

(c) The temperature to which the mixture must be heated in order that the relative saturation shall be 20%

3.102. A drier is removing C_6H_6 (mole weight = 78) from a solid material by exposing the material to a stream of N_2 in a drier. The N_2 stream entering the drier is at a total pressure of 800 mm Hg and a temperature of 15°C. The partial pressure of the C_6H_6 in the entering stream is 30 mm Hg. The N_2 stream leaving the drier is at a total pressure of 760 mm Hg, 40°C, and 80% relative saturation. The vapor pressure of benzene is given by the equation:

$$p^* = 5T - 15$$

where p^* = vapor pressure of benzene

T = temperature in °C

(a) If 1000 lb of pure N_2 is passing into the drier per hour, how much benzene is removed?

(b) If benzene is removed from the exit stream by cooling at 760 mm Hg, to what temperature must it be cooled in order to have the same amount of benzene per pound of N_2 as is entering the drier?

3.103. A drier must remove 50 lb of H_2O per hour from a certain material. Air at 50°F and 60% relative humidity enters the drier and leaves at 140°F and 70% relative humidity. What is the weight of bone-dry air used per hour? Barometer is 760 mm Hg.

3.104. A drier must remove 200 lb of H_2O per hour from a certain material. Air at 70°F and 50% relative humidity enters the drier and leaves at 140°F and 80% relative humidity. What is the weight of bone-dry air used per hour? Barometer is 760 mm Hg.

3.105. Acetone (C_3H_6O) at 25°C has a vapor pressure of 229.2 mm Hg, and a sp gr of $d_4^{25} = 0.780$. Dry air at 25°C and an absolute pressure of 715 mm Hg is bubbled through the acetone at 25°C; 15 gal of acetone evaporate. How many pounds of dry air are required?

3.106. On Thursday the temperature was 90°F, and the dew point was 70°F. At 2 P.M. the barometer read 29.83 in. Hg, but owing to an approaching storm it dropped by 5 P.M. to 29.08 in. Hg, with no other changes. What change occurred in (a) the relative humidity and (b) the percentage absolute humidity, between 2 and 5 P.M.?

3.107. Air is saturated with water at 140°F and a barometer reading of 29.68 mm Hg. If the temperature is reduced to 100°F and the gas compressed to 25 psia, what percentage of the water separates out?

3.108. A "wet" natural gas consists essentially of hexane (C_6H_{14}) and methane (CH_4). A natural gasoline plant of the pressure-refrigeration type is designed to recover the hexane from the gas, which is flowing at a pressure of 75 psi gauge and 30°C in a gas pipe line. One hundred grams of hexane is adsorbed and 100 ft³ (at 760 mm and 30°C) of CH_4 remains. To what temperature must the wet gas at 75 psi be cooled to recover 80% of the hexane?

3.109. Air saturated with water vapor is at 140°F and barometric pressure of 29.68 in. Hg.
(a) To what temperature must the air be cooled to separate 68% of the water in it (barometer is constant)?
(b) To what pressure must the air be compressed to separate 68% of the water in it (temperature is constant)?
(c) If the temperature is reduced to 100°F and the gas is compressed to 25 psia, what percentage of the water separates out?

3.110. Moist day air at 90°F, dew point 70°F, and barometer 29.8 in. Hg cools at night to a temperature of 50°F, barometer unchanged. Calculate:
(a) Cubic feet of night air per 1000 ft³ of day air
(b) Pounds of water deposited per 1000 ft³ of day air

3.111. A flue gas that analyzes CO_2, 12.0%; O_2, 8.0%; and N_2, 80.0%, by volume, has a dew point of 90°F. Calculate the density of the stack gas (flue gas +

water vapor with it) at 600°F and 29.4 in. Hg. What is its specific gravity compared with air at 80°F and 29.92 in. Hg?

3.112. Moist air is partially dehydrated and cooled before it is passed through a refrigerator room maintained at 0°F, to prevent excessive ice formation on the cooling coils. The cool air is passed through the room at the rate of 20,000 ft³/24 hr measured at the entrance temperature (40°F) and pressure. At the end of 30 days the refrigerator room must be warmed in order to remove the ice from the coils. How many pounds of water are removed?

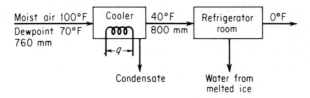

3.113. Nitrogen contains 6.5 grains of water vapor per cubic foot of wet N_2 at a temperature of 80°F. Calculate:
  (a) The per cent relative saturation of the mixture and its percentage composition by volume if the total pressure is 745 mm of Hg
  (b) The percentage saturation of the mixture under the conditions of part (a)
  (c) The weight of water which could be carried by 1 ft³ of the mixture were it saturated at the existing conditions

3.114. A natural gas contains 5.0% condensable hydrocarbons, of which the average molecular weight is 86 and the density in the liquid state is 0.659 g/cm³. What volume of natural gas at 120°F and 100 psig contains 1 gal of the condensable hydrocarbons? What volume of completely stripped gas would result at 60°F and 30.0 in. Hg? (Give answer in cubic feet.) If the gas is cooled to 32°F where the vapor pressure of the condensate is 43 mm Hg, what fraction of the condensable material is recovered?

3.115. One gallon of benzene (C_6H_6) vaporizes in a room 20 by 20 by 9 ft at a constant barometric pressure of 750 mm and 70°F. The lower explosive limit for benzene in air is 1.4%. Has this been exceeded?

3.116. Soybean flakes from an extraction process are reduced from 0.96 lb of C_2HCl_3/lb dry flakes to 0.05 lb of C_2HCl_3/lb dry flakes in a desolventizer by a stream of N_2 which vaporizes the C_2HCl_3. The entering N_2 contains C_2HCl_3 such that its dew point is 30°C. The N_2 leaves at 90°C with a relative saturation of 60%. The pressure in the desolventizer is 760 mm, and 1,000 lb/hr of dry flakes pass through the drier.
  (a) Compute the volume of N_2 plus C_2HCl_3 leaving the desolventizer at 90°C and 760 mm Hg in ft³/min.
  (b) The N_2 leaving the desolventizer is compressed and cooled to 40°C, thus condensing out the C_2HCl_3 picked up in the desolventizer. What must the pressure in the condenser be if the gas is to have a dew point of 30°C at the pressure of the desolventizer?

3.117. Methane gas contains CS_2 vapor in an amount such that the relative saturation at 35°C is 85%. To what temperature must the gas mixture be cooled to condense out 60% of the CS_2 by volume? The total pressure is constant at 750 mm Hg, and the vapor pressure of CS_2 (mol. wt 76.12) is given by the following relation:

$$p^* = 15.4T + 130$$

where p^* = vapor pressure of CS_2, mm Hg
T = temperature, °C

3.118. One thousand pounds of a slurry containing 10% by weight of $CaCO_3$ is to be filtered on a rotary vacuum filter. The filter cake from the filter contains 60% water. This cake is then placed in a drier and dried to a moisture content of 9.09% (9.09 lb H_2O/100 lb $CaCO_3$) on the dry basis. If the humidity of the air entering the drier is 0.005 lb of water per lb of dry air and the humidity of the air leaving the drier is 0.015 lb of water/lb of dry air, calculate:
(a) Pounds of water removed by the filter
(b) Pounds of dry air needed in the drier

3.119. An absorber receives a mixture of air containing 12% carbon disulfide (CS_2). The absorbing solution is benzene, and the gas exits from the absorber with a CS_2 content of 3% and a benzene content of 3% (because some benzene evaporates). What fraction of the CS_2 was recovered?

3.120. You are asked to design a silica-gel drier capable of removing 1000 lb of water per hour. Air is to be supplied to the drier at a temperature of 130°F, a pressure of 760 mm Hg, and a dew point of 80°F. If the air leaves the drier at a temperature of 90°F, a pressure of 760 mm Hg, and a dew point of 45°F, calculate the volume of air (at the initial conditions) which must be supplied per hour.

3.121. If air at 50% humidity and at 35°C and 745 mm Hg is to have 80% of its water content removed by isothermal compression, find the pressure required.

3.122. Toluene is evaporated into dry air. The resulting mixture at 100°F and a pressure of 14.7 psia has a percentage saturation of 50%. It is desired to condense 80% of the toluene present by a process of cooling and compressing. If the temperature is reduced to 40°F, to what pressure must the gas be compressed?

3.123. A gas mixture at a temperature of 77°F and a pressure of 760 mm Hg contains carbon disulfide vapor at 60% saturation. Calculate the temperature to which the gas must be cooled, at constant pressure, in order to condense 40% of the CS_2 present.

3.124. It is typical summer day, temperature 100°F, relative humidity 90%, and barometer 29.76 in. Hg. The corner Humble Oil station is compressing air for its "free air" supply and compresses the atmospheric air to a pressure of 50 psig, but the work of compression increases the temperature of the air to 120°F:

(a) Does water condense out of the air? If so, how many pounds of water condense per ton of *dry* air?

(b) What volume of atmospheric air has to be compressed to bring a 30-ft³ tank up to the final pressure of 50 psig?

3.125. In the manufacture of paper pulp by the sulfite process, a gas containing So_2 is passed through an absorption system containing a milk-of-lime suspension to produce a calcium bisulfite cooking liquor for the wood chips. The gas enters the absorption system at 150°F, at a total pressure of 36.4 in. Hg and a partial pressure of SO_2 of 3.8 in. Hg. The other gases are inert gases. The exit gas from the absorption system is at 80°F, at a total pressure of 30.2 in. Hg and a partial pressure of SO_2 of 0.4 in. Hg. Calculate:

(a) The ft³ dry exit gas/1000 ft³ dry entering gas

(b) The per cent loss of SO_2/1000 ft³ dry entering gas

3.126. A certain gas contains moisture, and you have to remove this by compression and cooling so that the gas will finally contain not more than 1% moisture (by volume). You decide to cool the final gas down to 70°F.

(a) Determine the minimum final pressure needed.

(b) If the cost of the compression equipment is

$$\text{cost in } \$ = (\text{pressure in psia})^{1.40}$$

and the cost of the cooling equipment is

$$\text{cost in } \$ = (350 - \text{temp. } °K)^{1.9}$$

is 70°F the best temperature to use?

3.127. It is desired to dry 12,350 ft³/hr of wet air at 190°F and 768 mm Hg pressure (with a relative humidity of 13.9%) by scrubbing with sulfuric acid in a packed tower. A recirculation system used for the acid is shown in the figure. The dried air will leave the scrubber at 120°F and 740 mm Hg pressure. The relative humidity of the dried air is to be 7.18%. Sufficient make-up acid containing 98.0% H_2SO_4 is added to maintain the concentration of the scrubbing solution entering the tower constant at 72.0% H_2SO_4. The weak acid analyzes 67.0% H_2SO_4. A certain amount of weak acid is continuously removed from the process. Calculate:

(a) The ft³/hr of air plus water vapor leaving the scrubber

(b) The lb/hr of make-up acid

(c) The lb/hr of acid entering the scrubber

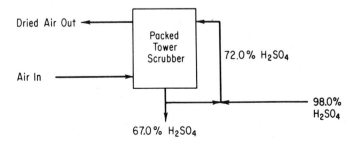

3.128. Refer to the process flow diagram for a process which produces maleic anhydride by the partial oxidation of benzene. The moles of O_2 fed to the reactor per mole of pure benzene fed to the reactor is 18.0. All the maleic acid produced in the reactor is removed with water in the bottom stream from the water scrubber. All the C_6H_6, O_2, CO_2, and N_2 leaving the reactor leave in the stream from the top of the water scrubber, saturated with H_2O. Originally, the benzene contains trace amounts of a nonvolatile contaminant which would inhibit the reaction. This contaminant is removed by steam distillation in the steam still. The steam still contains liquid phases of both benzene and water (benzene is completely insoluble in water). The benzene phase is 80 wt %, and the water phase is 20 wt % of the two-liquid phases in the still. Other process conditions are given on the flow sheet. Use the vapor pressure data given below. Calculate the:

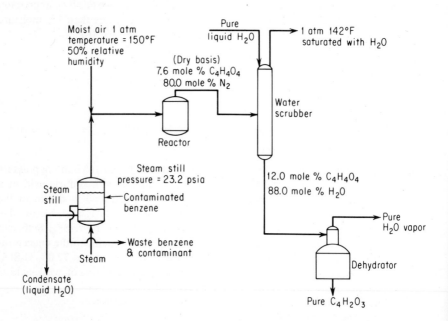

(a) Moles of benzene undergoing reaction (2) per mole of benzene feed to the reactor
(b) Pounds of H_2O removed in the top stream from the dehydrator per pound mole of benzene feed to the reactor
(c) Composition (mole %, wet basis) of the gases leaving the top of the water scrubber
(d) Pounds of pure liquid H_2O added to the top of the water scrubber per pound mole of benzene feed to the reactor
Vapor pressure data:

temperature, °F	benzene, psia	water, psia
110	4.045	1.275
120	5.028	1.692
130	6.195	2.223
140	7.570	2.889
150	9.178	3.718
160	11.047	4.741
170	13.205	5.992
180	15.681	7.510
190	18.508	9.339
200	21.715	11.526

3.129. In the Girbotol process to remove hydrogen sulfide from natural and refinery gases, monoethanolamine or other ethanolamines are allowed to react with the hydrogen sulfide, forming compounds which may be broken down by heat:

$$RNH_2 + H_2S \rightleftarrows RNH_3HS$$

(R represents an organic radical)

This plant uses monethanolamine (MEA) in aqueous solution which circulates through an absorber and a reactivator. As shown on the flow diagram, the products of this process are acid gas containing 40% hydrogen sulfide and purified gas of 0.2% hydrogen sulfide content. Five hundred cubic feet of impure gas at 15 psia and 60°F are fed with water into the absorber. The impure gas has the following composition:

methane	65%
ethane	20
propane	5
hydrogen sulfide	10

Compositions of the acid gas and purified gas are as shown.
(a) How many pounds of purified gas are obtained?
(b) Based on the entire amount of hydrogen sulfide entering the absorber, what weight of MEA is required for absorption, assuming 30% excess?
(c) If the reactivator is only 90% effective in removing the components of the acid gas from stream S, determine the pounds of liquid in streams R and S and determine their compositions.

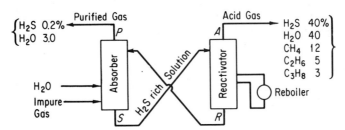

3.130. Examine the statements below:
  (a) Vapor pressure of gasoline is about 14 psia at 130°F.
  (b) The vapor pressure of the system, water-furfural diacetate, is 760 mm Hg at 99.96°C.
  Are the statements correct? If not, correct them. Assume the numerical values are correct.

3.131. A constant-volume bomb contains air at 66°F and 21.2 psia. One pound of liquid water is introduced into the bomb. The bomb is then heated to a constant temperature of 180°F. After equilibrium is reached, the pressure in the bomb is 33.0 psia. The vapor pressure of water at 180°F is 7.51 psia.
  (a) Did all of the water evaporate?
  (b) Compute the volume of the bomb in cubic feet.
  (c) Compute the humidity of the air in the bomb at the final conditions in pounds of water per pound of air.

Chapter 4

ENERGY BALANCES

One of the important problems encountered in industry is the determination and calculation of energy changes. In this chapter we will discuss energy balances, with the accessory background information needed to apply them correctly. You will find the energy balance another very useful tool to add to the fund of techniques you have accumulated so far. We will first discuss the balance itself and the methods engineers have developed to measure and evaluate various common types of energy. These types include heat, work, enthalpy, and internal energy. Next, the energy balance will be applied to practical and hypothetical problems of interest to chemical engineers. Finally, we will discuss the generation of energy as represented by the heat of reaction.

Certain terms which have been described in earlier parts of the text occur repeatedly in this chapter; these terms are repeated below with some elaboration in view of their importance.

(a) *System*. Any specified mass of material or piece of apparatus to which we would like to devote our attention. A system must be defined by surrounding it with a system boundary. A system enclosed by a boundary which prohibits the exchange of mass with the surroundings is termed a *closed* system, or *nonflow* system, in distinction to an *open* system, or *flow* system, in which the exchange of both mass and energy is permitted. All of the mass or apparatus external to the defined system is termed the *surroundings*. Reexamine some of the example problems in Chap. 2 for illustrations of the location of system boundaries. You should draw similar boundaries in the solution of your problems, since this will fix clearly the system and surroundings.

231

(b) *Property.* A characteristic of material which can be measured, such as pressure, volume, or temperature—or deduced or calculated, if not directly measured, such as internal energy. The properties of a system are dependent on its condition at any given time and not on what has happened to the system in the past.

An *extensive property* (variable, parameter) is one whose value is the sum of the values of each of the subsystems comprising the whole system. For example, a gaseous system can be divided into two subsystems, which have volumes or masses different from the original system. Consequently, mass or volume is an extensive property.

An *intensive property* (variable, parameter) is one whose values are not additive and do not vary with the quantity of the sample of the system. For example, temperature, pressure, density (mass per volume), etc. do not change if the system is sliced in half or if the halves are put together.

Two properties are *independent* of each other if at least one variation of state for the system can be found in which one property varies while the other remains fixed. The set of independent intensive properties necessary and sufficient to fix the state of the system can be ascertained from the phase rule of Sec. 3.7-1.

(c) *State.* Material with a given set of properties at a given time. The state of a system does not depend on the shape or configuration of the system, but only on its intensive properties.

It is necessary to keep in mind two important points as you read what follows. First, we will examine only systems that are homogeneous, not charged, and without surface effects, in order to make the energy balance as simple as possible. Second, the energy balance will be developed and applied from the macroscopic viewpoint (over-all about the system) rather than from a microscopic viewpoint, i.e., an elemental volume within the system.

4.1. Definitions and units

When you think about energy, what sort of image comes to mind? Perhaps it is an electric generator whirring at the bottom of a dam, or perhaps a bullet speeding through the air. If it is the latter, you instinctively feel that the bullet in motion is different from one at rest. You know a ball of iron in the sun is in a different state than one in the shade. If a gas confined in a cylinder at high pressure is allowed to expand, it can do work against a retarding force, and at the same time the temperature of the gas may fall. However, the same change in the properties of the gas can be brought about in other ways which seem to have very little to do with gas expansion; for example, the temperature of the gas might be reduced by placing the cylinder on a block of ice. To explain all these and many other phenomena, we postulate the existence of energy.

Normally we will express heat, work, or energy of any kind in the units of Btu (British thermal unit) or calories, although many other types of energy units can sometimes be effectively employed. The energy per unit mass then will be Btu per pound or calories per gram. The *calorie* is roughly defined as the amount of energy required to raise the temperature of 1 gram of water 1°C at a pressure of 1 atmosphere. (Similarly, the *Btu* is the amount of energy required to raise 1 pound of water 1°F.) However, since the heat capacity of water varies with temperature, it is necessary to be a little more precise and specify the temperature interval—for example, the temperature interval near 4°C, which is the temperature of the greatest density of water, or the temperature interval between 15°C and 16°C, which makes the calorie almost equal to the *mean* calorie. (The *mean* calorie is the energy required to raise 1 gram of water from 0°C to 100°C divided by 100.) One mean calorie is equal to 4.186 absolute joules.

Since electrical methods of measuring heat transfer are much more accurate than thermal measurements, we now primarily use an artificial calorie defined in terms of international or absolute joules called the *thermochemical* calorie, or 4.1833 international joules. This thermochemical calorie is independent of the heat capacity of water and is about the same as the calorie at 17°C. Another kind of calorie is the *steam* calorie, or the international Steam Table calorie (the IT calorie), which is $\frac{1}{860}$ of an international watthour, or 1.000654 thermochemical calories. For calculations made to slide-rule accuracy, there is hardly any reason for you to consider the differences between all these calories, but for precise measurements it is necessary to know their exact relationships.

Before formulating the general energy balance, we must discuss a few new terms that you should clearly understand. Unfortunately, many of them are used loosely in our ordinary conversation and writing, whereas others are so fundamental to our thinking that they defy exact definition. You may feel that you understand from long acquaintance—be sure that you really do.

(a) *Heat*. In a discussion of "heat" we enter an area in which our everyday use of the term may cause confusion, since we are going to use heat in a very restricted sense when we apply the laws governing energy changes. Heat (Q) is commonly defined as that part of the total energy flow across a system boundary that is caused by a temperature difference between the system and the surroundings. Heat may be exchanged by conduction, convection, or radiation. A more effective general qualitative definition is given by Callen:[1]

[1] H. B. Callen, *Thermodynamics*, John Wiley & Sons, Inc., New York, 1960, p. 7.

A macroscopic observation [of a system] is a kind of "hazy" observation which discerns gross features but not fine detail. .... Of the enormous number of atomic coordinates [which can exist], a very few with unique symmetric properties survive the statistical averaging associated with a transition to the macroscopic description [and are macroscopically observable]. Certain of these surviving coordinates are mechanical in nature [such as volume]. Others are electrical in nature [such as dipole moments]. ... It is equally possible to transfer energy to the hidden atomic modes of motion [of the atom] as well as to those modes which happen to be macroscopically observable. An energy transfer to the hidden atomic modes is called heat.

To evaluate heat transfer *quantitatively*, unless given a priori, you must apply the energy balance, Eq. (4.26) below, and evaluate all the terms except Q. Heat transfer can be *estimated* for engineering purposes by many empirical relations, which can be found in books treating heat transfer or transport processes.

(b) *Work*. Work (W) is commonly defined as energy transferred between the system and its surroundings by means of a vector force acting through a vector displacement on the system boundaries

$$W = \int F \, dl$$

where F is the direction of dl. However this definition is not exact inasmuch as:

(1) The displacement may not be easy to define.
(2) The product of $F \, dl$ does not always result in an equal amount of work.
(3) Work can be exchanged without a force acting on the system boundaries (such as through magnetic or electric effects).

Since heat and work are by definition mutually exclusive exchanges of energy, we will qualitatively classify work as energy which can be transferred to or from a mechanical state, or mode, of the system, while heat is the transfer of energy to atomic or molecular states, or modes, which are not macroscopically observable. To measure or evaluate work *quantitatively* by a mechanical device is difficult, so that, unless Eq. (4.26) or (4.32) below can be applied, in many instances the value of the work done must be given a priori.

(c) *Kinetic Energy*. Kinetic energy (K) is the energy a system possesses because of its velocity relative to the surroundings. Kinetic energy may be calculated from the relation

$$K = \tfrac{1}{2}mv^2 \tag{4.1}$$

or

$$\hat{K} = \tfrac{1}{2}v^2 \tag{4.1a}$$

where the superscript caret (^) refers to the energy per unit mass (or some-times per mole) and not the total kinetic energy as in Eq. (4.1).

(d) *Potential Energy.* Potential energy (P) is energy the system possesses because of the body force exerted on its mass by a gravitational field with respect to a reference surface. Potential energy can be calculated from

$$P = mgh \qquad (4.2)$$

or

$$\hat{P} = gh \qquad (4.2a)$$

where the symbol (^) again means potential energy for unit mass (or some-times per mole).

Example 4.1 Energy Changes

A 100-lb ball is dropped from the top of a 15-ft ladder and hits the ground. With reference to the ground, determine the following:

(a) What is the initial kinetic and potential energy of the ball in (ft)(lb$_f$)?

$$\text{initial } K = \tfrac{1}{2}mv^2 = 0$$

$$\text{initial } P = mgh = \cfrac{100 \text{ lb}_m \left|\, g \dfrac{\text{ft}}{\text{sec}^2}\, \right| 15 \text{ ft}}{\left|\, g_c \dfrac{(\text{ft})(\text{lb}_m)}{(\text{sec}^2)(\text{lb}_f)}\, \right|} = +1500 \text{ (ft)(lb}_f)$$

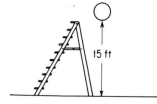

(b) What is the final kinetic and potential energy of the ball?

$$\text{final } K = 0$$
$$\text{final } P = 0$$

(c) What is the change in kinetic and potential energy for the process?

$$K_2 - K_1 = \tfrac{1}{2}m(v_2^2 - v_1^2) = 0$$
$$P_2 - P_1 = mg(h_2 - h_1) = 0 - (+1500) = -1500 \text{ (ft)(lb}_f)$$

A decrease in potential energy has occurred.

(d) If all the initial potential energy of the ball is converted into heat, how many Btu does this amount to?

$$\cfrac{1500 \text{ (ft)(lb}_f) \left|\, 1 \text{ Btu}\, \right|}{\left|\, 778 \text{ (ft)(lb}_f)\, \right|} = 1.93 \text{ Btu}$$

(e) *Internal Energy.* Internal energy (U) is the macroscopic observation of the molecular, atomic, and subatomic energies, all of which follow definite conservation rules for dynamic systems. Because no instruments exist with which to measure internal energy directly on a macroscopic scale, internal energy is calculated from certain variables which can be measured macroscopically, i.e., pressure, volume, temperature, and composition.

To calculate the internal energy per unit mass ($\hat{U}$), we make use of a special property of internal energy, namely, that it is an exact differential (because it is a "point" or "state" property, a matter to be described shortly) and, for a pure component, can be expressed in terms of the temperature and specific volume alone. If we say

$$\hat{U} = \hat{U}(T, \hat{V})$$

by taking the total derivative, we find

$$d\hat{U} = \left(\frac{\partial \hat{U}}{\partial T}\right)_{\hat{V}} dT + \left(\frac{\partial \hat{U}}{\partial \hat{V}}\right)_{T} d\hat{V} \tag{4.3}$$

By definition $\left(\frac{\partial \hat{U}}{\partial T}\right)_{\hat{V}}$ is the heat capacity at constant volume C_v, and for all practical purposes the term $\left(\frac{\partial \hat{U}}{\partial \hat{V}}\right)_{T}$ is so small that the second term on the right-hand side of Eq. (4.3) can be neglected. Consequently, changes in the internal energy can be computed by integrating Eq. (4.3) as follows:

$$\hat{U}_2 - \hat{U}_1 = \int_{T_1}^{T_2} C_v \, dT \tag{4.4}$$

Note that you can only calculate differences in internal energy, or calculate internal energy relative to a reference state, and not absolute values of internal energy. Instead of using Eq. (4.4), internal energy changes are usually calculated from enthalpy values, the next topic of discussion.

(f) *Enthalpy.* In applying the energy balance you will encounter a variable which is given the symbol H and the artificial name *enthalpy* (pronounced en'-thal-py). This variable is defined as the combination of two variables which will appear very often in the energy balance

$$H = U + pV \tag{4.5}$$

where p is the pressure and V the volume. The term enthalpy has replaced the now obsolete terms "heat content" or "total heat," to eliminate any connection whatsoever with heat as defined above.

To calculate the enthalpy per unit mass, we use the property that the enthalpy is an exact differential which can, for a pure substance, be expressed in terms of the temperature and pressure (a more convenient variable for enthalpy than volume). If we let

$$\hat{H} = \hat{H}(T, p)$$

by taking the total derivative of $\hat{H}$, we can form an expression corresponding to Eq. (4.3)

$$d\hat{H} = \left(\frac{\partial \hat{H}}{\partial T}\right)_p dT + \left(\frac{\partial \hat{H}}{\partial p}\right)_T dp \qquad (4.6)$$

By definition $\left(\frac{\partial \hat{H}}{\partial T}\right)_p$ is the heat capacity at constant pressure C_p, and for all

practical purposes $\left(\frac{\partial \hat{H}}{\partial p}\right)_T$ is so small at modest pressures that the second term

on the right-hand side of Eq. (4.6) can be neglected. Changes in enthalpy can then be calculated by integration of Eq. (4.6) as follows:

$$\hat{H}_2 - \hat{H}_1 = \int_{T_1}^{T_2} C_p \, dT \qquad (4.7)$$

As with internal energy, enthalpy has no absolute value; only changes in enthalpy can be calculated. Most often you will use a reference set of conditions in computing enthalpy changes. For example, the reference conditions used in the Steam Tables are liquid water at 32°F and its vapor pressure. This does not mean that the enthalpy is actually zero under these conditions but merely that the enthalpy has arbitrarily been assigned a value of zero at these conditions. In computing enthalpy changes, the reference conditions cancel out as can be seen from the following:

initial state of system   *final state of system*
enthalpy $= \hat{H}_1 - \hat{H}_{ref}$ enthalpy $= \hat{H}_2 - \hat{H}_{ref}$
   Net enthalpy change $= (\hat{H}_2 - \hat{H}_{ref}) - (\hat{H}_1 - \hat{H}_{ref}) = \hat{H}_2 - \hat{H}_1$

(g) *Point, or State, Functions.* The variables enthalpy and internal energy are called "point functions," or "state variables," which means that in their differential form they are exact differentials.[2] Another way to explain this is shown in Fig. 4.1. In proceeding from state 1 to state 2, the actual process is shown by the wiggly line. However, you may calculate $\Delta \hat{H}$ by method A or B, or any other method, and still obtain the same net enthalpy change as for the wiggly line. The change of enthalpy depends only on the initial

---

[2] To test if a differential dS is exact, where

$$dS = R \, dx + Z \, dy$$

form the partial derivatives $(\partial R/\partial y)_x$ and $(\partial Z/\partial x)_y$, and verify whether

$$\left(\frac{\partial R}{\partial y}\right)_x = \left(\frac{\partial Z}{\partial x}\right)_y$$

If so, dS is exact; if not, dS is not exact. The statement that dS is an exact differential is completely equivalent to saying that S is independent of path. As an example, applying the test to Eq. (4.6) yields

$$\frac{\partial}{\partial p}\left(\frac{\partial \hat{H}}{\partial T}\right)_p \overset{?}{=} \frac{\partial}{\partial T}\left(\frac{\partial \hat{H}}{\partial p}\right)_T$$

or

$$\left(\frac{\partial^2 \hat{H}}{\partial p \, \partial T}\right) = \left(\frac{\partial^2 \hat{H}}{\partial T \, \partial p}\right)$$

as expected.

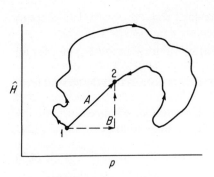

Fig. 4.1. Point function.

and final states of the system. The concept of the point function is the same as that of an airplane passenger who plans to go straight to Chicago from New York but is detoured because of bad weather by way of Cincinnati. His trip costs him the same whatever way he flies, and he eventually arrives at his destination. The gasoline consumption of the plane may vary considerably, and in analogous fashion heat (Q) or work (W), the two "path" functions with which we deal, may vary depending upon the specific path chosen, while $\Delta\hat{H}$ is the same regardless of path. If the plane were turned back by bad weather and landed at New York, the passenger might be irate, but at least he could get his money back. Thus $\Delta\hat{H} = 0$ if a cyclical process is involved which goes from state 1 to 2 and back to state 1 again, or

$$\oint d\hat{H} = 0$$

All the intensive properties we will work with, such as P, T, $\hat{U}$, p, $\hat{H}$, etc., are point functions and depend only on the state of the substance of interest, so that we can say, for example,

$$\oint dT = 0$$

$$\oint d\hat{U} = 0$$

Always keep in mind that the values for a difference in a point function can be calculated by taking the value in the final state and subtracting the value in the initial state, regardless of the actual path.

One property of ideal gases that should be noted is that their enthalpies and internal energies are functions of temperature only and are not influenced by changes in pressure or volume.

Before formulating the general energy balance, we will first discuss in some detail the calculation of enthalpy changes and provide some typical examples of such calculations. The discussion will be initiated with consideration of the heat capacity C_p.

4.2. Heat capacity

The two heat capacities have been defined as

(a) $$C_p = \left(\frac{\partial \hat{H}}{\partial T}\right)_p$$

(b) $$C_v = \left(\frac{\partial \hat{U}}{\partial T}\right)_{\hat{v}}$$

So that the quantities acquire some physical meaning, you can imagine they represent the amount of energy required to increase the temperature of a substance by 1 degree, energy which might be provided by heat transfer in certain specialized processes. To determine from experiment values of C_p (or C_v), the enthalpy (or internal energy) change must first be calculated from the general energy balance, Eq. (4.26), and then the heat capacity evaluated from Eq. (4.7) [or (4.4)] for small enthalpy changes.

In line with the definition of the calorie or Btu presented in the previous section, we can see that the heat capacity can be expressed in various systems of units and still have the same numerical value; for example, heat capacity may be expressed in

$$\frac{\text{cal}}{(\text{g mole})(^\circ\text{C})} = \frac{\text{kcal}}{(\text{kg mole})(^\circ\text{C})} = \frac{\text{Btu}}{(\text{lb mole})(^\circ\text{F})}$$

$$= \frac{\text{PCU}}{(\text{lb mole})(^\circ\text{C})} = \frac{\text{CHU}}{(\text{lb mole})(\text{C}^\circ)}$$

or it may be in terms of

$$\frac{\text{cal}}{(\text{gram})(^\circ\text{C})} = \frac{\text{Btu}}{(\text{lb})(^\circ\text{F})}$$

The PCU stands for the pound-centigrade heat unit, CHU for the centigrade heat unit. These relations are worth memorizing. Note that each form of the heat capacity consists of the unit of energy divided by the product of the unit of mass times the unit of the temperature *change*.

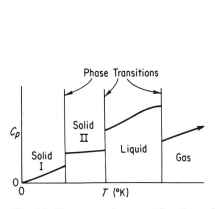

Fig. 4.2. Heat capacity as a function of temperature for a pure substance.

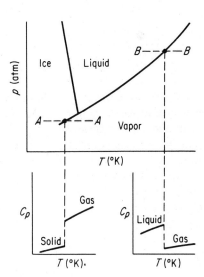

Fig. 4.3. Heat capacity and phase transitions.

The heat capacity over a wide temperature range for a pure substance is represented figuratively in Fig. 4.2, where the heat capacity is plotted as a function of the absolute temperature. We see that at zero degrees absolute the heat capacity is zero according to the third law of thermodynamics. As the temperature rises, the heat capacity also increases until a certain point is reached at which a phase transition takes place. The phase transitions are shown also on a p-T diagram in Fig. 4.3 for H_2O. The phase transition may take place between two solid states, or between a solid and a liquid state, or between a solid and a gaseous state, or between a liquid and a gaseous state. Figure 4.2 shows first a transition between solid state I and solid state II, then the transition between solid state II and the liquid state, and finally the transition between the liquid and the gaseous state. Note that the heat capacity is a continuous function *only* in the region between the phase transitions; consequently it is not possible to have a heat capacity equation for a substance which will go from absolute zero up to any desired temperature. What the engineer does is to determine experimentally the heat capacity equation between the temperatures at which the phase transitions occur, then stop and determine a new heat capacity equation for the next range of temperatures between the succeeding phase transitions.

For an actual substance, the heat capacity is not constant with temperature, although at times we may assume that it is constant in order to get approximate results. For the ideal gas, of course, the heat capacity at con-

TABLE 4.1 HEAT CAPACITIES OF IDEAL GASES

Type molecule	Approximate heat capacity (C_p)	
	High temperature	Room temperature
Monoatomic	$\frac{3}{2}R$	$\frac{3}{2}R$
Polyatomic, linear	$(3n - \frac{5}{2})R$	$\frac{5}{2}R$
Polyatomic, nonlinear	$(3n - 3)R$	$3R$

n = number of atoms per molecule

stant pressure is constant even though the temperature varies (see Table 4.1). For typical real gases, see Fig. 4.4; the heat capacities shown are for pure components. For ideal mixtures, the heat capacities of the individual components may be computed separately and each component handled as if it were alone (see Sec. 4.8 for additional details).

Most of the equations for the heat capacities of solids, liquids, and gases are empirical, and we usually express the heat capacity at constant pressure C_p as a function of temperature in a power series, with constants a, b, c, etc.; for example,

$$C_p = a + bT$$

or

$$C_p = a + bT + cT^2$$

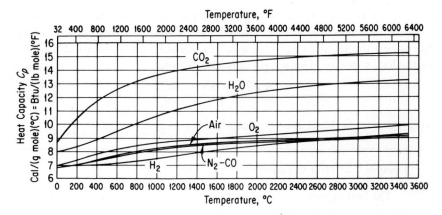

Fig. 4.4. Heat capacity curves for the combustion gases.

where the temperature may be expressed in degrees Centigrade, degrees Fahrenheit, degrees Rankine, or degrees Kelvin. If C_p is expressed in the form of

$$C_p = a + bT + cT^{-1/2}$$
$$C_p = a + bT - cT^{-2}$$

or a form such that we are dividing by T, then it is necessary to use degrees Kelvin or degrees Rankine in the heat capacity equations, because if degrees Centigrade or Fahrenheit were to be used, we might be dividing at some point in the temperature range by zero. Since these heat capacity equations are valid only over moderate temperature ranges, it is possible to have equations of different types represent with almost equal accuracy the experimental heat capacity data. The task of fitting heat capacity equations to heat capacity data is greatly simplified these days by the use of digital computers, which can determine the constants of best fit by means of a standard prepared program and at the same time find how precise the predicted heat capacities are. Heat capacity data can be found in the Appendix. The change of C_p with pressure at high pressures is beyond the scope of our work here. Details can be found in several of the references listed at the end of the chapter and in Comings.[3]

Specific heat is a term similar to "specific gravity" in that it is a ratio of the heat capacity of one substance to the heat capacity of a reference substance.[4] The common reference substance for solids and liquids is water, which is assigned the heat capacity of 1.0 at about 17°C. Since the heat

[3] E. W. Comings, *High Pressure Technology*, McGraw-Hill Book Company, New York, 1956.

[4] In some fields of engineering and science, specific heat means heat capacity based on a pound or gram.

capacity of water is approximately unity in the cgs and American engineering systems, the numerical values of specific heats and heat capacities are about the same although their units are not. For example, the net units of the ratio of the heat capacity of substance A to that of water are

$$\frac{C_{p_A}}{C_{p_{H_2O}}} = \frac{\text{Btu}/(\text{lb}_A)(°\text{F})}{\text{Btu}/(\text{lb}_{H_2O})(°\text{F})} = \frac{\text{lb}_{H_2O}}{\text{lb}_A}$$

although specific heats are never expressed as such units.

Example 4.2   Heat Capacity Equation

The heat capacity equation for CO_2 gas is

$$C_p = 6.393 + 10.100T \times 10^{-3} - 3.405T^2 \times 10^{-6}$$

with C_p expressed in cal/(g mole)(°K) and T in °K. Convert this equation into a form so that the heat capacity will be expressed over the entire temperature range in:

(a) Cal/(g mole)(°C) with T in °C
(b) Btu/(lb mole)(°F) with T in °F
(c) Cal/(g mole)(°K) with T in °F

Solution:
Changing a heat capacity equation from one set of units to another is merely a problem in the conversion of units. The heat capacity equation with t expressed in °C is

(a)

$$C_p \frac{\text{cal}}{(\text{g mole})(°\text{C})} = 6.393 \frac{\text{cal}}{(\text{g mole})(°\text{K})} \left| \frac{1°\text{K}}{1°\text{C}} \right.$$

$$+ 10.1000 \times 10^{-3} \frac{\text{cal}}{(\text{g mole})(°\text{K}^2)} \left| \frac{1°\text{K}}{1°\text{C}} \right| (t + 273)°\text{K}$$

$$-3.405 \times 10^{-6} \frac{\text{cal}}{(\text{g mole})(°\text{K}^3)} \left| \frac{1°\text{K}}{1°\text{C}} \right| (t + 273)^2 °\text{K}^2$$

To avoid confusion in the conversion recall that some of the °K's represent absolute temperature measurement and some represent Δ°K as explained in Chap. 1. For example, the temperature in the denominator of the third term, °K^3, is really $(°\text{K})^2(\Delta°\text{K})$, and the ratio 1°K/1°C is really 1 Δ°K/1 Δ°C. Thus we do not mean to imply in the above conversion that the temperature in °C is equal to the temperature in °K but only that the size of the temperature unit in °C is equal to that in °K.

$$C_p \frac{\text{cal}}{(\text{g more})(°\text{C})} = 6.393 + 10.100 \times 10^{-3}t + 2.757 - 3.405 \times 10^{-6}t^2$$

$$- 1.860 \times 10^{-3}t - 0.254$$

$$= 8.896 + 8.240 \times 10^{-3}t - 3.405 \times 10^{-6}t^2$$

where t is in °C.

(b)

$$C_p \frac{\text{Btu}}{\text{(lb mole)(°F)}} = 6.393 \frac{\text{cal}}{\text{(g mole)(°K)}} \left| \frac{454 \text{ g mole}}{\text{lb mole}} \right| \frac{\text{Btu}}{252 \text{ cal}} \left| \frac{1°\text{K}}{1.8°\text{F}} \right.$$

$$+ \; 10.100 \times 10^{-3} \frac{\text{cal}}{\text{(g mole)(°K}^2)} \left| \frac{454 \text{ g mole}}{\text{lb mole}} \right| \frac{\text{Btu}}{252 \text{ cal}} \left| \frac{1°\text{K}}{1.8°\text{F}} \right| \left[273 + \frac{t-32}{1.8} \right]°\text{K}$$

$$- \; 3.405 \times 10^{-6} \frac{\text{cal}}{\text{(g mole°)(K}^3)} \left| \frac{454 \text{ g mole}}{\text{lb mole}} \right| \frac{\text{Btu}}{252 \text{ cal}} \left| \frac{1°\text{K}}{1.8°\text{F}} \right| \left[273 + \frac{t-32}{1.8} \right]^2 °\text{K}^2$$

$$= 6.393 + 10.100 \times 10^{-3}[273 + (t-32)/1.8]$$
$$- \; 3.405 \times 10^{-6}[273 + (t-32)/1.8]^2$$

$$= 6.393 + 2.575 + 5.61 \times 10^{-3}t - 0.222$$
$$- \; 0.964 \times 10^{-3}t - 1.05 \times 10^{-6}t^2$$

$$= 8.746 + 4.646 \times 10^{-3}t - 1.05 \times 10^{-6}t^2$$

where t is in °F.

Note:

$$t(\text{in °F}) = 32 + t(\text{in °C})\left(\frac{1.8 \, \Delta°\text{F}}{1 \, \Delta°\text{C}} \right)$$

so that

$$t(\text{in °C}) = \frac{t(\text{in °F}) - 32}{1.8}$$

and

$$T(\text{in °K}) = 273 + t(\text{in °C})\left(\frac{1 \, \Delta°\text{K}}{1 \, \Delta°\text{C}} \right)$$

$$= 273 + \frac{t(\text{in °F}) - 32}{1.8}$$

If the equation for part (a) were available, the solution to part (b) would be simplified by employing it. For example, we use

$$C_p \frac{\text{cal}}{\text{(g mole)(°C)}} = 8.896 + 8.240 \times 10^{-3}t - 3.405 \times 10^{-6}t^2 \qquad (t \text{ in °C})$$

and convert it into

$$C_p \frac{\text{Btu}}{\text{(lb mole)(°F)}} = \frac{8.896 \text{ cal}}{\text{(g mole)(°C)}} \left| \frac{454 \text{ g mole}}{\text{lb mole}} \right| \frac{\text{Btu}}{252 \text{ cal}} \left| \frac{1°\text{C}}{1.8°\text{F}} \right.$$

$$+ \; 8.240 \times 10^{-3} \frac{\text{cal}}{\text{(g mole)(°C}^2)} \left| \frac{454 \text{ g mole}}{\text{lb mole}} \right| \frac{\text{Btu}}{252 \text{ cal}} \left| \frac{1°\text{C}}{1.8°\text{F}} \right| [(t-32)/1.8]°\text{C}$$

$$- \; 3.405 \times 10^{-6} \frac{\text{cal}}{\text{(g mole)(°C}^3)} \left| \frac{454 \text{ g mole}}{\text{lb mole}} \right| \frac{\text{Btu}}{252 \text{ cal}} \left| \frac{1°\text{C}}{1.8°\text{F}} \right| [(t-32)/1.8]^2 °\text{C}^2$$

$$= 8.746 + 4.646 \times 10^{-3}t - 1.05 \times 10^{-6}t^2$$

as before with t in °F.

(c) Since

$$\frac{\text{Btu}}{(\text{lb mole})(^\circ\text{F})} = \frac{\text{cal}}{(\text{g mole})(^\circ\text{K})}$$

the equation developed in part (b) gives the heat capacity in the desired units.

Example 4.3   Heat Capacity of the Ideal Gas

Show that $C_p = C_v + \hat{R}$ for the ideal gas.

Solution:

The heat capacity at constant volume is defined as

$$C_v = \left(\frac{\partial \hat{U}}{\partial T}\right)_{\hat{V}} \tag{a}$$

For any gas,

$$C_p = \left(\frac{\partial \hat{H}}{\partial T}\right)_p = \left[\frac{\partial \hat{U} + \partial(p\hat{V})}{\partial T}\right]_p = \left[\frac{\partial \hat{U} + p\,\partial \hat{V}}{\partial T}\right]_p \tag{b}$$

$$= \left(\frac{\partial \hat{U}}{\partial T}\right)_p + p\left(\frac{\partial \hat{V}}{\partial T}\right)_p$$

For the *ideal gas*, since $\hat{U}$ is a function of temperature only:

$$\left(\frac{\partial \hat{U}}{\partial T}\right)_p = \left(\frac{\partial \hat{U}}{\partial T}\right)_{\hat{V}} = C_v \tag{c}$$

and from $p\hat{V} = \hat{R}T$ we can calculate

$$\left(\frac{\partial \hat{V}}{\partial T}\right)_p = \frac{\hat{R}}{p} \tag{d}$$

so that

$$C_p = C_v + \hat{R}$$

We now mention a few ways by which to *estimate* heat capacities of solids, liquids, and gases. For the most accurate results you should employ actual experimental heat capacity data or equations in your calculations. However, if experimental data are not available, there are a number of approximate rules you may use which give rough estimates of values for the heat capacities of solids and liquids. The first two methods listed below are referred to primarily for their historical interest.

(a) *Law of Dulong and Petit* (1819) *for solids.* The heat capacity per gram atom, C_v, is equal to 6.2 ± 0.4 calories/$(^\circ\text{C})$(g atom). This rule does not hold well for elements below potassium (atomic weight 39) where C_v is lower than 6.2.

(b) *Kopp's rule* (1864) *for solids and liquids.* Kopp extended the law of Dulong and Petit to compounds. This rule, which is valid only around room temperature, is expressed as follows: The sum of the heat capacities of the individual elements is approximately equal to the heat capacity of a solid compound. For elements below potassium, numbers have been assigned from experimental data for the heat capacity for each element as shown in Table 4.2. For liquids Kopp's rule can be applied with a modified series of values for the various elements, as shown in Table 4.2.

TABLE 4.2 VALUES FOR MODIFIED KOPP'S RULE

Atomic Heat Capacity at 20°C in cal/(g atom)(°C)

Element	Solids	Liquids
C	1.8	2.8
H	2.3	4.3
B	2.7	4.7
Si	3.8	5.8
O	4.0	6.0
F	5.0	7.0
P or S	5.4	7.4
All others	6.2	8.0

Example 4.4   Use of Kopp's Rule

Determine the heat capacity at room temperature of $Na_2SO_4 \cdot 10 H_2O$.

Basis: 1 g mole $Na_2SO_4 \cdot 10 H_2O$

$$\begin{aligned}
\text{Na} \quad 2 \times 6.2 &= \quad 12.4 \text{ cal/(g atom)(°C)} \\
\text{S} \quad 1 \times 5.4 &= \quad 5.4 \\
\text{O} \quad 14 \times 4.0 &= \quad 56.0 \\
\text{H} \quad 20 \times 2.3 &= \quad \underline{46.0} \\
& \quad 119.8 \text{ cal/(g mole)(°C)}
\end{aligned}$$

The experimental value is about 141 cal/(g mole) (°C)

(c) *Aqueous solutions.* For the special but very important case of aqueous solutions, a rough rule in the absence of experimental data is to use the heat capacity of the water only. For example, a 21.6% solution of NaCl is assumed to have a heat capacity of 0.784 cal/(g)(°C); the experimental value at 25°C is 0.806 cal/(g)(°C).

(d) *Hydrocarbons.* An equation for the heat capacity of liquid hydrocarbons and petroleum products recommended by Fallon and Watson[5] is

[5] J. F. Fallon and K. M. Watson, *Natl. Petrol. News, Tech. Sec.*, June 7, 1944.

$$C_p = [(0.355 + 0.128 \times 10^{-2}\,°\text{API}) + (0.503 + 0.117 \times 10^{-2}\,°\text{API})$$
$$\times 10^{-3}t][0.05K + 0.41]$$

where $°\text{API} = \dfrac{141.5}{\text{sp gr }(60°\text{F}/60°\text{F})} - 131.5$ and is a measure of specific gravity.

$t = °\text{F}$

$K =$ The Universal Oil Products characterization factor which has been related to six easily applied laboratory tests. This factor is not a fundamental characteristic but is easy to determine experimentally. Values of K range from 10.0 to 13.0 and are discussed in Appendix K.

$C_p = \text{Btu/(lb)(°F)}$

(e) *Gases.* In the absence of experimental data, values for the heat capacity of a gas can be approximated by making use of generalized correlations based on the reduced properties; see footnotes 6 and 7 below. We do not have the space to discuss these techniques.

Additional methods of estimating solid and liquid heat capacities may be found in Reid and Sherwood,[7] who compare various techniques we do not have the space to discuss, and make recommendations as to their use.

4.3. Calculation of enthalpy changes

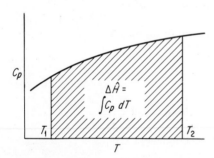

Fig. 4.5. Calculation of enthalpy change.

Now that we have examined the sources of heat capacity values, we can turn to the details of the calculation of enthalpy changes. If we omit for the moment consideration of phase changes and examine solely the problem of how to calculate enthalpy changes from heat capacity data, we can see that in general if we merely use Eq. (4.7), $\Delta\hat{H}$ is the area under the curve in Fig. 4.5.

$$\int_{\hat{H}_1}^{\hat{H}_2} d\hat{H} = \Delta\hat{H} = \int_{T_1}^{T_2} C_p\, dT \qquad (4.7)$$

(The technique of graphical integration is illustrated in Example 6.6.) If our heat capacity equation is expressed in the form $C_p = a + bT + cT^2$, then

[6] A. L. Lydersen, R. A. Greenkorn, and O. A. Hougen, "Thermodynamic Properties of Pure Fluids," *Univ. Wis. Eng. Expt. Sta. Rept.* No. 4, 1955.

[7] R. C. Reid and T. K. Sherwood, *The Properties of Gases and Liquids*, McGraw-Hill Book Company, New York, 1958.

$$\Delta \hat{H} = \int_{T_1}^{T_2} (a + bT + cT^2)\, dT = a(T_2 - T_1) + \frac{b}{2}(T_2^2 - T_1^2)$$

$$+ \frac{c}{3}(T_2^3 - T_1^3) \tag{4.8}$$

If a different form of the heat capacity equation is available, the integration can still be handled readily.

It is also possible to define a mean heat capacity, which is a quick and sometimes convenient way of calculating enthalpy changes. The *mean heat capacity*, C_{p_m}, is defined as the enthalpy change divided by the temperature difference for this change, or

$$C_{p_m} = \frac{\hat{H}_2 - \hat{H}_1}{t_2 - t_1} \tag{4.9}$$

Then it is possible to compute an enthalpy change, if C_{p_m} is available, as

$$\Delta \hat{H} = C_{p_m} \Delta t = C_{p_m}(t_2 - t_1) \tag{4.10}$$

where C_{p_m} is between t_1 and t_2.

If the heat capacity equation is a power series, $C_p = a + bt + ct^2$, then C_{p_m} is

$$C_{p_m} = \frac{\int_{t_1}^{t_2} C_p\, dt}{\int_{t_1}^{t_2} dt} = \frac{\int_{t_1}^{t_2} (a + bt + ct^2)\, dt}{t_2 - t_1}$$

$$= \frac{a(t_2 - t_1) + \frac{b}{2}(t_2^2 - t_1^2) + \frac{c}{3}(t_2^3 - t_1^3)}{t_2 - t_1} \tag{4.11}$$

Suppose we choose $t_1 = 0°$ for a reference state for our calculations. Equation (4.11) reduces to

$$C_{p_m} = a + \frac{b}{2}t_2 + \frac{c}{3}t_2^2 \tag{4.12}$$

Thus by choosing 0°F or 0°C as the reference temperature for C_{p_m}, you can simplify the expression for C_{p_m}. Table 4.3 lists mean heat capacities for combustion gases based on the same reference point (0°C) for two different temperature scales. Figure 4.6 compares C_p and C_{p_m}. As C_p gets bigger, C_{p_m} is always less since earlier smaller values are amalgamated in the C_{p_m} value.

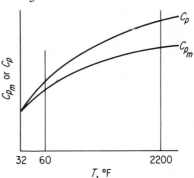

Fig. 4.6. Mean heat capacity.

TABLE 4.3a MEAN HEAT CAPACITIES OF COMBUSTION GASES
[cal/(g mole)(°C)]
Reference Temperature: 0°C; Pressure: 1 atm

°C	N_2	O_2	Air	H_2	CO	CO_2	H_2O
0	6.959	6.989	6.946	6.838	6.960	8.595	8.001
18	6.960	6.998	6.949	6.858	6.961	8.706	8.009
25	6.960	7.002	6.949	6.864	6.962	8.716	8.012
100	6.965	7.057	6.965	6.926	6.973	9.122	8.061
200	6.985	7.154	7.001	6.955	7.050	9.590	8.150
300	7.023	7.265	7.054	6.967	7.057	10.003	8.256
400	7.075	7.380	7.118	6.983	7.120	10.360	8.377
500	7.138	7.489	7.190	6.998	7.196	10.680	8.507
600	7.207	7.591	7.266	7.015	7.273	10.965	8.644
700	7.277	7.684	7.340	7.036	7.351	11.221	8.785
800	7.350	7.768	7.414	7.062	7.428	11.451	8.928
900	7.420	7.845	7.485	7.093	7.501	11.68	9.070
1000	7.482	7.916	7.549	7.128	7.570	11.85	9.210
1100	7.551	7.980	7.616	7.165	7.635	12.02	9.348
1200	7.510	8.039	7.674	7.205	7.688	12.17	9.482
1300	7.665	8.094	7.729	7.227	7.752	12.32	9.613
1400	7.718	8.146	7.781	7.260	7.805	12.44	9.740
1500	7.769	8.192	7.830	7.296	7.855	12.56	9.86

Source: Page 30 of Reference 12 in Table 4.5.

TABLE 4.3b MEAN HEAT CAPACITIES OF COMBUSTION GASES
[Btu/(lb mole)(°F)]
Reference Temperature: 32°F; Pressure: 1 atm

°F	N_2	O_2	Air	H_2	CO	CO_2	H_2O
32	6.959	6.989	6.946	6.838	6.960	8.595	8.001
60	6.960	6.996	6.948	6.855	6.961	8.682	8.008
77	6.960	7.002	6.949	6.864	6.962	8.715	8.012
100	6.961	7.010	6.952	6.876	6.964	8.793	8.019
200	6.964	7.052	6.963	6.921	6.972	9.091	8.055
300	6.970	7.102	6.978	6.936	6.987	9.362	8.101
400	6.984	7.159	7.001	6.942	7.007	9.612	8.154
500	7.002	7.220	7.028	6.961	7.033	9.844	8.210
600	7.026	7.283	7.060	6.964	7.065	10.060	8.274
700	7.055	7.347	7.096	6.978	7.101	10.262	8.341
800	7.087	7.409	7.134	6.981	7.140	10.450	8.411
900	7.122	7.470	7.174	6.984	7.182	10.626	8.484
1000	7.158	7.529	7.214	6.989	7.224	10.792	8.558
1100	7.197	7.584	7.256	6.993	7.268	10.948	8.634
1200	7.236	7.637	7.298	7.004	7.312	11.094	8.712
1300	7.277	7.688	7.341	7.013	7.355	11.232	8.790
1400	7.317	7.736	7.382	7.032	7.398	11.362	8.870
1500	7.356	7.781	7.422	7.054	7.439	11.484	8.950
1600	7.395	7.824	7.461	7.061	7.480	11.60	9.029
1700	7.433	7.865	7.500	7.073	7.519	11.71	9.107
1800	7.471	7.904	7.537	7.081	7.558	11.81	9.185
1900	7.507	7.941	7.573	7.093	7.595	11.91	9.263
2000	7.542	7.976	7.608	7.114	7.631	12.01	9.339

Source: Page 31 of Reference 12 in Table 4.5.

Example 4.5 Calculation of $\Delta\hat{H}$ Using Mean Heat Capacity

Calculate the enthalpy change for 1 lb mole of nitrogen dioxide (NO_2) which is heated at constant pressure (1 atm) from 60°F to 2200°F.

Solution:
Data from Kobe (Table 4.5, 12); reference conditions, 32°F:

$$C_{p_m} = 11.82 \text{ Btu/(lb mole)(°F)} \qquad \text{at } 2200°F$$

$$C_{p_m} = 8.73 \text{ Btu/(lb mole)(°F)} \qquad \text{at } 60°F$$

Basis: 1 lb mole of NO_2

$$\Delta\hat{H}_{2200-60} = \Delta\hat{H}_{2200} - \Delta\hat{H}_{60}$$

$$= \frac{11.82 \text{ Btu}}{\text{(lb mole)(°F)}} \left| (2200 - 32°F) - \frac{8.73 \text{ Btu}}{\text{(lb mole)(°F)}} \right| (60 - 32°F)$$

$$= 25,580 \text{ Btu/lb mole}$$

As shown in the example, if the reference conditions are not zero (0°K, 0°F etc.), the $\Delta\hat{H}_{2200-60}$ is

$$C_{p_{m_{2200}}}(t_{2200} - t_{\text{ref}}) - C_{p_{m_{60}}}(t_{60} - t_{\text{ref}})$$

and not $C_{p_{m_{2200}}}t_{2200} - C_{p_{m_{60}}}t_{60}$.

Example 4.6 Determination of Mean Heat Capacity

If the heat capacity equation in cal/(g mole)(°K) for SiC is expressed as

$$C_p = 8.89 + 0.00291T - \frac{28,400}{T^2}$$

for the temperature range 273° to 1600°K (within 2% accuracy), what is C_{p_m} at 1200°C in Btu/(lb mole) (°F)?

Solution:

Basis: 1 lb mole SiC

In order to calculate C_{p_m} it is necessary to select a reference temperature; 273°K will be used here. The question is: What is the mean heat capacity for the range 273°K to 1473°K with the answer expressed in Btu/(lb mole)(°F)?

$$C_{p_m} = \frac{\int_{273}^{1473} C_p \, dT}{1473 - 273} = \frac{\int_{273}^{1473} (8.89 + 0.00291T - 28,400/T^2) dT}{1200}$$

$$= \frac{8.89[1473 - 273]}{1200} + \frac{0.00291[(1473)^2 - (273)^2]}{2(1200)} + \frac{28,400\left[\frac{1}{1473} - \frac{1}{273}\right]}{1200}$$

$$= \frac{10,670 + 3050 - 84.6}{1200}$$

$$= 11.36 \text{ cal/(g mole)(°K)}$$

$$= 11.36 \text{ Btu/(lb mole)(°F)}$$

Example 4.7   Calculation of $\Delta \hat{H}$ Using Heat Capacity Equations

Coal is burned to a gas of the following composition (on a dry basis):

CO_2	9.2
CO	1.5
O_2	7.3
N_2	82.0
	100.0

What is the enthalpy difference for this gas between the bottom and the top of the stack if the temperature at the bottom of the stack is 550°F and the temperature at the top is 200°F? Ignore the water vapor in the gas, and neglect any energy effects resulting from the mixing of the gaseous components.

Solution:

Heat capacity equations from Kobe (Table 4.5, 12) (t in °F; C_p = Btu/(lb mole) (°F)) are

N_2: $C_p = 6.895 + 0.7624 \times 10^{-3}t - 0.7009 \times 10^{-7}t^2$

O_2: $C_p = 7.104 + 0.7851 \times 10^{-3}t - 0.5528 \times 10^{-7}t^2$

CO_2: $C_p = 8.448 + 5.757 \times 10^{-3}t - 21.59 \times 10^{-7}t^2 + 3.059 \times 10^{-10}t^3$

CO: $C_p = 6.865 + 0.8024 \times 10^{-3}t - 0.7367 \times 10^{-7}t^2$

Basis: 1.00 lb mole gas

By multiplying these equations by the respective mole fraction of each component, and then adding them together, you can save time in the integration.

N_2: $0.82(6.895 + 0.7624 \times 10^{-3}t - 0.7009 \times 10^{-7}t^2)$

O_2: $0.073(7.104 + 0.7851 \times 10^{-3}t - 0.5528 \times 10^{-7}t^2)$

CO_2: $0.092(8.448 + 5.757 \times 10^{-3}t - 21.59 \times 10^{-7}t^2 + 3.059 \times 10^{-10}t^3)$

CO: $0.015(6.865 + 0.8024 \times 10^{-3}t - 0.7367 \times 10^{-7}t^2)$

$C_{p_{net}} = 7.049 + 1.2243 \times 10^{-3}t - 2.6164 \times 10^{-7}t^2 + 0.2815 \times 10^{-10}t^3$

$$\Delta H = \int_{550}^{200} C_p \, dt = \int_{550}^{200} (7.049 + 1.2243 \times 10^{-3}t - 2.6164 \times 10^{-7}t^2 + 0.2815 \times 10^{-10}t^3)dt$$

$$= 7.049[(200) - (550)] + \frac{1.2243 \times 10^{-3}}{2} [(200)^2 - (550)^2]$$

$$- \frac{2.6164 \times 10^{-7}}{3} [(200)^3 - (550)^3]$$

$$+ \frac{0.2815 \times 10^{-10}}{4} [(200)^4 - (550)^4]$$

$$= -2465 - 160.6 + 13.8 - 0.633$$

$$= -2612 \text{ Btu/lb mole gas}$$

We now discuss briefly the use of enthalpy tables and charts. The simplest and quickest method of computing enthalpy changes is to use tabulated enthalpy data available in the literature or in reference books. Thus, rather than using integrated heat capacity equations or mean heat capacity data, you should first look to see if the actual enthalpy data are listed in tables as a function of temperature. Typical enthalpy data for a number of gases of interest in the chemical and petroleum industries are listed in Table 4.4. Some sources of enthalpy data are listed in Table 4.5. The most common source of enthalpy data for water is the Steam Tables. The reference by Kobe and Associates (Table 4.5, 12) lists heat capacity equations, enthalpy values, and many other thermodynamic functions for over one hundred compounds of commercial importance. Some of these data can be found in the Appendix. Remembering that enthalpy values are all relative to some

TABLE 4.4 ENTHALPIES OF COMBUSTION GASES
(Btu/lb mole)

Pressure: 1 atm

°R	N_2	O_2	Air	H_2	CO	CO_2	H_2O
492	0.0	0.0	0.0	0.0	0.0	0.0	0.0
500	55.67	55.93	55.57	57.74	55.68	68.95	64.02
520	194.9	195.9	194.6	191.9	194.9	243.1	224.2
537	313.2	315.1	312.7	308.9	313.3	392.2	360.5
600	751.9	758.8	751.2	744.4	752.4	963.0	867.5
700	1450.0	1471.0	1450.0	1433.0	1451.0	1914.0	1679.0
800	2150.0	2194.0	2153.0	2122.0	2154.0	2915.0	2501.0
900	2852.0	2931.0	2861.0	2825.0	2863.0	3961.0	3336.0
1000	3565.0	3680.0	3579.0	3511.0	3580.0	5046.0	4184.0
1100	4285.0	4443.0	4306.0	4210.0	4304.0	6167.0	5047.0
1200	5005.0	5219.0	5035.0	4917.0	5038.0	7320.0	5925.0
1300	5741.0	6007.0	5780.0	5630.0	5783.0	8502.0	6819.0
1400	6495.0	6804.0	6540.0	6369.0	6536.0	9710.0	7730.0
1500	7231.0	6712.0	7289.0	7069.0	7299.0	10942.0	8657.0
1600	8004.0	8427.0	8068.0	7789.0	8072.0	12200.0	9602.0
1700	8774.0	9251.0	8847.0	8499.0	8853.0	13470.0	10562.0
1800	9539.0	10081.0	9623.0	9219.0	9643.0	14760.0	11540.0
1900	10335.0	10918.0	10425.0	9942.0	10440.0	16070.0	12530.0
2000	11127.0	11760.0	11224.0	10689.0	11243.0	17390.0	13550.0

Source: Page 30 of Reference 12 in Table 4.5.

reference state, you can make enthalpy difference calculations merely by subtracting the final enthalpy from the initial enthalpy for any two sets of conditions. Of course, if the enthalpy data are not available, you will have to rely on calculations involving heat capacities or mean heat capacities.

If a pure material exists in solid, liquid, and gaseous form, a chart or diagram can be prepared showing its properties if sufficient reliable experi-

mental information is available. Examples of such charts are shown in
Appendix J; sources of such charts are listed in Table 4.6. Many forms
of charts are available. Some types that may occur to you would have as
coordinate axes

TABLE 4.5 SOURCES OF ENTHALPY DATA

1. American Petroleum Institute, Research Project 44, "Selected Values of Physical and
   Thermodynamic Properties of Hydrocarbons and Related Compounds," 1953.
2. Bichowsky, F. R., and F. D. Rossini, *Thermochemistry of Chemical Substances*,
   Reinhold Publishing Corp., New York, 1936.
3. Chermin, H. A. G., "Hydrocarbon Processing & Petroleum Refining," Parts 26–32,
   1961. (Continuation of Kobe compendium for gases; see item 12 below.)
4. Dow Chemical Co., "JANAF Thermodynamic Tables," issued periodically since 1961,
   Midland, Mich. (Metals and inorganics.)
5. Egloff, G., *Physical Constants of Hydrocarbons*, 5 vols., Reinhold Publishing Corp.,
   New York, 1939–1953.
6. Hilsenrath, J., and others, "Tables of Thermal Properties of Gases," *National Bureau
   of Standards (U.S.), Circ.* 564, 1955. (Additional single sheets issued as NBS-NACA
   sponsored tables.)
7. International Atomic Energy Agency, "Thermodynamics of Nuclear Materials,"
   Vienna, Austria, 1962.
8. *International Critical Tables*, 7 vols. and index, McGraw-Hill Book Company, New
   York, 1926–1933. (Now rather out of date.)
9. Keenan, J. H., and F. G. Keyes, *Thermodynamic Properties of Steam*, John Wiley
   & Sons, Inc., New York, 1936.
10. Keenan, J. H., and J. Kay, *Gas Tables*, John Wiley & Sons, Inc., New York, 1948.
11. Kelley, K. K., various *U.S. Bureau of Mines Bulletins* on the Thermodynamic Prop-
    erties of Substances.
12. Kobe, K. A., and Associates, "Thermochemistry of Petrochemicals," Reprint no. 44
    from the *Petroleum Refiner* (available from the Bureau of Engineering Research,
    University of Texas, Austin, 1958). A collection of a series of 24 articles covering
    105 different substances that appeared in the *Petroleum Refiner*.
13. Meadows, E. L., "Estimating Physical Properties," *Chem. Eng. Progr.*, vol. 61, p. 93
    (1965). (A. I. Ch. E. Machine Computation Committee report on the preparation of
    thermodynamic tables on tapes.)
14. Perry, J. H., *Chemical Engineers' Handbook*, 4th ed., McGraw-Hill Book Company,
    New York, 1964.
15. Rossini, F. K., and others, "Tables of Selected Values of Chemical Thermodynamic
    Properties," *National Bureau of Standards (U.S.), Circ.* 500, 1952. (Lithographed
    sheets are being issued periodically.)
16. Sage, B. H., and W. N. Lacey, "Thermodynamic Properties of the Lighter Paraffin
    Hydrocarbons and Nitrogen," American Petroleum Institute, New York, 1950.
17. Sage, B. H., and W. N. Lacey, "Some Properties of the Lighter Hydrocarbons,
    Hydrogen Sulfide, and Carbon Dioxide," American Petroleum Institute, New York,
    1955.
18. Stull, D. R., and G. C. Sinke, "Thermodynamic Properties of the Elements," Dow
    Chemical Co., Midland, Mich., 1956.
19. Zeise, H., *Thermodynamik*, Band III/I Taballen, S. Hirzel Verlag, Leipzig, 1954.
    (Tables of heat capacities, enthalpies, entropies, free energies, and equilibrium con-
    stants.)

TABLE 4.6 THERMODYNAMIC CHARTS SHOWING ENTHALPY DATA

Compound	Reference
Acetone	2
Acetylene	1
Air	Williams, V. C., *Am. Inst. Chem. Engrs. Trans.*, vol. 39, p. 93 (1943); *A. I. Ch. E. J.*, vol. 1, p. 302 (1955).
Benzene	1
1, 3-Butadiene	Meyers, C. H., *J. Res. Natl. Bur. Std., A.*, vol. 39, p. 507 (1947).
i-Butane	1, 3
n-Butane	1, 3
n-Butanol	Schemilt, L. W., in *Proc. Conf. Thermodyn. Transport Properties Fluids, London, 1957*, Inst. Mechanical Engrs. (1958).
Butanol, *tert.*	Maslan, F., *A. I. Ch. E. J.*, vol. 7, p. 172 (1961).
n-Butene	1
Chlorine	Hulme, R. E., and A. B. Tillman, *Chem. Eng.*, Jan. (1949).
Ethane	1, 3
Ethanol	Reid, R. C., and J. M. Smith, *Chem. Eng. Progr.*, vol. 47, p. 415 (1951).
Ethyl ether	2
Ethylene	1, 3
Ethylene oxide	Mock, J. E., and J. M. Smith, *Ind. Eng. Chem.*, vol. 42, p. 2125 (1950).
n-Heptane	Stuart, E. B., et al., *Chem. Eng. Progr.*, vol. 46, p. 311 (1950).
n-Hexane	1
Hydrogen sulfide	West, J. R., *Chem. Eng. Progr.*, vol. 44, p. 287 (1948).
Isopropyl ether	2
Mercury	General Electric Co. Report GET-1879A, 1949.
Methane	1, 3
Methanol	Smith, J. M., *Chem. Eng. Progr.*, vol. 44, p. 52 (1948).
Methyl ethyl ketone	2
Monomethyl hydrazine	Bizjak, F., and D. F. Stai, *A.I.A.A. J.*, vol. 2, p. 954 (1964).
Neon	Cryogenic Data Center, Nat. Bur. Std., Boulder, Colo.
Nitrogen	Lin, G. S., *Chem. Eng. Progr.*, vol. 59, no. 11, p. 69 (1963).
n-Pentane	1, 3
Propane	1, 3
n-Propanol	Schemilt, L. W. (see ref. for butanol).
Propylene	1, 3
Sulfur dioxide	West, J. R., and G. P. Giusti, *J. Phys. Colloid Chem.*, vol. 54, p. 601 (1950).
Combustion gases	Hottel, H. C., G. C. Williams, and C. N. Satterfield, *Thermodynamic Charts for Combustion Processes*, (I) Text, (II) Charts; John Wiley & Sons, Inc., New York, 1949.
Hydrocarbons	Edmister, W. C., *Applied Hydrocarbon Thermodynamics*, Gulf Publishing Co., Houston, Texas, 1961.

1. Canjar, L. N., et al., Thermodynamic Properties of Hydrocarbons, Gulf Publishing Co., Houston, Texas, 1967. (Series of articles which appeared in the magazine *Hydrocarbon Processing* from 1962 to 1965.)
2. Eubank, P. T., and J. M. Smith, *J. Chem. Eng. Data*, vol. 7, p. 75 (1962).
3. Edmister, W. C., *Applied Hydrocarbon Thermodynamics*, Gulf Publishing Co., Houston, Texas, 1961.

$$p \quad \text{vs.} \quad \hat{H}$$
$$p \quad \text{vs.} \quad \hat{V}$$
$$p \quad \text{vs.} \quad T$$
$$\hat{H} \quad \text{vs.} \quad \hat{S}^{8}$$

Since a chart has only two dimensions, the other parameters of interest have to be plotted as lines of constant value across the face of the chart. Recall,

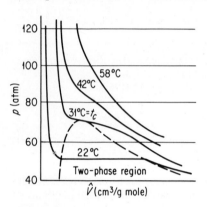

for example, that in the $p\hat{V}$ diagram for CO_2, Fig. 4.7, lines of constant temperature were shown as parameters. The two-phase region is shown only by a dotted line at its boundaries. Any point inside the two-phase region actually consists of liquid of one density in equilibrium with vapor of another density; no CO_2 exists as such at point A.

You can find a discussion of diagrams for pure components and mixtures in Chap. 3, and for further information you are referred to books dealing with physical chemistry or

Fig. 4.7. CO_2 chart: p-V-T relationships.

thermodynamics.

Although diagrams and charts are helpful in that they portray the relations among the phases and give approximate values for the physical properties of a substance, to get more precise data (unless the chart is quite large) usually you will find it best to see if tables are not available which list the physical properties you want.

Enthalpies and other thermodynamic properties can be *estimated* by generalized methods based on the theory of corresponding states.[9, 10, 11]

Example 4.8   Calculation of Enthalpy Change Using Tabulated Enthalpy Values

Recalculate Example 4.5 using data from enthalpy tables.

Solution:

For the same change as in Example 4.5, the data from Kobe (Table 4.5, 12) are

at 2200°F: $\Delta\hat{H} = 25,630$ Btu/lb mole⎫
at 60°F: $\Delta\hat{H} = 244.4$ Btu/lb mole⎭   ref. temp. = 32°F

---

[8] S is *entropy*—this diagram is called a *Mollier* diagram.

[9] Lyderson, Greenkorn, and Hougen, *op. cit.*

[10] Hougen, O. A., K. M. Watson, and R. A. Ragatz, *Chemical Process Principles, Part II*, 2nd ed., John Wiley & Sons, Inc., New York, 1959.

[11] Landis, E. K., M. T. Cannon, and L. N. Canjar, *Hydrocarbon Processing* vol. 44, p. 154 (1965).

Basis: 1 lb mole NO_2

$$\Delta \hat{H} = 25,630 - 244.4 = 25,386 \text{ Btu/lb mole}$$

Example 4.9   Use of the Steam Tables

What is the enthalpy change in Btu when 1 gal of water is heated from 60°F to 1150°F and 240 psig?
Solution:

Basis: 1 lb H_2O at 60°F

From Steam Tables (ref. temp. = 32°F),

$\hat{H} = 28.07 \text{ Btu/lb}$ at 60°F

$\hat{H} = 1,604.5 \text{ Btu/lb}$ at 1150°F and 240 psig (254.7 psia)

$\Delta \hat{H} = (1,604.5 - 28.07) = 1,576.4 \text{ Btu/lb}$

$\Delta H = 1576(8.345) = 13,150 \text{ Btu/gal}$

Note: The enthalpy values which have been used for liquid water as taken from the Steam Tables are for the saturated liquid under its own vapor pressure. Since the enthalpy of liquid water changes negligibly with pressure, no loss of accuracy is encountered for engineering purposes if the initial pressure on the water is not stated.

You may have noted for gases in the illustrated problems that we had to specify two physical properties such as temperature and pressure to definitely fix the *state* of the gas. Since we know from our previous discussion in Chap. 3 that specifying two properties for a pure gas will insure that all the other properties will have definite values, any two properties can be chosen at will. The ones usually selected are the ones easiest to measure (such as temperature and pressure), and then the others (specific volume, density, specific enthalpy, specific internal energy, etc.) are fixed. Since a particular state for a gas can be defined by any two independent properties, a two-dimensional thermodynamic chart can be seen to be a handy way to present combinations of physical properties.

4.4. Enthalpy changes for phase transitions

In making enthalpy calculations, we noted in Fig. 4.2 that the heat capacity data are discontinuous at the points of a phase transition. The name usually given to these phase transitions is *latent heat* changes, latent meaning "hidden" in the sense that the substance (for example, water) can absorb a large amount of heat without any noticeable increase in temperature.

Ice at 0°C can absorb heat amounting to 80 cal/g without undergoing a temperature rise or a pressure change. The enthalpy change from a solid to a liquid is called the *heat of fusion*, and the enthalpy change for the phase transition between solid and liquid water is thus 80 cal/g. The *heat of vaporization* is the enthalpy change for the phase transition between liquid and vapor, and we also have the *heat of sublimation*, which is the enthalpy change for the transition directly from solid to vapor. Dry ice at room temperature and pressure sublimes. The $\Delta \hat{H}$ for the phase change from gas to liquid is called the *heat of condensation*. You can find experimental values of latent heats in the references in Table 4.5, and a brief tabulation is shown in Appendix D. The symbols used for latent heat changes vary, but you usually find one or more of the following employed: $\Delta \hat{H}$, L, λ, Λ.

To calculate the enthalpy change for the vaporization of water using Steam Table data, the liquid or gaseous water should be heated or cooled to the dew point and vaporized at the dew point. Remember that the enthalpies given in the Steam Tables are for water under its vapor pressure at that temperature. *National Bureau of Standards Circular* 500 gives data at 25°C for the heat of vaporization of water:

°C	mm Hg	kcal/g mole	Btu/lb mole
25	23.75	10.514	18,925
25	760.	10.520	18,936

You can see that the effect of pressure is quite small and may be neglected under all ordinary conditions.

In the absence of experimental values for the heats of transition, the following approximate methods will give a rough estimate of the *molar latent heats*. Reid and Sherwood, *The Properties of Gases and Liquids*, give more sophisticated methods.[12]

4.4-1 Heat of Fusion. The heat of fusion for many elements and compounds can be expressed as

$$\frac{\lambda_f}{T_f} = \text{constant} = \begin{cases} 2\text{–}3 & \text{for elements} \\ 5\text{–}7 & \text{for inorganic compounds} \\ 9\text{–}11 & \text{for organic compounds} \end{cases} \qquad (4.13)$$

where λ_f = molal heat of fusion in cal/g mole

T_f = melting point in °K

4.4-2 Heat of Vaporization. (1) *Trouton's rule.* Trouton's rule states that the ratio of the molal heat of vaporization (λ_b) of a substance at its normal boiling point (1 atm) to the absolute temperature (T_b) is a constant

---

[12] Also see S. H. Fishtine, *Hydrocarbon Processing*, vol. 45 (No. 4), 173 (1965).

$$\frac{\lambda_b}{T_b} = \text{constant} = \begin{cases} 21 & \text{for nonpolar liquids} \\ 26 & \text{for water and lower alcohols} \end{cases} \qquad (4.14)$$

where λ_b = molal heat of vaporization in cal/g mole
   T_b = normal boiling point in °K

(2) *Kistyakowsky's equation*. Kistyakowsky[13] developed Eq. (4.15) for nonpolar liquids, and it provides quite accurate values of the molal heat of vaporization for these liquids

$$\frac{\lambda_b}{T_b} = 8.75 + 4.571 \log_{10} T_b \qquad (4.15)$$

where λ_b = molal heat of vaporization at T_b in cal/g mole
   T_b = normal boiling point in °K

(3) *Clausius-Clapeyron equation*. The Clapeyron equation itself is an exact thermodynamic relationship between the slope of the vapor-pressure curve and the molal heat of vaporization and the other physical factors as shown below:

$$\frac{dp^*}{dT} - \frac{\lambda}{T(V_g - V_l)} \qquad (4.16)$$

where p^* = the vapor pressure
   T = absolute temperature
   λ = molal heat of vaporization at T
   V_i = molal volume of gas or liquid as indicated by the subscript g or l

Any consistent set of units may be used. If we assume:

(a) V_l is negligible in comparison with V_g
(b) The ideal gas law is applicable

$$V_g = RT/p^*$$

(c) λ is constant over the temperature range of interest
then

$$\frac{dp^*}{p^*} = \frac{\lambda \, dT}{RT^2}$$

Rearranging the form

$$\frac{d \ln p^*}{d(1/T)} = -\frac{\lambda}{R} \qquad (4.17)$$

You can plot the $\log_{10} p^*$ vs. $1/T$ and obtain the slope $-(\lambda/2.303R)$.
   Integrating Eq. (4.17), we obtain an indefinite integral

$$\log_{10} p^* = -\frac{\lambda}{2.3RT} + B \qquad (4.18)$$

[13] W. Kistyakowsky, *Z. Physik u. Chem.*, vol. 107, p. 65 (1923).

or a definite one

$$\log_{10} \frac{p_1^*}{p_2^*} = \frac{\lambda}{2.3R}\left(\frac{1}{T_2} - \frac{1}{T_1}\right) \tag{4.19}$$

Either of these equations can be used graphically or analytically to obtain λ for a short temperature interval.

Example 4.10   Heat of Vaporization from the Clausius-Clapeyron Equation

Estimate the heat of vaporization of isobutyric acid at 200°C.

Solution:
The vapor-pressure data for isobutyric acid (from Perry) are:

pressure (mm)	*temperature (°C)*	*pressure (atm)*	*temp. (°C)*
100	98.0	1	154.5
200	115.8	2	179.8
400	134.5	5	217.0
760	154.5	10	250.0

Basis: 1 g mole isobutyric acid

Since λ remains essentially constant for short temperature intervals, the heat of vaporization can be estimated from Eq. (4.19) and the vapor-pressure data at 179.8°C and 217.0°C.

$$179.8°C = 452.8°K; \qquad 217°C = 490°K$$

$$\log_{10} \frac{2}{5} = \frac{\lambda}{(2.303)(1.987)}\left[\frac{1}{490} - \frac{1}{452.8}\right]$$

$$\lambda = 10,700 \text{ cal/g mole} = 19,500 \text{ Btu/lb mole}$$

A reduced form of the Clapeyron equation which gives good results is described in Hougen, Watson, and Ragatz.[14]

(4) *Reference substance plots.* Several methods have been developed to estimate the molal heat of vaporization of a liquid at any temperature (not just at its boiling point) by comparing the λ for the unknown liquid with that of a known liquid such as water.

(a) *Duhring plot.* The temperature of the wanted compound A is plotted against the temperature of the known (reference) liquid at *equal vapor pressure.* For example, if the temperatures of A (isobutyric acid) and the reference substance (water) are determined at 760, 400, and 200 mm pressure then a plot of the temperatures of A vs. the temperatures of the reference

[14] *Op. cit.*, pp. 273–75.

substance will be approximately a straight line over a wide temperature range.

(b) *Othmer plot.* The Othmer plot[15] is based on the same concepts as the Duhring plot except that the *logarithms* of vapor pressures are plotted against each other at *equal temperature*. As illustrated in Fig. 4.8, a plot of the $\log_{10}(p_A^*)$ against $\log_{10}(p_{ref}^*)$ chosen at the same temperature yields a straight line over a very wide temperature range. Applying the Clapeyron equation to each substance we have

$$\frac{d(\ln p_A^*)}{d(\ln p_{ref}^*)} = \frac{-\dfrac{\lambda_A\, d(1/T_A)}{R}}{-\dfrac{\lambda_{ref}\, d(1/T_{ref})}{R}} \qquad (4.20)$$

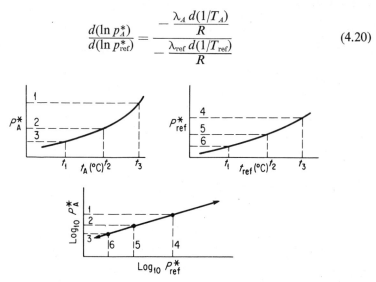

Fig. 4.8. Othmer plot and vapor pressure curves.

and choosing values of vapor pressure at equal temperature $(T_A = T_{ref})$

$$\frac{d(\ln p_A^*)}{d(\ln p_{ref}^*)} = \frac{\lambda_A}{\lambda_{ref}} = m = \text{slope of Othmer plot as in Fig. 4.8} \qquad (4.21)$$

The Othmer plot works well because the errors inherent in the assumptions made in deriving Eq. (4.21) cancel out to a considerable extent. At very high pressures the Othmer plot is not too effective. Incidentally, this type of plot has been applied to a wide variety of thermodynamic and transport relations, such as equilibrium constants, diffusion coefficients, solubility relations, ionization and dissociation constants, etc., with considerable success.

The Gordon method plots the log of the vapor pressure of A versus

---

[15] D. F. Othmer, *Ind. Eng. Chem.*, vol. 32, p. 841 (1940). For a complete review of the technique and a comparative statistical analysis among various predictive methods, refer to D. F. Othmer and H. N. Huang, *Ind. Eng. Chem.*, vol. 57, p. 40 (1965).

that of the reference substance at equal *reduced temperature*, and makes it possible to make better estimates in some cases.

Example 4.11   Use of Othmer Plot

Repeat the calculation for the heat of vaporization of isobutyric acid at 200°C using an Othmer plot.

Solution:
Data are as follows:

temperature (°C)	p_{iso}^* (atm)	log p*	$p_{H_2O}^*$ (atm)	log p*
154.5	1	0	5.28	0.723
179.8	2	0.3010	9.87	0.994
217.0	5	0.698	21.6	1.334
250.0	10	1.00	39.1	1.592

From Othmer plot:

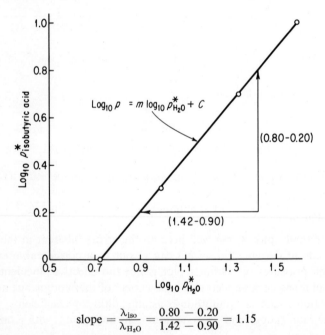

$$\text{slope} = \frac{\lambda_{iso}}{\lambda_{H_2O}} = \frac{0.80 - 0.20}{1.42 - 0.90} = 1.15$$

At 200°C (392°F), from the Steam Tables

$$\lambda_{H_2O} = 15{,}000 \text{ Btu/lb mole} \qquad (833.8 \text{ Btu/lb})$$

Then

$$\lambda_{iso} = (15{,}000)(1.15) = 17{,}250 \text{ Btu/lb mole}$$

The answer in this case is lower than that in Example 4.10. Without the experimental value, it is difficult to say what the proper answer is. However, at the normal boiling point (154°C), λ_{iso} is 17,700 Btu/lb mole, and λ_{iso} should be lower at 200°C.

---

(5) *Empirical relation of Watson.*[16] Watson found empirically that

$$\frac{\lambda_2}{\lambda_1} = \left(\frac{1 - T_{r_2}}{1 - T_{r_1}}\right)^{0.38}$$

where λ_2 = heat of vaporization of a pure liquid at T_2
$\quad\quad \lambda_1$ = heat of vaporization of the same liquid at T_1

4.5. The general energy balance

A description of the historical development of the energy balance and of special cases of it, particularly of the first law of thermodynamics, makes a most interesting story and can be found elsewhere.[17-21] The concept of the energy balance can be postulated as a fundamental law, i.e., as a statement that can neither be logically deduced from definitions nor established by any finite number of experiments. Fundamental laws are a generalization of experiment beyond the range of the experiments themselves and are assumed to be valid because we cannot find exceptions to them in practice. They are powerful tools which can be used in the solution of any practical problems.

The concept of the macroscopic energy balance is similar to the concept of the macroscopic material balance, namely,

$$\begin{Bmatrix} \text{Accumulation of} \\ \text{energy within the} \\ \text{system} \end{Bmatrix} = \begin{Bmatrix} \text{transfer of energy} \\ \text{into system through} \\ \text{system boundary} \end{Bmatrix} - \begin{Bmatrix} \text{transfer of energy out} \\ \text{of system through} \\ \text{system boundary} \end{Bmatrix}$$

$$+ \begin{Bmatrix} \text{energy genera-} \\ \text{tion within} \\ \text{system} \end{Bmatrix} - \begin{Bmatrix} \text{energy con-} \\ \text{sumption} \\ \text{within system} \end{Bmatrix} \tag{4.22}$$

While the formulation of the energy balance in words as outlined in Eq. (4.22) is easily understood and rigorous, you will discover in later courses that to express each term of (4.22) in mathematical notation requires certain

[16] K. M. Watson, *Ind. Eng. Chem.*, v. 23, p. 360 (1931); v. 35, p. 398 (1943).

[17] A. W. Porter, *Thermodynamics*, 4th ed., Methuen and Company, Ltd., London, 1951.

[18] D. Roller, *The Early Development of the Concepts of Temperature and Heat*, Harvard University Press, Cambridge, Massachusetts, 1950.

[19] E. N. Heibert, *Historical Roots of the Principle of Conservation of Energy*, State Historical Society of Wisconsin, 1962.

[20] J. Zernike, *Chem. Weekblad.*, vol. 61, pp. 270–74; 277–79 (1965).

[21] L. K. Nash, *J. Chem. Educ.*, vol. 42, p. 64 (1965). (A resource paper)

simplifications to be introduced, a discussion of which is beyond our scope here, but which have a quite minor influence on our final balance. We will split the energy associated with mass, mass either in the system or transported across the system boundaries, into three types: internal energy (U), kinetic energy (K), and potential energy (P). In addition to the energy transported across the system boundaries by mass flow into and out of the system, energy can be transferred by heat (Q) and work (W). Energy generation or consumption inside the system will be limited in this text to chemical reaction, or to energy generation throughout the material within the system caused by some external electric or magnetic field.

Figure 4.9 shows the various types of energy to be accounted for in Eq. (4.22), while Table 4.7 lists the specific individual terms which are to be employed in Eq. (4.22). As to the notation, the subscripts t_1 and t_2 refer to the initial and final time periods over which the accumulation is to be evaluated, with $t_2 > t_1$. The superscript caret (^) means that the symbol stands for energy per unit mass; without the caret, the symbol means energy of the total mass present. Other notation is evident from Fig. 4.10, a schematic diagram of a general process, or it can be found in the notation list at the end of the chapter.

With the aid of the symbols from Table 4.7, the general energy balance can be written as follows. (An alternative formulation of the balance is given in Chap. 6, where emphasis is placed on the instantaneous rate of change

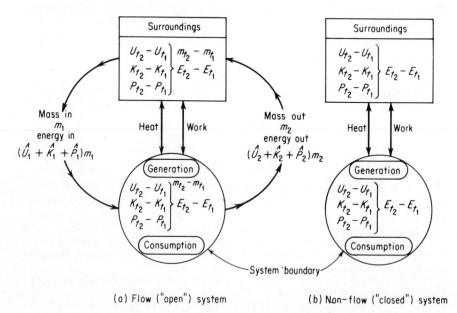

(a) Flow ("open") system   (b) Non-flow ("closed") system

Fig. 4.9. Energy balance for flow and nonflow systems.

TABLE 4.7   LIST OF SYMBOLS USED IN THE GENERAL ENERGY BALANCE

Accumulation term		
Type of energy	*At time t_1*	*At time t_2*
Internal	U_{t_1}	U_{t_2}
Kinetic	K_{t_1} $\Big\}E_{t_1}$	K_{t_2} $\Big\}E_{t_2}$
Potential	P_{t_1}	P_{t_2}
Mass	m_{t_1}	m_{t_2}
Energy accompanying mass transport		
Type of energy	*Transport in*	*Transport out*
Internal	U_1	U_2
Kinetic	K_1	K_2
Potential	P_1	P_2
Mass	m_1	m_2

Net heat input to system
$$Q$$

Net work done by system on surroundings
Mechanical work or work by moving parts: W
Work to introduce material into system, less work recovered
on removing material from system: $(p_2\hat{V}_2)m_2 - (p_1\hat{V}_1)m_1$

Net energy generation
$$S_R$$

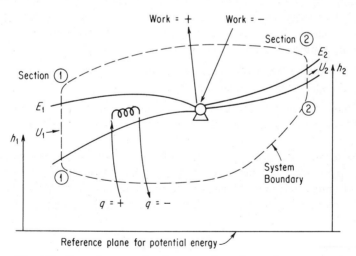

Fig. 4.10. General process showing system boundary and energy transport across boundary.

of energy of a system rather than the initial and final states of the system alone; the formulation in this chapter can be considered to be the result of integrating the balance in Chap. 6.):

$$m_{t_2}(\hat{U} + \hat{K} + \hat{P})_{t_2} - m_{t_1}(\hat{U} + \hat{K} + \hat{P})_{t_1} = (\hat{U}_1 + \hat{K}_1 + \hat{P}_1)m_1 \\ - (\hat{U}_2 + \hat{K}_2 + \hat{P}_2)m_2 + Q - W + p_1\hat{V}_1 m_1 - p_2\hat{V}_2 m_2 + S_R \tag{4.23}$$

or in simpler form, which is easier to memorize,

$$E_{t_2} - E_{t_1} = -\Delta[(\hat{H} + \hat{K} + \hat{P})m] + Q - W + S_R \tag{4.24}$$

where Δ = operator signifying *out* minus *in*, or *exit* minus *entrance*[22]

      Q = heat absorbed *by* the system *from* the surroundings (Q is positive for heat entering the system).

      W = mechanical work done *by* the system *on* the surroundings (W is positive for work going from the system to the surroundings).

      S_R = net energy generation within the system by chemical reaction or other source (S_R is positive for release of energy).

Keep in mind that a system may do work, or have work done on it, without some obvious mechanical device such as a turbine, pump, shaft, etc., being present. Often the nature of the work is implied rather than explicitly stated. For example, a cylinder filled with gas enclosed by a movable piston implies that the surrounding atmosphere can do work on the piston or the reverse; a batch fuel cell does no mechanical work, unless it produces bubbles, but delivers a current at a potential difference; etc.

Note that the expression $\Delta\hat{U} + \Delta p\hat{V} = \Delta\hat{H}$ has been employed in consolidating Eq. (4.23) into (4.24), so that the significance of the enthalpy term in the energy balance manifests itself. A more rigorous derivation of Eq. (4.24) may be found in a paper by Bird.[23] The terms of the equation can always be expressed in either one of two ways:

(a) As total energy quantities, such as Btu, as above

(b) As specific energies, such as Btu per pound

Be certain you use *consistent units* for all terms; the use of foot-pound, for example, and Btu in different places in Eq. (4.24) is a common error for the beginner.

The terms $p_1\hat{V}_1$ and $p_2\hat{V}_2$ in Eq. (4.23) and Table 4.7 represent the so-called "pV work," or "pressure energy" or "flow work," i.e., the work required to put a unit mass of matter into the system at ① in Fig. 4.10 and the work done by the system on a unit mass leaving the system at ②. If work is defined as

$$W = \int_0^l F\,dl$$

then, since the pressures at the entrance and exit to the system are constant for differential displacements of mass,

---

[22] In some texts the symbol Δ refers not only to *out* minus *in* but simultaneously to a value at t_2 minus a value at t_1 in the accumulation term, so that $\Delta E = E_{t_2} - E_{t_1}$.

[23] R. B. Bird, Reprint no. 293, *Univ. Wis. Eng. Expt. Sta. Rept.* 1957.

$$W_1 = \int_0^l F_1 \, dl = \int_0^{\hat{V}_1} p_1 \, d\hat{V} = p_1(\hat{V}_1 - 0) = p_1\hat{V}_1$$

where $\hat{V}$ is the volume per unit mass. Similarly the work recovered is $W_2 = p_2\hat{V}_2$.

In many problems you do not have to use all of the terms of the general energy balance equation because certain terms may be zero or may be so small that they can be neglected in comparison with the other terms. Several special cases of this nature, which can be deduced from the general energy balance, are of considerable industrial importance:

(a) No mass transfer ("closed" or "batch" system), no reaction

$$E_{t_2} - E_{t_1} = Q - W \tag{4.25}$$

Equation (4.25) is known as the *first law of thermodynamics*.

(b) No accumulation, no mass transfer, no reaction

$$Q = W \tag{4.26}$$

(c) No accumulation, no reaction, but with mass flow

$$Q - W = \Delta\,[(\hat{H} + \hat{K} + \hat{P})m] \tag{4.27}$$

(d) No accumulation, $Q = 0$, $W = 0$, $\hat{K} = 0$, $\hat{P} = 0$, $S_R = 0$

$$\Delta\hat{H} = 0 \tag{4.28}$$

Equation (4.28) is the so-called "enthalpy balance."

(e) No accumulation, no mass transfer, $W = 0$, $\hat{K} = 0$, $\hat{P} = 0$

$$Q = S_R \tag{4.29}$$

Take, for example, the flow system shown in Fig. 4.11. On an over-all basis between sections 1 and 5, we would find $\Delta P = 0$. In fact, the only portion of the system where ΔP would be of concern would be between section 4 and some other section. Between 3 and 4, ΔP may be consequential, but between 2 and 4 it may be negligible in comparison with the work introduced by the pump. Between section 3 and any further downstream point both Q and W are zero. You can find many additional examples of

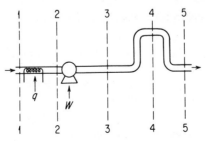

Fig. 4.11. Flow system.

other terms in the general energy balance which can be neglected in the subsequent examples in this chapter.

Some special process names are worth remembering:

(a) *Isothermal* ($dT = 0$)—constant-temperature process.

(b) *Adiabatic* ($Q = 0$)—no heat interchange, i.e., an insulated system. If we inquire as to the circumstances under which a process can be called adiabatic, the following include the most likely conditions:

    (1) The system is insulated.

    (2) Q is very small in relation to the other terms in the energy equation and may be neglected.

    (3) The process takes place so fast that there is no time for heat to be transferred.

(c) *Isobaric* ($dp = 0$)—constant-pressure process.

(d) *Isometric* or *isochoric* ($dV = 0$)—constant-volume process.

Occasionally in a problem you will encounter a special term called "sensible heat." Sensible heat is the enthalpy difference (normally for a gas) between some reference temperature and the temperature of the material under consideration, excluding any enthalpy differences for phase changes which we have previously termed latent heats.

One further remark that should be made is that the energy balance we have presented has included only the most commonly used energy terms. If a change in surface energy, rotational energy, or some other form of energy is important, these more obscure energy terms can be incorporated in the appropriate energy expression by separating the energy of special interest from the term in which it presently is incorporated in Eq. (4.23). As an example, kinetic energy might be split into linear kinetic energy (translation) and angular kinetic energy (rotation).

We turn now to some examples of the application of the general energy balance.

Example 4.12   Application of the Energy Balance

A rigid tank holds 2 lb of air at 100°F (the air has an internal energy of 100 Btu/lb with reference to fixed datum conditions). Heat is added to the air until the internal energy is 130 Btu/lb. (a) How much heat has been transferred to the air? (b) If by some means 10,000 (ft)(lb)$_f$ of work had been done *on* the gas at the same time, would this change your answer?

Solution:

(a) The air is chosen as the system, and the process is clearly a closed or batch system. The tank and everything outside the tank are the surroundings. Using Eq. (4.24) with the absence of K, P, and S_R inside the tank, and with no mass flow from the system to the surroundings or the reverse, we have (for $W = 0$)

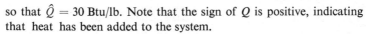

$$U_{t_2} - U_{t_1} = Q - W$$

Basis: 1 lb of air

$$\hat{U}_{t_2} - \hat{U}_{t_1} = 130 - 100 = 30 \text{ Btu/lb}$$

so that $\hat{Q} = 30$ Btu/lb. Note that the sign of Q is positive, indicating that heat has been added to the system.

Basis: 2 lb of air

$$Q = \frac{30 \text{ Btu}}{\text{lb}} \left| \frac{2 \text{ lb}}{} \right. = 60 \text{ Btu}$$

(b) If work is done somehow (by compression or otherwise) on the gas, then the work term is not zero but

$$W = - \frac{10{,}000 \text{ (ft)(lb}_f)}{} \left| \frac{1 \text{ Btu}}{778 \text{ (ft)(lb}_f)} \right. = -12.9 \text{ Btu}$$

Note that the sign on the work is negative since work is done *on* the gas.

$$Q = 60 - 12.9 = 47.1 \text{ Btu}$$

Less heat is required than before because some work has been done on the gas.

Example 4.13 Application of the Energy Balance

Air is being compressed from 1 atm and 460°R (where it has an enthalpy of 210.5 Btu/lb) to 10 atm and 500°R (where it has an enthalpy of 219.0 Btu/lb). The exit velocity of the air from the compressor is 200 ft/sec. What is the horsepower required for the compressor if the load is 200 lb/hr of air?

Solution:

This is clearly a flow process or open system as shown in the figure. Equation (4.24) can be used with the assumptions that $Q = 0$ (no heat exchange), $S_R = 0$, and no potential energy terms are of importance. Then

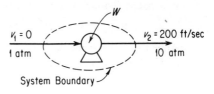

Basis: 1 lb of air

$$\hat{W} = -\Delta\left(\hat{H} + \frac{v^2}{2}\right)$$

$$\Delta\hat{H} = 219 - 210.5 = 8.5 \text{ Btu/lb}_m$$

Next, we will assume the entering velocity of the air is zero, so that

$$\frac{\Delta v^2}{2} = \frac{(200 \text{ ft})^2}{\text{sec}^2} \left| \frac{}{\dfrac{32.2 \text{ (ft)(lb}_m)}{(\text{sec}^2)(\text{lb}_f)}} \right| \frac{1 \text{ Btu}}{778 \text{ (ft)(lb}_f)} \left| \frac{1}{2} \right.$$

$$= 0.80 \text{ Btu/lb}_m$$

$$\hat{W} = -(8.5 + 0.8) = -9.3 \text{ Btu/lb}_m$$

(*Note:* the minus sign indicates work is done on the air.) To convert to power (work/time),

Basis: 200 lb air/hr

$$\text{hp} = \frac{9.3 \text{ Btu}}{\text{lb}} \left| \frac{200 \text{ lb}}{\text{hr}} \right| \frac{1 \text{ hp}}{2545 \dfrac{\text{Btu}}{\text{hr}}} = 0.73 \text{ hp}$$

Example 4.14   Application of the Energy Balance

A steel ball weighing 100 lb is dropped 100 ft to the ground. What are the values of Q and W and the change in U, K, and P for this process? What is the change in the total energy of the universe (system plus surroundings)?

Solution:

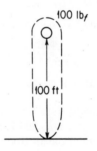

Let the system be the ball and the surroundings be everything else. This is a batch (nonflow) process. The general energy balance reduces to

$$[(\hat{U}_{t_2} + \hat{K}_{t_2} + \hat{P}_{t_2}) - (\hat{U}_{t_1} + \hat{K}_{t_1} + \hat{P}_{t_1})]m = Q - W$$

After the ball hits the ground and is at rest, we know that its velocity is zero, and we let the ground be the reference plane for potential energy. Consequently,

$$m(\hat{P}_{t_2} - \hat{P}_{t_1}) = m(g/g_c)(h_2 - h_1)$$

$$= (100 \text{ lb}_m)(g/g_c)(-100 \text{ ft}) = -10,000 \text{ (ft)(lb}_f)$$

If Q and W are zero, then $U_{t_2} - U_{t_1}$ may be calculated. If Q and W are not zero, then $(U_{t_2} - U_{t_1})$ is dependent upon, the values of Q and W, which are not specifically stated in the problem. If $U_{t_2} - U_{t_1}$ were known, then, $Q - W$ could be determined. Without more information or without making a series of assumptions concerning Q, W, and $U_{t_2} - U_{t_1}$, it is not possible to complete the requested calculations.

The change in the total energy of the universe is zero

Example 4.15   Application of the Energy Balance

Water is being pumped from the bottom of a well 150 ft deep at the rate of 200 gal/hr into a vented storage tank 30 ft above the ground. To prevent freezing in the winter a small heater puts 60,000 Btu/hr into the water during its transfer from the well to the storage tank. Heat is lost from the whole system at the constant rate of 25,000 Btu/hr. What is the rise or fall in the temperature of the water as it enters the storage tank, assuming the well water is at 35°F? A 2-hp pump is being used to pump the water. About 55% of the rated hp goes into the work of pumping and the rest is dissipated as heat to the atmosphere.

Solution:

Let the system consist of the well inlet, the piping, and the outlet at the storage tank. It is a flow process since material is continually entering and leaving the system.

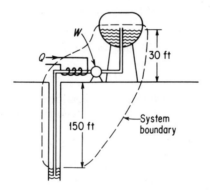

The general energy equation, for $S_R = 0$, reduces to

$$Q - W = \Delta [(\hat{H} + \hat{K} + \hat{P})m] \qquad \text{(a)}$$

The term $(E_{t_2} - E_{t_1})$ is zero because no accumulation of energy takes place in the pipe.

Basis: 1 hr operation

The total amount of water pumped is

$$\frac{200 \text{ gal}}{\text{hr}} \left| \frac{1 \text{ hr}}{} \right| \frac{8.33 \text{ lb}}{1 \text{ gal}} = 1666 \text{ lb/hr}$$

The water initially has a velocity of zero at the well inlet. The problem does not specify the size of pipe through which the water is being pumped so it is impossible to calculate the increase in kinetic energy experienced by the water as it leaves the pipe at the storage tank. Unless the pipe is exceptionally small, however, the kinetic energy term may be considered negligible in comparison with the other energy terms in the equation. Thus,

$$\hat{K}_1 = \hat{K}_2 \cong 0$$

$$\hat{P}_2 m_2 - \hat{P}_1 m_1 = \frac{1666 \ lb_f}{m}(180 \ ft) = 300{,}000 \ (ft)(lb_f)/hr$$

$$= \frac{300{,}000 \ (ft)(lb_f)/hr}{778 \ (ft)(lb_f)/Btu} = 386 \ Btu/hr$$

The heat lost by the system is 25,000 Btu/hr while the heater puts 60,000 Btu/hr into the system. The net heat exchange is

$$Q = 60{,}000 - 25{,}000 = 35{,}000 \ Btu/hr$$

The rate of work being done on the water by the pump is

$$W = - \frac{2 \ hp}{} \left| \frac{0.55}{} \right| \frac{33{,}000 \ (ft)(lb_f)}{(min)(hp)} \left| \frac{60 \ min}{hr} \right| \frac{Btu}{778 \ (ft)(lb_f)}$$

$$= - 2{,}800 \ Btu/hr$$

ΔH can be calculated from Eq. (a):

$$35{,}000 - (-2800) = \Delta H + 0 + 386$$

$$\Delta H = 37{,}414 \ Btu/hr$$

We know from Eq. (4.7) that, for an incompressible fluid such as water,

$$\Delta \hat{H} = \int_{T_1}^{T_2} C_p \, dT$$

Because the temperature range considered is small, the heat capacity of liquid water may be assumed to be constant and equal to 1.0 Btu/(lb)(°F) for the problem. Thus,

$$\Delta \hat{H} = C_p \, \Delta T = (1.0) \, (\Delta T)$$

$$\text{Basis: 1 lb } H_2O$$

Now

$$\Delta \hat{H} = \frac{37{,}414 \ Btu}{hr} \left| \frac{hr}{1666 \ lb} \right. = 22.5 \ Btu/lb$$

$$= (1.0) \, (\Delta T)$$

$$\Delta T = 22.5°F \text{ temperature rise}$$

Example 4.16   Energy Balance

Steam that is used to heat a batch reaction vessel enters the steam chest, which is segregated from the reactants, at 250°C saturated and is completely condensed. The reaction absorbs 1000 Btu/lb of material in the reactor. Heat loss from the steam chest to the surroundings is 5000 Btu/hr. The reactants are placed in the vessel at 70°F and leave at 212°F. If the charge consists of 325 lb of material and both products and reactants have an average heat capacity of $C_p = 0.78$ Btu/(lb)(°F), how many lb of steam are needed per lb of charge? The charge remains in the reaction vessel for 1 hr.

Solution:

Analysis of the process reveals that no potential energy, kinetic energy, or work terms are significant in the energy balance. The steam flows in and out, while the reacting material stays within the system.

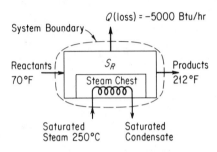

Basis: 1 hr of operation

System: Reaction vessel, including steam chest

The energy balance reduces to

$$(U_{t_2} - U_{t_1})_{\text{reactants}} = -\Delta H_{\text{steam}} + Q + S_R \tag{a}$$

However, since $\hat{U} = \hat{H} - p\hat{V}$,

$$[(\hat{H}_{t_2} - \hat{H}_{t_1}) + (p_{t_2}\hat{V}_{t_2} - p_{t_1}\hat{V}_{t_1})]m = Q + S_R - \Delta H_{\text{steam}}$$

Since no information is available concerning the $p\hat{V}$ difference, and it would no doubt be negligible if we could calculate it, it will be neglected, and then

$$(\hat{H}_{t_2} - \hat{H}_{t_1})m = -\Delta H_{\text{steam}} + Q + S_R \tag{b}$$

(1) The heat loss is given as $Q = -5000$ Btu/hr.

(2) The enthalpy change for the steam can be determined from the Steam Tables. The ΔH_{vap} of saturated steam at 250°C is 732.2 Btu/lb so that

$$-\Delta \hat{H}_{\text{steam}} = 737.2 \text{ Btu/lb}$$

(3) The enthalpy of the initial reactants, with reference to zero enthalpy at 70°F, is

$$\Delta H = m(\Delta \hat{H}) = m \int_{70}^{70} C_p \, dT = 0$$

Note that the selection of zero enthalpy at 70°F makes the calculation of the enthalpy of the reactants at the start quite easy. The enthalpy of the final products relative to zero enthalpy at 70°F is

$$\Delta H = m \int_{70}^{212} C_p \, dT = mC_p(212 - 70)$$

$$= \frac{325 \text{ lb}}{\text{hr}} \left| \frac{0.78 \text{ Btu}}{(\text{lb})(\text{°F})} \right| \frac{(212 - 70)\text{°F}}{} = 36{,}000 \text{ Btu/hr}$$

(4) In addition to the changes in enthalpy occurring in the material entering and leaving the system, the reaction absorbs 1000 Btu/lb.

$$S_R = \frac{-1000 \text{ Btu}}{\text{lb}} \bigg| \frac{325 \text{ lb}}{\text{hr}} = -325{,}000 \text{ Btu/hr}$$

Introducing these numbers into Eq. (b), we find

$$(36{,}000 - 0)\frac{\text{Btu}}{\text{hr}} = \left(737.2\frac{\text{Btu}}{\text{lb steam}}\right)\left(S\frac{\text{lb steam}}{\text{hr}}\right)$$

$$- 5000\frac{\text{Btu}}{\text{hr}} - 325{,}000\frac{\text{Btu}}{\text{hr}} \tag{c}$$

from which the lb steam/hr, S, can be calculated as

$$S = \frac{366{,}000 \text{ Btu}}{\text{hr}} \bigg| \frac{1 \text{ lb steam}}{737.2 \text{ Btu}} = 496\frac{\text{lb steam}}{\text{hr}}$$

or

$$\frac{366{,}000 \text{ Btu}}{\text{hr}} \bigg| \frac{1 \text{ lb steam}}{737.2 \text{ Btu}} \bigg| \frac{1 \text{ hr}}{325 \text{ lb charge}} = 1.53\frac{\text{lb steam}}{\text{lb charge}}$$

If the system is chosen to be everything but the steam coils and lines, then we would have a situation as shown in the second diagram. Under these circumstances we could talk about the heat transferred into the reactor from the steam chest. From a balance on the steam chest (no accumulation),

$$Q = \Delta H_{\text{steam}}$$

Both have negative values, but remember

$$Q_{\text{system I}} = -Q_{\text{system II}}$$

so that the value of $Q_{\text{system I}}$ is plus.

The energy balance on the system reduces to

$$(\hat{H}_{t_2} - \hat{H}_{t_1})m = Q + S_R \tag{d}$$

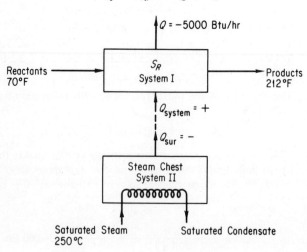

where $Q = Q_{\text{steam chest}} + (-5000 \text{ Btu})$. The steam used can be calculated from Eq. (d); the numbers will be identical to the calculation made for the original system.

Example 4.17   Energy Balance

Ten pounds of water at 35°F, 4 lb ice at 32°F, and 6 lb steam at 250°F and 20 psia are mixed together. What is the final temperature of the mixture? How much steam condenses?

Solution:

We will assume that the over-all batch process takes place adiabatically. The system is 20 lb of H_2O in various phases. Then the energy balance reduces to (superscripts are s = steam, w = water, i = ice)

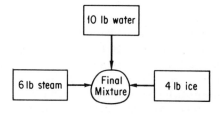

$$20\hat{U}_{t_2} - (6\hat{U}_{t_1}^s + 10\hat{U}_{t_1}^w + 4\hat{U}_{t_1}^i) = 0 \qquad \text{(a)}$$

If $\hat{U}$ is replaced with $\hat{H} - p\hat{V}$, we get

$$20\hat{H}_{t_2} - (6\hat{H}_{t_1}^s + 10\hat{H}_{t_1}^w + 4\hat{H}_{t_1}^i)$$
$$= 20(p\hat{V})_{t_2} - 6(p\hat{V})_{t_1}^s - 10(p\hat{V})_{t_1}^w - 4(p\hat{V})_{t_1}^i = \sum m(p\hat{V}) \qquad \text{(b)}$$

The term $\sum m(p\hat{V})$ here cannot be more than 1 Btu at the very most, and can safely be neglected.

It is not practical to sum up the enthalpy changes for each component in an expression involving the one unknown, the T_{final}, and then solve for this temperature. The reason is that we should use data from the Steam Tables, and a linear algebraic expression cannot be written down for the way the enthalpies change as a function of temperature. It is much simpler merely to assume the final conditions and to check the assumption by Eq. (b)

$$\text{Basis:} \begin{cases} 4 \text{ lb ice at 32°F} \\ 10 \text{ lb } H_2O \text{ at 35°F} \\ 6 \text{ lb steam at 250°F and 20 psia} \end{cases}$$

Since the heat of condensation of the steam is quite large we might expect that the final temperature of the mixture would be very near or at the saturation temperature of the 20 psia steam. Assume $T_{\text{final}} = 228°F$ (the sat. temp. of 20 psia steam).

We will also assume that *all* the steam condenses.

Using the Steam Tables (ref.: 0 enthalpy at 32°F, saturated liquid),

$$\Delta H_{\text{ice}} = \frac{4 \text{ lb}}{} \Bigg| \frac{143.6 \text{ Btu}}{\text{lb}} \text{ (heat of fusion at } 32°\text{F)}$$

$$+ 4 \text{ lb}(\Delta H_{228} - \Delta H_{32}) \quad \text{as liquid water}$$

$$= 574.4 + [196.2 - 0]$$

$$= 1359.2 \text{ Btu}$$

$$\Delta H_{\text{liquid}} = 10[\Delta H_{228} - \Delta H_{35}] \cdot$$

$$= 10(196.2 - 3.02)$$

$$= 1931.8 \text{ Btu}$$

$$\Delta H_{\text{steam}} = 6[\overset{\text{superheat}}{1156.1 - 1168.0}] + 6[\overset{\text{condensation}}{196.2 - 1156.1}]$$

$$= 6(-11.9 - 959.9)$$

$$= -71.4 - 5759.4$$

$$= -5830.8 \text{ Btu}$$

$$\Delta H_{\text{total}} = (1359.2 + 1931.8 - 5830.8) = -2539.8 \text{ Btu}$$

ΔH_{total} must be compared with $20 \hat{H}_{t_2} = 20(0) = 0$.

It is thus evident that our assumption that all the steam condenses is wrong, since the total enthalpy change is not zero. With this initial calculation, perhaps even without it, we can foresee that the final temperature of the mixture will be 228°F and that a saturated steam-liquid water mixture will finally exist in the vessel. The next question is, "How much steam condenses?"

Let $S=$ amount of steam which condenses at 228°F.

$$\Delta H_{\text{ice}} = 1359.2 \text{ Btu}$$

$$\Delta H_{\text{liquid}} = 1931.8 \text{ Btu}$$

$$\Delta H_{\text{steam}} = -71.4 + S[196.2 - 1156.1]$$

$$\Delta H_{\text{total}} \cong 0$$

$$\Delta H_{\text{steam}} + \Delta H_{\text{liquid}} + \Delta H_{\text{ice}} = 0$$

$$-71.4 - S(959.9) + 1931.8 + 1359.2 = 0$$

$$S = 3.355 \text{ lb}$$

If there had been only 1 lb of steam instead of 6 lb, then the first trial of $\sum \Delta H$ at $t = 228°\text{F}$ would yield

$$\sum \Delta H = 1359.2 + 1931.8 - 971.8 > 0$$

Hence, lower temperatures should be chosen until $\sum \Delta H = 0$.

4.6. Reversible processes and the mechanical energy balance

The energy balance of the previous section is concerned with various classes of energy without inquiring into how "useful" each form of energy is to man. Our experience with machines and thermal processes indicates that all types of energy transformation are not equally possible. For example, it is well known that heat cannot be transferred from a low temperature to a high temperature, but only in the reverse direction, nor can internal energy be completely converted into mechanical work. To account for these limitations on energy utilization, the second law of thermodynamics was eventually developed as a general principle.

As applied to fluid dynamic problems, one of the consequences of the second law of thermodynamics is that two categories of energy of different "quality" can be envisioned:

(a) The so-called "mechanical" forms of energy, such as kinetic energy, potential energy, and work, which are *completely* convertible by an *ideal* (frictionless, reversible) engine from one form to another within the class

(b) Other forms of energy, such as internal energy and heat, which are not so freely convertible

Of course, in any real process with friction, viscous effects, mixing of components, and other dissipative phenomena taking place which prevent the complete conversion of one form of mechanical energy to another, allowances will have to be made in making a balance on mechanical energy for these "losses" in "quality."

To describe the loss or transfer of energy of the freely convertible kind to energy of lesser "quality," a concept termed *irreversiblity* has been coined. A process which operates without the degradation of the convertible types of energy is termed a *reversible* process; one which does not is an irreversible process. A reversible process proceeds under conditions of differentially balanced forces. Only an infinitesimal change is required to reverse the process, a concept which leads to the name reversible.

Take, for example, the piston shown in Fig. 4.12. During the expansion process the piston moves the distance x and the volume of gas confined in the piston increases from V_1 to V_2. Two forces act on the reversible (frictionless) piston; one is the force exerted by the gas, equal to the pressure times the area of the piston, and the other is the force on the piston shaft. If the force exerted by the gas equals the force F, nothing happens. If F is greater than the force of the gas, the gas will be compressed, while if F is less than the force of the gas, the gas will expand.

In the latter case, the work done by the expanding gas and the piston will be $W = \int F\,dx$. The work of the

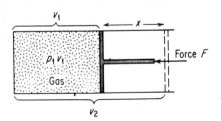

Fig. 4.12. Gas expansion.

gas would be $W = \int p\, dV$ if the process were reversible, i.e., if the force F divided by the piston area were differentially less at all times than the pressure of the gas, and if the piston were frictionless; but in a real process some of the work done by the gas is dissipated by viscous effects, and the piston will not be frictionless so that the work as measured by $\int F\, dx$ will be less than $\int p\, dV$. In order for these two measurements to be equal, none of the available energy of the system can be "wasted." To achieve such a situation we will have to insure that the movement of the piston is frictionless and that the motion of the piston proceeds under only a differential imbalance of forces so no shock or turbulence is present. Naturally such a process would take a long time to complete.

No real process which involves friction, shock, finite temperature differences, unrestricted expansion, viscous dissipation, or mixing can be reversible, and so we see that the dropping of a weight from a tower, the operation of a heat exchanger, and the combusion of gases in a furnace are all irreversible processes. Since practically all real processes are irreversible you may wonder why such attention is devoted to the theoretical reversible process. The reason is that it represents the best that can be done, the ideal case, and gives us a measure of our maximum accomplishment. In a real process we cannot do as well and so are less effective. A goal is provided by which to measure our effectiveness. And then, many processes are not too irreversible, so that there is not a big discrepancy between the practical and the ideal process.

A balance on mechanical energy can be written on a microscopic basis for an elemental volume by taking the scalar product of the local velocity and the equation of motion.[24] After integration over the volume of the system the *steady-state mechanical energy balance* (for a system with mass interchange with the surroundings) becomes, on a per unit mass basis,

$$\Delta(\hat{K} + \hat{P}) + \int_{p_1}^{p_2} \hat{V}\, dp + \hat{W} + \hat{E}_v = 0 \qquad (4.30)$$

where E_v represents the loss of mechanical energy, i.e., the irreversible conversion *by the flowing fluid* of mechanical energy to internal energy, a term which must in each individual process be evaluated by experiment (or, as occurs in practice, by use of already existing experimental results for a similar process). Equation (4.30) is sometimes called the Bernoulli equation, especially for the reversible process for which $E_v = 0$. The mechanical energy balance is best applied in fluid-flow calculations when the kinetic and potential energy terms and the work are of importance, and the friction losses can be evaluated from handbooks with the aid of *friction factors* or *orifice coefficients*.

[24] R. B. Bird, *op. cit.*

Example 4.18   Application of the Mechanical Energy Balance

Calculate the work per minute required to pump 1 lb of water per minute from 100 psia and 80°F to 1000 psia and 100°F.

Solution:

If the process is assumed to be reversible so that $E_v = 0$, if the pump is 100% efficient, and if no kinetic or potential energy terms are involved in the process, Eq. (4.30) reduces to

$$\hat{W} = -\int_{p_1}^{p_2} \hat{V}\, dp$$

From the Steam Tables, the specific volume of liquid water is 0.01608 ft³/lb$_m$ at 80°F and 0.01613 ft³/lb$_m$ at 100°F. For all practical purposes the water is incompressible, and the specific volume can be taken to be 0.0161 ft³/lb$_m$. Then,

$$\hat{W} = -\int_{100}^{1000} 0.0161\, dp = -0.0161(1000 - 100)$$

$$= -14.5(\text{lb}_f)(\text{in.})/\text{lb}_m = -2.68 \text{ Btu/lb}_m = -2.68 \text{ Btu/min}$$

About the same value can be calculated using Eq. (4.24) if $\hat{Q} = \hat{K} = \hat{P} = 0$, because the enthalpy change[25] for a reversible process for 1 lb of water going from 100 psia and 100°F to 1000 psia is 2.70 Btu. However, usually the enthalpy data for liquids other than water are missing, or not of sufficient accuracy to be of much value, which forces the engineer to turn to the mechanical energy balance.

One might now well inquire for the purpose of purchasing a pump motor, say, as to what the work would be for a real process, instead of the fictious reversible process assumed above. First, you would need to know the efficiency of the pump motor so that the actual input from the pump to the system would be known. Secondly, the friction losses in the pipe, valves, and fittings must be estimated so that the term E_v could be reintroduced into Eq. (4.30). Suppose, for the purposes of illustration, that E_v was estimated to be, from an appropriate handbook, 320 (ft)(lb$_f$)/lb$_m$ and the motor-pump efficiency was 60% (based on 100% efficiency for a reversible pump motor). Then,

$$E_v = \frac{320 \text{ (ft)(lb}_f)}{1 \text{ lb}_m} \left| \frac{1 \text{ Btu}}{778 \text{ (ft)(lb}_f)} \right| \frac{1 \text{ lb}_m}{\text{min}} = 0.41 \text{ Btu/min}$$

$$W = -(2.68 + 0.41) = -3.09 \text{ Btu/min}$$

Remember that the minus sign indicates work is done on the system. The pump motor must have the capacity

$$\frac{3.09 \text{ Btu}}{1 \text{ min}} \left| \frac{1}{0.60} \right| \frac{1 \text{ min}}{60 \text{ sec}} \left| \frac{1.415 \text{ hp}}{1 \text{ Btu/sec}} \right. = 0.122 \text{ hp}$$

[25] From J. H. Keenan and F. G. Keyes, *Thermodynamic Properties of Steam*, Table 3, John Wiley & Sons, Inc., New York, 1936.

Example 4.19   Calculation of Work for a Batch Process

One pound mole of N_2 is in a horizontal cylinder at 100 psia and 70°F. A 1-in.^{2} piston of 5-lb weight seals the cylinder and is fixed by a pin. The pin is released and the N_2 volume is doubled, at which time the piston is stopped again. What is the work done by the gas in this process?

Solution:

(1) Draw a picture.

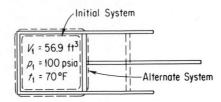

(2) Is the process a flow or nonflow process? Since no material leaves or enters the cylinder, let us analyze the process as a nonflow system.

(3) This process is definitely irreversible because of friction between the piston (and the gas) and the walls of the cylinder, turbulence in the the gas, the large pressure drops, etc.

(4) In selecting a system to work with, we can choose either the gas itself or the gas plus the piston. Let us initially select the N_2 gas as the system, with the surroundings being everything else including the piston and the cylinder.

(5) Since the gas expansion is a nonflow process, Eq. (4.30) does not apply. Even if you had an expression for the unsteady-state mechanical energy balance (which we have not discussed since it involves the concept of entropy), it would not be possible to calculate the work done by the gas because the process is irreversible and the E_v term would not be known. As might be expected, a direct application of $W = \int F \, dl$ fails for this problem because the pressure of the gas does not necessarily equal the force per unit area applied by the piston to the gas, i.e., the work cannot be obtained from $W = \int p \, dV$.

(6) Let us change our system to include the gas, the piston, and the cylinder. With this choice, the system expansion is still irreversible, but the pressure in the surroundings can be assumed to be atmospheric pressure and is constant. The work done in pushing back the atmosphere probably is done almost reversibly from the viewpoint of the surroundings, and can be closely estimated by calculating the work done by the surroundings:

$$W = \int F \, dl = \int p \, dV = p \, \Delta V$$

$$p = \frac{14.7 \text{ lb}_f}{\text{in.}^2} \left| \frac{144 \text{ in.}^2}{1 \text{ ft}^2} \right. = \frac{2120 \text{ lb}_f}{\text{ft}^2}$$

Assuming $z = 0.995$ and is constant, the initial volume of gas is

$$V_1 = \frac{359 \text{ ft}^3}{1 \text{ lb mole}} \left| \frac{530°R}{492°R} \right| \frac{14.7}{100} \left| 0.995 \right. = 56.9 \text{ ft}^3/\text{lb mole}$$

and ΔV of the gas is $2V_1 - V_1 = V_1 = 56.9 \text{ ft}^3/\text{lb mole}$ so that the volume change of the surroundings is -56.9 ft^3. Then the work done by the surroundings is

$$W = \frac{2120 \text{ lb}_f}{\text{ft}^2} \left| \frac{-56.9 \text{ ft}^3}{\text{lb mole}} \right| \frac{1 \text{ lb mole}}{}$$

$$= -120,000 \text{ (ft)(lb}_f)$$

The minus sign indicates work is done on the surroundings. From this we know the work done by the alternate system is

$$W_{\text{system}} = -W_{\text{surroundings}} = -(-120,000) = 120,000 \text{ (ft)(lb}_f)$$

(7) This still does not answer the question of what work was done by the gas, because our system now includes both the piston and the cylinder as well as the gas. You may wonder what happens to the energy transferred from the gas to the piston itself. Some of it goes into work against the atmosphere, which we have just calculated; where does the rest of it go? This energy can go into raising the temperature of the piston or the cylinder or the gas. With time, part of it can be transferred to the surroundings to raise the temperature of the surroundings. From our macroscopic viewpoint we cannot say specifically what happens to this "lost" energy.

(8) You should also note that if the surroundings were a vacuum instead of air, then *no work* would be done by the system, consisting of the piston plus the cylinder plus the gas, although the gas itself probably still would do some work.

4.7. Heat of reaction

The only term we have not yet discussed in the energy balance is S_R, the net generation—consumption term. The topic of energy liberation or absorption because of chemical reaction is frequently called *thermochemistry*, and the energy liberated or absorbed on reaction is termed the *heat of reaction*, a term which is a legacy of the days of the caloric theory. ("Heat of reaction" in terms of modern concepts is best translated as the energy release transferred as heat in certain types of experiments which are delineated below.) The energy released during a reaction comes from the rearrangement of the bonds holding together the atoms of the reacting molecules.

For an exothermic reaction, the energy required to hold the products of the reaction together is less than that required to hold the reactants together and the surplus energy is released. (It is usually transformed into the thermal energy of the molecules present but may appear as work, radiant energy, etc.)

To measure, i.e., calculate the values of, the heats of reaction, the experimenter usually selects either a simple flow process without kinetic energy, potential energy, or work effects (a flow calorimeter), or a simple batch process (a bomb calorimeter), in which to conduct the reaction. For the flow process the steady-state (no accumulation term) version of Eq. (4.24) reduces to

$$Q = \Delta H - S_R \qquad (4.31)$$

By determining Q for a flow system with $\Delta H = 0$, such as flows through a valve, or by determining ΔH with $Q = 0$, as in an insulated system, S_R can be evaluated. In a batch bomb, with no accumulation of internal energy, as might happen if the bomb were placed in a constant temperature bath and the system volume remained constant, Eq. (4.24) reduces to

$$Q = -S_R \qquad (4.32)$$

In each case the energy generation or consumption, S_R, is equal to the heat of reaction per mole (or per unit mass) of a designated substance that reacts times the number of moles (or mass) of the specified material that disappear:

$$S_R = (\Delta \hat{H}_{\mathrm{rxn}\,A})(m_A) \qquad (4.33)$$

When material A reacts, m_A is, by convention, a negative value because some of the A disappears. Remember that the term Q is plus when heat is absorbed by the system from the surroundings, so that Q will have a negative value when energy is liberated on reaction. Consequently, from Eq. (4.31) with $\Delta H = 0$, or from Eq. (4.32), S_R must be positive when energy is liberated. For Eq. (4.33) to be consistent with the previous sign conventions, $\Delta \hat{H}_{\mathrm{rxn}}$ must bear a *negative* value for exothermic reactions. Other texts may have other symbols and conventions the opposite of those used here, and consequently you must be sure that you employ the correct sign if you use different references as sources for thermochemical data. We can summarize the sign conventions used in this text as follows:

type of reaction	energy is	Q	$\Delta \hat{H}_{\mathrm{rxn}}$	S_R	surroundings Q
exothermic	evolved	−	−	+	+
endothermic	absorbed	+	+	−	−

The calculations we will make here will all be for low pressures, and, although the effect of pressure upon heats of reaction is relatively negligible under most conditions, if exceedingly high pressures are encountered, you should make the necessary corrections as explained in most texts on chemical thermodynamics.

There are certain conventions and symbols which you should always keep in mind concerning thermochemical calculations if you are to avoid difficulty later on. These conventions can be summarized as follows:

(a) The reactants are shown on the left-hand side of the equation, and the products are shown on the right—for example,

$$CH_4(g) + H_2O(l) \longrightarrow CO(g) + 3 H_2(g)$$

(b) The conditions of phase, temperature, and pressure must be specified unless the latter two are the standard conditions, as presumed in the example above, when only the phase is required. This is particularly important for compounds such as H_2O, which can exist as more than one phase under common conditions. If the reaction takes place at other than standard conditions, you might write

$$CH_4(g, 1.5 \text{ atm}) + H_2O(l) \xrightarrow{50°C} CO(g, 3 \text{ atm}) + H_2(g, 3 \text{ atm})$$

(c) Unless otherwise specified, the heats of reaction, the enthalpy changes, and all the constituents are at the standard state of 25°C (77°F) and 1 atm total pressure. The heat of reaction under these conditions is called the *standard heat of reaction*.

(d) Unless the amounts of material reacting are stated, it is assumed that the quantities reacting are the stoichiometric amounts as shown in the chemical equation.

Standard heat of reaction data are reported and tabulated in two essentially equivalent forms:

(a) Standard heats of formation
(b) Standard heats of combustion

We will first describe the standard heat of formation $(\Delta \hat{H}_f^\circ)$ and afterward the standard heat of combustion $(\Delta \hat{H}_c^\circ)$. The units of both quantities are usually tabulated as energy per mole, such as kilocalories per gram mole or Btu per pound mole. The "per mole" refers to the first substance in the related stoichiometric equation.

4.7-1 Standard Heat of Formation. This is a special type of heat of reaction, one for the formation of a compound from the elements. The initial reactants and final products must be stable and at 25°C and 1 atm. The reaction does not necessarily represent a real reaction that would proceed at constant temperature but can be a fictitious process for the formation of a compound from the elements. By defining the heat of formation as zero in the standard state for each *element*, it is possible to design a system to express the heats of formation for all *compounds* at 25°C and 1 atm. If you use the conventions discussed above, then the thermochemical calculations will all be consistent, and you should not experience any confusion as to signs. Consequently, with the use of well-defined standard heats of formation, it is not necessary to record the experimental heats of reaction for every reaction that can take place.

A formation reaction is understood by convention to be a reaction which forms 1 mole of compound from the elements which make it up. Standard heats of reaction for any reaction can be calculated from the tabulated (or experimental) standard heats of formation values by using Eq. (4.34) below, because the standard heat of formation is a point function,

$$\Delta H^{\circ}_{\text{rxn}} = \sum \Delta H^{\circ}_{f \text{ products}} - \sum \Delta H^{\circ}_{f \text{ reactants}}$$
$$= \sum n_{\text{prod}} \Delta \hat{H}^{\circ}_{f \text{ prod}} - \sum n_{\text{react}} \Delta \hat{H}^{\circ}_{f \text{ react}} \qquad (4.34)$$

Example 4.20   Heats of Formation

What is the standard heat of formation of HCl(g)?

Solution:

In the reaction at 25°C and 1 atm,

$$\tfrac{1}{2}H_2(g) + \tfrac{1}{2}Cl_2(g) \longrightarrow HCl(g)$$

Tabulated: $\Delta \hat{H}^{\circ}_f \left(\dfrac{\text{cal}}{\text{g mole}} \right)$ 0   0 $-22,063$

both $H_2(g)$ and $Cl_2(g)$ would be assigned $\Delta \hat{H}^{\circ}_f$ values of 0, and the value shown in Appendix F for HCl(g) of $-22,063$ cal/g mole is the standard heat of formation for this compound (as well as the standard heat of reaction for the reaction as written above). The value tabulated in the Appendix might actually be determined by carrying out the reaction shown for HCl(g) and measuring the energy liberated in a calorimeter, or by some other more convenient method. The superscript (°) on ΔH°_f indicates "standard state."

Example 4.21   Indirect Determination of Heats of Formation

Suppose you want to find the standard heat of formation of CO from experimental data. Can you prepare pure CO from C and O_2 and measure the energy liberated? This would be far too difficult. It would be easier experimentally to find the energy liberated for the two reactions shown below and add them as follows:

Basis: 1 g mole CO

$$\Delta \hat{H}^{\circ}_{\text{rxn}}(\textit{experimental})$$

$A:$ $C(\beta) + O_2(g) \longrightarrow CO_2(g)$	-94.052 kcal/g mole
$B:$ $CO(g) + \tfrac{1}{2}O_2(g) \longrightarrow CO_2(g)$	-67.636 kcal/g mole

---

$A - B:$ $C(\beta) + \tfrac{1}{2}O_2(g) \longrightarrow CO(g)$

$$\Delta H^{\circ}_{\text{rxn}} = \Delta H^{\circ}_f = (-94.052) - (-67.636) = -26.416 \text{ kcal/g mole}$$

The energy change for the over-all reaction scheme is the desired heat of formation per mole of CO(g).

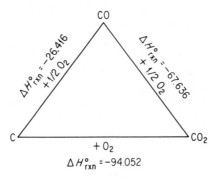

CO

$\Delta H^\circ_{rxn} = -26.416$
$+ 1/2\ O_2$

$\Delta H^\circ_{rxn} = -67.636$
$+ 1/2\ O_2$

C

CO$_2$

$+ O_2$

$\Delta H^\circ_{rxn} = -94.052$

Example 4.22   Calculation of S_R

Calculate S_R for the following reaction of 4 moles of NH$_3$:

$$4\ NH_3(g) + 5\ O_2(g) \longrightarrow 4\ NO(g) + 6\ H_2O(g)$$

Solution:

Basis: 4 g mole NH$_3$

tabulated	NH$_3$(g)	O$_2$(g)	NO(g)	H$_2$O(g)
$\Delta \hat{H}^\circ_f$ per mole at 25°C and 1 atm (kcal/g mole)	-11.04	0	$+21.60$	-57.80

$$\Delta H^\circ_{rxn} = [4(21.60) + 6(-57.80)] - [5(0) + 4(-1104)]$$
$$= -216.24\ \text{kcal/4 g mole} \quad \text{or} \quad -54.0\ \text{kcal/g mole NH}_3$$
$$S_R = 216.24\ \text{kcal}$$

Example 4.23   Heat of Formation with a Phase Change

If the standard heat of formation for H$_2$O(l) is $-68,317$ cal/g mole and the heat of evaporation is $+10,519$ cal/g mole at 25°C and 1 atm, what is the standard heat of formation of H$_2$O(g)?

Solution:

Basis: 1 g mole H$_2$O

$\Delta \hat{H}^\circ_f$	0	0	-68.317

A: $H_2(g) + \frac{1}{2} O_2(g) \longrightarrow H_2O(l)$ $\Delta H^\circ_{rxn} = -68.317$ kcal/g mole

B: $H_2O(l) \longrightarrow H_2O(g)$ $\Delta H^\circ_{vap} = +10.519$ kcal/g mole

---

$A + B$: $H_2(g) + \frac{1}{2} O_2(g) \longrightarrow H_2O(g)$

$$\Delta H^\circ_{rxn} + \Delta H^\circ_{vap} = \Delta H^\circ_{f\,H_2O(g)} = -57.798\ \text{kcal/g mole}$$

You can see that these equations (or any number of equations) can be handled by algebraic methods, and the heats of reaction can be added or subtracted in the same fashion as are the equations. By carefully following these rules of procedure, you will avoid most of the common errors in thermochemical calculations.

To simplify matters, the value selected for ΔH_{vap} was at 25°C and 1 atm. More precisely, if the final state for water is specified as $H_2O(g)$ at 25°C and 1 atm, the following enthalpy changes should be taken into account if you start with $H_2O(l)$ at 25°C and 1 atm; practically, ΔH_{vap} at 25°C and the vapor pressure of water will be adequate for calculations:

$$
\Delta H_{vap} \text{ at } 25°C \text{ and 1 atm}
\begin{cases}
H_2O(l)\ 25°C,\ 1\ atm \\
\quad \downarrow \Delta H_1 \\
H_2O(l)\ 25°C,\ \text{vapor pressure at } 25°C \\
\quad \downarrow \Delta H_2 = \Delta H_{vap} \text{ at the vapor pressure of water} \\
H_2O(g)\ 25°C,\ \text{vapor pressure at } 25°C \\
\quad \downarrow \Delta H_3 \\
H_2O(g)\ 25°C,\ 1\ atm
\end{cases}
$$

There are many sources of tabulated values for the standard heats of formation. A good source of extensive data is the *National Bureau of Standards Bulletin* 500, and its supplements, by F. K. Rossini. A condensed set of values for the heats of formation may be found in Appendix F. If you cannot find a standard heat of formation for a particular compound in reference books or in the chemical literature, $\Delta \hat{H}_f^\circ$ may be estimated by the methods described in Verma and Doraiswamy[26] or by some of the authors listed as references in their article. Note that most of the values for the standard heats of formation are negative, i.e., they are for exothermic reactions, but not all of them are.

4.7-2 Standard Heat of Combustion. Standard heats of combustion are another method of expressing thermochemical data useful for thermochemical calculations. The standard heats of combustion do not have the same standard states as the standard heats of formation. The conventions used with the standard heats of combustion are:

(a) The compound is oxidized with oxygen or some other substance to the products $CO_2(g)$, $H_2O(l)$, $HCl(aq)$,[27] etc.

(b) The reference conditions are still 25°C and 1 atm.

(c) Zero values of $\Delta \hat{H}_c^\circ$ are assigned to certain of the oxidation products as, for example, $CO_2(g)$, $H_2O(l)$, and $HCl(aq)$.

[26] K. K. Verma and L. K. Doraiswamy, *Ind. Eng. Chem. Fundamentals*, vol. 4, p. 389 (1965).

[27] HCl(aq) represents an infinitely dilute solution of HCl (see Sec. 4.8).

(d) If other oxidizing substances are present, such as S or N_2, or if Cl_2 is present, it is necessary to make sure that states of the products are carefully specified and are identical to (or can be transformed into) the final conditions which determine the standard state as shown in Appendix F.

The enthalpy change for the standard heat of combustion can never be positive but is always negative. A positive value would mean that the substance would not burn or oxidize.

In the search for better high-energy fuels, the heat of combustion of each element in terms of energy per unit mass is of interest. You can see from Fig. 4.13 that the best fuels will use H, Be, or B as building blocks. With everything else held constant, the greater the heat of combustion per pound, the longer the range of an airplane or missile.

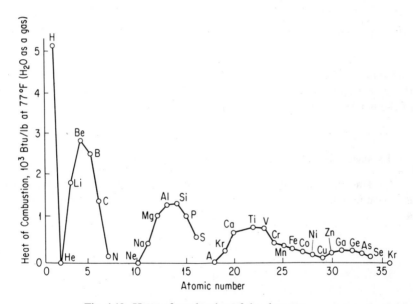

Fig. 4.13. Heats of combustion of the elements.

For a fuel such as coal or oil, the standard heat of combustion is known as the *heating value* of the fuel. To determine the heating value, a weighed sample is burned in oxygen in a calorimeter bomb, and the energy given off is detected by measuring the temperature increase of the bomb and surrounding apparatus.

Because the water produced in the calorimeter is in the vicinity of room temperature (although the gas within the bomb is saturated with water vapor at this temperature), essentially all the water formed in the combustion process is condensed into liquid water. This is not like a real combustion process in a furnace where the water remains as a vapor and passes up the stack. Consequently we have two heating values for fuels containing hydrogen: (1) the gross, or higher, heating value, in which all the water formed is condensed into the liquid state, and (2) the net, or lower, heating value, in which all the water formed remains in the vapor state. The value you determine in the calorimeter is the gross heating value; this is the one reported along with the fuel analysis and should be presumed unless the data state specifically that the net heating value is being reported.

You can estimate the heating value of a coal within about 3 per cent from the Dulong formula:[28]

The higher heating value (HHV) in Btu/lb

$$= 14{,}544\,C + 62{,}028\!\left(H - \frac{O}{8}\right) + 4050\,S$$

where C = weight fraction carbon
     S = weight fraction net sulfur

$H - \dfrac{O}{8}$ = weight fraction net hydrogen = total weight fraction hydrogen

$-\,\frac{1}{8}$ weight fraction oxygen

The values of C, H, S, and O can be taken from the fuel or flue-gas analysis. If the heating value of a fuel is known and the C and S are known, the value of the net H can be determined from the Dulong formula.

Example 4.24 Heating Value of Coal

The following coal has a reported heating value of 12,810 Btu/lb as received. Assuming this is the gross heating value, calculate the net heating value.

comp.	%
C	71.0
H_2	5.6
N_2	1.6
net S	2.7
ash	6.1
O_2	13.0
	100.0

Solution:

The corrected ultimate analysis shows 5.6% hydrogen on the as-received basis

Basis: 100 lb coal as received

The water formed on combustion is:

[28] H. H. Lowry, ed., *Chemistry of Coal Utilization*, Chap. 4, John Wiley & Sons, Inc., New York, 1945.

$$\frac{5.6 \text{ lb } H_2}{} \left| \frac{1 \text{ lb mole } H_2}{2.02 \text{ lb } H_2} \right| \frac{1 \text{ lb mole } H_2O}{1 \text{ lb mole } H_2} \left| \frac{18 \text{ lb } H_2O}{1 \text{ lb mole } H_2O} \right. = 50 \text{ lb } H_2O$$

The energy required to evaporate the water is

$$\frac{50 \text{ lb } H_2O}{100 \text{ lb coal}} \left| \frac{1020 \text{ Btu}}{\text{lb } H_2O} \right. = \frac{510 \text{ Btu}}{\text{lb coal}}$$

The net heating value is

$$12,810 - 510 = 12,300 \text{ Btu/lb}$$

The value 1020 Btu/lb is not the latent heat of vaporization of water at 77°F (1050 Btu/lb) but includes the effect of a change from a heating value at constant volume to one at constant pressure (-30 Btu/lb) as described in a later section of this chapter.

A general relation between the gross heating value and the net heating value is

net Btu/lb coal $=$ gross Btu/lb coal $- 91(\%$ total H by weight$)$

Standard heats of reaction can be calculated from standard heats of combustion by Eq. (4.35)

$$\Delta H_{rxn}^{\circ} = -\left[\sum \Delta H_{c \text{ products}}^{\circ} - \sum H_{c \text{ reactants}}^{\circ} \right] \qquad (4.35)$$

$$= -\left[\sum n_{prod} \Delta \hat{H}_{c \text{ prod}}^{\circ} - \sum n_{react} \Delta \hat{H}_{c \text{ react}}^{\circ} \right]$$

Note: the minus sign in front of the summation expression occurs because the choice of reference states is zero for the right-hand side of the standard equations.

Example 4.25   Calculation of Heat of Reaction from Heat of Combustion Data

What is the heat of reaction of the following reaction:

$$C_2H_5OH(l) + CH_3COOH(l) \longrightarrow C_2H_5OOCCH_3(l) + H_2O(l)$$
  ethyl alcohol   acetic acid   ethyl acetate

Solution:

Basis: 1 g mole C_2H_5OH

Tabulated	$C_2H_5OH(l)$	$CH_3COOH(l)$	$C_2H_5OOCCH_3(l)$	$H_2O(l)$
$\Delta \hat{H}_c^{\circ}$ per mole at 25°C and 1 atm (kcal/g mole)	-326.70	-208.34	-538.75	0

$$\Delta H_{rxn}^{\circ} = -[-538.75 - (-326.70 - 208.34)] = +3.72 \text{ kcal/g mole}$$

Example 4.26   Calculation of Heat of Formation from Heats of Combustion

Calculate the standard heat of formation of $C_2H_2(g)$ (acetylene) from the standard heat of combustion data.

Solution:

The standard heat of formation for $C_2H_2(g)$ would be expressed in the following manner (Basis: 1 g mole C_2H_2):

$$2\,C(\beta) + H_2(g) \longrightarrow C_2H_2(g) \qquad \Delta H_f^\circ = ?$$

How can we obtain this equation using known standard heat of combustion data? The procedure is to take the chemical equation which gives the standard heat of combustion of $C_2H_2(g)$ (Eq. *A* below) and add or subtract other known combustion equations (*B* and *C*) so that the desired equation is finally obtained algebraically. The details are shown below:

$$\Delta \hat{H}_c^\circ (\text{kcal/g mole})$$

A:	$C_2H_2(g) + 2\frac{1}{2}\,O_2(g) \longrightarrow 2\,CO_2(g) + H_2O(l)$	-310.615
B:	$C(\beta) + O_2(g) \longrightarrow CO_2(g)$	-94.052
C:	$H_2(g) + \frac{1}{2}\,O_2(g) \longrightarrow H_2O(l)$	-68.312

$-A + 2B + C$:
$$2\,C(\beta) + H_2(g) \longrightarrow C_2H_2(g)$$

$$\Delta H_{\text{net}}^\circ = \Delta H_f^\circ = -(-310.615) + 2(-94.052) + (-68.317) = +54.194\frac{\text{kcal}}{\text{g mole}}$$

Example 4.27   Combination of Heats of Reaction Changes at 25°C

The following heats of reaction are known from experiment for the reactions below at 25°C in the standard thermochemical state:

		$\Delta \hat{H}_{\text{rxn}}^\circ$
	rxn	*kcal/g mole*
1. $C_3H_6(g) + H_2(g)$	$\longrightarrow C_3H_8(g)$	-29.6
2. $C_3H_8(g) + 5\,O_2(g)$	$\longrightarrow 3\,CO_2(g) + 4\,H_2O(l)$	-530.6
3. $H_2(g) + \frac{1}{2}\,O_2(g)$	$\longrightarrow H_2O(l)$	-68.3
4. $H_2O(l)$	$\longrightarrow H_2O(g)$	$+10.5\ (\Delta H_{\text{vap}}^\circ)$
5. C (diamond) $+ O_2(g)$	$\longrightarrow CO_2(g)$	-94.50
6. C (graphite) $+ O_2(g)$	$\longrightarrow CO_2(g)$	-94.05

Calculate:

(a) The standard heat of formation of propylene (C_3H_6 gas)

(b) The standard heat of combustion of propylene (C_3H_6 gas)

(c) The net heating value of propylene in Btu/ft³ measured at 60°F and 30 in. Hg saturated with water vapor

Solution:

(a) Reference state: 25°C, 1 atm; $C(\beta)$ (graphite) and $H_2(g)$ have zero enthalpies

Desired: $3\ C(\beta) + 3\ H_2(g) \longrightarrow C_3H_6(g)$

$$\Delta H_f^\circ = ?$$

kcal/g mole

(1) $C_3H_6(g) + H_2(g) \longrightarrow C_3H_8(g)$ $\Delta H_1 = -29.6$

(2) $C_3H_8(g) + 5\ O_2(g) \longrightarrow 3\ CO_2(g) + 4\ H_2O(l)$ $\Delta H_2 = -530.6$

(3) $-4[H_2(g) + \tfrac{1}{2}\ O_2(g) \longrightarrow H_2O(l)]$ $-4\ \Delta H_3 = +273.2$

(6) $-3[C(\beta) + O_2(g) \longrightarrow CO_2(g)]$ $-3\ \Delta H_6 = +282.2$

---

(7) = (1) + (2) + (3) + (6):

$C_3H_6(g) \longrightarrow 3\ C(\beta) + 3\ H_2(g)$ $\Delta H_{\mathrm{rxn}}^\circ = \quad -4.8$

$$\Delta H_{f_{C_3H_6(g)}}^\circ = +4.8 \text{ kcal/g mole}$$

(b) Reference state: 25°C, 1 atm; $CO_2(g)$ and $H_2O(l)$ have zero enthalpies

Desired: $C_3H_6(g) + \tfrac{9}{2}\ O_2(g) \longrightarrow 3\ CO_2(g) + 3\ H_2O(l)$

kcal/g mole

(1) $C_3H_6(g) + H_2(g) \longrightarrow C_3H_8(g)$ $\Delta H_1 = -29.6$

(2) $C_3H_8(g) + 5\ O_2(g) \longrightarrow 3\ CO_2(g) + 4\ H_2O(l)$ $\Delta H_2 = -530.6$

(3) $-[H_2(g) + \tfrac{1}{2}\ O_2(g) \longrightarrow H_2O(l)]$ $-\Delta H_3 = +68.3$

---

(8) = (1) + (2) + (3):

$C_3H_6(g) + \tfrac{9}{2}\ O_2(g) \longrightarrow 3\ CO_2(g) + 3\ H_2O(l)$ $\Delta H_{\mathrm{rxn}}^\circ = -491.9$

$$\Delta H_{c_{C_3H_6(g)}}^\circ = -491.9 \text{ kcal/g mole}$$

(c) Net heating value

Desired: $C_3H_6(g) + \tfrac{9}{2}\ O_2(g) \longrightarrow 3\ CO_2(g) + 3\ H_2O(g)$

kcal/g mole

(8) $C_3H_6(g) + \tfrac{9}{2}\ O_2(g) \longrightarrow 3\ CO_2(g) + 3\ H_2O(l)$ $\Delta H_8 = -491.9$

(4) $3\ H_2O(l) \longrightarrow 3\ H_2O(g)$ $3\ \Delta H_4 = +31.5$

---

(9) = (8) + (4):

$C_3H_6(g) + \tfrac{9}{2}\ O_2(g) \longrightarrow 3\ CO_2(g) + 3\ H_2O(g)$ $\Delta H_{\mathrm{rxn}} = -460.4$

$$\Delta H_c' = -460{,}400 \text{ cal/g mole}$$

$$\Delta H_c' = (-460{,}400)(1.8) = -829{,}000 \text{ Btu/lb mole}$$

At 60°F, 30 in. Hg, saturated with water vapor,

vapor pressure of H_2O at 60°F = 13.3 mm Hg

pressure on gas $= (760)\left(\dfrac{30.00}{29.92}\right) - 13.3$

$$= 763 - 13.3 = 749.7 \simeq 750 \text{ mm Hg}$$

$$\text{molal volume} = \frac{359}{750} \frac{760}{(460+32)} \frac{(460+60)}{} = 384 \text{ ft}^3/\text{lb mole}$$

$$\text{heating value} = \frac{829{,}000}{384} = 2160 \text{ Btu/ft}^3 \text{ measured at } 60°\text{F and 30 in. Hg satd.}$$

At 60°F, 30 in. Hg, dry,

$$\text{molal volume} = 379 \text{ ft}^3/\text{lb mole}$$

$$\text{net heating value} = \frac{829{,}000}{379} = 2185 \text{ Btu/ft}^3$$

One of the common errors to make in these thermochemical calculations is to forget that the standard state for heat of combustion calculations is liquid water, and if gaseous water is present, a phase change (the heat of vaporization or heat of condensation) must be included in the calculations. If the final product in Example 4.25 had been $H_2O(g)$ rather than $H_2O(l)$, we would have incorporated the phase transition for water as follows:

A: $C_2H_5OH(l) + CH_3COOH(l) \longrightarrow C_2H_5OOCCH_3(l) + H_2O(l)$

$$\Delta H_{rxn}^° = +3.72$$

B: $H_2O(l) \quad \longrightarrow \quad H_2O(g) \quad \Delta H_{vap} = +10.52$

$A + B$: $C_2H_2OH(l) + CH_3COOH(l) \longrightarrow C_2H_5OOCCH_3(l) + H_2O(g)$

$$\Delta H_{rxn}^° = (+3.72) + (10.52) = +14.24 \text{ kcal/g mole}$$

With adequate data available you will find it simpler to use only the heats of combustion or only the heats of formation in the same algebraic calculation for a heat of reaction. Mixing these two sources of enthalpy change data, unless you take care, will only lead to error and confusion. Of course, when called upon, you should be able to calculate the heat of formation from the heat of combustion, or the reverse, being careful to remember and take into account the fact that the standard states for these two types of calculations are different. Since the heat-of-combustion values are so large, calculations made by subtracting these large values from each other can be a source of considerable error. To avoid other major errors, carefully check all signs and make sure all equations are not only balanced but are written according to the proper convention.

4.7-3 Heats of Reaction at Constant Pressure or at Constant Volume. Heats of reaction obtained by calorimetric methods are usually determined in a constant volume process, such as in a bomb, in which the volume is constant but not the pressure. For such a process (the system is the material in the bomb), the general energy balance, Eq. (4.24), reduces to (with no work, mass flow, nor kinetic or potential energy effects)

$$U_{t_2} - U_{t_1} = Q_v + S_R \qquad (4.36)$$

In a flow process which takes place at constant pressure the general energy balance reduces to Eq. (4.31)

$$\Delta H = Q_p + S_R \tag{4.31}$$

If we subtract Eq. (4.36) from Eq. (4.31), we find

$$Q_p - Q_v = \Delta H - (U_{t_2} - U_{t_1}) = (U_2 - U_1) - (U_{t_2} - U_{t_1})$$
$$+ (m_2 p_2 \hat{V}_2 - m_1 p_1 \hat{V}_1) \tag{4.37}$$

Suppose, furthermore, that the internal energy change per unit mass for the batch, constant volume process is identical to the internal energy difference between the outlet and inlet in the flow process. Then

$$(U_{t_2} - U_{t_1}) = (U_2 - U_1)$$

and

$$Q_p - Q_v = (m_2 p_2 \hat{V}_2 - m_1 p_1 \hat{V}_1) \tag{4.38}$$

To evaluate the terms on the right-hand side of Eq. (4.38), we can assume for solids and liquids that the $\Delta m \, p\hat{V}$ change is negligible and can be ignored. Therefore, the only change which must be taken into account is for gases present as products and/or reactants. If, for simplicity, the gases are assumed to be ideal, then at constant temperature

$$mp\hat{V} = nRT$$
$$\Delta m \, p\hat{V} = \Delta n \, RT$$

and

$$Q_p - Q_v = \Delta n \, (RT) \tag{4.39}$$

Example 4.28   Difference Between Heat of Reaction at Constant Pressure and at Constant Volume

Find the difference between the heat of reaction at constant pressure and at constant volume for the following reaction at 25°C (assuming it could take place):

$$C(s) + \tfrac{1}{2} O_2(g) \longrightarrow CO(g)$$

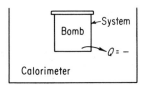

Solution:

Basis: 1 mole of C(s)

System: bomb $Q = +$ when heat is absorbed by the bomb.

From Eq. (4.41), $Q_p - Q_v = \Delta n \, (RT)$.

$$\Delta n = 1 - \tfrac{1}{2} = +\tfrac{1}{2}$$

since C is a solid.

$$Q_p - Q_v = \tfrac{1}{2}RT = 0.5(1.987)(298) = 296 \text{ cal}$$

If the measured heat evolved from the bomb was 26,711 cal.,

$$Q_p = Q_v + 296 = -26,711 + 296 = -26,416 \text{ cal}$$

The size of this correction is relatively insignificant compared to either the quantity Q_p or Q_v. In any case, the heat of reaction calculated from the bomb experiment is, from Eqs. (4.32) and (4.33):

$$Q = -S_R = -(\Delta \hat{H}_{\text{rxn}})(m)$$

$$\Delta \hat{H}_{\text{rxn}_v} = -\frac{Q_v}{m} = -\frac{-26,711}{-1} = -\frac{26,711 \text{ cal}}{\text{g mole}}$$

Since reported heats of reaction are normally for constant pressure processes, the value of $-26,711$ would be corrected to

$$\Delta \hat{H}_{\text{rxn}_p} = -\frac{Q_p}{m} = -\frac{-26,416}{-1} = -\frac{26,416 \text{ cal}}{\text{g mole}}$$

4.7-4 Incomplete Reactions. If an incomplete reaction occurs, you should calculate the standard heat of reaction only for the products which are actually formed from the reactants which actually react. In other words, only the portion of the reactants which actually undergo some change and liberate or absorb some energy are to be considered in calculating the overall standard heat of the reaction. If some material passes through unchanged, then you should not include it in the *standard heat of reaction* calculations; however, when the reactants or products are at conditions *other* than 25°C and 1 atm, whether they react or not, you must include them in the enthalpy calculations as explained in Sec. 4.7-5.

Example 4.29 Incomplete Reactions

If 10 kg of PbS and 3 kg of O_2 react to yield 6 kg of Pb and 1 kg of PbO_2 and the only other product is SO_2, what is the total heat of reaction at 25°C and 1 atm?

Solution:

The stoichiometry for this problem has been worked out in Example 1.26 based on the following data:

data	PbS(c)	$O_2(g)$	Pb(c)	$SO_2(g)$	$PbO_2(c)$
kg	10	3	6	?	1
mol. wt	239	32	207	64	239
g moles	41.9	93.7	29.0		4.19
$-\Delta \hat{H}_f^\circ \left(\dfrac{\text{kcal}}{\text{g mole}} \right)$	22.38	0	0	70.96	65.0

Recall that stoichiometric amounts of materials are *not* mixed in this example.

$$\text{Basis: 10 g PbS}$$

PbS reacting: 33.2 g mole O_2 reacting: 37.4 g mole

$$\text{SO}_2 \text{ formed: } 33.2 \text{ g mole}$$

Heat of reaction at 25°C and 1 atm:

$$\overset{\textbf{Pb}}{} \quad \overset{\textbf{SO}_2}{} \quad \overset{\textbf{PbO}_2}{}$$
$$\Delta H_{\text{rxn}}^\circ = [29.0(0) + 33.2(-70.96) + 4.19(-65.00)]$$
$$\overset{\textbf{PbS}}{} \quad \overset{\textbf{O}_2}{}$$
$$-[33.2(-22.38) + 37.4(0)] = -1.89 \text{ kcal}$$

4.7-5 Effect of Temperature on Heat of Reaction (at Constant Pressure). You realize the standard state of 25°C which we have chosen is only by accident the temperature at which any given reaction will take place. In most reactions the products enter and leave at temperatures other than 25°C; these temperatures may be higher or lower than 25°C. Since enthalpy and heats of reaction are point functions, we can set up a schematic diagram

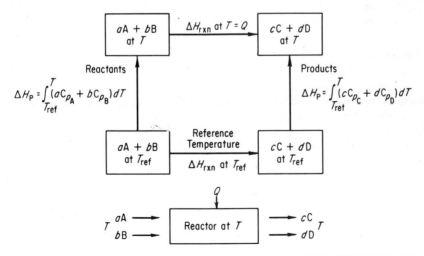

Fig. 4.14. Heat of reaction at a temperature other than standard conditions.

as shown in Fig. 4.14 which will enable us to take into account varying temperature conditions.

(a) *Reaction in which the reactants enter and the products leave at the same temperature—temperature different from the standard state of 25°C.* Suppose a reaction such as the following

$$aA + bB \longrightarrow cC + dD$$

takes place at T, a temperature different than the reference temperature T_{ref} of 25°C, and all streams enter and leave at T. We can draw a diagram which shows the enthalpy relations for this reaction as in Fig. 4.14. The arrows indicate directions of flow of the hypothetical transitions while ΔH_R and ΔH_P indicate the (positive) enthalpy change of reactants and products, respectively, *from the reference state.*

The general energy balance, Eq. (4.24), reduces to Eq. (4.31) for this type of process,

$$Q = \Delta H - S_R \tag{4.31}$$

or

$$Q = (\Delta H_P - \Delta H_R) - (\Delta \hat{H}_{rxn_{T_{ref}}})(m) \tag{4.40}$$

in terms of the notation in Fig. 4.14. (Keep in mind that m earlier has been arbitrarily made a negative number (mass lost) so that S_R is positive for exothermic reactions.) By definition, Q, as calculated by Eq. (4.40) is equal to the "heat of reaction at the temperature T" so that, if $m = -1$ g mole (or -1 g),

$$- (m)(\Delta \hat{H}_{rxn_{T_{ref}}}) = -(-1)\Delta \hat{H}_{rxn_{T_{ref}}} = + \Delta H_{rxn_{T_{ref}}}$$

and

$$\Delta H_{rxn_T} = \Delta H_{rxn_{T_{ref}}} + \Delta H_P - \Delta H_R \tag{4.41}$$

If the heat capacity equation is expressed as

$$C_p = \alpha + \beta T + \gamma T^2 \tag{4.42}$$

then to obtain $\Delta H_P - \Delta H_R$ we add up the enthalpy changes for the products and subtract those for the reactants. Rather than integrate separately, let us consolidate like terms as follows. Each heat capacity equation is multiplied by the proper number of moles

$$aC_{p_A} = a[\alpha_A + \beta_A T + \gamma_A T^2] \tag{4.43a}$$

$$bC_{p_B} = b[\alpha_B + \beta_B T + \gamma_B T^2] \tag{4.43b}$$

$$cC_{p_C} = c[\alpha_C + \beta_C T + \gamma_C T^2] \tag{4.43c}$$

$$dC_{p_D} = d[\alpha_D + \beta_D T + \gamma_D T^2] \tag{4.43d}$$

Then we define a new term ΔC_p which is equal to

original expression   equivalent
new term

$$cC_{pC} + dC_{pD} - (aC_{pA} + bC_{pB}) = \Delta C_p$$

where

$$[(c\alpha_C + d\alpha_D) - (a\alpha_A + b\alpha_B)] = \Delta\alpha \qquad (4.44)$$

$$T[c\beta_C + d\beta_D) - (a\beta_A + b\beta_B)] = T\Delta\beta$$

$$T^2[c\gamma_C + d\gamma_D) - (a\gamma_A + b\gamma_B)] = T^2\,\Delta\gamma$$

Simplified, this can be expressed as

$$\Delta C_p = \Delta\alpha + \Delta\beta T + \Delta\gamma T^2 \qquad (4.45)$$

Furthermore,

$$(\Delta H_P - \Delta H_R) = \int_{T_R}^{T} \Delta C_p\, dT = \int_{T_R}^{T} (\Delta\alpha + \Delta\beta T + \Delta\gamma T^2)\, dT$$

$$= \Delta\alpha(T - T_R) + \frac{\Delta\beta}{2}(T^2 - T_R^2) + \frac{\Delta\gamma}{3}(T^3 - T_R^3) \qquad (4.46)$$

where $T_R = T_{\text{ref}}$ for simplicity.

If the integration is carried out without definite limits,

$$(\Delta H_P - \Delta H_R) = \int (\Delta C_p)\, dT = \Delta\alpha T + \frac{\Delta\beta}{2}T^2 + \frac{\Delta\gamma}{3}T^3 + C \qquad (4.47)$$

where C is the integration constant. Finally ΔH_{rxn} at the new temperature T is

$$\Delta H_{\text{rxn}_T} = \Delta H_{\text{rxn}_{T_R}} + \Delta\alpha(T - T_R) + \frac{\Delta\beta}{2}(T^2 - T_R^2) + \frac{\Delta\gamma}{3}(T^3 - T_R^3) \quad (4.48a)$$

or

$$\Delta H_{\text{rxn}_T} = \Delta H_{\text{rxn}_{T_R}} + \Delta\alpha T + \frac{\Delta\beta}{2}T^2 + \frac{\Delta\gamma}{3}T^3 + C \qquad (4.48b)$$

as the case may be. Using Eq. (4.48a) and knowing $\Delta\hat{H}_{\text{rxn}}$ at the reference temperature T_R, you can easily calculate ΔH_{rxn} at any other temperature. Equation (4.48b) can be consolidated into

$$\Delta H_{\text{rxn}_T} = \Delta H_0 + \Delta\alpha T + \frac{\Delta\beta}{2}T^2 + \frac{\Delta\gamma}{3}T^3 \qquad (4.49)$$

with

$$\Delta H_0 = (\Delta H_{\text{rxn}_{T_R}} + C)$$

Now, if ΔH_{rxn} is known at any temperature T, you can calculate ΔH_0 as follows:

$$\Delta H_0 = \Delta H_{\text{rxn}_T} - \Delta\alpha(T) - \frac{\Delta\beta}{2}(T^2) - \frac{\Delta\gamma}{3}T^3 \qquad (4.50)$$

and then you can use this value of ΔH_0 to assist in the calculation of ΔH_{rxn} at any other temperature. These methods of using definite or indefinite integration of the C_p equations yield, of course, identical results. Still another method of handling these enthalpy change calculations would be to use mean heat capacity data or enthalpy data obtained directly from published tables. If a phase change takes place, it also must be included in the enthalpy calculations.

Example 4.30 Calculation of Heat of Reaction at a Temperature Different than Standard Conditions

An inventor thinks he has developed a new catalyst which can make the gas phase reaction

$$CO_2 + 4 H_2 \longrightarrow 2 H_2O + CH_4$$

proceed with 100 per cent conversion. Estimate the heat which must be provided or removed if the products enter and leave at 500°C.

Solution:

In effect we need to calculate the heat of reaction at 500°C from Eq. (4.41) or Q in Eq. (4.40). For illustrative purposes we first use the technique based on Eqs. (4.49) and (4.50).

$$\text{Basis: 1 g mole } CO_2(g)$$

$$CO_2(g) + 4 H_2(g) \longrightarrow 2 H_2O(g) + CH_4(g)$$

$$-\Delta \hat{H}_f^\circ \left(\frac{kcal}{kg \; mole} \right) \quad 94,052 \qquad 0 \qquad \quad 57,798 \qquad 17,889$$

$$\Delta \hat{H}_{rxn_{298}{}^\circ K} = [-17,889 - (2)(57,798)] - [(4)(0) - 94,052]$$

$$= -39,433 \text{ cal/g mole } CO_2$$

First we will calculate ΔC_p:

$$C_{p_{CO_2}} = 6.339 + 10.14 \times 10^{-3}T - 3.415 \times 10^{-6}T^2 \quad T \text{ in } {}^\circ K$$

$$C_{p_{H_2}} = 6.424 + 1.039 \times 10^{-3}T - 0.078 \times 10^{-6}T^2 \quad T \text{ in } {}^\circ K$$

$$C_{p_{H_2O}} = 6.970 + 3.464 \times 10^{-3}T - 0.483 \times 10^{-6}T^2 \quad T \text{ in } {}^\circ K$$

$$C_{p_{CH_4}} = 3.204 + 18.41 \times 10^{-3}T - 4.48 \times 10^{-6}T^2 \quad T \text{ in } {}^\circ K$$

$$\Delta \alpha = [(1)(3.204) + (2)(6.970)] - [(1)(6.339) + (4)(6.424)]$$
$$= -14.891$$

$$\Delta \beta = [(1)(18.41) + (2)(3.464)](10^{-3}) - [(1)(10.14) + (4)(1.039)](10^{-3})$$
$$= 11.047 \times 10^{-3}$$

$$\Delta \gamma = [(1)(-4.48) + (2)(-0.483)](10^{-6}) - [(1)(-3.415) + (4)(-0.078)](10^{-6})$$
$$= -1.719 \times 10^{-6}$$

$$\Delta C_p = -14.891 + 11.042 \times 10^{-3}T - 1.719 \times 10^{-6}T^2$$

Next we find ΔH_0, using as a reference temperature 25°C,

$$\Delta H_0 = \Delta H_{rxn_{298}} - \Delta \alpha T - \frac{\Delta \beta}{2} T^2 - \frac{\Delta \gamma}{3} T^3$$

$$= -39{,}443 - (-14.891)(298) - \frac{11.042 \times 10^{-3}}{2}(298)^2$$

$$- \frac{(-1.719 \times 10^{-6})}{3}(298)^3$$

$$= -39{,}443 + 4{,}430 - 491 + 15.16 = -35{,}479 \text{ cal}$$

Then, with ΔH_0 known, the ΔH_{rxn} at 773°K can be determined.

$$\Delta H_{rxn_{773}°K} = \Delta H_0 + \Delta \alpha T + \frac{\Delta \beta}{2} T^2 + \frac{\Delta \gamma}{3} T^3$$

$$= -35{,}479 - 14.891(773) + \frac{11.042 \times 10^{-3}}{2}(773)^2$$

$$= - \frac{1.719 \times 10^{-6}}{3}(773)^3$$

$$= -43{,}943 \text{ cal}$$

or 43,943 kcal/kg mole CO_2 must be removed.

Example 4.31 Calculation of Heat of Reaction at a Temperature Different than Standard Conditions

Repeat the calculation of the previous example using enthalpy values from Kobe (reference 12 in Table 4.5).

Solution:

Enthalpy data have been taken from Kobe's *Thermochemistry of Petrochemicals*. The heat of reaction at 25°C and 1 atm from the previous example is

$$\Delta \hat{H}_{rxn_{298}°K} = -39{,}433 \ \frac{\text{kcal}}{\text{kg mole}}$$

$\Delta \hat{H}$ (kcal/kg mole); reference is 0°C

temperature	CO_2	H_2	H_2O	CH_4
25°C	218	172	200	210
500°C	5340	3499	4254	5730

From Eq. (4.41) or Fig. 4.14 you can see

$$\Delta H_{rxn_{500}°C} = \Delta H_{rxn_{25}°C} + \Delta H_{products} - \Delta H_{reactants}$$

$$= -39{,}433 + [(1)(5730 - 210) + 2(4254 - 200)]$$

$$- [(1)(5340 - 218) + 4(3499 - 172)]$$

$$= 44{,}235 \ \frac{\text{kcal}}{\text{kg mole } CO_2}$$

Note that the enthalpy of the products and of the reactants are both based on the reference temperature of 25°C. The answer is not quite the same as in the previous example, because the heat capacity data used in Example 4.29 were not quite the same as those used by Kobe in calculating his ΔH values.

(b) *Reaction for case in which products leave and reactants enter at different temperatures.* The method of procedure in this more general case is to first choose a reference state at which the heat of reaction is known. This usually turns out to be 25°C and 1 atm. Then the next step is to calculate the enthalpy changes for each stream entering and leaving *relative to this reference state.* Finally, the enthalpy changes are summed up and the heat of reaction calculated for the actual process which is taking place. Even though the actual temperature of the reaction itself is unknown, or is known but is different than that of any of the entering or leaving streams, the heat of reaction can be computed from Eqs. (4.40) or (4.41) for the process with the conditions of the streams as stated.

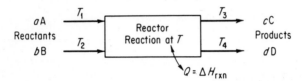

Fig. 4.15. Heat of reaction, general case.

Enthalpy changes can be clearly shown schematically on enthalpy-temperature plots. The arrows which represent the direction of the enthalpy change have some significance, since an arrow with a positive component parallel to the H axis indicates a positive enthalpy change, while an arrow with a negative component indicates a negative enthalpy change. The energy liberated on reaction then can be indicated to be a summing-up of the enthalpy changes as indicated by the arrows in Fig. 4.16. Drawing one of these diagrams for each problem involving enthalpy changes will materially assist you in its solution.

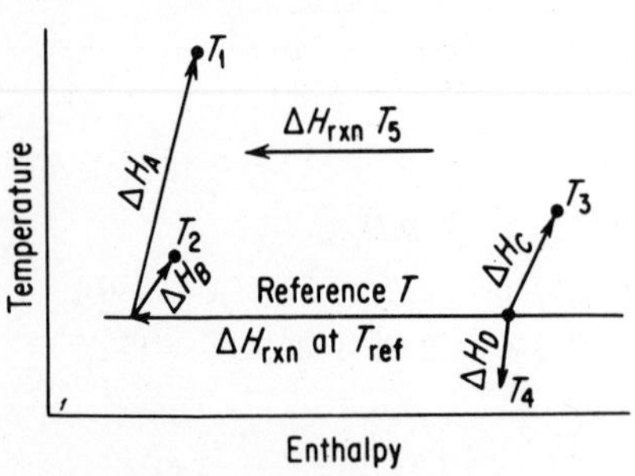

Note that, if the products do not leave the reactor at the temperature of the (well-mixed) reactor, some heat must be removed from the exit stream by cooling, radiation, or the like, or else the exit stream did not come to thermal equilibrium with the reactor contents.

Fig. 4.16. Enthalpy-temperature diagram.

Methods you can use to determine ΔH values for the individual streams are:

1. Obtain the enthalpy values from a set of published tables, e.g., the tables by Kobe.

2. Use $\Delta H = C_{p_m} \Delta t$ or

$$\Delta H = C_{p_{m_2}}(T_2 - T_{\text{ref}}) - C_{p_{m_1}}(T_1 - T_{\text{ref}})$$

as previously discussed.

3. Find ΔH from

$$\Delta H = \int (\Delta C_p)\, dT$$

for all components.

4. Analytically or graphically find

$$\Delta H = \int C_p\, dT$$

for each component individually.

Any phase changes taking place among the reactants or products not accounted for in the chemical equation must be included in the calculations.

Example 4.32   Heat of Reaction—General Case

Carbon monoxide at 50°F is completely burned at 2 atm pressure with 50% excess air which is at 1000°F. The products of combustion leave the combustion chamber at 800°F. Calculate the heat evolved from the combustion chamber in terms of Btu/lb of CO entering.

Solution:
The diagram is as shown below.

Basis: 1 lb mole of CO

$$CO(g) + \tfrac{1}{2} O_2(g) \longrightarrow CO_2(g)$$

Material balance:
amount of air entering:

$$= \frac{1 \text{ lb mole CO}}{} \left| \frac{0.5 \text{ lb mole } O_2}{1 \text{ lb mole CO}} \right| \frac{1.5 \text{ lb mole } O_2 \text{ used}}{1.0 \text{ lb } O_2 \text{ mole needed}} \left| \frac{1 \text{ lb mole air}}{0.21 \text{ lb mole } O_2} \right.$$

$= 3.57$ lb mole air

amount of O_2 leaving, unreacted:

$= (0.21)(3.57) - 0.5$

$= 0.25$ lb mole O_2

amount of N_2 leaving:

$= (0.79)(3.57)$

$= 2.82$ lb mole N_2

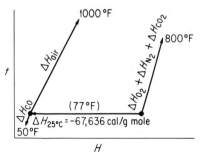

Enthalpy data have been taken from Kobe's *Thermochemistry of Petrochemicals*. The heat of reaction at 25°C (77°F) and 1 atm from Example 4.21 is −67,636 cal/g mole or −121,745 Btu/lb mole. We can assume that the slightly higher pressure at 2 atm has no effect on the heat of reaction or enthalpy values.

$$\Delta H \text{ (Btu/lb mole); reference is } 32°F$$

temperature	CO	air	O_2	N_2	CO_2
50°F	125.2	—	—	—	—
77°F	313.3	312.7	315.1	312.2	392.2
800°F	—	—	5690	5443	8026
1000°F	—	6984	—	—	—

$$Q = \Delta H_{rxn_{77°F}} + \Delta H_{products} - \Delta H_{reactants}$$

(a) $\Delta \hat{H}_{rxn_{77°F}} = -121,745 \text{ Btu/lb mole}$

(b) $\Delta H_{products} = \Delta H_{800°F} - \Delta H_{77°F}$

$$\overset{CO_2}{= (1)(8026} - 392.2) + \overset{N_2}{(2.82)(5443} - 312.2)$$

$$+ \overset{O_2}{(0.25)(5690} - 315.1)$$

$$= 7633.8 + 14,480 + 1343$$

$$= 23,457 \text{ Btu/lb mole}$$

(c) $\Delta H_{reactants} = \overset{Air}{\Delta H_{1000°F}} - \Delta H_{77°F} + \overset{CO}{\Delta H_{50°F}} - \Delta H_{77°F}$

$$= (3.57)(6984 - 312.7) + (1)(125.2 - 313.3)$$

$$= 23,800 - 188.1 = 23,612 \text{ Btu/lb mole}$$

(d) $Q = -121,745 + 23,457 - 23,612$

$$= -121,900 \text{ Btu/lb mole}$$

$$\frac{-121,900 \text{ Btu}}{\text{lb mole CO}} \left| \frac{1 \text{ lb mole CO}}{28 \text{ lb CO}} \right. = -4360 \text{ Btu/lb CO}$$

4.7-6 Temperature of a Reaction. We are now equipped to determine what is called the *adiabatic reaction temperature*. This is the temperature obtained when (a) the reaction is adiabatic, i.e., there is no heat interchange between the container in which the reaction is taking place and the surroundings, and (b) when there are no other effects present, such as electrical effects, work, ionization, free radical formation, etc. In calculations of flame temperatures for combustion reactions, the adiabatic reaction temperature assumes complete combustion. Equilibrium considerations may dictate less than complete combustion for an actual case. For example, the adiabatic flame temperature for the combustion of CH_4 with theoretical air has been calculated to be 2010°C; allowing for incomplete combustion, it would be 1920°C. The actual temperature when measured is 1885°C.

This calculation of the adiabatic reaction temperature tells us the temperature ceiling that thermodynamics puts on a process. We can do no better, but of course the actual temperature may be less. The adiabatic reaction temperature helps us select the types of materials that must be specified for the container in which the reaction is taking place.

The principle behind the calculation of the adiabatic reaction temperature is to assume that all the energy liberated from the reaction at some base temperature plus that brought in by the entering stream (relative to the same base temperature) is available to raise the energy of the products. We assume that the products leave at the temperature of the reaction, and thus, if you know the temperature of the products, you automatically know the temperature of the reaction. This concept is sometimes called the "energy pool." In effect for this adiabatic process the general energy balance reduces to:

$$\Delta H = \Delta H_{\text{products}} - \Delta H_{\text{reactants}} = S_R = (\Delta \hat{H}_{\text{rxn}})(m)$$

Since no heat escapes and the energy liberated is allowed only to increase the enthalpy of the products of the reaction, we have (see also Fig. 4.17)

$$\Delta H_{\text{products}} = \boxed{\Delta H_{\text{reactants}} + S_R} \qquad (4.51)$$

"energy pool"

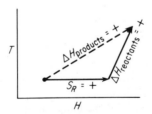

Fig. 4.17. Adiabatic reaction temperature.

Any phase changes that take place and are not accounted for by the chemical equation must be incorporated into the "energy pool." Because of the character of the information available, the determination of the adiabatic reaction temperature or flame temperature may involve a trial-and-error solution.

Example 4.33 Adiabatic Flame Temperature

Calculate the theoretical flame temperature for CO burned at constant pressure with 100% excess air, when the reactants enter at 200°F.

Solution:

$$CO(g) + \tfrac{1}{2} O_2(g) \longrightarrow CO_2(g)$$

Basis: 1 g mole $CO(g)$; ref. temp. 25°C (77°F)

Material balance:

entering reactants		exit products	
comp.	*moles*	*comp.*	*moles*
$CO(g)$	1.00	$CO_2(g)$	1.00
O_2(req.)	0.50	$O_2(g)$	0.50
O_2(xs)	0.50	$N_2(g)$	3.76
O_2(total)	1.00		
N_2	3.76		
air	4.76		

$$\Delta H_{\text{rxn}} \text{ at } 25°C = -67{,}636 \text{ cal} \qquad (200°F = 93.3°C)$$

Note: For the purposes of illustration, in this example mean heat capacities have been calculated using 25°C as the reference temperature rather than 0°C.

Then, for Eq. (4.51), $\Delta H_{\text{reactants}}$:

reactants

comp.	*moles*	Δt	C_{p_m}	ΔH
$CO(g)$	1.00	68.3	6.981	476
Air	4.76	68.3	6.993	2270
			$\sum \Delta H_R =$	2746 cal

$$S_R = (-67{,}636)(-1) = 67{,}636 \text{ cal}$$

$$\Delta H_{\text{products}} = 2746 + 67{,}636 = 70{,}382 \text{ cal}$$

To find the temperature which yields a $\Delta H_{\text{products}}$ of 70,382 cal, the simplest procedure is to assume various values of the exit temperature of the products until the $\sum \Delta H_P = 70{,}382$.

Assume TFT (theoretical flame temperature) = 1800°C:

$$\Delta t = 1800 - 25 = 1775°C$$

comp.	*moles*	C_{p_m}	*total* ΔH
CO_2	1.00	12.94	23,000
O_2	0.50	8.349	7,400
N_2	3.76	7.924	52,900
		$\sum \Delta H_P =$	83,300 cal

Assume TFT = 1500°C:

$$\Delta t = 1500 - 25 = 1475°C$$

comp.	moles	C_{p_m}	total ΔH
CO_2	1.00	12.70	18,740
O_2	0.50	8.305	6,120
N_2	3.76	7.879	43,600

$$\Sigma \, \Delta H_P = 68,460 \text{ cal}$$

Make a linear interpolation:

$$\text{TFT} = 1500 + \frac{70,382 - 68,460}{83,300 - 68,460}(300) = 1500 + 39$$

$$\text{TFT} = 1539°C = 2798°F$$

4.8 Heats of solution and mixing

So far in our energy calculations, we have been considering each substance to be a completely pure and separate material. The physical properties of an "ideal" solution or mixture may be computed from the sum of the properties in question for the individual components. For gases, mole fractions can be used as weighting values, or, alternatively, each component can be considered to be independent of the others. In most instances so far in this book we have used the latter procedure. Using the former technique, as we did in a few instances, we could write down for the heat capacity of an ideal mixture,

$$C_{p \text{ mixture}} = x_A C_{p_A} + x_B C_{p_B} + x_C C_{p_C} + \cdots \tag{4.52}$$

or, for the enthalpy,

$$\Delta \hat{H}_{\text{mixture}} = x_A \Delta \hat{H}_A + x_B \Delta \hat{H}_B + x_C \Delta \hat{H}_C + \cdots \tag{4.53}$$

These equations are applicable to ideal mixtures only.

When two or more pure substances are mixed to form a gas or liquid solution, we frequently find energy is absorbed or evolved upon mixing. Such a solution would be called a "real" solution. For example, in a binary system with a fixed reference for the enthalpies,

$$\Delta H_{\text{total}} = \Delta H_1 + \Delta H_2 + \Delta H_{\text{mixing}} \tag{4.54}$$

where the subscripts 1 and 2 represent the pure components and where ΔH represents the total enthalpy and not the enthalpy per pound. The total heat of mixing (ΔH_{mixing}) has to be determined experimentally, but can be retrieved from tabulated experimental (smoothed) results, once such data are available. This type of energy change has been given the formal name *heat of solution* when one substance dissolves in another, and there is also the negative of the heat of solution, the *heat of dissolution*, for a substance which separates from a solution. Tabulated data for heats of solution appear in Table 4.8 in terms of energy per mole for consecutively added quantities of solvent to solute; the gram mole refers to the gram mole of solute. Heats of solution are somewhat similar to heats of reaction in that an energy change takes place because of differences in the forces of attraction of the solvent and solute molecules. Of course, these energy changes are much smaller than those we find accompanying the breaking and combining of

TABLE 4.8   HEAT OF SOLUTION OF HCl
(at 25°C and 1 atm)

Composition	Total moles H_2O added to 1 mole HCl	$-\Delta\hat{H}°$ for each incremental step (cal/g mole)	Integral heat of solution: The cumulative $-\Delta\hat{H}°$ (cal/g mole)
HCl (g)	0		
HCl·1 H_2O	1	6,268	6,268
HCl·2 H_2O	2	5,400	11,668
HCl·3 H_2O	3	1,920	13,588
HCl·4 H_2O	4	1,040	14,628
HCl·5 H_2O	5	680	15,308
HCl·8 H_2O	8	1,000	16,308
HCl·10 H_2O	10	300	16,608
HCl·15 H_2O	15	359	16,967
HCl·25 H_2O	25	305	17,272
HCl·50 H_2O	50	242	17,514
HCl·100 H_2O	100	136	17,650
HCl·200 H_2O	200	85	17,735
HCl·500 H_2O	500	76	17,811
HCl·1000 H_2O	1,000	39	17,850
HCl·5000 H_2O	5,000	59	17,909
HCl·50,000 H_2O	50,000	35	17,944
HCl·∞ H_2O		16	17,960

Source: National Bureau of Standards Circular 500 (Reference 15 in Table 4.5).

chemical bonds. When incorporated into the energy balance, heats of solution are best treated identically to heats of reaction, i.e., the energy liberated is incorporated into the S_R term in Eq. (4.24).

The solution process can be represented by an equation such as the following:

$$HCl(g) + 5\,H_2O \longrightarrow HCl{:}5\,H_2O$$

or

$$HCl(g) + 5\,H_2O \longrightarrow HCl(5\,H_2O)$$
$$\Delta\hat{H}°_{soln} = -15{,}308 \text{ cal/g mole}$$

The expression HCl(5 H_2O) means that 1 mole of HCl has been dissolved in 5 moles of water, and the enthalpy change for the process is −15,308 cal/g mole of HCl. Table 4.8 shows the heat of solution for additional numbers of moles of water added to 1 mole of HCl.

The *standard integral heat of solution* is the cumulative $\Delta \hat{H}^{\circ}_{\text{soln}}$ as shown in the last column for the indicated number of molecules of water. As successive increments of water are added to the mole of HCl, the cumulative heat of solution or the integral heat of solution increases, but the incremental enthalpy change decreases as shown in Table 4.8. Note that both the reactants and products have to be at standard conditions. The heat of dissolution would be just the negative of these values. The integral heat of solution is plotted in Fig. 4.18, and you can see that an asymptotic value is approached as the solution becomes more dilute. At infinite dilution this value is called

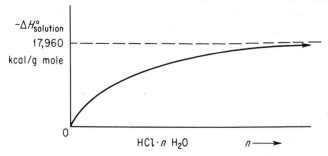

Fig. 4.18. Integral heat of solution of HCl in water.

the *standard integral heat of solution at infinite dilution* and is $-17{,}960$ cal/g mole of HCl. In the Appendix are other tables presenting standard integral heat of solution data. Since the energy changes for heats of solution are point functions, you can easily go between any two concentrations of HCl and find the energy change caused by adding or subtracting water.

Example 4.34　Heat of Solution

Calculate the standard heat of formation of HCl in 5 g moles of water.

Solution:
We treat the solution process in an identical fashion to a chemical reaction:

kcal/g mole

$\Delta \hat{H}^{\circ}_{f}$ = -22.063	$\frac{1}{2} H_2(g) + \frac{1}{2} Cl_2(g)$	$= HCl(g)$
$\Delta \hat{H}^{\circ}_{\text{soln}}$ = -15.308	$HCl(g) + 5 H_2O$	$= HCl(5 H_2O)$
$\Delta \hat{H}^{\circ}_{f}$ = -37.371	$\frac{1}{2} H_2(g) + \frac{1}{2} Cl_2(g) + 5 H_2O$	$= HCl(5 H_2O)$

It is important to remember that the heat of formation of H_2O itself does not enter into the calculation. The heat of formation of HCl in an infinitely dilute solution is

$$\Delta \hat{H}_f^\circ = -22.063 - 17.960 = -40.023 \text{ kcal/g mole}$$

Another type of heat of solution which is occasionally encountered is the partial molal heat of solution. Information about this thermodynamic property can be found in most standard thermodynamic texts or in books on thermochemistry.

One point of special importance concerns the formation of water in chemical reaction. When water participates in a chemical reaction in solution as a reactant or product of the reaction, you must include the heat of formation of the water as well as the heat of solution in the calculation of the over-all enthalpy change. Thus, if HCl reacts with sodium hydroxide to form water and the reaction is carried out in only 2 moles of water to start with, it is apparent that you will have 3 moles of water at the end of the process. In calculating S_R, not only do you have to take into account the water formed, but there is also a heat of solution factor. If gaseous HCl reacts with crystalline sodium hydroxide and the product is 1 mole of gaseous water vapor, then you could calculate the heat of reaction without worrying about the heat of solution effect.

If an enthalpy-concentration diagram is available for the system in which you are interested, then the enthalpy changes can be obtained directly from the diagram by convenient graphical methods. See Chap. 5 for illustrations of this technique.

Example 4.35   Application of Heat of Solution Data

An ammonium hydroxide solution is to be prepared at 77°F by dissolving gaseous NH_3 in water. Prepare charts showing:

(a) The amount of cooling needed in Btu to prepare a solution containing 1 lb mole of NH_3 at any concentration desired

(b) The amount of cooling needed in Btu to prepare 100 gal of a solution of any concentration up to 35% NH_3

(c) If a 10.5% NH_3 solution is made up without cooling, to what temperature will the solution rise?

Solution:

Heat of solution data have been taken from *NBS Circular* 500.

(a)   Basis: 17 lb NH_3 = 1 lb mole NH_3

Reference temperature = 77°F = 25°C

To convert from kcal/g mole to Btu/lb mole, multiply by 1800.

description	state	$-\Delta\hat{H}_f^\circ$ kcal/g mole	$-\Delta\hat{H}_f^\circ$ Btu/lb mole	$-\Delta\hat{H}_{soln}^\circ$ Btu/lb mole	weight % NH_3
	g	11.04	19,900	0	100
1 H_2O	aq	18.1	32,600	12,700	48.5
2 H_2O	aq	18.7	33,600	13,700	32.0
3 H_2O	aq	18.87	34,000	14,100	23.9
4 H_2O	aq	18.99	34,200	14,300	19.1
5 H_2O	aq	19.07	34,350	14,450	15.9
10 H_2O	aq	19.23	34,600	14,700	8.63
20 H_2O	aq	19.27	34,700	14,800	4.51
30 H_2O	aq	19.28	34,700	14,800	3.05
40 H_2O	aq	19.28	34,700	14,800	2.30
50 H_2O	aq	19.29	34,750	14,850	1.85
100 H_2O	aq	19.30	34,750	14,850	0.94
200 H_2O	aq	19.32	34,800	14,900	0.47
∞ H_2O	aq	19.32	34,800	14,900	0.0

Standard heats of solution can be calculated from the cumulative data as follows:

$$\Delta\hat{H}_{soln}^\circ = \Delta\hat{H}_f^\circ - \Delta\hat{H}_{f_{gas}}^\circ$$
$$\Delta\hat{H}_{soln}^\circ = [-32,600 - (-19,900)]$$
$$= -12,700 \text{ Btu/lb mole } NH_3$$

Weight per cents are computed as follows:

$$\text{wt } \% \text{ } NH_3 = \frac{\text{lb } NH_3(100)}{\text{lb } H_2O + \text{lb } NH_3}$$

$$\% \text{ } NH_3 \text{ for 1 } H_2O: = \frac{17(100)}{18(1) + 17} = 48.5\%$$

The heat of solution values shown in diagram a are equivalent to the cooling duty required.

(b) Part (b) of the problem requires that a new basis be selected, 100 gal of solution. Additional data concerning densities of NH_4OH are shown on next page.

Sample calculations are as follows:

$$\text{density, lb/100 gal} = \frac{(\text{sp gr soln})(62.4 \text{ lb/ft}^3)(1.003)(100)}{(7.48 \text{ gal/ft}^3)}$$

Note: 1.003 is the specific gravity of water at 77°F.

$$\text{density @ 32.0\% } NH_3 = \frac{(0.889)(62.4)(1.003)(100)}{7.48} = 741 \text{ lb/100 gal}$$

$$\left.\begin{array}{l}\text{cooling req'd} \\ \text{Btu/100 gal}\end{array}\right\} = \left(\frac{\text{lb moles } NH_3}{100 \text{ gal}}\right)\left(-\Delta H_{soln}^\circ \frac{\text{Btu}}{\text{lb mole } NH_3}\right)$$

$$\left.\begin{array}{l}\text{cooling req'd} \\ \text{for 100 gal} \\ 32.0\% \text{ } NH_3 \text{ soln}\end{array}\right\} = (13.94)(13,700) = 191,000 \text{ Btu/100 gal soln}$$

These data are portrayed in diagram b.

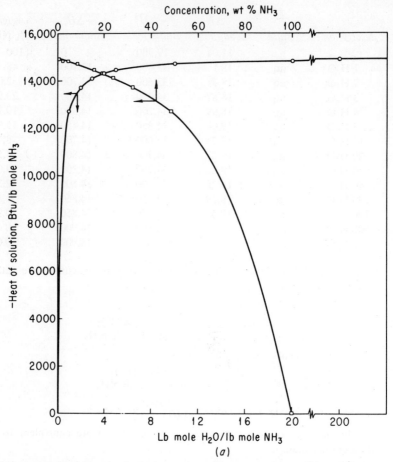

(a)

Basis: 100 gal of solution at concentrations and densities shown

% NH_3	sp gr* @ 4°C	density, lb/100 gal	lb NH_3 100 gal	lb mole NH_3 100 gal	$-\Delta \hat{H}^\circ_{soln}$ Btu lb mole NH_3	cooling req'd per 100 gal, Btu
32.0	0.889	741	237	13.94	13,700	191,000
23.9	0.914	761	182	10.70	14,100	151,000
19.1	0.929	774	148	8.70	14,300	124,000
15.9	0.940	784	124.7	7.32	14,450	106,000
8.63	0.965	805	69.4	4.08	14,700	60,000
4.51	0.981	819	37.0	2.18	14,800	32,200
3.05	0.986					
2.30	0.990	826	19.0	1.12	14,800	16,600
1.85	0.992					
0.94	0.995	830	7.8	0.46	14,850	6,800
0.47	0.998					
0.0	1.000	834	0	0	14,900	0

*Source: N. A. Lange, *Handbook of Chemistry*, 8th ed., Handbook Publishers Inc., Sandusky, Ohio, 1958.

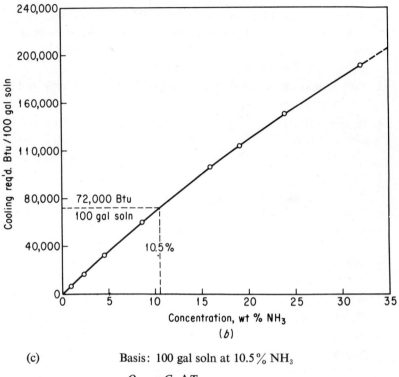

Concentration, wt % NH₃

(b)

(c)   Basis: 100 gal soln at 10.5% NH_3

$$Q = mC_p \, \Delta T$$

$$Q = 72{,}000 \text{ Btu/100 gal} \quad (\text{cf Fig. b})$$

$$\text{sp gr soln} = 0.955$$

$$m = \frac{(0.955)(62.4)(1.003)(100)}{7.48} = 800 \text{ lb}$$

$$C_p \, 10.5\% \, NH_3 \text{ soln} = 4.261 \text{ joules/(g)(°C)}$$

$$= 1.02 \text{ Btu/(lb)(°F)} \ (I.C.T., \text{ vol. V})$$

$$\Delta T = \frac{Q}{mC_p} = \frac{72{,}000}{(800)(1.02)} = 88°F$$

$$T_{\text{final}} = 77 + 88 = 165°F$$

WHAT YOU SHOULD HAVE LEARNED FROM THIS CHAPTER

1. You should know what the energy balance is in words and in mathematical equations. You should be able to explain what each term in the equations means and be able to apply the equations to practical or simulated problems, i.e., be able to state what each term is in light of the conditions in the problem, know what assumptions can and cannot be made, and know what terms can be omitted.

2. In analyzing problems by means of energy balances, you should be able to set up a suitable system, be able to distinguish between flow and nonflow processes, and be able to judge whether the process can be considered to be reversible or irreversible.

3. You should know the difference between thermal energy and heat, and between heat and work.

4. In applying the energy balance, you should be able to locate enthalpy or heat capacity data for a wide range of compounds and, if such data are not available, be able to make suitable approximations.

5. You should know what a point function is and how it differs from a path function.

6. You should be familiar with the principles of thermochemistry, and especially how to use a reference temperature, how to calculate heats of reaction with the products and reactants entering and leaving at various temperatures, and how to calculate standard heats of formation and heats of combustion from experimental data.

7. When applicable, you should be able to compute the heats of solution or mixing and know where to find information of this type.

8. You should be able to calculate the adiabatic reaction temperature for simple or complex reactions, whether they go to completion or not and whether or not the participants are in the proper stoichiometric proportions.

NOMENCLATURE

(Units are discussed in the text)

a, b, c = constants in heat capacity equation
c = crystalline
C_p = heat capacity at constant pressure
C_v = heat capacity at constant volume
C_{p_m} = mean heat capacity
E = total energy in accumulation term
E_v = irreversible conversion of mechanical energy to internal energy
F = force
(g) = gas
g = acceleration due to gravity
g_c = conversion factor of $\dfrac{32.2\ (\text{ft})(\text{lb}_m)}{(\text{sec}^2)(\text{lb}_f)}$
h = distance above reference plane

H = enthalpy
ΔH_c° = standard heat of combustion
ΔH_f° = standard heat of formation
ΔH_{rxn} = heat of reaction
ΔH_{soln} = heat of solution
ΔH_0 = constant defined in Eq. (4.50)
K = kinetic energy
(l) = liquid
l = distance
m = mass of material
n = moles of material
p = pressure
Pcu = pound centigrade unit
p^* = vapor pressure
P = potential energy
Q = heat transferred
Q_p = heat evolved in a constant pressure process
Q_v = heat evolved in a constant volume process
R = universal gas constant
(s) = solid
S_R = energy generated or absorbed
t = relative temperature in °C or °F
T = absolute temperature or temperature in general
T_b = normal boiling point in °K
T_f = melting point in °K
T_r = reduced temperature = T/T_c
U = internal energy
v = velocity
V = volume
V_g = molal volume of gas
V_l = molal volume of liquid
W = work done
x = mole fraction (with a subscript)

α, β, γ = constants in heat capacity equation
Δ = difference between exit and entering streams
λ = molal heat of vaporization
λ_b = molal heat of vaporization at the normal boiling point
λ_f = molal latent heat of fusion at the melting point
ρ = density

Superscripts:
$\wedge$ = per unit mass or per mole

Subscripts:
1, 2 = system boundaries
t = time

R = reactants
R = reference temperature
P = products
ref = reference
rxn = reaction

SUPPLEMENTARY REFERENCES

1. Everdell, M. H., *Fundamental Thermodynamics for Engineers*, The English Universities Press, Ltd., London, 1958.

2. Hall, N. A., and W. E. Ibele, *Engineering Thermodynamics*, Prentice-Hall, Inc., Englewood Cliffs, N.J., 1960.

3. Henley, E. J., and H. Bieber, *Chemical Engineering Calculations*, McGraw-Hill Book Company, New York, 1959.

4. Hougen, O. A., K. M. Watson, and R. A. Ragatz, *Chemical Process Principles*, Part I, 2nd ed., John Wiley & Sons, Inc., New York, 1956.

5. Hougen, O. A., K. M. Watson, and R. A. Ragatz, *Chemical Process Principles*, Part II, 2nd ed., John Wiley & Sons, Inc., New York, 1959.

6. Littlejohn, C. E., and G. F. Meenaghan, *An Introduction to Chemical Engineering*, Reinhold Publishing Corp., New York, 1959.

7. Schmidt, A. X., and H. L. List, *Material and Energy Balances*, Prentice-Hall, Inc., Englewood Cliffs, N.J., 1962.

8. Smith, J. M., and H. C. Van Ness, *Introduction to Chemical Engineering Thermodynamics*, 2nd ed., McGraw-Hill Book Company, New York, 1959.

9. Weber, H. C., and H. P. Meissner, *Thermodynamics for Chemical Engineers*, 2nd ed., John Wiley & Sons, Inc., New York, 1957.

10. Williams, E. T., and R. C. Johnson, *Stoichiometry for Chemical Engineers*, McGraw-Hill Book Company, New York, 1958.

PROBLEMS

4.1. Are the following variables intensive or extensive variables? Explain for each:
(a) Pressure
(b) Volume
(c) Specific volume
(d) Refractive index
(e) Surface tension

4.2. A missile is fired vertically from the earth's surface so that it reaches a height of 150,000 ft above the ground. Calculate the potential and kinetic energy per pound of the missile at 150,000 ft.

4.3. If a pail weighing $\frac{1}{2}$ lb is dropped into a well 50 ft deep, what is the kinetic and potential energy of the pail (a) just before it hits the water, and (b) after it hits the water surface (at 50 ft)?

4.4. Explain specifically what the system is for each of the following processes; indicate the portions of the energy transfer which are heat and work by the symbols Q and W, respectively:

(a) A liquid inside a metal can, well-insulated on the outside of the can, is shaken very rapidly in a vibrating shaker.

(b) Hydrogen is exploded in a calometric bomb and the water layer outside the bomb rises in temperature by 1°C.

(c) A motor boat is driven by an outboard-motor propeller.

(d) Water flows through a pipe at 10 ft/min, and the temperature of the water and the air surrounding the pipe are the same.

4.5. Draw a simple sketch of each of the following processes, and, in each, label the system boundary, the system, the surroundings, and the streams of material and energy which cross the system boundary:

(a) Water enters a boiler, is vaporized, and leaves as steam. The energy for vaporization is obtained by combustion of a fuel gas with air outside the boiler surface.

(b) The steam enters a rotary steam turbine and turns a shaft connected to an electric generator. The steam is exhausted at a low pressure from the turbine.

(c) A battery is charged by connecting it to a source of current.

(d) A tree obtains water and minerals through its roots and gives off carbon dioxide from its leaves. The tree, of course, gives off oxygen at night.

4.6. Draw a simple sketch of the following processes; indicate the system boundary, and classify the system as open or closed:

(a) Automobile engine   (e) A river
(b) Water wheel   (f) The earth and its atmosphere
(c) Pressure cooker   (g) An air compressor
(d) Man himself   (h) A coffee pot

4.7. Before it lands, a vehicle returning from space must convert its enormous kinetic energy to heat. To get some idea of what is involved, a vehicle returning from the moon at 25,000 mph can, in converting its kinetic energy, increase the internal energy of the vehicle sufficiently to vaporize it. Obviously a large part of the total kinetic energy must be transferred from the vehicle. How much kinetic energy does the vehicle have in Btu? How much energy must be transferred by heat if the vehicle is to heat up only 20°F/lb?

4.8. A 100-hp engine is doing work at the rate of how many (a) Btu/hr, (b) cal/sec, (c) kw?

4.9. By use of the heat capacity data for liquid water, calculate the enthalpy of liquid water at 150°F and 1 atm relative to (a) 32°F and 1 atm and (b) relative to 100°F and 1 atm.

4.10. Given that the heat capacity C_p for mercury at -20°C is 0.0335 cal/g, while at 100°C the value of C_p is 0.0327, compute the change of enthalpy of 10 g of mercury from $-20°C$ to $100°C$. Given that the heat capacity at constant volume, C_v, is 0.0294 at $-20°C$ and 0.0276 cal/g at $100°C$, compute the change in internal energy for the same temperature range. Then compute ΔpV for mercury for the same temperature range.

4.11. One hundred and fifty pounds of CO_2 have a specific enthalpy of 45,000 $(ft)(lb_f)/lb_m$ with reference to $0°F$ and 1 psia. What is the enthalpy of this CO_2 in Btu/lb mole? What is the total internal energy if the pressure is 6 atm and the temperature is $50°F$?

4.12. One gram mole of air is heated from $400°$ tto $1000°C$. Calculate ΔH by integrating the heat capacity equation. Calculate ΔU also.

4.13. One pound mole of the following gas:

$$20\% \text{ He}; \quad 20\% \text{ CH}_4; \quad 40\% \text{ CO}_2; \quad 20\% \text{ N}_2$$

is heated from 100 to $300°F$ at constant pressure of 1 atm. Find ΔH and ΔU for the process.

4.14. Calculate the enthalpy change in cooling 10,000 ft³ (measured at the initial conditions) of the following mixture from $500°F$ to $300°F$: gas (at 1 atm)— $50\% \text{ N}_2$, $50\% \text{ C}_2\text{H}_2$; solid—C(graphite), 1 lb/100 ft³ of gas at entering conditions.

4.15. One pound mole of NO is heated at constant pressure from $50°F$ to $300°F$. What is the enthalpy change? Compare with that for NO as an *ideal* gas.

4.16. (a) Ten-pound moles of an ideal gas are originally in a tank at 100 atm and $40°F$. The gas is heated to $440°F$. The specific molal enthalpy, $\Delta \hat{H}$, of the ideal gas is given by the equation

$$\Delta \hat{H} = 300 + 8.00t$$

where $\Delta \hat{H} = $ Btu/lb mole
$t = $ temperature, $°F$

(1) Compute the volume of the container (ft³).
(2) Compute the final pressure of the gas (atm).
(3) Compute the enthalpy change of the gas.

(b) Use the equation above to develop an equation giving the molal internal energy, $\Delta \hat{U}$, in cal/g mole as a function of temperature t in $°C$.

(c) What is the temperature for the reference enthalpy ($\Delta \hat{H} = 0$)?

4.17. The differential change in the volume of a gas is given by the relation

$$dV = nR\left[\left(\frac{1}{p} + a\right) dT - \frac{T}{p^2} dp\right]$$

Show that the volume V is a point or state function.

4.18. State which of the following variables are point, or state, variables, and which are not; explain your decision in one sentence for each one:

(a) Pressure
(b) Density
(c) Molecular weight
(d) Heat capacity
(e) Internal energy
(f) Ionization constant

4.19. Experimental values of the heat capacity C_p have been determined in the laboratory as follows; fit a second-order polynomial in temperature to the data ($C_p = a + bT + cT^2$):

$T, °C$	$C_p, cal/(g\ mole)(°C)$
100	9.69
200	10.47
300	11.23
400	11.79
500	12.25
600	12.63
700	12.94

(The data are for carbon dioxide; if a computer is used in the data fitting process, also calculate the confidence limits for the predicted value of C_p.)

4.20. If the equation for the mean heat capacity of a compound is

$$C_{p_m}\ (Btu)/(lb\ mole)(°F) = 3.44 + 1.25 \times 10^{-2}t + 4.27 \times 10^{-5}t^2$$

where t is in °C and the reference temperature is 0°C,
(a) What is the equation for the heat capacity?
(b) What is the value of the heat capacity at 200°C?
(c) What is the enthalpy change per mole from 100 to 200°C?

4.21. Determine the mean heat capacity between T_1 and T_2 if C_p is expressed as
(a) $C_p = a + bT$ (T in degrees absolute)
(b) $C_p = a + bT - cT^{-2}$ (T in degrees absolute)
(c) $C_p = a - bT - cT^{1.2}$ (T in degrees C)

4.22. Look up the molal heat capacity equations for the gases listed below and calculate:
(a) C_p at 300°C
(b) C_p at 200°F
(c) The mean C_p to 300°C from a reference temperature
(d) The mean C_p to 200°F from a reference temperature
(e) The heat required to heat the gas from 77°F to the above temperatures.
Gases: SO_2, H_2O, NO, CO_2

4.23. The instantaneous molal heat capacity of CO_2 is

$$C_p = 9.085 + 0.0048t - 0.83 \times 10^{-6}t^2$$

where $t = °C$
$C_p = cal/(g\ mol)(°C)$

Calculate the mean molal heat capacity of 1 lb mole of CO_2 between 0 and 1000°C.

4.24. The instantaneous molal heat capacity of carbon monoxide is

$$C_p = 6.935 + 6.77 \times 10^{-4}t + 1.3 \times 10^{-7}t^2$$

where $C_p = cal/(g\ mol)(°C)$
$t = °C$

Calculate the mean molal heat capacity between 500 and 1000°C.

4.25. The mean molal heat capacity of air over the temperature range 0 to $t°C$ is given by the equation

$$C_{p_m} = 6.935 + 0.338 \times 10^{-3}t + 0.433 \times 10^{-7}t^2$$

Calculate the instantaneous molal heat capacity at 1000°C.

4.26. Harrison (see reference 12, Table 4.5) has calculated the heat capacity values for ammonia from $-40°C$ to 1200°C. These values are:

$t, °C$	$C_p^°$ cal/(g mole)(°C)	$t, °C$	$C_p^°$ cal/(g mole)(°C)
−40	8.180	500	12.045
−20	8.268	600	12.700
0	8.371	700	13.310
18	8.472	800	13.876
25	8.514	900	14.397
100	9.035	1000	14.874
200	9.824	1100	15.306
300	10.606	1200	15.694
400	11.347		

These data have been represented by the equations

$$C_p^° = 8.3810 + 7.9891 \times 10^{-3}t - 1.5055 \times 10^{-6}t^2$$

and

$$C_p^° = 8.4017 + 7.0601 \times 10^{-3}t + 1.0567 \times 10^{-6}t^2 - 1.5981 \times 10^{-9}t^3$$

with average deviations of 0.55% and 0.36% and maximum deviations of 1.48% and 0.91%.

(a) Plot the heat capacity curve for ammonia (use actual data).

(b) Plot first and second difference curves. What do they indicate?

From the first equation calculate the mean heat capacity of ammonia in the following ways:

(1) In kilocalories per kilogram per degree Centigrade from 0 to $t°C$

(2) In Pcu per pound per degree Centigrade from 0 to $t°C$

(3) In kilocalories per cubic meter per degree Centigrade from 0 to $t°C$

(4) In kilocalories per kilogram per degree Centigrade from 500 to 1000°C

(5) In Btu per pound mole per degree Fahrenheit from 32 to $t°F$

(6) In Btu per cubic foot per degree Fahrenheit from 32 to $t°F$

(7) In Btu per pound per degree Fahrenheit from 1000 to 2000°F

4.27. Calculate, using Kopp's rule, the heat capacities in Btu/(lb)(°F) for $CaCO_3$, Na_2CO_3, $Na_2CO_3 \cdot 10\ H_2O$, $(NH_4)_2SO_4$, and compare with experimental values at 25°C.

4.28. Calculate, using Kopp's rule for liquids, the heat capacities of liquid CCl_4, CH_3OH, and HNO_3, and compare with experimental values at 25°C.

4.29. (a) Estimate the heat of vaporization of n-butane at its normal boiling point of 31.1°F using the Kistyakowsky equation. The experimental value is 165.8 Btu/lb.

(b) Make an Othmer plot for n-butane, and calculate the latent heat of vaporization at 280°F; compare this value with the one calculated from the following experimental data:

$t°F$	$p*(atm)$	$V_{(1)} (ft^3/lb)$	$V_{(g)} (ft^3/lb)$
260	24.662	0.0393	0.222
270	27.134	0.0408	0.192
280	29.785	0.0429	0.165
290	32.624	0.0458	0.138
305.56(t_c)	37.47	0.0712	0.0712

Data are from Prengle, Greenhaus, and York, *Chem. Eng. Progress*, v. 44, p. 863 (1948). The reported value of ΔH is 67.3 Btu/lb.

4.30. The normal boiling point (760 mm Hg) of anhydrous hydrogen chloride is −85.03°C. At 0°C its vapor pressure is 25.94 atm. Construct an Othmer plot against liquid ethylene and calculate the latent heat of vaporization of HCl at its normal boiling point.

4.31. Benzene boils at about 80°C. Estimate the heat of vaporization at the boiling point in Btu/lb of benzene using Trouton's rule, and compare your answer with the actual heat of vaporization.

4.32. The vapor pressure of benzene is 271.3 mm at 50°C and 757.6 mm at 80°C. What is the vapor pressure of benzene at 70°C?

4.33. It is found that the normal boiling point of n-heptane is 98.5°C and of n-octane is 124.7°C. At what temperatures will they have the same vapor pressure as does n-decane at 100°C?

4.34. The vapor pressure of phenylhydrazine has been found to be (from 25 to 240°C)

$$\log_{10} p* = 7.9046 - \frac{2366.4}{t + 230}$$

where $p*$ is in atm and t is in °C. What is the heat of vaporization of phenylhydrazine in Btu/lb at 200°F?

4.35. (a) Using the following data on the vapor pressure of Cl_2, plot $\log p*$ against $1/T$, and calculate the latent heat of vaporization of Cl_2 as a function of temperature:

t (°F)	$p*$ (psia)
−22	17.8
32	53.5
86	126.4
140	258.5
194	463.5
248	771
284	1050

How satisfactory are these data?

(b) The vapor pressure of Cl_2 is given by Lange[29] by the equation

$$\log p^* = A - \frac{B}{(C + t)}$$

where p^* = vapor pressure in mm Hg
t = °C; and for chlorine
$A = 6.86773$
$B = 821.107$
$C = 240$

Calculate the latent heat of vaporization of chlorine at the normal boiling point in Btu/lb. Compare with experimental value.

4.36. Compute the specific enthalpy (Btu/lb) of carbon tetrachloride (M = 153.84) as a vapor at 250°F relative to the solid at its melting point. From Kobe and Long,[30] the molal heat capacity of carbon tetrachloride vapor is

$$C_p = 12.24 + 3.40 \times 10^{-2}T - 3.00 \times 10^{-5}T^2$$

where T is the temperature in °K.

4.37. Use of the Steam Tables and CO_2 chart:
(a) What is the enthalpy change needed to change 3 lb of liquid water at 32°F to steam at 1 atm and 300°F?
(b) What is the enthalpy change needed to heat 3 lb of water from 60 psia and 32°F to steam at 1 atm and 300°F?
(c) What is the enthalpy change needed to heat 1 lb of water at 60 psia and 40°F to steam at 300°F and 60 psia?
(d) What is the enthalpy change needed to change 1 lb of a water-steam mixture of 60% quality to one of 80% quality if the mixture is at 300°F?
(e) Calculate the ΔH value for an isobaric (constant pressure) change of steam from 120 psia and 500°F to saturated liquid.
(f) Do the same for an isothermal change to saturated liquid.
(g) Does an enthalpy change from saturated vapor at 450°F to 210°F and 7 psia represent an enthalpy increase or decrease? A volume increase or decrease?
(h) In what state is water at 40 psia and 267.24°F; at 70 psia and 302°F; and at 70 psia and 304°F?
(i) A 2.5 ft³ tank of water at 160 psia and 363.5°F has how many ft³ of liquid water in it? Assume you start with 1 lb of H_2O. Could it contain 5 lb of H_2O under these conditions?
(j) What is the volume change when 2 lb of H_2O at 1000 psia and 200°F expand to 245 psia and 460°F?
(k) Ten pounds of wet steam at 100 psia have an enthalpy of 9000 Btu. Find the quality of the wet steam.

[29] N. A. Lange, *Handbook of Chemistry*, 9th ed., Handbook Publishers Inc., Sandusky, Ohio, 1956, p. 1426.
[30] K. A. Kobe and E. G. Long, *Petrol. Refiner*, v. 29, no. 3, p. 159 (1950).

(l) Compute the enthalpy change, volume change, and internal energy change for CO_2 compressed from 1 atm and 60°F to 200 psia, saturated liquid.

(m) If 2 lb of solid CO_2 are vaporized at 1 atm into a tank 8 ft³ in volume, what fraction of the CO_2 remains as solid?

(n) If one pound of CO_2 gas is expanded at constant enthalpy from 1200 psia and 100°F to 1 atm, what is the final temperature, enthalpy, and volume?

4.38. Write the simplified energy expressions for the following changes:

(a) A fluid flows steadily through a poorly designed coil in which it is heated from 70 to 250°F. The pressure at the coil inlet is 120 psia, and at the coil outlet is 70 psia. The coil is of uniform cross section, and the fluid enters with a velocity of 2 ft/sec.

(b) A fluid is expanded through a well-designed adiabatic nozzle from a pressure of 200 psia and a temperature of 650°F to a pressure of 40 psia and a temperature of 350°F. The fluid enters the nozzle with a velocity of 25 ft/sec.

(c) A turbine directly connected to an electric generator operates adiabatically. The working fluid enters the turbine at 200 psia and 640°F. It leaves the turbine at 40 psia and at a temperature of 350°F. Entrance and exit velocities are negligible.

(d) The fluid leaving the nozzle of part (b) is brought to rest by passing through the blades of an adiabatic turbine rotor and leaves the blades at 40 psia and at 400°F.

(e) A fluid is allowed to flow through a cracked (slightly opened) valve from a region where its pressure is 200 psia and 670°F to a region where its pressure is 40 psia, the whole operation being adiabatic.

4.39. Write the appropriate simplified energy expressions for the following changes; in each case the amount of material to be used as a basis of calculation is 1 lb and the initial condition is 100 psia and 370°F:

(a) The substance, enclosed in a cylinder fitted with a movable frictionless piston, is allowed to expand at constant pressure until its temperature has risen to 550°F.

(b) The substance, enclosed in a cylinder fitted with a movable frictionless piston, is kept at constant volume until the temperature has fallen to 250°F.

(c) The substance, enclosed in a cylinder fitted with a movable frictionless piston, is compressed adiabatically until its temperature has risen to 550°F.

(d) The substance, enclosed in a cylinder fitted with a movable frictionless piston, is compressed at constant temperature until the pressure has risen to 200 psia.

(e) The substance is enclosed in a container which is connected to a second evacuated container of the same volume as the first, there being a closed valve between the two containers. The final condition is reached by opening the valve and allowing the pressures and temperatures to equalize adiabatically.

4.40. One pound mole of an *ideal* gas whose C_p is 7 Btu/(lb mole)(°R) is confined in a reservoir with a floating top such that the pressure on the gas is 60 psig no matter what its volume is. In the morning the gas is at 50°F, but late in the afternoon its temperature rises to 90°F.

   (a) Determine how much heat has been transferred into the tank, the work done by the gas, and the internal energy change for the gas.

   (b) If the system returns to its original state in the evening, again find Q, W, and the internal energy and enthalpy changes for the cooling process.

   (c) What are Q, W, and the internal energy and enthalpy changes for the over-all process of heating and cooling?

4.41. One pound mole of an *ideal* gas ($C_p = \frac{5}{2}R$) is confined in a cylinder at 100°F and 2000 psia. This cylinder is connected through a valve to a second cylinder of equal volume which is completely evacuated. If the valve between the cylinders is opened, find Q, W, and the internal energy and enthalpy changes for the gas. Assume the cylinder walls do not absorb any heat, and assume the cylinders exist alone in the universe. List any other assumptions you have to make to obtain the desired quantities. In order to recompress the above gas back into the original cylinder at the original conditions, what is the minimum work that has to be done, and what will Q, and the internal energy and enthalpy changes be for this process?

4.42. (a) A large piston does 12,500 ft-lb of work in compressing 3 ft³ of air to 25 psia. Five pounds of water circulate into and out of the water jacket around the piston and increase in temperature 2.3°F by the end of the process. What is the change of internal energy of the air?

   (b) Suppose the water does not circulate but is stationary and increases in temperature the same amount. What is the change now in the internal energy of the air?

   (c) Suppose the piston after compressing the gas returns to its original position, and all the 12,500 ft-lb of work are recovered. What will the water temperature be in case (b)? Explain any assumptions you have made to get your answer.

4.43. A system consists of 25 lb of water vapor at the dew point. The system is compressed isothermally at 400°F, and 988 Btu of work are done on the system by the surroundings. What volume of liquid was present in the system before and after compression?

4.44. Steam fills tank 1 at 1000 psia and 700°F. The volume of tank 1 equals the volume of tank 2. A vacuum exists in tank 2 initially. The valve connecting the two tanks is opened, and isothermal expansion of the steam occurs from

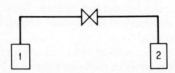

tank 1 to tank 2. Find per pound of steam for the entire process:

   (a) The enthalpy change

(b) The work done by the steam

(c) The heat transferred to or from the steam (state which)

State all assumptions clearly.

4.45. Ammonia at 50°F and 9 atm pressure is supplied to a heat exchanger to cool a liquid hydrocarbon solution. The NH_3 leaves the exchanger at 0°F and 1.18 atm pressure. The heat duty is 10,000 Btu/hr. How much NH_3 is required per hour? NH_3 data are available in most reference books and the *Chemical Engineers' Handbook*.

4.46. Water is being pumped from a pond through a long fire hose. A 50-hp motor drives the pump, and the over-all efficiency of the motor pump is 75% (i.e., 75% of the energy supplied by the motor is transferred to the water). The nozzle of the hose is 25 ft above and 250 ft from the pond. 100 gpm are being pumped, and the water velocity at the nozzle exit is 50 ft/sec. Estimate the temperature change in the water between the pond and the nozzle exit.

4.47. A desalted crude oil (40 API) is being heated in a parallel-flow heat exchanger from 70 to 200°F with a straight-run gasoline vapor available at 280°F. If 400 gal/hr of gasoline are available (measured at 60°F, API 63), how much crude can be heated per hour? Would countercurrent flow of the gasoline to the crude change your answer to this problem? Assume $K = 11$ for both streams.

4.48. Kerosene (API 42) is to be cooled from 420 to 300°F by means of 35 API crude oil. The crude is available at 270°F and rises to 285°F. Estimate the volumetric ratio of kerosene to crude flowing through the heat exchanger.

4.49. The process of throttling, i.e., expansion of a gas through a small orifice, is an important part of refrigeration. If wet steam (fraction vapor is 0.975) at 100 psia is throttled to 1 atm, find the following for the process: heat transferred to or from steam; work done; enthalpy change; internal energy change; exit temperature.

4.50. Calculate the work done when 1 lb mole of water evaporates completely at 212°F. Express your results in Btu.

4.51. Oil of average C_p of 0.8 Btu/(lb)(°F) flows at 2000 lb/min from an open reservoir standing on a hill 1000 ft high into another open reservoir at the bottom. To insure rapid flow, heat is put into the pipe at the rate of 100,000 Btu/hr. What is the enthalpy change in the oil per pound? Suppose a 1-hp pump (50% efficient) is added to the pipe line to assist in moving the oil. What is the enthalpy change per pound in the oil now?

4.52. A car weighing 3000 lb, which initially is at rest, is pushed up an inclined hill for a linear distance of 50 ft, at which time it is 5 ft higher than when it started and is moving at the speed of 10 mph. The average force exerted was 600 lb.

(a) What was the total work done on the car?

(b) What was the potential energy, kinetic energy, and total energy acquired by the car?

(c) Why are the calculated values obtained in parts (a) and (b) not the same?

4.53. An anvil is fastened to a thin steel wire the other end of which is attached to a big ball of iron. The wire is suspended from a frictionless pulley 100 ft from the ground. Neglect friction, the weight of the wire, and the heat capacity of the wire and pulley. If the anvil weighs 200 lb and rests on the ground, and the iron ball weighs 300 lb and is initially 50 ft from the ground, calculate Q, W, and the internal energy change for the following systems when everything comes to rest. (Assume all elements move relatively slowly in changing positions and that the process is isothermal.)

(a) The anvil, ball, and wire are a closed system.

(b) The anvil and wire are the system, and the ball is the surroundings.

(c) The wire is the system.

(d) The pulley is the system.

4.54. (a) If 2 lb of $H_2O(l)$ are flashed isothermally at 300°F into steam at 1 atm pressure, what is the change of enthalpy? Assume $H_2O(l)$ is incompressible and that steam $[H_2O(g)]$ is an ideal gas. Assume the specific heat of $H_2O(l)$ is 1.0 and that of steam is 0.5. The latent heat of vaporization at 212°F and 1 atm is 970.3 Btu/lb.

(b) If the $H_2O(l)$ in (a) is flashed to 0.20 atm, will this change your answer to (a)? If so, how much?

(c) Estimate the change in internal energy for the process (a) above.

(d) Can you calculate a mean heat capacity for the process? If so, calculate it.

(e) If the water in (a), after flashing, is compressed back to its original conditions, what is the over-all enthalpy change for the 2 lb of water?

(f) Check you calculations using the Steam Tables.

4.55. Ten pounds of steam in an engine at 118 psia and 340°F are allowed to expand isothermally into surrounding steam at 340°F and at a constant pressure of 30 psia. Calculate Q, W, and the internal energy and enthalpy changes for the 10 lb for this process.

4.56. A steam turbine receives 20,000 lb/hr of steam and delivers 1 MW (1000 kw). Neglect any heat losses.

(a) Neglecting velocity changes, find the change in enthalpy across the turbine.

(b) Assume the entrance velocity is 50 ft/sec and the exit velocity 1000 ft/sec; find ΔH.

(c) Assume the inlet steam pipe is 10 ft higher than the exhaust; find ΔH.

4.57. A power plant is as shown. If the pump moves 100 gal/min into the boiler with an over-all efficiency of 40%, find the horsepower required for the pump. List all additional assumptions required.

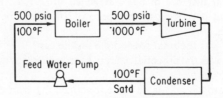

4.58. What is T_4 for two perfect gas streams flowing at the same (mole) rate in a countercurrent heat exchanger? Assume $C_{p_A} = C_{p_B}$ and are constant. Neglect any heat loss from the exchanger.

$T_1 = 200°C$
$T_2 = 100°C$
$T_3 = \ \ 0°C$
$T_4 = \ ?$

4.59. (a) One pound of nitrogen is contained in a vertical cylinder at a pressure of 500 psia and 70°F by a piston which has a mass of 5.0 lb/in.² of surface area. If the piston, which is held in place by a pin, is suddenly released and rises until the N_2 volume is 20 times as large as before and then is held in the new position, what is the work done by the gas? (*Note:* this is *not* a frictionless piston.) List all assumptions and justify them.

(b) What is the work done on the surroundings if the system consists of the piston plus the gas? Is this the same as the answer to part (a)? Explain.

4.60. One pound of steam goes through the following reversible process: In its initial state (state 1) it is at 500 psia and 1000°F. It is then compressed isothermally to state 2 which is at 100 psia. Then it is cooled at constant volume to 60 psia (state 3). Next it is cooled at constant pressure to a volume of 7.000 ft³/lb (state 4). Then it is compressed adiabatically to 500 psia and 800°F (state 5), and finally it is heated at constant pressure back to the original state.

(a) Sketch the path of each step in a *p-V* diagram.

(b) Compute the internal energy and enthalpy changes for each step and for the entire process.

(c) Compute Q and W whenever possible for each step of the process.

4.61. A thousand pounds of ethane per hour are continuously compressed in a reciprocating compressor from 15 to 100 psia. The compressor is jacketed and sufficient cooling water supplied so that the *p-V* data tabulated below represent the conditions of the gas within the cylinder. Find the compression work done on the gas per hour. Assume the friction to be negligible.

pressure-volume data

pressure, psia	specific volume, ft³/lb
15	13.23
20	9.89
25	7.90
30	6.57
40	4.90
50	3.90
60	3.24
80	2.40
100	1.90

If enthalpy of ethane at 15 psia, 13.23 ft³/lb, is 470 Btu/lb and the enthalpy at 100 psia, 1.90 ft³/lb, is 460 Btu/lb, how much heat is removed in the cooling water per 1000 pounds of ethane compressed? What is the internal energy change of the ethane?

4.62. A compressor station delivers gas at 290°F and 1200 psia from a supply at 200°F and 200 psia. If 3000 Btu/lb mole of gas that is compressed is removed from the compressor by intercooling, find the work done in Btu by the compressor per lb mole of gas delivered. The gas is: (a) air, (b) propane, (c) methane, (d) CO_2, (e) N_2. If the compression were adiabatic, what would your answer be now? If the compression were isothermal at 200°F (with the same heat interchange), what would your answer be?

4.63. A cylinder, closed at one end, is fitted with a movable piston. Originally the cylinder contains 1.2 ft³ of gas at 7.3 atm pressure. If the gas pressure is slowly reduced to 1 atm by withdrawing the piston, calculate the work done by the gas on the piston face, assuming the following relationships to hold:
(a) pV = constant
(b) $pV^{1.3}$ = constant
(c) Suppose the pressure is reduced while V is constant.
State all assumptions you must make in order to calculate the work.

4.64. An ideal gas with a heat capacity of $C_p = 6.5 + 1.5T \times 10^{-3}$ [where T is in °R and C_p is in Btu/(lb mole)(°F)] passes through a compressor at the rate of 100 lb moles/min. The entering conditions of the gas are 1 atm and 70°F. The exit conditions are 15 atm and 1200°F. Ignore potential and kinetic energy effects, and assume the process is adiabatic. Is it a reversible process? Show how you can prove it is or is not by equations.

4.65. A fireman drives a pumper up to a river and pumps water through his hose to a fire 100 ft higher than the river. The water comes out of the fire hose at 100 ft/sec. Ignoring friction, what hp engine is required to deliver 5000 gal of water per minute? The river flows at 2 mph.

4.66. Water is flowing in a straight horizontal pipe of 2-in. I.D. at 10 ft/sec when suddenly it comes into a section of pipe where the I. D. is 1 in. Assuming the pipe is insulated, what is the change in enthalpy of the water between the two sections?

4.67. Frozen-food quality is taking a big step forward with the introduction of ultrafast freezing as a commercial reality. The key to this process is the use of −320°F liquid nitrogen to do the freezing. For example, in the freezing of fish fillets, after precooling by vaporized nitrogen, the fillets enter a freezing section where they pass through a liquid nitrogen spray, which vaporizes into −320°F gas. The resulting cold gas is used to remove sensible heat from the entering fish and exhausts to the atmosphere at −10°F or warmer.

A well-insulated tunnel, 6 ft wide by 32 ft long, has a capacity of 1000 lb/hr of fish fillets. Estimate the gallons of liquid N_2 used per hour. (The actual consumption was reported to be 130 to 150 gal/hr.)

4.68. Determine the steam rate required in the diagrammed still. Assume K cf exit streams $\cong 11$.

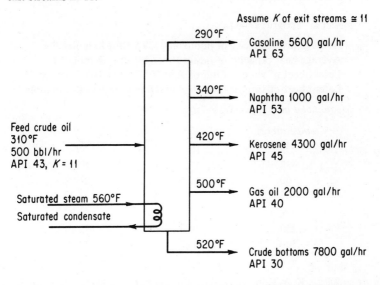

4.69. A distillation tower separates an acetone (A)-isopropanol (P) mixture into an A-rich distillate and a P-rich bottoms. The bottoms are used to preheat the feed in the countercurrent heat exchanger. Some process conditions are given in the figure. Compute:

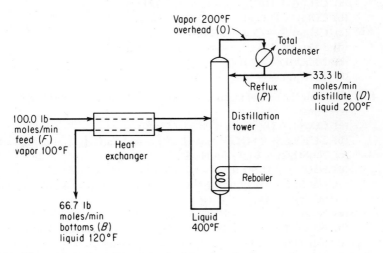

(a) The temperature, °F, of the feed leaving the heat exchanger, assuming no heat losses in the heat exchanger
(b) The heat removed in the condenser, Btu/min, assuming no heat losses in the distillation tower

(c) The heat added in the reboiler, Btu/min, assuming no heat losses in the distillation tower

PHYSICAL PROPERTY DATA:

Average heat capacity of liquid $A = 29.5$ Btu/(lb mole)(°F).
Average heat capacity of liquid $P = 41.7$ Btu/(lb mole)(°F).
Latent heat of vaporization of A at 77°F = 13,140 Btu/lb mole.
Latent heat of vaporization of P at 77°F = 18,990 Btu/lb mole.

Mean molal heat capacities relative to 32°F:

temperature, °F	A C_{p_m}	P C_{p_m}
32	17.20	20.50
60	17.55	21.09
77	17.77	21.23
100	18.06	21.62
200	19.46	23.13
300	20.57	24.67
400	21.67	26.11

Source: K. A. Kobe, R. H. Harrison, and R. E. Pennington, *Petrol. Refiner*, v. 30, no. 8, p. 119 (1951).

4.70. Calculate the heat of reaction at 77°F and 1 atm for the following reactions (these are all methods of manufacturing $H_2(g)$):
(a) $CH_4(g) + H_2O(g) \longrightarrow CO(g) + 3 H_2(g)$
(b) $CO(g) + H_2O(g) \longrightarrow CO_2(g) + H_2(g)$
(c) $CH_4(g) \longrightarrow C(s) + 2H_2(g)$
(d) $3 Fe(s) + 4 H_2O(g) \longrightarrow Fe_3O_4(s) + 4 H_2(g)$
(e) $2 H_2O(l) \longrightarrow 2 H_2(g) + O_2(g)$
(f) $2 NH_3(g) \longrightarrow N_2(g) + 3 H_2(g)$

4.71. Calculate the heat of reaction at the standard reference state for the following reactions:
(a) $CO_2(g) + H_2(g) \longrightarrow CO(g) + H_2O(l)$
(b) $2 CaO(s) + 2 MgO(s) + 4 H_2O(l) \longrightarrow 2 Ca(OH)_2(s) + 2 Mg(OH)_2(s)$
(c) $Na_2SO_4(s) + C(s) \longrightarrow Na_2SO_3(s) + CO(g)$
(d) $NaCl(s) + H_2SO_4(l) \longrightarrow NaHSO_4(s) + HCl(g)$
(e) $NaCl(s) + 2 SO_2(g) + 2 H_2O(l) + O_2(g) \longrightarrow 2 Na_2SO_4(s) + 4 HCl(g)$
(f) $SO_2(g) + \frac{1}{2} O_2(g) + H_2O(l) \longrightarrow H_2SO_4(l)$
(g) $N_2(g) + O_2(g) \longrightarrow 2 NO(g)$
(h) $Na_2CO_3(s) + 2 Na_2S(s) + 4 SO_2(g) \longrightarrow 3 Na_2S_2O_3(s) + CO_2(g)$
(i) $NaNO_3(s) + Pb(s) \longrightarrow NaNO_2(s) + PbO(s)$
(j) $Na_2CO_3(s) + 2 NH_4Cl(s) \longrightarrow 2 NaCl(s) + 2 NH_3(g) + H_2O(l) + CO_2(g)$
(k) $Ca_3(PO_4)_2(s) + 3 SiO_2(s) + 5 C \longrightarrow 3 CaSiO_3(s) + 2 P(s) + 5 CO(g)$
(l) $P_2O_5(s) + 3 H_2O(l) \longrightarrow 2 H_3PO_4(l)$

(m) $CaCN_2(s) + 2 NaCl(s) + C(s) \longrightarrow CaCl_2(s) + 2 NaCN(s)$

(n) $NH_3(g) + HNO_3(aq) \longrightarrow NH_4NO_3(aq)$

(o) $2 NH_3(g) + CO_2(g) + H_2O(l) \longrightarrow (NH_4)_2CO_3(aq)$

(p) $(NH_4)_2CO_3(aq) + CaSO_4 \cdot 2 H_2O(s) \longrightarrow CaCO_3(s) + 2 H_2O(l)$
    $+ (NH_4)_2SO_4(aq)$

(q) $CuSO_4(aq) + Zn(s) \longrightarrow ZnSO_4(aq) + Cu(s)$

(r) $\underset{\text{benzene}}{C_6H_6(l)} + Cl_2(g) \longrightarrow \underset{\text{chlorobenzene}}{C_6H_5Cl(l)} + HCl(g)$

(s) $CS_2(l) + Cl_2(g) \longrightarrow S_2Cl_2(l) + CCl_4(l)$

(t) $\underset{\text{ethylene}}{C_2H_4(g)} + HCl(g) \longrightarrow \underset{\text{ethyl chloride}}{CH_3CH_2Cl(g)}$

(u) $\underset{\text{methyl alcohol}}{CH_3OH(g)} + \tfrac{1}{2} O_2(g) \longrightarrow \underset{\text{formaldehyde}}{H_2CO(g)} + H_2O(g)$

(v) $\underset{\text{acetylene}}{C_2H_2(g)} + H_2O(l) \longrightarrow \underset{\text{acetaldehyde}}{CH_3CHO(l)}$

(w) $\underset{\text{n-butane}}{n\text{-}C_4H_{10}(g)} \longrightarrow \underset{\text{ethylene}}{C_2H_4(g)} + \underset{\text{ethane}}{C_2H_6(g)}$

(x) $\underset{\text{ethylene}}{C_2H_4(g)} + \underset{\text{benzene}}{C_6H_6(l)} \longrightarrow \text{ethyl benzene(l)}$

(y) $\underset{\text{ethylene}}{2 C_2H_4(g)} \longrightarrow \underset{\text{1-butane}}{C_4H_8(l)}$

(z) $\underset{\text{propene}}{C_3H_6(g)} + \underset{\text{benzene}}{C_6H_6(l)} \longrightarrow \underset{\text{(isopropyl benzene)}}{\text{cumene(l)}}$

4.72. (a) Calculate the standard heat of reaction of $NH_4Cl(s)$ from $NH_3(g)$ and $HCl(g)$ based on the following data:

compound	$-\Delta H_f^\circ$ (cal/g mole)
$NH_4Cl(s)$	42,150
$NH_3(g)$	10,890
$HCl(g)$	21,700

(b) The standard heats of combustion of various compounds are listed below. Calculate the standard heat of formation of each.

compound	$-\Delta H_c^\circ$ (kcal/g mole)
(1) cyclopentane(g)—C_5H_{10}	793.39
(2) cyclopentane(1)—C_5H_{10}	786.54
(3) n-propylbenzene(l)—C_9H_{12}	1247.19
(4) 3-ethylhexane(g)—C_8H_{18}	1316.87
(5) n-hexane(g)—C_6H_{14}	1002.57

4.73. The process of converting SO_2 to sulfuric acid with the aid of nitrogen oxides can be expressed on an over-all basis as follows:

$$SO_2(g) + NO_2(g) + H_2O(l) \longrightarrow H_2SO_4(l) + NO(g)$$

This process has been used by the chemical industry for over a century in what is known as the "chamber process." With the high dilution of N_2 that accompanies the SO_2, the raw gases have to pass at low velocities through large lead chambers in order to react sufficiently. If 10,000 ft³/hr

of NO (measured at S.C.) and 2700 lb/hr of H_2SO_4 are produced, what is
the cooling required if the reaction is to proceed isothermally at 77°F?

4.74. An off-gas from a crude oil topping plant has the following composition:

component	vol %
methane	88
ethane	6
propane	4
butane	2

(a) Calculate the higher heating value on the following bases: (1) Btu per
pound, (2) Btu per mole, (3) Btu per cubic foot of off-gas measured at
60°F and 760 mm.
(b) Calculate the lower heating value on the same three bases indicated
above.

4.75. Calcium carbide is made in an electric furnace from calcium oxide and
carbon as follows:

$$CaO(s) + 3\ C(\beta) \longrightarrow CO(g) + CaC_2(s)$$

CaC_2 yields acetylene when it reacts with water:

$$CaC_2(s) + 2\ H_2O(l) \longrightarrow Ca(OH)_2(s) + C_2H_2(g)$$

as found by Wöhler in 1862. Calculate the heat of reaction at 77°F and
1 atm and at 1200°F and 1 atm for both these reactions and for the over-all
combination of the two reactions. Since H_2O at 1200°F is above its critical
temperature, assume the entering water is a gas for the second calculation.

4.76. A technician determined the following standard heats of combustion at
25°C and 1 atm for benzene:

$$C_6H_6(g) \qquad \Delta H_c^\circ = -789.08\ \text{kcal/g mole}$$
$$C_6H_6(l) \qquad \Delta H_c^\circ = -780.98\ \text{kcal/g mole}$$

What is the heat of combustion for both liquid and gaseous C_6H_6 if the
final product is $H_2O(g)$?

4.77. When CO and steam are mixed, there occurs the reversible reaction
$CO + H_2O(g) = CO_2 + H_2$. The degree of completion of the reaction
depends on the equilibrium temperature and the reaction rate.
(a) What is the heat of reaction at standard conditions (25°C and 1 atm)?
(b) Write an expression for the heat of reaction assuming n_{CO} moles of CO
are supplied, n_{H_2O} of steam are supplied, and x_{CO} is the fraction of CO
which reacts. Then calculate, per mole of CO supplied, what the heat
of reaction will be at 25°C and 1 atm if 30% of the CO reacts.

4.78. The net heating value of CH_4 at 50°C is 191,870 cal/g mole. What is the gross
heating value at 0°C?

	t, °C	p^*_{mm}	ΔH_{vap} cal/g
C_p for $CH_4 = 8.52 + 0.0096t$	0	4.6	595
C_p = cal/(g mole)(°C)	18	15.5	586
t = °C	25	23.7	582
	50	92.3	568
	100	760.	539

4.79. What is the gross heating value of H_2 at 0°C? Gross heating value means the heat of reaction with the product H_2O as a liquid at 1 atm.

$$H_2(g) + \tfrac{1}{2} O_2(g) \longrightarrow H_2O(l)$$

$$\Delta H_{rxn} \text{ at } 25°C = -68,310 \text{ cal/g mole } H_2$$

$$C_p \text{ of } O_2 \text{ and } N_2 = \tfrac{2}{3} \text{ cal/g mole}$$

What is the net heating value, i.e., heat of reaction with the H_2O as a gas?

4.80. The chemist for a gas company finds a gas analyzes CO_2, 9.2; C_2H_4, 0.4; CO, 20.9; H_2, 15.6; CH_4, 1.9; N_2, 52.0%. What shall he report as the heating value of the gas?

4.81. If 1 lb mole of Cu and 1 lb mole of H_2SO_4 (100%) react together completely in a bomb calorimeter, how many Btu are absorbed (or evolved)? Assume the products are $H_2(g)$ and solid $CuSO_4$. The initial and final temperatures in the bomb are 25°C.

4.82. Calculate the heat of reaction of the following reactions at the stated temperature:

(a) $$MgO(s) + C(s) + Cl_2(g) \xrightarrow{850°C} MgCl_2(g) + CO(g)$$

(b) $$\underset{\text{methyl alcohol}}{CH_3OH(g)} + \tfrac{1}{2} O_2(g) \xrightarrow{200°C} \underset{\text{formaldehyde}}{H_2CO(g)} + H_2O(g)$$

(c) $$SO_2(g) + \tfrac{1}{2} O_2(g) \xrightarrow{300°C} SO_3(g)$$

4.83. Pyrites is converted to sulfur dioxide by the reaction:

$$4 FeS_2 + 11 O_2 \longrightarrow 2 Fe_2O_3 + 8 SO_2$$

at about 400°C. Owing to imperfect burner operation, unburned lumps of FeS_2 remain. Also because of equilibrium and rate considerations, the reaction is not complete. If $2\tfrac{1}{2}$ ton of pyrites is burned with 20% excess air (based on the equation above) and 1 ton of Fe_2O_3 is produced, calculate the heat of reaction at:
(a) 25°C and 1 atm
(b) 400°C and 1 atm

4.84. Sulfur can be recovered from the H_2S in natural gas by the following reaction:

$$3 H_2S(g) + 1\tfrac{1}{2} O_2(g) \longrightarrow 3 S(s) + 3 H_2O(g)$$

For the materials as shown, with H_2S and O_2 entering the process at 300°F and the products leaving the reactor at 100°F, calculate the heat of reaction

in Btu/lb of S formed. Assume the reaction is complete. If it is only 75%
complete, will this change your answer, and if so, how much?

4.85. The reaction $SO_2 + \frac{1}{2} O_2 \longrightarrow SO_3$ would seem to offer a simple method of
making sulfur trioxide. However, both the reaction rate and equilibrium
considerations are unfavorable for this reaction. At 600°C the reaction is
only about 70% complete. If the products leave the reactor at 600°C and
the reactants enter at 25°C, what is the heat evolved or absorbed from
the system under these conditions?

4.86. If CO at constant pressure is burned with excess air and the theoretical
flame temperature is 1800°F, what was the per cent excess air used? The
reactants enter at 200°F.

4.87. Which substance will give the higher theoretical flame temperature if the
inlet per cent excess air and temperature conditions are identical: (a) CH_4,
(b) C_2H_6, (c) C_4H_8?

4.88. If methane at 77°F and 1 atm is burned with excess air at the same temperature and pressure, set up an expression and plot the equation between
T, the theoretical adiabatic flame temperature, and S, the per cent excess
air. Assume complete reaction takes place.

4.89. A power plant burns natural gas (90% CH_4, 10% C_2H_6) at 77°F and 1 atm
with 70% excess air at the same conditions. Calculate the theoretical
maximum temperature in the boiler if all products are in the gaseous state.

4.90. In the problem above, if the air is preheated to 500°F, what will be the
maximum temperature?

4.91. Sulfur dioxide gas is oxidized in 100% excess air with 80% conversion to
SO_3. The gases enter the converter at 400°C and leave at 450°C. How many
Btu are absorbed in the heat interchanger of the converter per pound mole
of SO_2 introduced?

4.92. *n*-Heptane is dehydrocyclicized in the hydroforming process to toluene by
means of catalysts as follows:

$$C_7H_{16} \longrightarrow C_6H_5CH_3 + 4 H_2$$

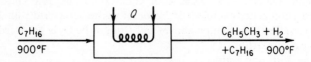

Assuming that a yield of 35% of the theoretical is obtained under the
conditions shown in the flow diagram, how much heat is required in the
process per 1000 lb of toluene produced? *Note:*

$$C_{p_m} (C_7H_{16})_{65-900°F} = 0.56 \text{ Btu/(lb)(°F)}$$

$$C_{p_m} (C_6H_5CH_3)_{65-900°F} = 0.62 \text{ Btu/(lb)(°F)}$$

4.93. In the manufacture of benzaldehyde, a mixture of toluene and air is passed through a catalyst bed where it reacts to form benzaldehyde,

$$C_6H_5CH_3 + O_2 \longrightarrow C_6H_5CHO + H_2O$$

Dry air and toluene gas are fed to the converter at a temperature of 350°F and at atmospheric pressure. To maintain a high yield, air is supplied in 100% excess over that required for complete conversion of the toluene charged. The degree of completion of the reaction, however, is only 13%. Owing to the high temperature in the catalyst bed, 0.5% of the toluene charged burns to form CO_2 and H_2O,

$$C_6H_5CH_3 + 9 O_2 \longrightarrow 7 CO_2 + 4 H_2O$$

Cooling water is circulated through a jacket on the converter, entering at 80°F and leaving at 105°F. The hot gases leave the converter at 379°F. During a 4-hr test run, a water layer amounting to 29.3 lb was collected after the exit gases had been cooled. Calculate:

(a) Composition of inlet stream to converter
(b) Composition of exhaust gas from converter
(c) Gallons per hour of cooling water required in converter jacket

Additional data: The heat of combustion of liquid benzaldehyde is −841.3 kcal/g mole at 18°C; the heat of vaporization of benzaldehyde is 86.5 cal/g at its boiling point of 179°C; the heat of vaporization of toluene is 98.6 cal/g at 25°C; the *specific* heats of both toluene and benzaldehyde *gas* may be taken as 31 Btu/(lb mole)(°F); C_p for benzaldehyde liquid is 0.43 cal/(g)(°C).

4.94. Carbon is burned with air (under pressure) at a pressure of 100 psia and a temperature of 350°C. The products of combustion flow from the pressure system, leaving at 1 atm and 350°C. The off-gas analysis is:

CO_2	18.0
O_2	3.0
N_2	79.0
	100.0%

All entering reactants are (a) at 350°C, (b) at 77°F, (c) at 60°F. Compute ΔH_{rxn} per pound of C burned under these conditions.

4.95. Ammonia oxidation furnishes a large amount of nitric acid for industry. When NH_3 is oxidized using either air or oxygen in the presence of a suitable catalyst, at least two reactions are possible:

(a) $\qquad\qquad 4 NH_3 + 5 O_2 \longrightarrow 4 NO + 6 H_2O(g)$
(b) $\qquad\qquad 4 NH_3 + 3 O_2 \longrightarrow 2 N_2 + 6 H_2O(g)$

The first reaction yields NO, which can be converted into HNO_3, while the second results in a loss of fixed nitrogen. At 1000°C, 92% of the NH_3

can be converted into NO, while the remainder goes by reaction (b). What is the heat of reaction at 1000°C per pound of NH_3 supplied to the reactor if the catalytic burning is with the stoichiometric amount of pure oxygen? What would be the change in the heat of reaction if 10% excess air at 1000°C [based on reaction (a)] were used?

4.96. In the production of ethylene from ethane and propane, the following yields were found:

reaction	per cent of reactant proceeding by process shown
$C_2H_6 \longrightarrow C_2H_4 + H_2$	100%
$C_3H_8 \longrightarrow C_2H_4 + CH_4$	60
$C_3H_8 \longrightarrow C_3H_6 + H_2$	30
$2 C_3H_8 \longrightarrow 2 C_2H_6 + C_2H_4$	10

If a mixture of 50% ethane (C_2H_6) and 50% propane (C_3H_8) is passed through the reactor, what is the standard heat of reaction per mole of feed?

4.97. (a) In a petrochemical plant 1 ton/hr of 50% (by wt) H_2SO_4 is being produced at 250°F by concentrating 30% H_2SO_4 supplied at 100°F. From the data provided below, find the heat which has to be supplied per hour:

Btu evolved at 100°F per lb mole H_2SO_4	moles of H_2O per mole of H_2SO_4
18,000	2
21,000	3
23,000	4
24,300	5
27,800	10
31,200	22

C_p (Btu/(lb)(°F))	30% H_2SO_4	50% H_2SO_4
100°F	0.80	0.70
250°F	0.75	0.60

C_p of water vapor is about 0.50, and for water use, 1.0.

(b) Using the same data as in (a) above, what is the temperature of a solution of 30% (by wt) H_2SO_4 if it is made from 50% H_2SO_4 at 100°F and pure water at 200°F if the process is adiabatic?

4.98. (a) From the data below plot the enthalpy of 1 *mole of solution* at 80°F as a function of the weight % HNO_3. Use as reference states liquid water at 32°F and liquid HNO_3 at 32°F. You can assume C_p for H_2O is 18 cal/(g mole)(°C) and for HNO_3, 30 cal/(g mole)(°C).

$-\Delta H_{soln}$ at 80°F (cal/g mole HNO₃)	moles H₂O added to 1 mole HNO₃
0	0
800	0.1
1300	0.2
1650	0.3
2000	0.5
2600	0.67
3400	1.0
4100	1.5
4850	2.0
5750	3.0
6200	4.0
6650	5.0
7300	10.0
7450	20.0

(b) Compute the energy absorbed or evolved at 80°F on making a solution of 4 moles of HNO_3 and 4 moles of water by mixing a solution of $33\frac{1}{3}$ mole % acid with one of 60 mole % acid.

4.99. *National Bureau of Standards Circular* 500 gives the following data for calcium chloride (mol. wt 111) and water:

formula	state	$-\Delta H_f$ at 25°C (kcal/g mole)
H_2O	liq	68.317
	g	57.798
$CaCl_2$	c	190.0
	in 25 moles of H_2O	208.51
	50	208.86
	100	209.06
	200	209.20
	500	209.30
	1000	209.41
	5000	209.60
	∞	209.82
$CaCl_2 \cdot H_2O$	c	265.1
$CaCl_2 \cdot 2\ H_2O$	c	335.5
$CaCl_2 \cdot 4\ H_2O$	c	480.2
$CaCl_2 \cdot 6\ H_2O$	c	623.15

Calculate:
(a) Energy evolved when 1 lb mole $CaCl_2$ is made into a 20% solution at 77°F
(b) Heat of hydration of the dihydrate to the hexahydrate
(c) Energy evolved when a 20% solution containing 1 lb mole $CaCl_2$ is diluted with water to 5% at 77°F

Chapter 5

COMBINED MATERIAL

AND ENERGY BALANCES

Now that you have accumulated some experience in making energy balances, and in the principles of thermochemistry, it is time to apply this knowledge to situations and problems involving both material and energy balances. You have already encountered some simple examples of combined material and energy balances, as, for example, in the calculation of the adiabatic reaction temperature, where a material balance provides the groundwork for the writing of an energy balance. In fact, in all energy balance problems, however trifling they may seem, you must know the amount of material entering and leaving the process if you are to apply successfully the appropriate energy balance equation(s).

In this chapter we will consider those problems which require you to make a preliminary material balance prior to making an energy balance, and also problems which require you to use in their solution simultaneous material and energy balances. In line with this discussion we will take up two special types of charts, enthalpy-concentration charts and humidity charts, which are prepared by combining material and energy balances, and which are useful in a wide variety of practical problems.

5.1 Simultaneous use of material and energy balances
   for the steady state

For any specified system or piece of equipment the law of the conservation of mass will provide you with one complete series of equations comprised of:

334

(a) A total material balance
(b) A material balance for each component (or each atomic species, if preferred)

You can use the energy balance to add one additional independent over-all equation to your arsenal, but you cannot make energy balances for each individual component. As we have mentioned previously, you need one independent equation for each unknown in a given problem or situation. The energy balance often provides the extra piece of information to help you resolve an apparently insuperable calculation composed solely of material balances.

Applying the "black box" technique to any given system or piece of equipment *in the steady state*, let us draw a diagram such as Fig. 5.1. This could be a boiler, or a distillation column, or a drier, or perhaps some type of process involving a chemical reaction.

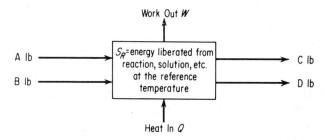

Fig. 5.1. Sketch of generalized flow process with chemical reaction.

Let x_i = weight fraction of any component
$\hat{H}_i$ = enthalpy, Btu/lb, with respect to some reference temperature of any component

If the subscript numbers 1, 2, 3, etc., represent the components in each stream, you can write the following material balances in algebraic form:

balance	*in*	=	*out*
total:	$A + B$	=	$C + D$
component 1:	$Ax_{A_1} + Bx_{B_1}$	=	$Cx_{C_1} + Dx_{D_1}$
component 2:	$Ax_{A_2} + Bx_{B_2}$	=	$Cx_{C_2} + Dx_{D_2}$
etc.			

As previously discussed, the number of independent equations is one less than the total number of equations.

In addition, an over-all energy balance can be written (ignoring kinetic and potential energy changes):

$$Q - W = (C\hat{H}_C + D\hat{H}_D) - (A\hat{H}_A + B\hat{H}_B) - S_R$$

For a more complex situation, examine the interrelated pieces of equipment in Fig. 5.2.

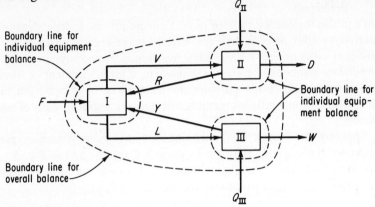

Fig. 5.2. Sketch for interrelated processes and streams.

Again the streams are labeled, and the components are 1, 2, 3, etc. How should you attack a problem of this nature? From an over-all viewpoint, the problem reduces to that shown in Fig. 5.1. In addition, a series of material balances and an energy balance can be made around each piece of equipment, I, II, and III. Naturally, all of these equations are not independent, because, if you add up the total material balances around boxes I, II, and III, you simply have the grand over-all material balance around the whole process. Similarly, if you add up the component balances for each box, you have a grand component balance for the entire process, and the sum of the energy balances around boxes I, II, and III gives the over-all energy balance. The following is a list of the material and energy balances that you can write for Fig. 5.2:

balance	*in*	*out*

Entire process:

total
$$F = D + W$$

component
$$Fx_{F_i} = Dx_{D_i} + Wx_{W_i}$$

energy
$$Q_{III} + F\Delta\hat{H}_F = D\Delta\hat{H}_D + W\Delta\hat{H}_W + Q_{II}$$

Process I:

total
$$F + R + Y = V + L$$

component
$$Fx_{F_i} + Rx_{R_i} + Yx_{Y_i} = Vx_{V_i} + Lx_{L_i}$$

energy
$$F\Delta\hat{H}_F + R\Delta\hat{H}_R + Y\Delta\hat{H}_Y = V\Delta\hat{H}_V + L\Delta\hat{H}_L$$

Process II:

total
$$V = R + D$$

component
$$Vx_{V_i} = Rx_{R_i} + Dx_{D_i}$$

energy
$$V\Delta\hat{H}_V = R\Delta\hat{H}_R + D\Delta\hat{H}_D + Q_{II}$$

Process III:

total
$$L = Y + W$$

component
$$Lx_{L_i} = Yx_{Y_i} + Wx_{W_i}$$

energy
$$Q_{III} + L\Delta\hat{H}_L = Y\Delta\hat{H}_Y + W\Delta\hat{H}_W$$

Note the symmetry among these equations. The methods of writing and applying these balances are now illustrated by an example.

In practice, the solution of steady-state material and energy balances is quite tedious, a situation which has led engineers to the use of digital and hybrid computer routines. Certain special problems are encountered in the solution of large-scale sets of equations, problems of sufficient complexity to be beyond our scope here. However, the problems are clearly explained and resolved to some extent in the article by Ravicz and Norman.[1] You might also refer to Nagiev.[2]

Example 5.1   Simultaneous Material and Energy Balances

A distillation column separates 10,000 lb/hr of a 40% benzene, 60% chlorobenzene liquid solution which is at 70°F. The liquid product from the top of the column is 99.5% benzene, while the bottom (stream from the reboiler) contains 1% benzene. The condenser uses water which enters at 60°F and leaves at 140°F, while the reboiler uses saturated steam at 280°F. The reflux ratio (the ratio of the liquid overhead returned to the column to the liquid overhead product removed) is 6 to 1. Assume both the condenser and reboiler operate at 1 atm pressure; that the temperature calculated for the condenser is 178°F, for the reboiler 268°F; and that the calculated fraction benzene in the vapor from the reboiler is 3.9 wt % (5.5 mole %). Calculate the following:

(a) The pounds of overhead product (distillate) and bottoms per hour
(b) The pounds of reflux per hour
(c) The pounds of liquid entering the reboiler and the reboiler vapor per hour
(d) The pounds of steam and cooling water used per hour

Solution:
(a) A diagram will help visualize the process and assist in pointing out what additional data have to be determined.

First we have to get some pertinent enthalpy or heat capacity data. Then we can make our material and energy balances. (The exit streams have the same composition as the solutions in the condenser or reboiler.)

(b) Convert the reboiler analysis into mole fractions.

Basis: 100 lb B

comp.	lb	mol. wt	lb moles	mole fr.
Bz	1	78.1	0.0128	0.014
Cl	99	112.6	0.88	0.986
			0.8928	1.000

[1] A. E. Ravicz and R. L. Norman, *Chem. Eng. Progr.*, v. 60, p. 71 (1964).

[2] M. F. Nagiev, *The Theory of Recycle Processes in Chemical Engineering*, Pergamon Press, New York, 1964.

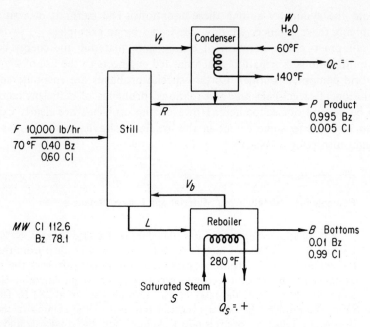

(c) The heat capacity data for liquid benzene and chlorobenzene will be assumed to be as follows[3] (no enthalpy tables are available):

| Temp. (°F) | C_p, Btu/(lb)(°F) | | $\Delta\hat{H}_{\text{vaporization}}$, Btu/lb | |
	Cl	Bz	Cl	Bz
70	0.31	0.405		
90	0.32	0.415		
120	0.335	0.43		
150	0.345	0.45		
180	0.36	0.47	140	170
210	0.375	0.485	135	166
240	0.39	0.50	130	160
270	0.40	0.52	126	154

Basis: 10,000 lb feed/hr

(d) Over-all material balances:
Over-all total material balance:

$$F = P + B$$

$$10,000 = P + B$$

Over-all benzene balance:

$$Fx_F = Px_P + Bx_B$$

[3] Data estimated from tabulations in the Appendix of *Process Heat Transfer* by D. Q. Kern, McGraw-Hill Book Company, New York, 1950.

$$10,000(0.40) = P(0.995) + B(0.01)$$

$$10,000(0.40) = P(0.995) + (10,000 - P)(0.01)$$

$$P = 3960 \text{ lb/hr} \longleftarrow \text{a}_1$$

$$B = 6040 \text{ lb/hr} \longleftarrow \text{a}_2$$

(e) Material balances around the condenser:

$$\frac{R}{P} = 6 \quad \text{or} \quad R = 6P = 6(3960) = 23,760 \text{ lb/hr} \longleftarrow \text{ⓑ}$$

$$V_t = R + P = 23,760 + 3960 = 27,720 \text{ lb/hr}$$

(f) Material balances around the reboiler:
Total:
$$L = B + V_b$$

Benzene:
$$Lx_L = Bx_B + V_b x_{V_b}$$

$$L = 6040 + V_b$$

$$Lx_L = 6040(0.01) + V_b(0.039)$$

We have three unknown and only two *independent* equations. We can write additional equations around the still, but these will not resolve the problem since we would still be left with one unknown more than the number of *independent* equations. This is the stage at which energy balances can be used effectively.

(g) Over-all energy balance: Let the reference temperature be 70°F; this will eliminate the feed from the enthalpy calculations. Assume the solutions are ideal so that the thermodynamic properties (enthalpies and heat capacities) are additive. No work or potential or kinetic energy change is involved in this problem. Thus:

$$Q_{\text{steam}} + Q_{\text{condenser}} = \underbrace{P \int_{70}^{178} C_{p_P} \, dt}_{\Delta H_P} + \underbrace{B \int_{70}^{268} C_{p_B} \, dt}_{\Delta H_B} - \underbrace{F \int_{70}^{70} C_{p_F} \, dt}_{\Delta H_F = 0}$$

We know all the terms, except Q_{steam} and $Q_{\text{condenser}}$, and still need more equations.

(h) Energy balance on the condenser: This time we will let the reference temperature equal 178°F; this choice simplifies the calculation, because then neither the R nor P streams have to be included. Assume the product leaves at the saturation temperature in the condenser of 178°F. With the condenser as the system and the water as the surroundings we have

system (condenser)	surroundings (water)
$\Delta H_{\text{condenser}} = Q_{\text{condenser}}$	$\Delta H_{\text{water}} = Q_{\text{water}}$

and, since $Q_{\text{system}} = -Q_{\text{surroundings}}$, $\Delta H_{\text{condenser}} = -\Delta H_{\text{water}}$

$$V_t(-\Delta \hat{H}_{\text{vaporization}}) = -WC_{p_{\text{H}_2\text{O}}}(t_2 - t_1)$$

$$27,720[170(0.995) + 140(0.005)] = W(1)(140 - 60) = Q_{\text{water}} = -Q_{\text{condenser}}$$

We have weighted the enthalpies of the components in V_t by their weight fractions for simplicity. Solving, $Q_C = -4.71 \times 10^6$ Btu/hr (heat evolved), and the cooling water used is

$$W = 5.89 \times 10^4 \text{ lb } H_2O/\text{hr} \longleftarrow \boxed{d_1}$$

(i) Amount of steam used: We will use the over-all energy balance from step (g).

$$Q_{\text{steam}} = 3960 \frac{\text{lb}}{\text{hr}}\left(46.9 \frac{\text{Btu}}{\text{lb}}\right) + 6040 \frac{\text{lb}}{\text{hr}}\left(68.3 \frac{\text{Btu}}{\text{lb}}\right) + 4.71 \times 10^6 \frac{\text{Btu}}{\text{hr}}$$

In the preceding equation the $\int C_p \, dt$ was determined by first graphically integrating $\int C_p \, dt$ to get $\Delta \hat{H}$ for each component and then weighting the $\Delta \hat{H}$ values by their respective weight fractions:

$$\Delta \hat{H}_P = \int_{70}^{178} C_{p_P} \, dt \quad \text{Btu/lb} \qquad \Delta \hat{H}_B = \int_{70}^{268} C_{p_B} \, dt \quad \text{Btu/lb}$$

Bz	Cl	Avg
47.0	36.2	46.9

Bz	Cl	Avg
88.1	68.0	68.3

An assumption that the P stream was pure benzene and the B stream was pure chlorobenzene would be quite satisfactory since the value of Q_C is one order of magnitude larger than the "sensible heat" terms

$$Q_{\text{steam}} = 5.31 \times 10^6 \text{ Btu/hr}$$

From the Steam Tables, $\Delta \hat{H}_{\text{vap}}$ at 280°F is 923 Btu/lb. Assume the steam leaves at its saturation temperature and is not subcooled. Then,

$$\text{lb steam used/hr} = \frac{5.31 \times 10^6 \text{ Btu/hr}}{923 \text{ Btu/lb}} = 5760 \text{ lb/hr} \longleftarrow \boxed{d_2}$$

(j) Energy balance around the reboiler:

$$Q_{\text{steam}} + L(\Delta \hat{H}_L) = V_b(\Delta \hat{H}_{V_b}) + B(\Delta \hat{H}_B)$$

We know $Q_{\text{steam}} = 5.31 \times 10^6$ Btu/hr. We do not know L or the value of $\Delta \hat{H}_L$. However, even if $\Delta \hat{H}_L$ is not known, the temperature of stream L entering the reboiler would not be more than 20°F lower than 268°F at the very most, and the heat capacity would be about that of chlorobenzene. We will assume a difference of 20°F, but you can note in the calculations below that the effect of including $\Delta \hat{H}_L$, as opposed to ignoring it, is minor.

The value of V_b is still unknown, but all the other values ($\Delta \hat{H}_{V_b}$, B, $\Delta \hat{H}_B$) are known or can be calculated. Thus, if we combine the energy balance around the reboiler with the over-all material balance around the reboiler, we can find both L and V_b.

Reference temperature: 268°F

Energy balance:

$$5.31 \times 10^6 \frac{\text{Btu}}{\text{hr}} + (L \text{ lb})\left(0.39 \frac{\text{Btu}}{\text{(lb)(°F)}}\right)(-20°F) = V_b[(0.99)(126)$$
$$+ (0.01)(154)] + B(0)$$

Material balance:

$$L = 6040 + V_b$$

$$5.31 \times 10^6 - (6040 + V_b)(7.8) = 126.3 V_b$$

$$5.31 \times 10^6 - 0.047 \times 10^6 = 126.3 V_b + 7.8 V_b$$

$$V_b = \frac{5.26 \times 10^6}{134} = 39{,}300 \text{ lb/hr} \longleftarrow \quad \boxed{c_1}$$

$$L = V_b + B = 39{,}300 + 6040 = 45{,}340 \text{ lb/hr} \longleftarrow \boxed{c_2}$$

If we had ignored the enthalpy of the L stream, then V_b would have been

$$V_b = \frac{5.31 \times 10^6}{126.3} = 42{,}100/\text{lb/hr}$$

a difference of about 7.1%.

5.2 Enthalpy-concentration charts

Enthalpy-concentration charts are convenient methods of representing enthalpy data for binary mixtures. If available,[4] they are useful in making combined material and energy balances in distillation, crystallization, and all sorts of mixing and separation problems. You will find a few examples of enthalpy-concentration charts in Appendix I.

At some time in your career as engineer you may find you have to make numerous repetitive material and energy balance calculations on a given binary system. Perhaps you decide an enthalpy-concentration chart for the system would be of some use, but you cannot find one in the literature or in your files. How do you go about constructing such a chart?

5.2-1 Construction of an Enthalpy-Concentration Chart. As usual, the first thing to do is choose a basis—some given amount of the mixture, usually 1 lb or 1 lb mole. Then choose a reference temperature ($H_0 = 0$ at T_0) for the enthalpy calculations. Assuming 1 lb is the basis, you then make an energy balance for solutions of various compositions at various temperatures

$$\Delta \hat{H}_{\text{mixture}} = x_A \Delta \hat{H}_A + x_B \Delta \hat{H}_B + \Delta \hat{H}_{\text{mixing}} \tag{5.1}$$

where $\Delta \hat{H}_{\text{mixture}}$ = the enthalpy of 1 lb of the mixture

$\Delta \hat{H}_A, \Delta \hat{H}_B$ = the enthalpies of the pure components per lb relative to the reference temperature. (The reference temperature does not have to be the same for A as for B.)

$\Delta \hat{H}_{\text{mixing}}$ = the heat of mixing (solution) per lb at the temperature of the given calculation

---

[4] For a literature survey as of 1957 see Robert Lemlich, Chad Gottschlich, and Ronald Hoke, *Chem. Eng. Data Series*, v. 2, p. 32 (1957). Additional refs. are: for CCl_4, see M. M. Krishnaiah et al., *J. Chem. Eng. Data*, v. 10, p. 117 (1965); and for EtOH-EtAc see Robert Lemlich, Chad Gottschlich, and Ronald Hoke, *Brit. Chem. Eng.*, v. 10, p. 703 (1965).

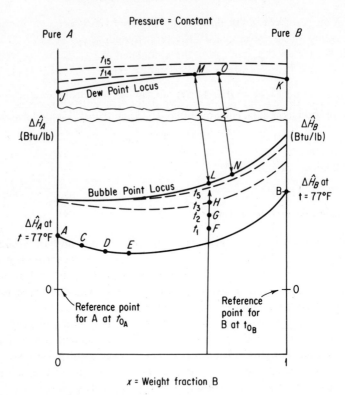

Fig. 5.3. Enthalpy-concentration diagram.

In the common case where the $\Delta \hat{H}_{\text{mixing}}$ is known only at one temperature (usually 77°F), a modified procedure as discussed below would have to be followed to calculate the enthalpy of the mixture.

The choice of the reference temperatures for A and B locates the zero enthalpy datum on each side of the diagram (see Fig. 5.3). From enthalpy tables such as the Steam Tables, or by finding

$$(\hat{H}_A - \hat{H}_{A_0}) = \int_{t_0}^{t=77°F} C_{p_A} \, dt$$

you can find $\Delta \hat{H}_A$ at 77°F and similarly obtain $\Delta \hat{H}_B$ at 77°F. Now you have located points A and B. If one of the components is water, it is advisable to choose 32°F as t_0 because then you can use the Steam Tables as a source of data. If both components have the same reference temperature, the temperature isotherm will intersect on both sides of the diagram at 0, but there is no particular advantage in this.

Now that you have $\Delta \hat{H}_A$ and $\Delta \hat{H}_B$ at 77°F (or any other temperature at which $\Delta \hat{H}_{\text{mixing}}$ is known), you can calculate $\Delta \hat{H}_{\text{mixture}}$ at 77°F by Eq.

(5.1). You can review the details about how to get $\Delta \hat{H}_{\text{mixing}}$ in Chap. 4. For various mixtures such as 10 per cent A and 90 per cent B, 20 per cent A and 80 per cent B, etc., plot the calculated $\Delta \hat{H}_{\text{mixture}}$ as shown by the points C, D, E, etc., in Fig. 5.3, and connect these points with a continuous line.

You can calculate $\Delta \hat{H}_{\text{mixture}}$ at any other temperature t, once this 77°F isotherm has been constructed, by again making an enthalpy balance as follows:

$$\Delta \hat{H}_{\text{mixture at any } t} = \Delta \hat{H}_{\text{mixture at 77°F}} + \int_{77°F}^{t} C_{p_x}\, dt \qquad (5.2)$$

where C_{p_x} is the heat capacity of the solution at concentration x. These heat capacities must be determined experimentally, although in a pinch they might be estimated. Points F, G, H, etc., can be determined in this way for a given composition, and then additional like calculations at other fixed concentrations will give you enough points so that all isotherms can be drawn up to the bubble-point line for the mixture (1 atm).

In order to include the vapor region on the enthalpy concentration chart you need to know:

(a) The heat of vaporization of the pure components (to get points J and K)

(b) The composition of the vapor in equilibrium with a given composition of liquid (to get the tie lines L-M, N-O, etc.)

(c) The dew-point temperatures of the vapor (to get the isotherms in the vapor region)

(d) The heats of mixing in the vapor region, usually negligible [to fix the points M, O, etc., by means of Eq. (5.1)]. (Alternatively, the heat of vaporization of a given composition could be used to fix points M, O, etc.)

The construction and use of enthalpy-concentration diagrams for combination material-energy balance problems will now be illustrated.

Example 5.2   Preparation of an Enthalpy-Concentration Chart for Ideal Mixtures

Prepare an enthalpy-concentration chart from the data listed below for the n-butane, n-heptane system. Assume heats of mixing (solution) are negligible.

Solution:

The compositions of the vapor and liquid phases as a function of temperature are also essential data and are listed in the first columns of the calculations

100 PSIA, n-BUTANE–n-HEPTANE SYSTEM*

Enthalpy of Saturated Hydrocarbon Liquids at 100 psia
Reference State: 32°F and 14.7 psia

Temperature, °F	$\Delta \hat{H}_{C_4}$ (n-Butane) Btu/lb mole	$\Delta \hat{H}_{C_7}$ (n-Heptane) Btu/lb mole
140	3,800	7,100
160	4,500	7,700
200	6,050	9,100
240	7,700	11,400
280	9,400	14,000
320	11,170	16,700
360	13,350	19,400

Enthalpy of Saturated Hydrocarbon Vapors at 100 psia
Reference State: 32°F and 14.7 psia

Temperature	$\Delta \hat{H}_{C_4}$ (n-Butane) Btu/lb mole	$\Delta \hat{H}_{C_7}$ (n-Heptane) Btu/lb mole
140	11,300	19,300
160	11,800	20,100
200	12,820	21,600
240	13,900	23,250
280	15,030	25,000
320	16,200	26,900
360	17,550	29,300

* Calculated from data of E. G. Scheibel, *Petroleum Refiner*, v. 26, p. 116 (1947).

below. Intermediate values of enthalpy were interpolated from a plot of enthalpy vs. temperature prepared from the data given above.

Basis: 1 lb mole mixture

Reference conditions: 32°F and 14.7 psia

Step 1: Plot the boiling points of pure C_4 (146°F) and pure C_7 (358°F). Fix the enthalpy scale from 0 to 30,000 Btu/lb mole mixture. By plotting the temperature-enthalpy data on separate graphs you can find that the enthalpy of the pure C_4 at 146°F is 3970 Btu/lb mole and that of C_7 at 358°F is 19,250 Btu/lb mole. These are marked in the diagram (p. 346) as points A and B, respectively.

Step 2: Now choose various other compositions of liquid between A and B (at known temperatures), and multiply the enthalpy of the pure component per mole by the mole fraction present:

$$\Delta \hat{H}_{\text{liquid mixture}} = \Delta \hat{H}_{C_4} x_{C_4} + \Delta \hat{H}_{C_7} x_{C_7}$$

No heat of mixing is present since ideality was assumed. In this way the bubble-point line between A and B can be established.

$H\text{-}x$ Calculations for $C_4\text{-}C_7$ Liquid (Saturated) at 100 psia

Enthalpy, Btu/lb mole

Temp., °F	Mole fr.		$\Delta\hat{H}_{C_4}$	$\Delta\hat{H}_{C_7}$	$\Delta\hat{H}_{C_4}x_{C_4}$	$\Delta\hat{H}_{C_7}x_{C_7}$	$\Delta\hat{H}_L = \Delta\hat{H}_{C_4}x_{C_4} + \Delta\hat{H}_{C_7}x_{C_7}$
	x_{C_4}	x_{C_7}					
358	0	1.0	13,200	19,250	0	19,250	19,250
349	0.02	0.98	12,700	18,650	254	18,250	18,504
340.5	0.04	0.96	12,220	18,000	490	17,280	17,770
331.5	0.06	0.94	11,750	17,380	710	16,300	17,010
315	0.10	0.90	11,000	16,200	1,100	14,600	15,700
296	0.15	0.85	10,100	14,900	1,515	12,650	14,165
278.5	0.20	0.80	9,350	13,750	1,870	11,000	12,870
248	0.30	0.70	8,050	11,850	2,420	8,300	10,720
223.5	0.40	0.60	7,000	10,400	2,800	6,240	9,040
204	0.50	0.50	6,200	9,400	3,100	4,700	7,800
188	0.60	0.40	5,600	8,700	3,360	3,480	6,840
173.8	0.70	0.30	5,000	8,120	3,500	2,440	5,940
160.5	0.80	0.20	4,500	7,700	3,600	1,540	5,140
151.0	0.90	0.10	4,150	7,400	3,740	740	4,480
147.8	0.95	0.05	4,000	7,310	3,800	366	4,166
146.0	1.0	0	3,970	7,280	3,970	0	3,970

Step 3: Plot the enthalpy values for the saturated pure vapor (dew point), points C and D. A supplementary graph again is required to assist in interpolating enthalpy values.

Step 4: Fill in the saturated-vapor curve between C and D by the following calculation:

$$\Delta\hat{H}_V = \Delta\hat{H}_{C_4}y_{C_4} + \Delta\hat{H}_{C_7}y_{C_7}$$

Enthalpy, Btu/lb mole

Temp., °F	Mole fr.		$\Delta\hat{H}_{C_4}$	$\Delta\hat{H}_{C_7}$	$\Delta\hat{H}_{C_4}y_{C_4}$	$\Delta\hat{H}_{C_7}y_{C_7}$	$\Delta\hat{H}_V = \Delta\hat{H}_{C_4}y_{C_4} + \Delta\hat{H}_{C_7}y_{C_7}$
	y_{C_4}	y_{C_7}					
358	0	1.0	17,500	29,250	0	29,250	29,250
349	0.084	0.914	17,150	28,700	1,440	26,200	27,640
340.5	0.160	0.84	16,850	28,100	2,700	23,600	26,300
331.5	0.241	0.759	16,500	27,550	3,970	20,860	24,830
315	0.378	0.622	16,050	26,700	6,060	16,600	22,660
296	0.518	0.482	15,800	25,800	8,050	12,420	20,470
278.5	0.630	0.370	14,980	24,900	9,425	9,210	18,635
248	0.776	0.224	14,100	23,600	10,950	5,290	16,240
223.5	0.857	0.143	13,420	22,550	11,500	3,220	14,720
204	0.907	0.093	12,950	21,700	11,750	2,020	13,770
188	0:942	0.058	12,500	21,100	11,780	1,225	13,005
173.8	0.968	0.032	12,100	20,600	11,700	659	12,359
160.5	0.986	0.014	11,800	26,100	11,620	282	11,902
151.0	0.996	0.004	11,500	19,720	11,450	79	11,529
147.8	0.999	0.001	11,450	19,600	11,430	20	11,450
146.0	1.000	0	11,400	19,540	11,400	0	11,400

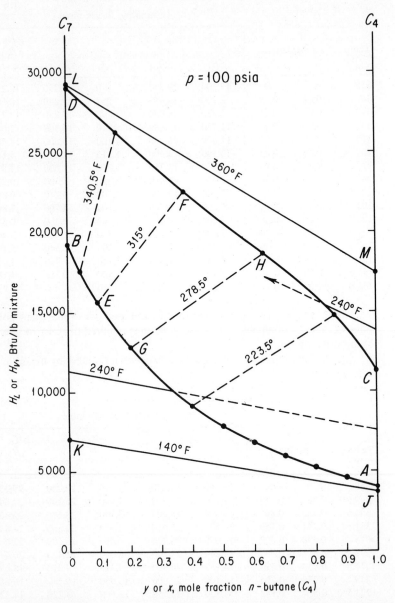

Step 5: Draw tie lines (dashed lines) between the bubble-point and dew-point lines (lines *E-F*, *G-H*, etc.). These lines of constant temperature show the equilibrium concentrations in the vapor and liquid phases. The experimental data were selected so that identical temperatures could be used in the above calculations for each phase; if such data were not available, you would have to prepare additional graphs to use in interpolating the isobaric data (data at 100

psia) with respect to the mole fraction y or x. If you wanted to draw the lines at even temperature intervals, such as 140, 160, 180°F, etc., you would also have to interpolate.

Step 6: Draw isothermal lines at 140, 160°F, etc., in the liquid and vapor regions. Presumably these will be straight lines since there is no heat of mixing. Since:

$$x_{C_7} + x_{C_4} = 1 \qquad\qquad (a)$$

$$\Delta\hat{H}_L = \Delta\hat{H}_{mixture} = x_{C_4}\Delta\hat{H}_{C_4} + x_{C_7}\Delta\hat{H}_{C_7} = x_{C_4}\Delta\hat{H}_{C_4} + (1 - x_{C_4})\Delta\hat{H}_{C_7}$$

$$= (\Delta\hat{H}_{C_4} - \Delta\hat{H}_{C_7})x_{C_4} + \Delta\hat{H}_{C_7} \qquad\qquad (b)$$

Because $\Delta\hat{H}_{C_4}$ and $\Delta\hat{H}_{C_7}$ are constant at any given temperature, $\Delta\hat{H}_{C_4} - \Delta\hat{H}_{C_7}$ is constant, and Eq. (b) is the equation of a straight line of a plot of $\Delta\hat{H}_{mixture}$ vs. x_{C_4}.

The 140°F isotherm is fixed by the points J and K in the liquid region, and the 360°F isotherm is fixed by points L and M in the vapor region:

	140°F, *liquid* $\Delta\hat{H}_L$ (*Btu/mole*)		360°F, *vapor* $\Delta\hat{H}_V$ (*Btu/mole*)
J (C$_4$)	3800	L (C$_4$)	17,550
K (C$_7$)	7100	M (C$_7$)	29,300

The 240°F isotherm (and others higher than 140°F) in the liquid region is real only up to the saturated-liquid line—the dotted portion is fictitious. Portions of isotherms in the vapor region lower than 360°F would also be fictitious, as, for example, at 240°F.

Example 5.3   Applications of the Enthalpy-Concentration Chart

One hundred pounds of a 73% NaOH solution at 350°F are to be diluted to give a 10% solution at 80°F. How many pounds of water at 80°F and ice at 32°F are required if there is no external source of cooling available? Use the Steam Tables and the NaOH-H$_2$O enthalpy-concentration chart in Appendix I as your source of data. (The reference conditions for this chart are $H = 0$ at 32°F for liquid water and $H = 0$ for an infinitely dilute solution of NaOH, with pure caustic having an enthalpy at 68°F of 455 Btu/lb above this datum.)

Solution:
The data required to make a material and an energy balance are as follows:

	From Appendix I		*From the Steam Tables*
NaOH			$\Delta\hat{H}$ of liquid H$_2$O
conc.	*temp.,* °F	$\Delta\hat{H}$, *Btu/lb*	= 48 Btu/lb
73	350	468	$\Delta\hat{H}$ of ice = -143 Btu/lb
10	80	42	(or minus the heat of fusion)

We can make a material balance first.

Basis: 100 lb 73% at 350°F

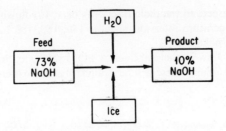

The tie element in the material balance is the NaOH, and using it we can find the total H_2O added (ice plus H_2O):

$$\frac{100 \text{ lb product}}{10 \text{ lb NaOH}} \Bigm| \frac{73 \text{ lb NaOH}}{100 \text{ lb feed}} = 730 \text{ lb product/100 lb feed}$$

less 100 lb feed

gives 630 lb H_2O added/100 lb feed

Next we make an energy (enthalpy) balance,

$$\Delta H_{\text{over-all}} = 0 \qquad \text{or} \qquad \Delta H_{\text{in}} = \Delta H_{\text{out}}$$

In order to differentiate between the ice and the liquid water added, let us designate the ice as x lb and then the H_2O becomes $(630 - x)$ lb:

in

73% NaOH solution	H_2O	ice
$\dfrac{100 \text{ lb}}{} \Bigm\| \dfrac{468 \text{ Btu}}{\text{lb}}$	$+ \dfrac{(630 - x) \text{ lb}}{} \Bigm\| \dfrac{48 \text{ Btu}}{\text{lb}}$	$+ \dfrac{x \text{ lb}}{} \Bigm\| \dfrac{-143 \text{ Btu}}{\text{lb}} =$

out, 10% NaOH solution

$$\frac{730 \text{ lb}}{} \Bigm| \frac{52 \text{ Btu}}{\text{lb}}$$

$$46{,}800 + 30{,}240 - 191x = 30{,}660$$

$$x = 243 \text{ lb ice at } 32°\text{F}$$

$$\text{liquid } H_2O \text{ at } 80°\text{F} = 387 \text{ lb}$$

Example 5.4   Applications of the Enthalpy-Concentration Chart

Six hundred pounds of 10% NaOH at 200°F are added to 400 lb of 50% NaOH at the boiling point. Calculate:

(a) The final temperature of the solution
(b) The final concentration of the solution
(c) The pounds of water evaporated during the mixing process

Solution:

Basis: 1000 lb final solution

Use the same NaOH-H_2O enthalpy-concentration chart as in the previous problem to obtain the enthalpy data. We can write down the following material balance:

comp.	10% solution	+ 50% solution	= final solution	wt %
NaOH	60	200	260	26
H_2O	540	200	740	74
total	600	400	1000	100

Next, the energy (enthalpy) balance (in Btu) is:

10% solution		50% solution		final solution
600(152)	+	400(290)	=	ΔH
91,200	+	116,000	=	207,200

Note that the enthalpy of the 50% solution at its boiling point is taken from the bubble-point curve at $x = 0.50$. The enthalpy per pound is

$$\frac{207{,}200 \text{ Btu}}{1000 \text{ lb}} = 207 \text{ Btu/lb}$$

On the enthalpy-concentration chart for NaOH-H_2O, for a 26% NaOH solution with an enthalpy of 207 Btu/lb, you would find that only a two-phase mixture of (a) saturated H_2O vapor and (b) NaOH-H_2O solution at the boiling

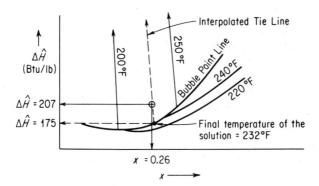

point could exist. To get the fraction H_2O vapor, we have to make an additional energy (enthalpy) balance. By interpolation, draw the tie line through the point $x = 0.26$, $H = 207$ (make it parallel to the 200° and 250°F tie lines). The final temperature appears from the diagram to be 232°F; the enthalpy of the liquid at the bubble point is about 175 Btu/lb. The enthalpy of the saturated water vapor (no NaOH is in the vapor phase) from the Steam Tables at 232°F is 1158 Btu/lb. Let $x = $ lb H_2O evaporated.

Basis: 1000 lb final solution

$$x(1158) + (1000 - x)175 = 1000(207)$$

$$983x = 32{,}000$$

$$x = 32.6 \text{ lb } H_2O \text{ evaporated}$$

5.2-2 Graphical Solutions on an Enthalpy-Concentration Chart. One of the major advantages of an enthalpy-concentration chart is that the same problems we have just used as examples, and a wide variety of other problems, can be solved graphically directly on the chart. We will just indicate the scope of this technique, which in its complete form is usually called the Ponchon-Savaritt method; you can refer to some of the references for enthalpy-concentration charts at the end of this chapter for additional details.

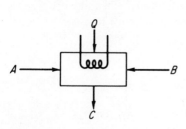

Fig. 5.4. A typical process with mass and heat interchange.

For any steady-state process with three streams and a net heat interchange Q with the surroundings, we can draw a simple diagram as in Fig. 5.4. A, B, and C are in pounds or moles. An over-all material balance gives us

$$A + B = C \tag{5.3}$$

and a component material balance gives

$$Ax_A + Bx_B = Cx_C \tag{5.4}$$

An energy balance for a flow process (neglecting the work and the kinetic and potential energy effects) gives us[5]

$$Q = \Delta H$$

or

$$Q + AH_A + BH_B = CH_C \tag{5.5}$$

First we must choose some basis for carrying out the calculations, and then Q is dependent on this basis. Thus, if A is chosen as the basis, Q_A will be Q per unit amount of A, or

$$Q_A = \frac{Q}{A} \tag{5.6}$$

Similarly, if B is the basis,

$$Q_B = \frac{Q}{B} \tag{5.7}$$

Also

$$Q = AQ_A = BQ_B = CQ_C \tag{5.8}$$

Let us choose A as the basis for working the problem, and then Eq. (5.5) becomes

$$AQ_A + AH_A + BH_B = CH_C \tag{5.9}$$

---

[5] In what follows H is always the enthalpy relative to some reference value, and we suppress the caret ($\wedge$) to make the notation more compact.

or

$$A(H_A + Q_A) + BH_B = CH_C \tag{5.10}$$

Similar equations can be written down if B or C is chosen as the basis.

(a) *Adiabatic processes.* As a special case, consider the adiabatic process ($Q = 0$). Then (with A as the basis) the energy balance becomes

$$AH_A + BH_B = CH_C = (A + B)H_C = AH_C + BH_C$$

or

$$A(H_A - H_C) = B(H_C - H_B)$$

or

$$\frac{A}{B} = \frac{H_C - H_B}{H_A - H_C} \tag{5.11}$$

Combining material balances,

$$Ax_A + Bx_B = Cx_C = (A + B)x_C = Ax_C + Bx_C$$

or

$$A(x_A - x_C) = B(x_C - x_B)$$

or

$$\frac{A}{B} = \frac{x_C - x_B}{x_A - x_C} \tag{5.12}$$

Obviously then:

$$\frac{A}{B} = \frac{x_C - x_B}{x_A - x_C} = \frac{H_C - H_B}{H_A - H_C} \tag{5.13}$$

Similarly, solving the energy and material balances for A and C instead of A and B, we can get

$$\frac{A}{C} = \frac{x_C - x_B}{x_A - x_B} = \frac{H_C - H_B}{H_A - H_B} \tag{5.14}$$

and in terms of B and C we could get a like relation. Rearranging the two right-hand members of Eq. (5.13) we can find that

$$\frac{H_C - H_B}{x_C - x_B} = \frac{H_A - H_C}{x_A - x_C} \tag{5.13a}$$

Also, from Eq. (5.14),

$$\frac{H_C - H_B}{x_C - x_B} = \frac{H_A - H_B}{x_A - x_B} \tag{5.14a}$$

On an enthalpy-concentration diagram (an H-x plot) the distances H_C-H_B, H_A-H_B, and H_A-H_C are projections on the H axis of a curve, while the distances x_C-x_B, x_A-x_B, x_A-x_C are the corresponding projections on the x axis (see Fig. 5.5). The form of Eqs. (5.13a) and (5.14a) is such that they tell us that they are each equations of a straight line on an H-x plot and that these lines pass through the points A, B, and C which are represented on an H-x diagram by the coordinates $A(H_A, x_A)$, $B(H_B, x_B)$, and $C(H_C, x_C)$, respectively.

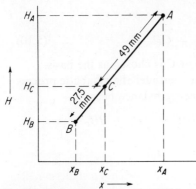

Fig. 5.5. Projections of the line BCA on the H and x axes.

Since Eqs. (5.13a) and (5.14a) both pass through point C, a common point, and have the same slope $(H_C - H_B)/(x_C - x_B)$, mathematical logic tells us they must be equations of the same line, i.e., the lines are actually a single line passing through B, C, and A as shown in Fig. 5.5. The symmetry of this type of arrangement leads to use of the "lever arm" rule.

If $A + B = C$, then point C lies on a line *between* A and B, and *nearer* to the quantity present in the *largest* amount. If more B is added, C will lie nearer B. When two streams are subtracted, the resulting stream will lie *outside* the region of a line between the two subtracted streams, and *nearer* the one present in the larger amount. Thus if $C - B = A$, and C is larger than A, then A will lie on a straight line through C and B nearer to C than B. Look at Fig. 5.5 and imagine B is removed from C. A represents what is left after B is taken from C.

The "inverse" lever arm principle tells us how far to go along the line through A and B to find C if $A + B = C$, or how far to go along the line through C and B if $C - B = A$. In the case of $A + B = C$, we saw that the weight (or mole) ratio of A to B was given by Eq. (5.13). From the symmetry of Fig. 5.5, you can see that, if the ratio of A to B is equal to the ratio of the projections of line segments BC and AC on the H or x axes, then the amount of $A + B$ should be proportional to the sum of the line segments $(x_C - x_B) + (x_A - x_C)$, or $(H_C - H_B) + (H_A - H_C)$. Furthermore, the amount of A should be proportional to the measured distance $\overline{BC}$ and the amount of B proportional to the distance $\overline{AC}$. Also the ratio of A to B should be

$$\frac{A}{B} = \frac{\text{distance } \overline{BC}}{\text{distance } \overline{AC}} \tag{5.15}$$

This relation is the *inverse lever arm rule*. The distances $\overline{BC}$, $\overline{AC}$, and $\overline{AB}$ can be measured with a ruler.

As an example of the application of Eq. (5.15), if A were 100 lb and the measured distances were

$$\overline{BC} = 27.5 \text{ mm}$$

$$\overline{AC} = 49 \text{ mm}$$

$$\overline{AB} = 76.5 \text{ mm}$$

then

$$\frac{A}{B} = \frac{100}{B} = \frac{\overline{BC}}{\overline{AC}} = \frac{27.5 \text{ mm}}{49 \text{ mm}} = 0.561$$

and

$$B = \frac{100}{0.561} = 178 \text{ lb}$$

The sum of $A + B = C$ is $100 + 178 = 278$ lb. Alternatively,

$$\frac{A}{C} = \frac{\overline{BC}}{\overline{AB}} = \frac{27.5 \text{ mm}}{76.5 \text{ mm}} = 0.360$$

$$C = \frac{A}{0.360} = \frac{100}{0.360} = 278 \text{ lb}$$

(b) *Nonadiabatic processes.* Let us now consider the circumstances under which Q is not equal to zero in Eq. (5.5). This time, for variety, let us take C as a basis so that $Q = CQ_C$. Then we have two pairs of equations to work with again,

$$AH_A + BH_B = C(H_C - Q_C) \qquad (5.16)$$

$$Ax_A + Bx_B = Cx_C \qquad (5.4)$$

Briefly, Eqs. (5.16) and (5.4) tell us that on an H-x diagram points A, B, and C lie on a straight line if the coordinates of the points are $A(H_A, x_A)$, $B(H_B, x_B)$, and $C[(H_C - Q_C), x_C]$, respectively,[6] as illustrated in Fig. 5.6. Since the coordinates of C are really fictitious coordinates and the enthalpy projection of C is $(H_C - Q_C)$, we will designate the point through which the line passes $[(H_C - Q_C), x_C]$ by the more appropriate notation C_Q. If A or B had been chosen as the basis, we would have set up diagrams such as Figs. 5.7 and 5.8.

A different series of figures could be drawn for other typical problems,

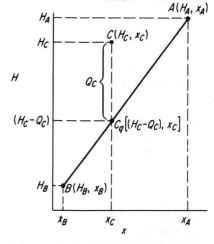

Fig. 5.6. Inverse lever arm rule applied to a nonadiabatic process.

[6] Proof of these relations is analogous to the previous development.

Material balances:

$$Ax_A + Bx_B = Cx_C = (A + B)x_C = Ax_C + Bx_C \qquad (a)$$

$$A(x_A - x_C) = B(x_C - x_B) \qquad (b)$$

Energy balance:

$$AH_A + BH_B = C(H_C - Q_C) = (A + B)(H_C - Q_C)$$

$$= A(H_C - Q_C) + B(H_C - Q_C) \qquad (c)$$

$$A[H_A - (H_C - Q_C)] = B(H_C - Q_C) - H_B \qquad (d)$$

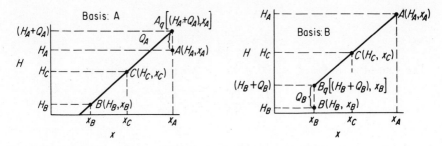

Figs. 5.7. and 5.8. Inverse lever arm principle for different bases.

as, for example, C being split up into two streams with heat being absorbed or evolved. Additional details related to more complex problems will be found in the references on enthalpy-concentration charts at the end of the chapter.

Example 5.5   Graphical Use of Enthalpy-Concentration Charts

Do Example 5.3 again by graphical means.

Solution:

Plot the known points A and C on the H-x diagram for NaOH. The known points are as follows (with the given coordinates or data):

solution		x	H, Btu/lb	t, °F
initial	(A)	0.73	468	350
final	(C)	0.10		80
added	(D)	0.00		80
	(E)	0.00		32 (ice)

What we will do is remove solution A from the final solution C to obtain solution B, i.e., subtract $C - A$ to get B. This is the reverse of adding A to B to get C.

Draw a line through A and C until it intersects the $x = 0$ axis (for pure water). The measured (with a ruler) ratio of the lines $\overline{BC}$ to $\overline{AC}$ is the ratio of 73% NaOH solution to pure water.

Thus

$$\frac{A}{B} = \frac{x_C - x_B}{x_A - x_C} = \frac{(H_C - Q_C) - H_B}{H_A - (H_C - Q_C)} \tag{e}$$

and, rearranging,

$$\frac{H_A - (H_C - Q_C)}{x_A - x_C} = \frac{(H_C - Q_C) - H_B}{x_C - x_B} \tag{f}$$

A similar equation can be obtained for the ratio A/C.

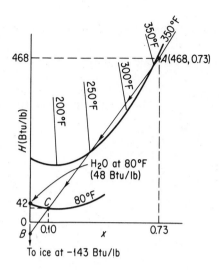

Basis: 100 lb 73 % NaOH solution at 350°F (A)

$$\frac{100 \text{ lb } (A)}{\text{lb } H_2O \ (B)} = \frac{\overline{BC}}{\overline{AC}} = \frac{2.85 \text{ units}}{17.95 \text{ units}} = 0.159$$

$$\frac{100}{0.159} = \text{lb } H_2O = 630 \text{ lb ice plus liquid water } (B)$$

To obtain the proportions of ice and water, we want to subtract D from B to get E.

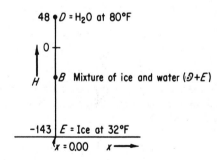

We measure the distances $\overline{DE}$ and $\overline{BE}$. Then,

$$\frac{\text{lb } H_2O \ (D)}{\text{lb total } (B)} = \frac{\overline{BE}}{\overline{DE}} = \frac{3.65 \text{ units}}{5.95 \text{ units}} = 0.613$$

$$\text{lb } H_2O \ (D) = 630(0.613) = 386 \text{ lb}$$

$$\text{lb ice } (E) = 630 - 386 = 244 \text{ lb}$$

Example 5.6   Graphical Use of Enthalpy-Concentration Charts

Do Example 5.4 again by graphical means.

Solution:

Basis: 1000 lb of total solution

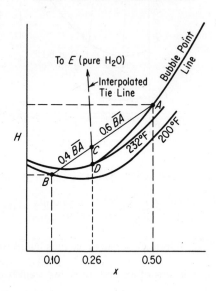

Again plot the known data on an *H-x* chart. Point C, the sum of solutions A and B, is found graphically by noting by the inverse lever arm rule

$$\frac{\text{distance } \overline{BC}}{\text{distance } \overline{BA}} = \frac{\text{lb } A}{\text{lb } A + B} = \frac{400}{1000} = 0.4$$

Now measure $\overline{BA}$ on the diagram, and plot $\overline{BC}$ as $0.4(\overline{BA})$. This fixes point C.

Since C is in the two-phase region, draw a tie line through C (parallel to the nearby tie lines) and measure the distances $\overline{CD}$ and $\overline{ED}$. They will give the H_2O evaporated as follows:

$$\frac{\overline{CD}}{\overline{ED}} = \frac{\text{lb } H_2O \text{ evaporated}}{1000 \text{ lb mixture}}$$

$$\text{lb } H_2O \text{ evaporated} \cong 33 \text{ lb}$$

The final concentration of the solution and the temperature of the solution can be read off the *H-x* chart as before as

$$T = 232°F, \qquad x = 26\%$$

Example 5.7   Graphical Use of Enthalpy-Concentration Charts with a Process Involving Heat Transfer

An acetic acid-water mixture is being concentrated as shown in the diagram. Calculate (a) the enthalpy per pound mole of stream A, (b) the mole fraction of stream A, and (c) the number of pounds each of A and B.

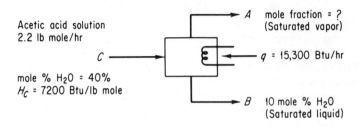

Solution:

Basis: 2.2 lb mole acetic acid solution, 40% H_2O

First we have to prepare an enthalpy concentration chart by plotting the data for the acetic acid-water system from Appendix I.

Basis: 2.2 lb mole C

This diagram is used for the graphical solution we are now going to describe. The line connecting A, B, and C must pass through the following points (if Q is based on C):

$$
\begin{array}{ccc}
A & B & C_Q \\
(H_A, y_A) & (H_B, x_B) & [(H_C + Q_C), x_C]
\end{array}
$$

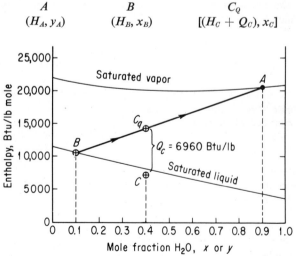

since the material and energy balances are based on the equations:

$$Cx_C = Ay_A + Bx_B$$

$$Q + CH_C = AH_A + BH_B = CQ_C + CH_C = C(H_C + Q_C)$$

The points we know are B and C,

B	C
H_B = saturated liquid	$H_C = 7200$ Btu/lb mole
$x_C = 0.10$	$x_C = 0.40$

Plot these two points, and then determine where the point C_Q lies:

$$C_Q \text{ is at } x_C = 0.40$$

and

$$H_{C_Q} = 7200 + \frac{15{,}300 \text{ Btu/hr}}{2.2 \text{ lb mole/hr}} = 7200 + 6960 = 14{,}160 \text{ Btu/lb mole}$$

Plot C_Q, and draw a line through B and C_Q. Extend the line to the saturated-vapor line to get point A, which is at about $x = 0.91$. ←—— ⓑ

From the chart, the enthalpy of A is about 20,500 Btu/lb mole. ←—— ⓐ

By measuring the length of the distances $\overline{BC_Q}$, $\overline{C_QA}$, and $\overline{BA}$, or their projections on the x axis, we can find the amount of A and B.

$$\frac{A}{C} = \frac{\overline{BC_Q}}{\overline{AB}} = \frac{0.4 - 0.1}{0.91 - 0.1} = \frac{0.3}{0.81} = 0.370$$

$$A = 0.370C = 0.370(2.2) = 0.815 \text{ lb mole}$$

$$B = 2.2 - 0.815 = 1.385 \text{ lb mole}$$

Example 5.8 Graphical Use of Enthalpy-Concentration Charts with Processes Involving Heat Transfer

An acetic acid-water mixture is being concentrated as shown in the diagram. How much heat is added or removed?

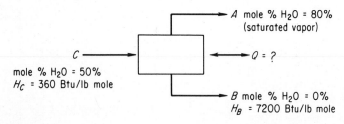

Solution:

The coordinates of all the points, A, B, and C, are known. These points can be plotted on the H-x chart, and then some basis chosen, A, B, or C:

$$\text{Basis: 1 lb mole } A$$

The governing material and energy balances in this case are (assuming Q is added and is $+$)

$$Cx_C = Ax_A + Bx_B$$

$$Q + CH_C = AH_A + BH_B = AQ_A + CH_C$$

or

$$A(H_A - Q_A) + BH_B = CH_C$$

Connect points B and C with a line, and extend the line toward the right-hand axis (see diagram). What we are looking for is the point A_Q located at the coordinates $H = (H_A - Q_A)$ and $x = 0.80$ on the extension of the line $\overline{BC}$

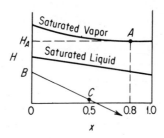

through B and C. To reach A_Q from A, we must subtract Q_A; by measuring on the diagram we find a plus value has to be subtracted from H_A, or

$$Q_A = +24,000 \text{ Btu/lb mole } A \quad \text{(heat added)}$$

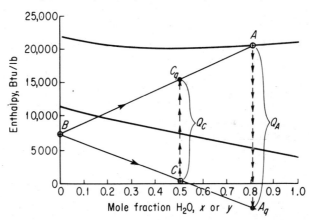

If point A_Q had fallen above A, then heat would have been removed from the system and Q_A would have been negative.

If we convert our answer to the basis of 1 lb mole of C, we find

$$\frac{A}{C} = \frac{\overline{BC}}{\overline{AB}} = \frac{0.5 - 0}{0.8 - 0} = 0.625$$

or

$$C = \frac{1}{0.625} = 1.60 \text{ lb mole}$$

Basis: 1 lb mole C

$$Q_C = \frac{24,000 \text{ Btu}}{\text{lb mole } A} \left| \frac{1.00 \text{ lb mole } A}{1.60 \text{ lb mole } C} \right. = 15,000 \text{ Btu/lb mole } C$$

As an alternative solution, we could have selected C as the basis to start with and used the equations:

$$Cx_C = Ax_A + Bx_B$$

$$Q + CH_C = AH_A + BH_B = C(H_C + Q_C)$$

In this case, join A and B and find point C_Q at $x = 0.50$ on the line $\overline{AB}$. Measure $\overline{C_QC}$; it is 14,900 Btu, which is close enough to the value of 15,000 Btu/lb mole C calculated above.

A similar calculation might have been made with B as the basis, by joining points A and C and extending to the $x = 0$ axis in order to get B_Q. Q_B would be measured from B_Q to B on the $x = 0$ axis.

5.3 Humidity charts and their use

We have previously (Chap. 3) discussed humidity, condensation, and vaporization from the viewpoint of the material balance. In this section we are going to combine material and energy balances for mixtures of water vapor and air and apply our results to problems such as humidification, air conditioning, water cooling towers, and the like. Before proceeding further, you should review briefly the sections in Chap. 3 dealing with vapor pressure, saturation, and partial saturation. You will also find it indispensable to learn the following special definitions and relations.

(a) The *humidity* $\mathscr{H}$ is the pounds of water vapor per pound of bone-dry air (some texts use moles of water vapor per mole of dry air as the humidity)

$$\mathscr{H} = \frac{18p_{H_2O}}{29(p_T - p_{H_2O})} = \frac{18n_{H_2O}}{29(n_T - n_{H_2O})}, \qquad (5.17)$$

As long as the total pressure is 1 atm (or fixed) and the partial pressure of the water vapor is low, $\mathscr{H}$ is directly proportional to p_{H_2O}. The *per cent humidity* is the

$$\frac{\text{lb water vapor/lb dry air}}{\text{lb water vapor carried by 1 lb}}(100)$$
$$\text{dry air at saturation}$$

(b) The *humid heat* is the heat capacity of an air-water vapor mixture expressed on the *basis of one pound of bone-dry air*. Thus the humid heat C_S is

$$C_S = C_{p_{air}} + (C_{p_{H_2O\,vapor}})(\mathscr{H}) \qquad (5.18)$$

where the heat capacities are all per pound and not per mole. Assuming the heat capacities of air and water vapor are constant under the narrow range of conditions found for air conditioning and humidity calculations, we can write

$$C_S = 0.240 + 0.45\,(\mathscr{H})\tag{5.19}$$

where C_S is in Btu/(°F)(lb dry air).

(c) The *humid volume* is the volume of 1 lb of dry air plus the water vapor in the air,

$$V = \frac{359 \text{ ft}^3}{1 \text{ lb mole}}\left|\frac{1 \text{ lb mole air}}{29 \text{ lb air}}\right|\frac{t+460}{32+460}$$

$$+ \frac{359 \text{ ft}^3}{1 \text{ lb mole}}\left|\frac{1 \text{ lb mole H}_2\text{O}}{18 \text{ lb H}_2\text{O}}\right|\frac{t+460}{32+460}\left|\frac{\mathscr{H} \text{ lb H}_2\text{O}}{\text{lb air}}\right.$$

$$= (0.730t + 336)\left(\frac{1}{29} + \frac{\mathscr{H}}{18}\right)\tag{5.20}$$

where V is in ft³/lb dry air and t is in °F.

(d) The *dry-bulb temperature* (t_{DB}) is the ordinary temperature you always have been using for a gas in °F.

(e) The *wet-bulb temperature* (t_{WB}) you may guess, even though you may never have heard of this term before, has something to do with water (or other liquid, if we are concerned not with humidity but with saturation) evaporating from around an ordinary mercury thermometer bulb. Suppose you put a wick, or porous cotton cloth, on the mercury bulb of a thermometer and wet the wick. Next you either (a) whirl the thermometer in the air as in Fig. 5.9 (this apparatus is called a sling psychrometer when the wet-bulb and dry-bulb thermometers are mounted together), or (b) set up a fan to blow rapidly on the bulb at 1000 ft³/min or more. What happens to the temperature recorded by the wet-bulb thermometer?

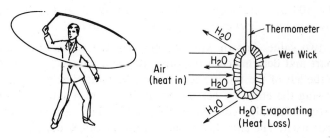

Fig. 5.9. The wet-bulb temperature obtained with a sling psychrometer.

As the water from the wick evaporates, the wick cools down and continues to cool until the rate of heat transferred to the wick by the air blowing on it equals the rate of loss of heat caused by the water evaporating from the wick. We say that the temperature at

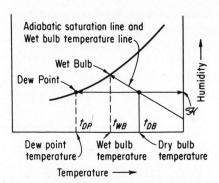

Fig. 5.10. General layout of the humidity chart showing the location of the wet-bulb and dry-bulb temperatures, the dew point and dew-point temperature, and the adiabatic saturation line and wet-bulb line.

equilibrium with the wet wick is the wet-bulb temperature. (Of course, if water continues to evaporate, it eventually will all disappear, and the wick temperature will rise.) The final temperature for the process described above lies on the 100 per cent relative humidity curve (saturated-air curve), while the so-called wet-bulb line showing how the wet-bulb temperature changes on approaching equilibrium is approximately a straight line and has a negative slope as illustrated in Fig. 5.10.

Now that we have an idea of what the various features portrayed on the *humidity chart* (psychrometric chart) are, let us look at the chart itself, Figs. 5.11(a) and 5.11(b) (inside back cover). It really is nothing more than a graphical means of presenting the relationships for and between the material and energy balances in water vapor-air mixtures. Its skeleton consists of a humidity ($\mathscr{H}$) — temperature ($t_{\text{dry bulb}}$) set of coordinates together with the additional parameters (lines) of:

(a) Constant relative humidity (10 to 90%)
(b) Constant moist volume (humid volume)
(c) Adiabatic cooling lines which are the same (for water vapor only[7]) as the wet-bulb or psychrometric lines
(d) The 100 per cent relative humidity (identical to the 100 per cent absolute humidity) curve or saturated-air curve.

With any two values known, you can pinpoint the air-moisture condition on the chart and determine all the other required values.

Off to the left of the 100 per cent relative humidity line you will observe scales showing the enthalpy per pound of dry air of a saturated air-water vapor mixture. Enthalpy corrections for air less than saturated are shown on the chart itself. The enthalpy of the wet air, in Btu/lb dry air, is:

$$\Delta \hat{H} = \Delta \hat{H}_{\text{air}} + \Delta \hat{H}_{\text{H}_2\text{O vapor}}(\mathscr{H}) \qquad (5.21)$$

We should mention at this point that the reference conditions for the humidity chart are liquid water at 32°F and 1 atm (not the vapor pressure of H_2O) for water, and 0°F and 1 atm for air. The chart is suitable for use

---

[7] For a detailed discussion of the uniqueness of this coincidence, consult any of the references at the end of this chapter.

only at normal atmospheric conditions and must be modified[8] if the pressure is significantly different than 1 atm. If you wanted to, you could calculate the enthalpy values shown on the chart directly from tables listing the enthalpies of air and water vapor by the methods described in Chap. 4, or you could, by making use of Eq. (5.21), compute the enthalpies with reasonable accuracy from the following equation for 1 lb of air:

$$\Delta \hat{H} = \underbrace{0.240(t - 0)}_{C_p(\Delta t) \text{ for air}} + \underbrace{\mathcal{H}[1075}_{\substack{\text{heat of vaporization} \\ \text{of water at } 32°F}} + \underbrace{0.45(t - 32)]}_{\substack{C_p(\Delta t) \text{ for} \\ \text{water vapor}}} \qquad (5.22)$$

Consolidating terms:

$$\Delta \hat{H} = 0.240t + \mathcal{H}(1061 + 0.45t) \qquad (5.23)$$

You will recall that the idea of the wet-bulb temperature is based on the equilibrium between the *rates* of heat transfer and evaporation of water. Rates of processes are a topic we have not discussed. The fundamental idea is that a large amount of air is brought into contact with a little bit of water, and that presumably the evaporation of the water leaves the temperature and humidity of the air unchanged. Only the temperature of the water changes. The equation of the wet-bulb line is

$$h_c(t - t_{WB}) = k'_g \Delta \hat{H}_{vap}(\mathcal{H}_{WB} - \mathcal{H}) \qquad (5.24)$$

where h_c = heat transfer coefficient for convection
k'_g = mass transfer coefficient
$\Delta \hat{H}_{vap}$ = latent heat of vaporization
$\mathcal{H}$ = humidity of moist air
t = temperature of moist air

The equation for the wet-bulb lines is based on a number of assumptions, a discussion of which is beyond the scope of this book. However, you can see that the ratio

$$\frac{(\mathcal{H}_{WB} - \mathcal{H})}{(t_{WB} - t)} = -\frac{h_c}{(k'_g)\Delta \hat{H}_{vap}} \qquad (5.25)$$

For water only, it so happens that $h_c/k'_g \cong C_S$, i.e., the numerical value is about 0.25, which gives the wet-bulb lines the slope of

$$\frac{(\mathcal{H}_{WB} - \mathcal{H})}{(t_{WB} - t)} = -\frac{C_S}{\Delta \hat{H}_{vap}} \qquad (5.26)$$

For other substances, the value of h_c/k'_g can be as much as twice that of water.

Another type of process of some importance occurs when an adiabatic cooling or humidification takes place between air and water that is recycled

---

[8] See G. E. McElroy, *U.S. Bur. Mines Rept. Invest.*, No. 4165, Dec., 1947.

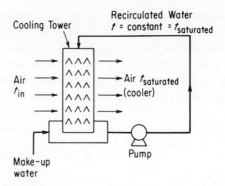

Fig. 5.12. Adiabatic humidification with recycle of water.

as in Fig. 5.12. In this process the air is both cooled and humidified (its water content rises) while a little bit of the recirculated water is evaporated. At equilibrium, in the steady state, the temperature of the air is the same as the temperature of the water, and the air is saturated at this temperature. By making an over-all energy balance around the process ($Q = 0$), we can obtain the equation for the adiabatic cooling lines. Employing a version of Eq. (5.22) with the equilibrium temperature of the water, t_S, taken as a reference temperature rather than 0 or 32°F, we get, ignoring the small amount of make-up water or assuming it enters at t_S,

$$\overbrace{0.240(t_{air} - t_S)}^{\substack{\text{enthalpy of air} \\ \text{entering}}} + \overbrace{\mathscr{H}_{air}[\Delta \hat{H}_{H_2O \text{ at } t_S} + 0.45(t_{air} - t_S)]}^{\substack{\text{enthalpy of water vapor} \\ \text{in air entering}}}$$

$$= \overbrace{0.240(t_S - t_S)}^{\substack{\text{enthalpy of air} \\ \text{leaving}}} + \overbrace{\mathscr{H}_S[\Delta \hat{H}_{H_2O \text{ at } t_S} + 0.45(t_S - t_S)]}^{\substack{\text{enthalpy of water vapor} \\ \text{in air leaving}}} \quad (5.27)$$

This can be reduced to

$$t_{air} = \frac{\Delta \hat{H}_{H_2O \text{ at } ts}(\mathscr{H}_S - \mathscr{H}_{air})}{0.240 + 0.45\mathscr{H}_{air}} + t_S \quad (5.28)$$

which is the equation of the adiabatic cooling curve.

Notice that this equation can be written as:

$$\frac{(\mathscr{H}_S - \mathscr{H})}{(t_S - t_{air})} = -\frac{C_S}{\Delta \hat{H}_{vap}} \quad (5.29)$$

because $C_S = 0.240 + 0.45\mathscr{H}$ and $t_{WB} = t_S$. Thus the wet-bulb equation, for water only, is the same as the adiabatic saturation equation [Eq. (5.26)]. For other materials these two equations have different slopes.

Only two of the quantities in Eq. (5.28) are variables, if t_S is known, because $\mathscr{H}_S$ is the humidity of saturated air at t_S and $\Delta \hat{H}_{H_2O \text{ at } t_S}$ is fixed by t_S. Thus, for any value of t_S, you can make a plot of Eqs. (5.25) and/or (5.29) on the humidity chart in the form of $\mathscr{H}$ vs. t_{air}. These curves, which are essentially linear, will intersect the 100 per cent relative humidity curve at $\mathscr{H}_S$ and t_S, as described earlier.

The adiabatic cooling lines are lines of almost constant enthalpy for the entering air-water mixture, and you can use them as such without much error (1 or 2 per cent). However, if you want to correct a saturated enthalpy value for the deviation which exists for a less-than-saturated air-water vapor mixture, you can employ the enthalpy deviation lines which appear on the chart and which can be used as illustrated in the examples below. Any process which is not a wet-bulb process or an adiabatic process with recirculated water can be treated by the usual material and energy balances, taking the basic data for the calculation from the humidity charts. If there is any increase or decrease in the moisture content of the air in a psychrometric process, the small enthalpy effect of the moisture added to the air or lost by the air may be included in the energy balance for the process to make it more exact as illustrated in Examples 5.11 and 5.12.

You can find further details regarding the construction of humidity charts in the references at the end of this chapter. Tables are also available listing all the thermodynamic properties (p, $\hat{V}$, $\mathscr{H}$, ΔH, and S) in great detail.[9] Although we will be discussing humidity charts exclusively, charts can be prepared for mixtures of any two substances in the vapor phase, such as CCl_4 and air or acetone and nitrogen, by use of Eqs. (5.17) to (5.28) if all the values of the physical constants for water and air are replaced by those of the desired gas and vapor. The equations themselves can be used for humidity problems if charts are too inaccurate or are not available.

Example 5.9   Properties of Moist Air from the Humidity Chart

List all the properties you can find on the humidity chart for moist air at a dry-bulb temperature of 90°F and a wet-bulb temperature of 70°F.

Solution:

A diagram will help explain the various properties obtained from the humidity chart. You can find the location of point A for 90°F DB (dry bulb) and 70°F WB (wet bulb) by following a vertical line at $t_{DB} = 90°F$ until it crosses the wet-bulb line for 70°F. This wet-bulb line can be located by searching along the 100% humidity line until the saturation temperature of 70°F is reached, or, alternatively, by proceeding up a vertical line at 70°F until it intersects the 100% humidity line. From the wet-bulb temperature of 70°F, follow the adiabatic cooling line (which is the same as the wet-bulb temperature line on the humidity chart) to the right until it intersects the 90°F DB line.

[9] Microfilms of Psychrometric Tables, 1953, by Byron Engelbach are available from University Microfilms, Ann Arbor, Mich.

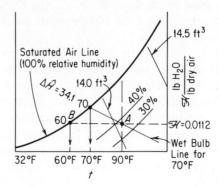

Now that point A has been fixed, you can read the other properties of the moist air from the chart.

(a) *Dew point.* When the air at A is cooled at constant pressure (and in effect at *constant humidity*), as described in Chap. 3, it eventually reaches a temperature at which the moisture begins to condense. This is represented by a horizontal line, a constant-humidity line, on the humidity chart, and the dew point is located at B, or about 60°F.

(b) *Relative humidity.* By interpolating between the 40% R.H. and 30% R.H. lines with a ruler, you can find that point A is at about 37% R.H.

(c) *Humidity* ($\mathscr{H}$). You can read the humidity from the right-hand ordinate as 0.0112 lb H_2O/lb air.

(d) *Humid volume.* By interpolation again between the 14.0 and the 14.5 ft³ lines, you can find the humid volume to be 14.097 ft³/lb dry air.

(e) *Enthalpy.* The enthalpy value for saturated air with a wet-bulb temperature of 70°F is $\hat{H} = 34.1$ Btu/lb dry air (a more accurate value can be obtained from psychrometric tables if needed). The enthalpy deviation for less-than-saturated air is about -0.2 Btu/lb dry air; consequently the actual enthalpy of air at 37% R.H. is $34.1 - 0.2 = 33.9$ Btu/lb dry air.

Example 5.10   Heating at Constant Humidity

Moist air at 50°F and 50% R.H. is heated in your furnace to 100°F. How much heat has to be added per ft³ of initial moist air, and what is the final dew point of the air?

Solution:

As shown in the diagram, the process goes from point A to point B on a horizontal line of constant humidity. The initial conditions are fixed at $t_{DB} = $ 50°F and 50% R.H. Point B is fixed by the intersection of the horizontal line from A and the vertical line at 100°F. The dew point is unchanged in this process and is located at C at 32.5°F.

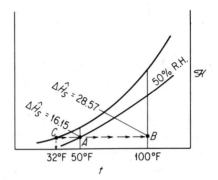

The enthalpy values are as follows (all in Btu/lb dry air):

point	$\Delta\hat{H}_{\text{satd}}$	δH	$\Delta\hat{H}_{\text{actual}}$
A	16.15	−0.02	16.13
B	28.57	−0.26	28.31

Also at A the volume of the moist air is 12.92 ft³/lb dry air. Consequently the heat added is $(Q = \Delta\hat{H})$ 28.31 − 16.13 = 12.18 Btu/lb dry air.

$$\frac{12.18 \text{ Btu}}{\text{lb dry air}} \mid \frac{1 \text{ lb dry air}}{12.92 \text{ ft}^3} = 0.942 \text{ Btu/ft}^3 \text{ initial moist air added}$$

Example 5.11   Cooling and Humidification

One way of adding moisture to air is by passing it through water sprays or air washers. Normally, the water used is recirculated rather than wasted. Then, in the steady state, the water is at the adiabatic saturation temperature which is the same as the wet-bulb temperature. The air passing through the washer is cooled, and if the contact time between the air and the water is long enough, the air will be at the wet-bulb temperature also. However, we will assume the washer is small enough so that the air does not reach the wet-bulb

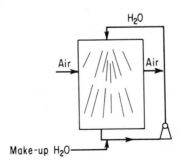

temperature but the following conditions prevail:

	t_{DB}, °F	t_{WB}, °F
entering air	100	70
exit air	80	

Find the moisture added per pound of dry air.

Solution:

The whole process is assumed to be *adiabatic*, and, as shown in the diagram, takes place between points A and B. The wet-bulb temperature remains constant.

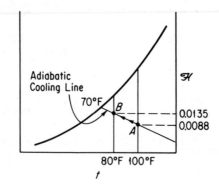

Humidity values are:

$$\mathcal{H},\ \frac{\text{lb H}_2\text{O}}{\text{lb air}}$$

B	0.0135
A	0.0088

Difference:

$$0.0047\ \frac{\text{lb H}_2\text{O}}{\text{lb dry air}} \quad \text{added.}$$

Example 5.12   Cooling and Dehumidification

A process which takes moisture out of the air by passing the air through water sprays sounds peculiar but is perfectly practical as long as the water temperature is below the dew point of the air. Equipment such as shown in the diagram would do the trick. If the entering air has a dew point of 70°F and is at 40% R.H., how much heat has to be removed by the cooler, and how much water vapor is removed, if the exit air is at 56°F with a wet-bulb temperature of 54°F?

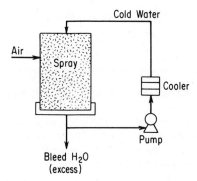

Solution:

The initial and final values of the enthalpies and humidities are:
Data for the process:

	A	*B*
$\mathscr{H}\left(\dfrac{\text{grains } H_2O}{\text{lb dry air}}\right)$	111	62
$\Delta\hat{H}\left(\dfrac{\text{Btu}}{\text{lb dry air}}\right)$	$41.3 - 0.2 = 41.1$	$23.0 - 0 = 23.0$

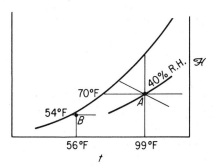

The grains of H_2O removed are

$$111 - 62 = 49 \text{ grains/lb dry air}$$

The cooling duty is approximately

$$41.1 - 23.0 = 18.1 \text{ Btu/lb dry air}$$

In the upper left of the humidity chart is a little insert which gives the value of the small correction factor for the water condensed from the air which leaves the system. Assuming the water leaves at the wet-bulb temperature of 54°F, read for 49 grains a correction of -0.15 Btu/lb dry air. You could calculate the same value by taking the enthalpy of liquid water from the Steam Tables and saying,

$$\frac{22 \text{ Btu}}{\text{lb } H_2O} \left|\frac{1 \text{ lb } H_2O}{7000 \text{ grains}}\right| \frac{49 \text{ grains rejected}}{1 \text{ lb dry air}} = 0.154 \text{ Btu/lb dry air}$$

The exact energy (enthalpy) balance will then give us the cooling load:

air in   air out   H₂O out

$41.1 - 23.0 - 0.15 = 17.9$ Btu/lb dry air

Example 5.13   Combined Material and Energy Balances for a Cooling Tower

You have been requested to redesign a water-cooling tower which has a blower with a capacity of 8.30×10^6 ft³/hr of moist air (at 80°F and a wet-bulb temperature of 65°F). The exit air leaves at 95°F and 90°F wet bulb. How much water can be cooled in lb/hr if the water to be cooled is not recycled, enters the tower at 120°F, and leaves the tower at 90°F?

Solution:

Enthalpy, humidity, and humid volume data taken from the humidity chart are:

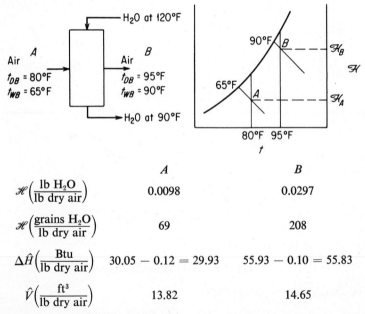

	A	B
$\mathscr{H}\left(\dfrac{\text{lb H}_2\text{O}}{\text{lb dry air}}\right)$	0.0098	0.0297
$\mathscr{H}\left(\dfrac{\text{grains H}_2\text{O}}{\text{lb dry air}}\right)$	69	208
$\Delta\hat{H}\left(\dfrac{\text{Btu}}{\text{lb dry air}}\right)$	$30.05 - 0.12 = 29.93$	$55.93 - 0.10 = 55.83$
$\hat{V}\left(\dfrac{\text{ft}^3}{\text{lb dry air}}\right)$	13.82	14.65

The cooling water exit temperature can be obtained from an energy balance around the process.

Basis: 8.30×10^6 ft³/hr of moist air

$$\frac{8.30 \times 10^6 \text{ ft}^3}{} \; \frac{\text{lb dry air}}{13.82 \text{ ft}^3} = 6.00 \times 10^5 \text{ lb dry air/hr}$$

The enthalpy of the entering water stream is (reference temperature is 32°F and 1 atm)

$$\Delta\hat{H} = C_{p_{\text{H}_2\text{O}}}\,\Delta T = 1(120 - 32) = 88 \text{ Btu/lb H}_2\text{O}$$

while that of the exit stream is 58 Btu/lb H_2O. (The value from the Steam Tables at 120°F for liquid water of 87.92 Btu/lb H_2O is slightly different since it represents water at its vapor pressure (1.69 psia) based on reference conditions of 32°F and liquid water at its vapor pressure.) Any other datum could be used instead of 32°F for the liquid water. For example, if you chose 90°F, one water stream would not have to be taken into account because its enthalpy would be zero.

The loss of water to the air is

$$0.0297 - 0.0098 = 0.0199 \text{ lb } H_2O/\text{lb dry air}$$

(a) *Material balance for water stream:*

Let $\qquad W = $ lb H_2O entering the tower in the water stream per lb dry air

Then $(W - 0.0199) = $ lb H_2O leaving tower in the water stream per lb dry air

(b) *Energy balance (enthalpy balance) around the entire process:*

air and water in air entering

$$\frac{29.93 \text{ Btu}}{\text{lb dry air}} \left| \; 6.00 \times 10^5 \text{ lb dry air} \right.$$

water stream entering

$$+ \; \frac{88 \text{ Btu}}{\text{lb } H_2O} \left| \; \frac{W \text{ lb } H_2O}{\text{lb dry air}} \right| 6.00 \times 10^5 \text{ lb dry air}$$

air and water in air leaving

$$= \; \frac{55.83 \text{ Btu}}{\text{lb dry air}} \left| \; 6.00 \times 10^5 \text{ lb dry air} \right.$$

water stream leaving

$$+ \; \frac{58 \text{ Btu}}{\text{lb } H_2O} \left| \; \frac{(W - 0.0199) \text{ lb } H_2O}{\text{lb dry air}} \right| 6.00 \times 10^5 \text{ lb dry air}$$

$$29.93 + 88W = 55.83 + 58(W - 0.0199)$$

$$W = 0.825 \text{ lb } H_2O/\text{lb dry air}$$

$$(W - 0.0199) = 0.805 \text{ lb } H_2O/\text{lb dry air}$$

The total water leaving the tower is

$$\frac{0.805 \text{ lb } H_2O}{\text{lb dry air}} \left| \; \frac{6.00 \times 10^5 \text{ lb dry air}}{\text{hr}} \right. = 4.83 \times 10^5 \text{ lb/hr}$$

5.4 Complex problems

In this book we have treated only small segments of material and energy balance problems. Put a large number of these segments together and you will have a real industrial process. We do not have the space to describe the details of any specific process, but for such information you can consult the references at the end of this chapter. It is always wise to read about a process and gain as much information as you can about the stoichiometry and energy relations involved before undertaking to make any calculations. Do not be unnerved by the complexity of a large-scale detailed plant. With the techniques you have accumulated while studying this text you will find that you will be able to break down the over-all scheme into small units involving three or four streams which can be handled in the same way you have handled the material in this text. Perhaps you can find a tie element (or make one up) that will permit you to work from one unit of the process to the next. Example 5.14 briefly outlines, without much descriptive explanation, how you should apply your knowledge of material and energy balances to a not-too-complex alcohol plant.

Example 5.14   A More Complex Problem

The Blue Ribbon Sour Mash Company plans to make commercial alcohol by a process shown in the diagram. Grain mash is fed through a heat exchanger

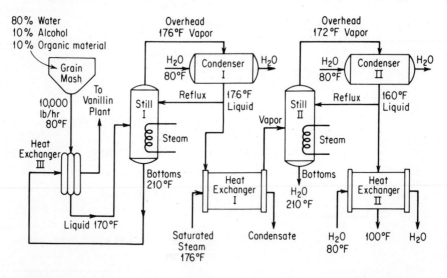

where it is heated to 170°F. The alcohol is removed as 60% (wt) alcohol from the first fractionating column; the bottoms contain no alcohol. The 60% alcohol is further fractionated to 95% alcohol and essentially pure water in the second column. Both stills operate at a 3-to-1 reflux ratio and heat is supplied to the bottom of the columns by steam. Condenser water is obtainable at 80°F. The operating data and physical properties of the streams have been accumulated and are listed for convenience:

operating information and data

stream	state	b.p. (°F)	C_p, Btu/(lb)(°F) liquid	C_p, Btu/(lb)(°F) vapor	heat of vaporization (Btu/lb)
feed	liquid	170	0.96		950
60% alcohol	liquid or vapor	176	0.85	0.56	675
bottoms (I)	liquid	212	1.00	0.50	970
95% alcohol	liquid or vapor	172	0.72	0.48	650
bottoms (II)	liquid	212	1.00	0.50	970

Make a complete material balance on the process and:

(a) Determine the weight of the following streams per hour:
   (1) Overhead product, column (I)
   (2) Reflux, column (I)
   (3) Bottoms, column (I)
   (4) Overhead product, column (II)
   (5) Reflux, column (II)
   (6) Bottoms, column (II)
(b) Calculate the temperature of the bottoms leaving the heat exchanger III.
(c) Determine the total heat input to the system in Btu/hr.
(d) Calculate the water requirements for each condenser and heat exchanger II in gallons per hour if the maximum exit temperature of water from this equipment is 130°F.

Solution:
Let us call the alcohol A for short and the organic matter M.

Basis: 10,000 lb/hr mash

(a) *Material balance around column I and condenser:*

		In				*Out*	
Feed	A	$(0.10)(10{,}000) =$	1000 lb	Product	A		= 1000 lb
	H₂O	$(0.80)(10{,}000) =$	8000		H₂O	$\left(\dfrac{1000}{0.60}\right) - 1000 =$	667
	M	$(0.10)(10{,}000) =$	1000	Bottoms	H₂O	$(8000 - 667) =$	7333
			—		M		1000
			10,000 lb				10,000 lb

(b) *Material balance around column I only:*

Feed	A	=	1000 lb	Overhead Vapor	A	$4(1000)$	= 4000 lb
	H₂O	=	8000		H₂O	$4(667)$	= 2667
	M	=	1000	Bottoms	H₂O		= 7333
Reflux	A	$(3)(1000)$	= 3000		M		= 1000
	H₂O	$(3)(667)$	= 2000				
			15,000 lb				15,000 lb

(c) *Material balance around column II and condenser:*

Feed	A	=	1000 lb	(d) Overhead Product	A		= 1000 lb
	H₂O	=	667		H₂O	$\left(\dfrac{1000}{0.95} - 1000\right)$	= 50
			1667 lb	Bottoms	H₂O	$(667 - 50)$	= 617
							1667 lb

374

(d) *Material balance on column II cutting reflux and overhead vapor:*

In

Feed $\begin{cases} A \\ H_2O \end{cases}$ = 1000 lb
                = 667

(e)
Reflux $\begin{cases} A & 3(1000) \\ H_2O & (3)(50) \end{cases}$ = 3000
                         = 150
                        4817 lb

Out

Vapor $\begin{cases} A & (4)(1000) \\ H_2O & (4)(50) \end{cases}$ = 4000 lb
                         = 200

Bottoms $\{ H_2O \;\; (667 - 50)$ = 617
                        4817 lb

STEP 2: ENERGY BALANCES

(a) *Energy balance on heat exchanger III:*

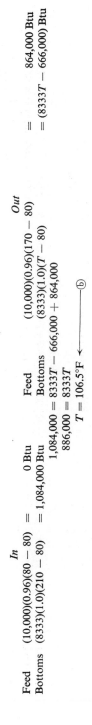

Reference
Temperature
= 80°F

In

Feed $(10{,}000)(0.96)(80 - 80)$ = 0 Btu

Bottoms $(8333)(1.0)(210 - 80)$ = 1,084,000 Btu

Out

Feed $(10{,}000)(0.96)(170 - 80)$ = 864,000 Btu

Bottoms $(8333)(1.0)(T - 80)$ = $(8333T - 666{,}000)$ Btu

$$1{,}084{,}000 = 8333T - 666{,}000 + 864{,}000$$
$$886{,}000 = 8333T$$
$$T = 106.5°F$$

375

(b) *Energy balance around heat exchanger III inlet, and overhead vapor and reflux line from I:*

Reference temperature = 176°F

	In		Out

Feed   (10,000)(0.96)(80 − 176) =   −921,000

Reflux   (5000)(0.85)(176 − 176) =   0

Steam ΔH_{S_1}

$\overline{(\Delta H_{S_1} - 921,000)}$

Bottoms to

Vanillin Plant   (8333)(1.0)(106.5 − 176) =   −579,000

Vapor   (6667)(0.85)(176 − 176) + (6667)(675) = 4,500,000

$\overline{3,921,000}$

$\Delta H_{S_1} - 921,000 = 3,921,000$

$\Delta H_{S_1} = 4,842,000$ Btu/hr

(c) *Energy balance around heat exchanger I outlet and overhead vapor and reflux from II:*

Reference temperature = 172°F

	In		Out

Feed to II   (1667)(0.85)(176 − 172) =   5,650

$\Delta H_{\text{vaporization}} \equiv \text{steam@176°F}$

$+ (1667)(675) =$ 1,125,000

Reflux   (3150)(0.72)(160 − 172) =   −27,200

Steam ΔH_{S_2}

$\overline{(\Delta H_{S_2} + 1,103,450)}$

Vapor   (4200)(0.72)(172 − 172) + (4200)(650) = 2,725,000

Bottoms   (617)(1.0)(210 − 172) =   23,400

$\overline{2,748,400}$

$\Delta H_{S_2} + 1,103,450 = 2,748,400$

$\Delta H_{S_2} = 1,645,000$ Btu/hr

(d) *Total energy input into system:*

$\Delta H_{S_1} + \Delta H_{S_2}$ + steam heater = 4,842,000 + 1,645,000 + 1,125,000 = 7,612,000 Btu/hr

(e) *Energy balance on condenser I:*

$W = $ lb H$_2$O/hr;   Reference temperature = 176°F

ⓒ

In   *Out*

Vapor $(6667)(0.85)(176 - 176) + (6667)(675) =$ $4{,}500{,}000$ Condensate $(6667)(0.85)(176 - 176) =$ 0

Cooling H_2O $(W)(1.0)(80 - 176) =$ $-96W$ Cooling H_2O $(W)(1.0)(130 - 176) =$ $-46W$

       $(-96W + 4{,}500{,}000)$ $-46W$

$$50W = 4{,}500{,}000 \quad \text{or} \quad W = \frac{4{,}500{,}000}{50} = 90{,}000 \text{ lb } H_2O/hr$$

$$\frac{90{,}000 \text{ lb } H_2O/hr}{8.345 \text{ lb/gal}} = 10{,}800 \text{ gal } H_2O/hr \qquad \text{(d}_1\text{)}$$

(f) Energy balance on condenser II:

$$W = \text{lb } H_2O/hr; \qquad \text{Reference temperature} = 172°F$$

In   *Out*

Vapor $(4200)(0.72)(172 - 172) + (4200)(650) =$ $2{,}725{,}000$ Condensate $(4200)(0.72)(160 - 172) =$ $-36{,}000$

Cooling H_2O $(W)(1.0)(80 - 172) =$ $-92W$ Cooling H_2O $(W)(1.0)(172 - 130) =$ $-42W$

       $(-92W + 2{,}725{,}000)$ $(-42W - 36{,}000)$

$$50W = 2{,}761{,}000 \quad \text{or} \quad W = \frac{2{,}761{,}000}{50} = 55{,}200 \text{ lb } H_2O/hr$$

$$\frac{55{,}200 \text{ lb } H_2O}{8.345 \text{ lb/gal}} = 6620 \text{ gal } H_2O/hr \qquad \text{(d}_2\text{)}$$

(g) Energy balance on heat exchanger II:

$$W = \text{lb } H_2O/hr; \qquad \text{Reference temperature} = 80°F$$

In   *Out*

Condensate $(1050)(0.72)(160 - 80) =$ $60{,}500$ Product $(1050)(0.72)(100 - 80) =$ $15{,}120$

Cooling H_2O $(W)(1.0)(80 - 80) =$ 0 Cooling H_2O $(W)(1.0)(130 - 80) =$ $50W$

       $60{,}500$ $50W + 15{,}120$

$$50W + 15{,}120 = 60{,}500$$

$$W = 907 \text{ lb } H_2O/hr \quad \text{or} \quad 109 \text{ gal } H_2O/hr \qquad \text{(d}_3\text{)}$$

WHAT YOU SHOULD HAVE LEARNED FROM THIS CHAPTER

1. By the end of this chapter you should have perfected your techniques in using material and energy balances separately or in combination to such an extent that you should be able to analyze any type of process and write down the appropriate balances in an accomplished manner.
2. You should know how to use humidity charts and enthalpy-concentration charts as aids in the solution of problems.

NOMENCLATURE

C_p = heat capacity
C_S = humid heat defined by Eq. (5.18)
$\Delta\hat{H}$ = enthalpy per unit mass or mole
h_c = heat transfer coefficient in Eq. (5.24)
H = enthalpy, with appropriate subscripts, relative to a reference enthalpy
ΔH = enthalpy change, with appropriate subscripts
$\mathscr{H}$ = humidity, lb water vapor/lb dry air
k_g' = mass transfer coefficient in Eq. (5.24)
n = moles
p = pressure with appropriate subscript
Q = heat transferred (on the basis shown by the appropriate subscript, if needed)
S = entropy
t = temperature in °F or °C, with appropriate subscript
t_{DB} = dry-bulb temperature
t_{WB} = wet-bulb temperature
$\hat{V}$ = humid volume defined in Eq. (5.20)
W = work done by the system
w = pounds of a substance
x = mass or mole fraction in general
x = mass or mole fraction in the liquid phase for two-phase systems
y = mass or mole fraction in the vapor phase for two-phase systems

SUPPLEMENTARY REFERENCES

Combustion of Solid, Liquid, and Gaseous Fuels

1. Griswold, John, *Fuels, Combustion and Furnaces*, McGraw-Hill Book Company, New York, 1946.
2. Hougen, O. A., K. M. Watson, and R. A. Ragatz, *Chemical Process Principles*, Part I, 2nd ed., John Wiley & Sons, Inc., New York, 1954.
3. Lewis, W. K., A. H. Radasch, and H. C. Lewis, *Industrial Stoichiometry*, 2nd ed., McGraw-Hill Book Company, New York, 1954.
4. Popovich, M., and C. Hering, *Fuels and Lubricants*, John Wiley & Sons, Inc., New York, 1959.

Gas Producers and Producer Gas

5. Arne, Francis, "Manufactured Gas," *Chem. Eng.*, Mar. 24, 1958, pp. 121–23.

6. Griswold, John, *Fuels, Combustion and Furnaces*, McGraw-Hill Book Company, New York, 1946.

7. Gumz, Wilhelm, *Gas Producers and Blast Furnaces*, John Wiley & Sons, Inc., New York, 1958.

8. Lewis, W. K., A. H. Radasch, and H. C. Lewis, *Industrial Stoichiometry*, 2nd ed., McGraw-Hill Book Company, New York, 1954.

Enthalpy-Concentration Charts

*9. Badger, W. L., and J. T. Banchero, *Introduction to Chemical Engineering*, McGraw-Hill Book Company, New York, 1955.

*10. Brown, G. G., et al., *Unit Operations*, John Wiley & Sons, Inc., New York, 1950.

*11. Ellis, S. R. M., *Chem. Eng. Sci.*, vol. 3, p. 287 (1954).

**12. Lemlich, Robert, Chad Gottschlich, and Ronald Hoke, *Chem. Eng. Data Series*, vol. 2, p. 32 (1957).

*13. McCabe, W. L., *Am. Inst. Chem. Engrs. Trans.*, vol. 31, p. 129 (1935).

**14. Othmer, D. F., et al., *Ind. Eng. Chem.*, vol. 51, p. 89 (1959).

*15. Robinson, C. S., and E. R. Gilliland, *Elements of Fractional Distillation*, 3rd ed., McGraw-Hill Book Company, New York, 1939.

*16. White, R. R., *Petroleum Refiner*, vol. 24, no. 8, p. 101; vol. 24, no. 9, p. 127 (1945).

Humidity Charts and Calculations

17. Badger, W. L., and J. T. Banchero, *Introduction to Chemical Engineering*, McGraw-Hill Book Company, New York, 1955.

18. McCabe, W. L., and J. C. Smith, *Unit Operations of Chemical Engineering*, McGraw-Hill Book Company, New York, 1956.

19. Treybal, R. E., *Mass Transfer Operations*, McGraw-Hill Book Company, New York, 1955.

20. Woolrich, W. R., and W. R. Woolrich, Jr., *Air Conditioning*, The Ronald Press Co., New York, 1957.

Industrial Process Calculations

21. Hougen, O. A., K. M. Watson, and R. A. Ragatz, *Chemical Process Principles*, Part I, 2nd ed., John Wiley & Sons, Inc., New York, 1954.

* Concerned with H-x chart calculations.
** Concerned with H-x chart construction.

22. Lewis, W. K., A. H. Radasch, and H. C. Lewis, *Industrial Stoichiometry*, 2nd ed., McGraw-Hill Book Company, New York, 1954.

23. Nelson, W. L., *Petroleum Refinery Engineering*, 4th ed., McGraw-Hill Book Company, New York, 1958.

24. Shreve, R. N., *The Chemical Process Industries*, 2nd ed., McGraw-Hill Book Company, New York, 1956.

PROBLEMS

Enthalpy Concentration Chart Problems

5.1. Draw the saturated-liquid line (1 atm isobar) on an enthalpy concentration chart for caustic soda solutions. Show the 200, 250, 300, 350, and 400°F isotherms in the liquid region, and draw tie lines for these temperatures through the vapor region. Using the data from *N.B.S. Circular* 500, show where molten NaOH would be on this chart. Take the remaining data from the following table and the Steam Tables.

temp. (°F)	x satd. liquid conc., wt fr.	$\Delta \hat{H}$ enthalpy, satd. liquid, Btu/lb
200	0	168
250	0.34	202
300	0.53	314
350	0.68	435
400	0.78	535

C_p for NaOH solutions, Btu/(lb)(°F)

wt % NaOH	temperature, °F				
	32	60	100	140	180
10	0.882	0.897	0.911	0.918	0.922
20	0.842	0.859	0.875	0.884	0.886
30		0.837	0.855	0.866	0.869
40		0.815	0.826	0.831	0.832
50			0.769	0.767	0.765

Source: J. W. Bertetti and W. L. McCabe, *Ind. Eng. Chem.*, v. 28, p. 375 (1936).
Note: All H_2O tie lines extend to pure water vapor.

5.2. Refer to the Figure in Appendix I.1, the enthalpy-composition chart for the system *A-B* at 1 atm, where *A* = ethanol and *B* = water.
 (a) What are the reference states?
 (b) What is the normal boiling point (°F) of pure *A*?
 (c) What is the normal boiling point (°F) of pure *B*?
 (d) What is the heat of vaporization (Btu/lb) of pure *B* at the normal boiling point?

(e) What is the bubble point (°F) of a mixture of A and B which is 45 wt % A?

(f) Estimate the heat capacity in Btu/(lb)(°F) of a vapor mixture of A and B which is 45 wt % at 185°F.

(g) One hundred pounds of a liquid A-B mixture at 150°F and 90 wt % A is mixed with 38.5 lb of pure B vapor at 215°F in a steady-flow process. The process is adiabatic. Determine the temperature (°F), the compositions (wt % A), and the masses (lb) of the vapor and liquid streams leaving the process.

5.3. An evaporator at atmospheric pressure is designed to concentrate 10,000 lb/hr of a 10% NaOH solution at 70°F into a 40% solution. The steam pressure inside the steam chest is 40 psig. Determine the lb of steam needed per hour if the exit strong caustic preheats the entering weak caustic in a heat exchanger, leaving the heat exchanger at 100°F.

5.4. A 50% caustic solution at 280°F is to be diluted to a 17.5% solution at 70°F. How much of the water added must be in the form of ice?

5.5. One thousand pounds of 10% NaOH solution at 100°F is to be fortified to 30% NaOH by adding 73% NaOH at 200°F. How much 73% solution must be used? How much cooling must be provided so that the final temperature will be 70°F?

5.6. In a battery plant pure H_2SO_4 at 80°F is mixed with pure water at 60°F to make a 20% solution at 70°F. How much heat was removed per pound of final solution? If the mixing had been adiabatic, what would have been the temperature of the final solution?

5.7. Fifteen per cent H_2SO_4 at 70°F is to be concentrated to 90% H_2SO_4. Steam is available at 800 psig, and a pressure of 1 atm can be maintained in an available evaporator. Calculate the steam required per pound of weak H_2SO_4 supplied.

5.8. Saturated steam at 300°F is blown continuously into a tank of 30% H_2SO_4 at 70°F. What is the highest concentration of liquid H_2SO_4 that can result from this process?

5.9. To a closed tank containing 100 lb of water at 90°F is added 200 lb of 80% H_2SO_4 solution at 294°F and 100 lb of 40% H_2SO_4 solution at 140°F. In order to cool the solution, a 30-lb cake of ice is dropped into the tank. What is the final composition and temperature of the mixture in the tank? Use the chart provided for enthalpies of H_2SO_4 solutions in Appendix I (note the abscissa is wt % of H_2SO_4). Latent heat of fusion of ice is 79.7 cal/g. Heat capacity of H_2O is about 1 Btu/lb. Heat of formation of H_2O (g) is -57.80 kcal/g mole.

5.10. For the ammonia-water system at . . . psia, calculate the unknown quantities for each of the three cases below:

	stream	wt % NH_3	enthalpy Btu/lb	amount lb
A.	A	10	satd. liquid	150
	B	70	satd. vapor	300
	C	unknown	unknown	unknown
	$Q = -400,000$ Btu			

stream	wt % NH$_3$	enthalpy Btu/lb	amount lb
B. A	80	satd. vapor	unknown
B	10	1700	unknown
C	50	100	100
Q = unknown			
C. A	90	1200	100
B	unknown	1500	unknown
C	35	800	400
Q = unknown			

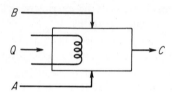

5.11. A mixture of ammonia and water in the vapor phase, saturated at 250 psia and containing 80 wt % ammonia, is passed through a condenser at a rate of 10,000 lb/hr. Heat is removed from the mixture at the rate of 5,800,000 Btu/hr while the mixture passes through a cooler. The mixture is then expanded to a pressure of 100 psia and passes into a separator. A flow sheet of the process is given below. If the heat loss from the equipment to the surroundings is neglected, determine the composition of the liquid leaving the separator, by:
(a) A material and energy balance set of equations
(b) Using the enthalpy-concentration diagram method

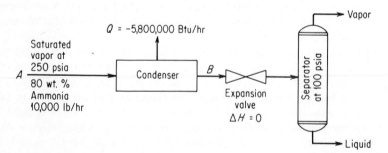

5.12. (a) Plot an enthalpy-concentration diagram for the ethyl alcohol-water system at 760 mm Hg total pressure (enthalpy of the mixture in Btu/lb vs. weight fraction ethanol). Plot the diagram on 11- by 17-in. graph paper. Be sure to include the following: (a) saturated-vapor line, (b) saturated-liquid line, and (c) lines of constant temperature in the subcooled-liquid region from 0 to 200°F. Notice that even though the EtOH-water system is a nonideal system, the saturated-vapor and liquid lines are almost straight lines and could have been drawn from the enthalpies of the pure components without serious error.

(b)

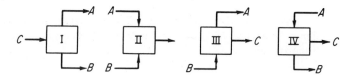

In each of the four cases diagramed the following data apply:

stream	wt % EtOH	condition	amount
A	80	unknown	unknown
B	10	70°F	unknown
C	60	superheated vapor at 800 Btu/lb	100 lb

(1) For diagram I:
    (a) By a material and energy balance, find the weights of streams A and B and the enthalpy of stream A.
    (b) Prove by analytical geometry that A, B, and C will lie on a straight line when plotted on an H-x diagram.
    (c) Repeat part (a), but this time use the method of Ponchon instead of a system of material and energy balance equations.
(2) Repeat 1 (c) for diagram II.
(3) Repeat 1 (c) for diagram III.
(4) Repeat 1 (c) for diagram IV.

    Note: For part (a) you must plot the actual data and show your points clearly. For part (b), use $8\frac{1}{2}$ by 11 graph paper with the abscissa marked from 0.1 to 0.9 wt fraction. If you use more than one graph for the solution of part (b), you may plot the saturated-vapor and liquid lines from the enthalpies of the pure components and connect them with a straight line. See Appendix I.

References for data: L. W. Cornell and R. E. Montonna, *Ind. Eng. Chem.*, v. 25, pp. 1331–35 (1933); J. H. Perry, *Chemical Engineers' Handbook*, 2nd ed., McGraw-Hill Book Company, New York, 1941, p. 1364; Noyes and Wurfle, *J. Am. Chem. Soc.*, v. 23, p. 463 (1901).

Humidity and Saturation Chart Problems

5.13. Construct a "saturation" chart for CO_2 and acetone at 1 atm pressure and include:
    (a) 100, 50, and 25 per cent saturation lines
    (b) Saturated acetone vs. temperature line
    (c) Latent heat of acetone vs. temperature
    (d) "Humid heat" vs. saturation
    (e) Adiabatic cooling lines for adiabatic saturation temperatures of 40, 80, and 100°F

(f) Wet- and dry-bulb temperature lines for temperatures of 40, 80, and 100°F

　　Data: Take the vapor pressure data for acetone from any reference book. Acetone, $C_{p(\text{avg})} = 0.347$ cal/(g)(°C). Acetone, latent heat of vaporization:

t (°C)	cal/g
0	134.74
20	131.87
40	128.05
60	123.51
80	118.26
100	112.76

$h_c/k_c' = 0.38$ for acetone vapor.

5.14. (a) Calculate the:
   (1) Humidity of air saturated at 120°F
   (2) Saturated volume at 120°F
   (3) Adiabatic saturation temperature and wet-bulb temperature of air having a dry-bulb $t = 120°F$ and a dew point $= 60°F$
   (4) Per cent saturation when the air in (3) is cooled to 82°F
   (5) Pounds of water condensed/100 lb of moist air in (3) when the air is cooled to 40°F

(b) Compute the wet-bulb temperature and per cent *relative* humidity before and after for the following cases:

dry bulb t (°F)	% humidity	new dry bulb t (°F)
80	40	100
150	60	100
100	10	60
60	95	150

5.15. Air at 100°F having a wet-bulb temperature of 65°F is used to dry clay pottery. The air leaves the drier with 95% humidity.
   (a) What is the *relative* humidity of the air leaving?
   (b) How many pounds of water will be removed per 100 lb of dry air?
   (c) If the air from the drier is heated to 150°F, how much heat is required per 100 lb of dry air?
   (d) If the air heated to 150°F is passed again over the clay and leaves at 120°F, what is the % humidity of the air leaving?
   (e) How many pounds of water are removed from the clay in the second operation per 100 lb of dry air?
   (f) What is the humid volume of the air after the second operation?

5.16. Moist air at 1 atm, a dry-bulb temperature of 195°F, and a wet-bulb temperature of 115°F is enclosed in a rigid container. The container and its contents are cooled to 110°F.

(a) What is the molal humidity of the cooled moist air?
(b) What is the final total pressure in atm in the container?
(c) What is the dew point in °F of the cooled moist air?
(d) What is the final wet-bulb temperature in °F?

5.17. Temperatures taken around a forced-draft cooling tower are as follows:

	in	out	
air	85	90	°F
water	102	89	°F

The wet-bulb temperature of the entering air is 77°F. Assuming the air leaving the tower to be saturated, calculate with the aid of the data given below the:
(a) Humidity of the entering air
(b) Pound of dry air through the tower per lb of water into the tower
(c) Percentage of water vaporized in passing through the tower
   Data:

	77°F	85°F	89°F	90°F	100°F	102°F
Saturated $\mathscr{H}$	0.0202	0.0264	0.030	0.031	0.0425	0.0455

C_p air $= 0.24$; C_p water vapor $= 0.45$; $\lambda = 1040$ Btu/lb at any of the temperatures encountered in this problem.

5.18. Your nephew has seen his teacher demonstrate a sling psychrometer in high school and is slightly puzzled as to how it works.
(a) Tell precisely what happens in each of the cases given below (i.e., direction of mass transfer, direction of transfer of latent and sensible heat, and tell what happens to the water temperature in each case).
(b) Calculate the initial humidity of the air in each case.

case	initial water temp. on wick	room condition (temp. and press. water)
A	60°F	80°F and saturated
B	60°F	100°F and 26 mm Hg
C	80°F	100°F and 5 mm Hg

The barometer reads 760 mm Hg. The vapor pressure of water is:

°F	mm Hg
40	6.4
50	13.6
80	26
100	49

5.19. Derive the expressions for humid heat, saturated volume, and adiabatic cooling lines.

5.20. A wet material is to be dried by the passage over it of hot combustion gases. Can the ordinary humidity chart for air-water vapor mixtures be employed in the design of a drier for such a purpose?

5.21. What advantage is derived from plotting humidity charts on a molar basis?

5.22. Air, dry-bulb 100°F, wet-bulb 80°F, is scrubbed with water to remove dust. The water is maintained at 75°F. Assume that the time of contact is sufficient to reach complete equilibrium between air and water. The air is then heated to 200°F by passing it over steam coils. It is then used in an adiabatic rotary drier from which it issues at 120°F. It may be assumed that the material to be dried enters and leaves at 115°F. The material loses 0.1 lb H_2O per lb of product. The total product is 2000 lb/hr.

(a) What is the humidity:
   (1) Of the initial air?
   (2) After the water sprays?
   (3) After reheating?
   (4) Leaving the drier?
(b) What is the per cent humidity at each of the above points?
(c) What is the total weight of dry air used per hour?
(d) What is the total volume of air leaving the drier?
(e) What is the total amount of heat supplied to the cycle in Btu per hour?

5.23. Your boss wants to air-condition a service building 100 ft long by 60 ft wide by 16 ft average height by cooling and dehumidifying the necessary fresh air with cold water in a spray chamber. The average occupancy of the building is 100 persons per hour with a total emission of 800 Btu/(person)(hr). The severest atmospheric conditions for the city are 100°F with 95% humidity. It is believed that air at 70°F and 60% humidity will be satisfactory, provided the total circulation is sufficient to hold the temperature rise of the air to 2°F. Neglecting radiation from the building and using the sensible heat of the recirculated air for reheating, calculate the:

(a) Volume of recirculated air at the inlet conditions
(b) Volume of fresh air under the worst conditions
(c) Tons of refrigeration (1 ton = 12,000 Btu/hr) required
(d) Volume of the dehumidifier spray chamber, assuming the air approaches within 2°F of the water temperature

5.24. Sodium chloride from an evaporator contains 88% NaCl, the balance water. This material is to be dried in a countercurrent rotary drier, using hot air at a dry bulb of 140°F, 10% relative humidity. This hot air stream is made up of fresh air with a humidity of 0.0145 mole of water per mole of dry air plus a recycled stream of moist air from the drier. This recycle stream represents 15% by weight of the total air in the drier. Required drier conditions are 80 lb of dry air for every pound of dry stock. Compute the per cent water content on a wet basis of the dried stock leaving the drier and also the humidity of the air leaving the drier. Is this process satisfactory?

5.25. A countercurrent drier, with valves set so that 25% of the exit air is recycled, is used to dry glue. The fresh air enters at a temperature of 140°F and a humidity of 0.01 lb H_2O/lb air. The operation of the drier is adiabatic, and the air leaves at its wet-bulb temperature. The glue enters with a water content of 19% on a wet basis and leaves bone dry. How many pounds of wet glue can be dried for every pound of dry air recycled?

5.26. A drier produces 7250 lb/day of "dry" product containing 5% moisture (wet basis) from a charge to the drier containing 20% moisture (dry basis). Air enters at 140°F and a humidity of 0.008 lb H_2O/lb BD air; air leaves at 110°F and a humidity of 0.018 lb H_2O/lb BD air. The stock temperature throughout is 100°F. The latent heat of vaporization of H_2O at 100°F = 1036 Btu/lb; $C_{S_1} = 0.243$ and $C_{S_2} = 0.248$ Btu/(lb)(°F). Determine the heat input into the drier from the heaters in Btu/day. (1 = in, 2 = out.)

5.27. (a) An air stream from a plant drying operation contains CCl_4 vapor. To estimate the loss of CCl_4 from the process, a thermometer was provided with a cloth wick wetted with liquid CCl_4 and inserted into the air stream. A dry thermometer indicated the temperature to be 158°F. The wet-bulb thermometer read 72°F. The pressure in the duct was 800 mm Hg. The air-CCl_4 flow rate was 200 ft³/sec.

   Data: CCl_4 latent heat of vap. at 72°F = 94 Btu/lb; CCl_4 vapor pressure at 72°F = 98 mm; heat transfer coeff., gas to wet bulb = 8.5 Btu/(hr)(ft²)(°F); $h_c/k_g' = 0.5$.

   Estimate the pounds of CCl_4 lost per hour.

   (b) It was proposed that the CCl_4 be removed from the air by compression in an isothermal compressor at 100°F to 100 psia. What per cent of the CCl_4 originally in the air stream could be recovered by this method? Vapor pressure of CCl_4 at 100°F = 190 mm Hg.

5.28. In one of the hotter regions of the country a home owner decides to keep his home at an average temperature of 80°F and 40% humidity. On a typical day the outside conditions are as follows: dry-bulb temperature = 95°F and wet-bulb = 85°F. The city water supply is at 70°F and scarce. He therefore decides to use an electric refrigeration unit to cool the air entering the ventilating ducts. Summary of conditions:

   Size of home: 50,000 ft³.

   Recirculation rate: 1 complete change every 3 min.

   Average outlet temperature of air: 82°F.

   Increase in humidity in house may be considered as zero.

   Make-up air may be considered at 15% of inlet air.

Give a complete flow sheet of the process and determine the amount of refrigeration and reheating necessary to maintain the above conditions.

5.29. Hunicke and Wagner in U.S. Patent 2,005,422 (June 18, 1935) concentrate sulfite waste liquor (s.w.l.) from the pulping of wood by blowing hot stack gas through sparger pipes immersed in the liquid. The foam that forms is knocked down by a spray of liquid s.w.l. feed. Because most of the substances in s.w.l. are colloidal, its vapor pressure and thermal properties may be considered to be the same as those of water. The flue gas analyzes CO_2, 12.0%; O_2, 7.0%; N_2, 81.0% and has a dew point of 90°F. It enters the apparatus at 800°F. The s.w.l. from the blowpits is fed into the apparatus at 120°F. The weather is partly cloudy, temperature 80°F, barometer 29.84 in. Hg, and the wind is 10 mph NNE. Calculate:

   (a) The boiling or equilibrium temperature of the s.w.l. in the evaporator

   (b) The cubic feet of stack gas entering per pound of water evaporated

General Problems

5.30. One of the ways in which steel can be welded is to take a mixture of powdered aluminum and finely divided iron oxide and ignite it. A vigorous reaction takes place, and aluminum oxide and molten iron are formed at a temperature up to 2300°C:

$$2\text{ Al} + \text{Fe}_2\text{O}_3 \longrightarrow \text{Al}_2\text{O}_3 + 2\text{ Fe}$$

A mixture of this type is called thermite; it has been used to weld together the ends of steel rails, to repair machinery, etc. A manufacturer is considering making a new type of thermite which combines powdered magnesium with iron oxide. Which stoichiometric mixture weighs less, the $2\text{ Al} + \text{Fe}_2\text{O}_3$ or the $3\text{ Mg} + \text{Fe}_2\text{O}_3$, to get the desired temperature of 3000°F if the heat lost by convection and radiation is 20% of the heat of reaction? Assume the initial thermite mixture is at 65°F. The heat capacities of Al_2O_3 and MgO can be considered constant at 0.20 Btu/(lb)(°F). For iron and steel use the following data:

$$C_p(\text{s}) = 0.12 \text{ Btu/(lb)(°F)}$$

$$C_p(\text{l}) = 0.25 \text{ Btu/(lb)(°F)}$$

$$\Delta H_{\text{fusion}} = 86.5 \text{ Btu/lb}, \qquad \text{melting point} = 2800°\text{F}$$

5.31. A process involving catalytic dehydrogenation in the presence of hydrogen is known as "hydroforming." In the Second World War this process was of importance in helping to meet the demand for toluene for the manufacture of explosives. Toluene, benzene, and other aromatic materials can be economically produced from naptha feeds in this way. After the toluene is separated from the other components it is condensed and cooled in a process such as

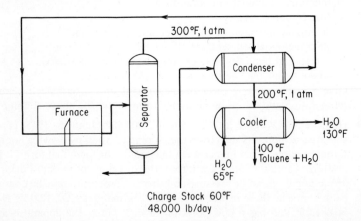

that shown in the flow sheet. For every 100 lb of stock charged to the system, 27.5 lb of a toluene and water mixture (9.1% by weight water) are produced as overhead vapor and condensed by the charge stream. Calculate (a) the temperature of the charge stock after it leaves the condenser, and (b) the pounds of cooling water required per hour.

Additional data:

stream	C_p Btu/(lb)(°F)	b.p. (°F)	latent heat vap (Btu/lb)
$H_2O(l)$	1.0	212	970
$H_2O(g)$	0.5	—	—
toluene(l)	0.4	260	100
toluene(g)	0.3	—	—
charge stock	0.5	—	—

5.32. Toluene, manufactured by the conversion of *n*-heptane with a Cr_2O_3 on Al_2O_3 catalyst,

$$CH_3CH_2CH_2CH_2CH_2CH_2CH_3 \longrightarrow \bigcirc^{CH_3} + 4\,H_2$$

by the method of hydroforming described in the previous problem, is recovered by use of a solvent. The process and conditions are as diagramed.

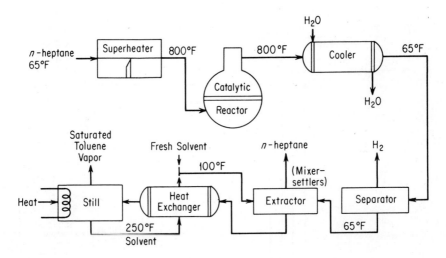

The yield of toluene is 15% based on the *n*-heptane charged to the furnace. Assume 10 lb of solvent are used per lb of toluene in the extractors.

(a) Calculate how much heat has to be added or removed from the catalytic reactor to make it isothermal at 800°F.

(b) Find the temperature of the *n*-heptane and solvent stream leaving the mixer settlers if both streams are at the same temperature.

(c) Find the temperature of the solvent stream after it leaves the heat exchanger.

(d) Calculate the heat duty of the fractionating column in Btu/lb *n*-heptane feed to the process.

Additional data:

	$-\Delta H_c^\circ$ *	C_p Btu/(lb)(°F)		$\Delta H_{\text{vaporization}}$	b.p.
	cal/g mole	liquid	vapor	Btu/lb	°F
toluene	934,500	0.53	0.55	157	231
n-heptane	1,160,000	0.51	0.45	137	210
solvent	—	0.40	0.60	—	322

* As liquids.

The heat of solution of toluene in the solvent is -10 Btu/lb toluene.

5.33. As shown in the diagram, a mixture of 10 wt % C_2H_6, 20 wt % C_3H_8, and 70 wt % C_4H_{10} are charged as liquid from storage to a dehydrogenation furnace at the rate of 5000 lb/hr. In the furnace the C_2H_6 goes through unchanged; 10% of the C_3H_8 passing through the furnace is dehydrogenated

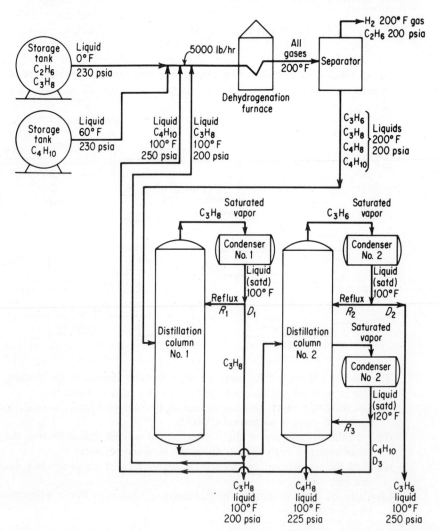

$(C_3H_8 \longrightarrow C_3H_6 + H_2)$; and 70% of the n-butane is dehydrogenated $(C_4H_{10} \longrightarrow C_4H_8 + H_2)$. In the separator all of the H_2 and C_2H_6 are separated and withdrawn from the system. The C_3H_6, C_3H_8, C_4H_8 and n-C_4H_{10} are sent to fractionator no. 1, where the C_3H_8 is separated. Fractionator no. 2 separates the C_3H_6, C_4H_{10}, and C_4H_8. All C_4H_{10} and 20 lb/hr of C_3H_8 are recycled to the furnace. The distillation columns (fractionators) operate at a 5 to 1 reflux ratio, i.e., $R/D = 5/1$.

(a) Determine the volume of gas in ft³ from the separator per hour measured at 200°F and 200 psia.

(b) What weight of C_3H_8 is being refluxed into the distillation tower per hour?

(c) What weight of C_3H_8 has to be removed from the separator per hour?

(d) Determine the ratio of the recycle n-C_4H_{10} to the fresh feed of C_4H_{10} from storage.

(e) What weights of C_4H_8 and C_3H_6 are being recovered per hour?

(f) Determine the heat duty (cooling or heating) required for the furnace, assuming no heat losses to the surroundings.

(g) If cooling water is available at 70°F, how many gallons per hour are required for all three condensers if the maximum allowable discharge temperature of the water is 100°F?

Note: In computing enthalpies, preferably use actual data from p-H charts or tables. If ideal gas values at 1 atm are used, assume ΔH from 1 atm to 200 psia is as follows:

PRESSURE CORRECTION
ΔH^* (Btu/lb)

	200°F	100°F
C_2H_6 (g)	− 8	−12
C_3H_6 (g)	−14	−20
C_3H_8 (g)	−12	−18
C_4H_{10} (g)	−18	− 7†
H_2 (g)	0	0

Source: W. C. Edmister, *Applied Hydrocarbon Thermodynamics*, Gulf Publishing Co., Houston, Tex., 1961.

* $\Delta H_{200\ psia} - \Delta H_{1\ atm}$.

† From 1 atm to 52 psia where C_4H_{10} is satd. vapor.

5.34. One hundred thousand pounds of a mixture of 50% benzene, 40% toluene, and 10% o-xylene are separated every day in a distillation-fractionation plant as shown on the flow sheet.

Data:

	b.p. °C	C_p liquid cal/(g)(°C)	latent ht. vap. cal/g	C_p vapor cal/(g)(°C)
benzene	80	0.44	94.2	0.28
toluene	109	0.48	86.5	0.30
o-xylene	143	0.48	81.0	0.32
charge	90	0.46	88.0	0.29
overhead T_I	80	0.45	93.2	0.285
residue T_I	120	0.48	83.0	0.31
residue T_{II}	143	0.48	81.5	0.32

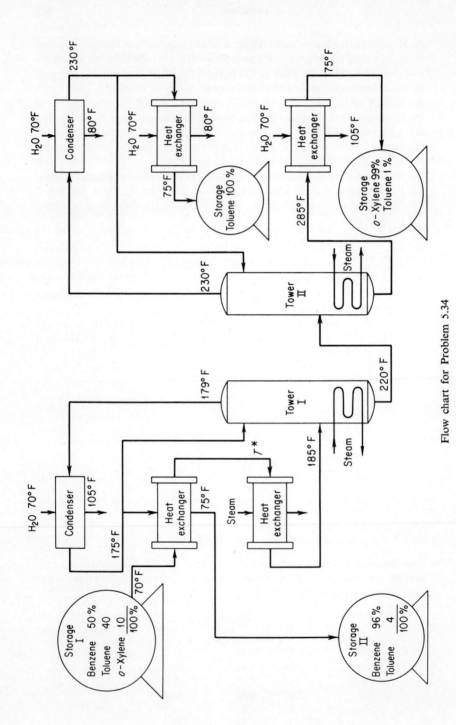

Flow chart for Problem 5.34

The reflux ratio for Tower I is 6:1.
The reflux ratio for Tower II is 4:1.
The charge to Tower I is liquid.
The charge to Tower II is liquid.

Compute the:

(a) Temperature of the mixture at the outlet of the heat exchanger (marked as T^*)
(b) Btu supplied by the steam reboiler in each column
(c) Quantity of cooling water required in gallons per day for the whole plant
(d) Energy balance around Tower I

5.35. The initial process in most refineries is a simple distillation in which the crude oil is separated into various fractions. The flow sheet for one such process is illustrated. Make a complete material and energy balance around the entire

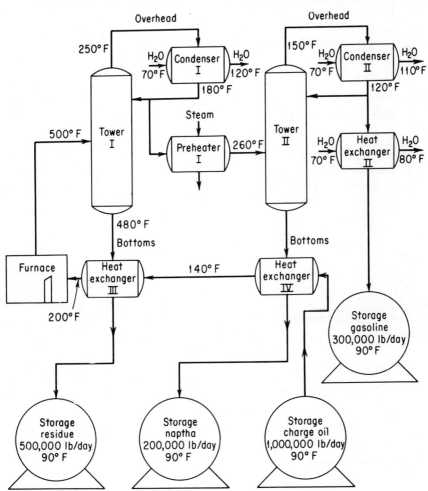

distillation system and for each unit including the heat exchangers and condensers. Also:

(a) Calculate the heat load that has to be supplied by the furnace in Btu/hr.
(b) Determine the additional heat that would have to be supplied by the furnace if the charge oil were not preheated to 200°F before it entered the furnace.

Do the calculated temperatures of the streams going into storage from the heat exchangers seem reasonable?

Additional data:

	specific heat of liquid Btu/(lb)(°F)	latent heat of vaporization Btu/lb	specific heat of vapor Btu/(lb)(°F)	condensation temp., °F
charge oil	0.53	100	0.45	480
overhead, Tower I	0.59	111	0.51	250
bottoms, Tower I	0.51	92	0.42	500
overhead, Tower II	0.63	118	0.58	150
bottoms, Tower II	0.58	107	0.53	260

The reflux ratio of Tower I is 3 recycle to 1 product.
The reflux ratio of Tower II is 2 recycle to 1 product.

5.36. Sulfuric acid is a basic raw material used in a wide range of industries. It has been claimed that the state of civilization of a country can be determined by the amount of sulfuric acid consumed per capita. Sulfuric acid was one of the earliest known acids because it could be made by the absorption in H_2O of the SO_3 formed when naturally occurring sulfates or sulfides were roasted. Innumerable man-years of design effort have gone into developing methods of obtaining economic production of sulfuric acid from various starting materials. The source of sulfur in this problem is sulfur itself.

From an over-all viewpoint the preparation of sulfuric acid is quite simple. The sulfur is burned to SO_2

$$S(s) + O_2(g) \longrightarrow SO_2(g)$$

which is then oxidized to SO_3 with additional air

$$SO_2(g) + \tfrac{1}{2} O_2(g) \longrightarrow SO_3(g)$$

and the SO_3 formed is finally absorbed in water to yield H_2SO_4.

$$SO_3(g) + H_2O(l) \longrightarrow H_2SO_4(l)$$

The details of the process are shown in the flow sheet, as are the operating details of the plant. One hundred and fifty per cent excess air (based on the oxidation of sulfur to SO_2) is used. The conversion of SO_2 to SO_3 is 98%.

(a) Calculate the tons of sulfur needed per day.
(b) Calculate the tons of SO_3 absorbed in Towers I and II per day.
(c) Calculate the ft³ of air at S.C. needed per hour for combustion of the sulfur.
(d) Make energy balances around Towers I and II.
(e) Calculate the heat loss from the burner per hour.

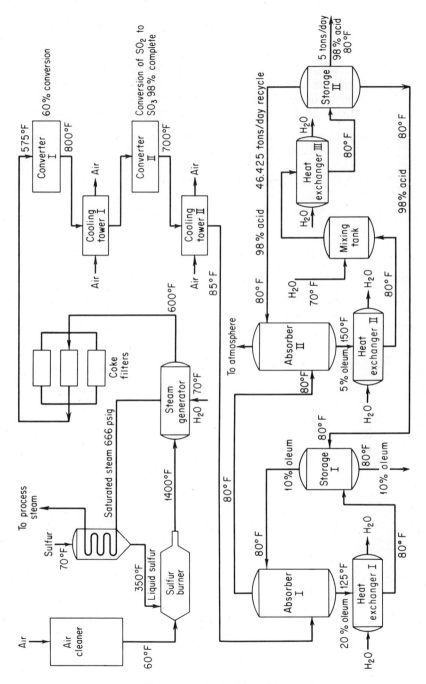

Flow chart for Problem 5.36

395

Additional data: Heat of solution data can be assumed to be as follows:

solution	$\Delta H_{\text{solution}}$
SO_3 in 10% oleum	10 Btu/lb of 20% oleum formed
SO_3 in 98% H_2SO_4	50 Btu/lb of 5% oleum formed
20% oleum in 98% H_2SO_4	40 Btu/lb of 10% oleum formed
H_2O in 5% oleum	80 Btu/lb of 98% H_2SO_4 formed

Note: % oleum equals the wt. % free SO_3 in the H_2SO_4-SO_3 mixture. All H_2O is considered combined with SO_3 to form H_2SO_4.

Use the following values for the heat capacities of the streams:

stream	C_p, Btu/(lb)(°F)
S(s)	0.163
S(l)	0.235
SO_3(g)*	$6.08 + 13.1 \times 10^{-3}T - 0.382 \times 10^{-6}T^2$
98% H_2SO_4	0.5
5% oleum	0.45
10% oleum	0.43
20% oleum	0.40

* C_p in Btu/(lb mole)(°F) and T in °R.

Other data can be found in the Appendix.

Chapter 6

UNSTEADY-STATE

MATERIAL AND

ENERGY BALANCES

In previous chapters all of the material and all of the energy balances you
have encountered, except for the batch energy balances, were *steady-state*
balances, i.e., balances for processes which did not require an accumulation
term. Now it is time for us to focus our attention briefly on *unsteady-
state* processes. These are processes in which quantities or operating conditions *change with time*. Sometimes you will hear the word *transient state*
applied to such problems. The unsteady state is much more complicated
than the steady state and in general is more difficult to handle mathematically.
However, a wide variety of important industrial problems fall into this
category, such as the start-up of equipment, batch heating or reactions,
the change from one set of operating conditions to another, and the pertur-
bations which develop as process conditions fluctuate. We can consider
here only some very simple examples of what is really a most complex subject.
But the fundamentals to be presented are valid no matter how complex
the actual situation may be.

The basic expression for either the material or the energy balance should
by now be well known to you. However, you should also realize that these
principles can be applied at various levels, or stratum, of description. In
other words, the engineer can portray the operation of a real process by
writing balances on a number of physical scales. A typical illustration of

this concept might be in meterology where the following different models can be used on a descending scale of magnitude in the real world:

Global weather pattern
Local weather pattern
Individual clouds
Convective flow in clouds
Molecular transport
The molecules themselves

Similarly, in chemical engineering we write material and energy balances from the viewpoint of various scales of information:

(1) Molecular and atomic balances
(2) Microscopic balances
(3) Multiple gradient balances
(4) Maximum gradient balances
(5) Macroscopic balances

in decreasing order of degree of detail about a process.[1] In this chapter, the type of balance to be described and applied is the simplest one, namely, the macroscopic balance (number 5 in the tabulation above).

The macroscopic balance ignores all the detail within a system and consequently results in a balance about the entire system. Only time remains as a differential independent variable in the general balance. The dependent variables, such as concentration and temperature, are not functions of position but represent over-all averages throughout the entire volume of the system. In effect, the system is assumed to be sufficiently well mixed so that the output concentrations and temperatures are equivalent to the concentrations and temperatures inside the system.

As usual, the first task is to reduce the general balance expressed in words in Fig. 6.1 to mathematical statements which are quantitative in nature. Equation (6.1) can be applied to the mass of a single component or to the total amount of material or energy. Let us now write down Eq. (6.1) in mathematical symbols for the small time interval Δt, and, using the "delta" technique, work out a material or energy balance for the system shown in Fig 6.1. Let the accumulation be positive in the direction in which time is positive, i.e., as time increases from t to $t + \Delta t$. The mass transport through the system boundary is split into two parts, transport through defined surfaces S_1 and S_2, whose areas may be known, and transport across the system boundary through other (undefined) surfaces.

---

[1] Additional information together with applications concerning these various types of balances can be found in D. M. Himmelblau and K. B. Bischoff, *Process Analysis and Simulation*, John Wiley & Sons, Inc., New York, 1967.

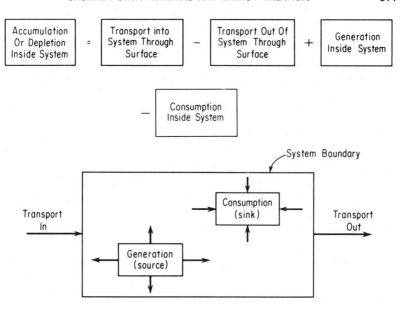

Fig. 6.1. A general unsteady-state process with transport in and out and internal generation and consumption.

Component material balances:

$$\rho_A V|_{t+\Delta t} - \rho_A V|_t = \rho_A v S \, \Delta t|_{S_1} - \rho_A v S \, \Delta t|_{S_2} + \tilde{w}_A \, \Delta t + r_A \, \Delta t$$

accumulation   transport through defined boundaries   transport through other boundaries   generation or consumption

$$(6.2)^2$$

Total material balance:

$$\rho V|_{t+\Delta t} - \rho V|_t = \rho v S \, \Delta t|_{S_1} - \rho v S \, \Delta t|_{S_2} + \tilde{w} \, \Delta t \qquad (6.3)$$

accumulation   transport through defined boundaries   transport through other boundaries

Energy balance:

$$E|_{t+\Delta t} - E|_t = \left| \left(\hat{H} + \frac{v^2}{2} + gh \right) \tilde{m} \, \Delta t \right|_{S_1} - \left| \left(\hat{H} + \frac{v^2}{2} + gh \right) \tilde{m} \, \Delta t \right|_{S_2}$$

accumulation   transport through defined boundaries

$$+ \tilde{Q} \, \Delta t - \tilde{W} \, \Delta t + \tilde{B} \, \Delta t + \tilde{S}_R \, \Delta t \qquad (6.4)$$

heat   work   transport through other boundaries   generation or consumption

where $\tilde{B}$ = rate of energy transfer accompanying w

$\tilde{m}$ = rate of mass transfer through defined surfaces

---

[2] The symbol $|_t$ means the quantities preceding the vertical line are evaluated at time t, or time $t + \Delta t$, or at surface S_1, or at surface S_2, as the case may be.

$\tilde{Q}$ = rate of heat transfer

r_A = rate of generation or consumtion of component A by chemical reaction

S = defined cross-sectional area perpendicular to material flow

$\tilde{S}_R$ = rate of generation of energy

t = time

v = fluid velocity in a duct of cross section S

V = system volume

$\tilde{W}$ = rate of work done by the system

$\tilde{w}_A, \tilde{w}$ = rate of mass flow of component A, or total mass flow, respectively, through the system boundaries other than through the defined surfaces S_1 and S_2

ρ_A, ρ = mass of component A, or total mass, respectively, per unit volume

The other notation for the energy balance is identical to that of Chap. 4; note that the work, heat, generation, and mass transport can now all be expressed as rate terms (mass or energy per unit time).

If each side of Eq. (6.2) is divided by Δt, we obtain:

$$\frac{\rho_A V|_{t+\Delta t} - \rho_A V|_t}{\Delta t} = \rho_A v S|_{S_1} - \rho_A v S|_{S_2} + \tilde{w}_A + r_A \tag{6.5}$$

Similar relations can be obtained from Eqs. (6.3) and (6.4). Next, if we take the limit of each side of Eq. (6.5) as $\Delta t \longrightarrow 0$, we get

$$\frac{d(\rho_A V)}{dt} = -\Delta(\rho_A v S) + \tilde{w}_A + r_A \tag{6.6}$$

Similar treatment of the total mass balance and the energy balance yields the following two equations:

$$\frac{d(\rho V)}{dt} = -\Delta(\rho v S) + \tilde{w} \tag{6.7}$$

$$\frac{d(E)}{dt} = -\Delta\left[\left(\hat{H} + \frac{v^2}{2} + gh\right)\tilde{m}\right] + \tilde{Q} - \tilde{W} + \tilde{B} + \tilde{S}_R \tag{6.8}$$

The relation between the energy balance given by Eq. (6.8), which has the units of energy per unit time, and the energy balance given by Eq. (4.24), which has the units of energy, should be fairly clear. Equation (4.24) represents the integration of Eq. (6.8), expressed formally as follows:

$$E_{t_2} - E_{t_1} = \int_{t_1}^{t_2} \{-\Delta[(\hat{H} + \hat{K} + \hat{P})\tilde{m}] + \tilde{Q} + \tilde{B} - \tilde{W} + \tilde{S}_R\}\, dt \tag{6.9}$$

The quantities designated in Eq. (4.24) without the tilde ($\sim$) are integrated values.

To solve one of the very general equations (6.6), (6.7), or (6.8) analytically is usually quite difficult, and in the following examples we will have to restrict our analyses to simple cases. If we make enough (reasonable) assumptions and work with simple problems, we can consolidate or eliminate enough terms of the equations to be able to integrate them and develop some analytical answers.

In the solution of unsteady-state problems you have to apply the usual procedures of problem-solving initially discussed in Chap. 1. Two major tasks exist:

(a) To set up the unsteady-state equation
(b) To solve it once the equation is established

After you draw a diagram of the system and set down all the information available, you should try to recognize the important variables and represent them by letters. Next, decide which variable is the independent one, and label it. The independent variable is the one you select to have one or a series of values, and then the other variables are all dependent ones—they are determined by the first variable(s) you selected. Which is chosen as an independent and which as a dependent variable is usually fixed by the problem but may be arbitrary. Although there are no general rules applicable to all cases, the quantities which appear prominently in the statement of the problem are usually the best choices. You will need as many equations as you have dependent variables.

As mentioned before, in the macroscopic balance the independent variable is time. In mathematics, when the quantity x varies with time, we consider dx to be the change in x that occurs during time dt if the process continues through the interval beginning at time t. Let us say t is the independent variable and x is the dependent one. In solving problems you can use one or a combination of Eqs. (6.6), (6.7), and (6.8) directly, or alternatively you can proceed, as shown in some of the examples, to set up the differential equations from scratch exactly in the same fashion as Eqs. (6.2) through (6.4) were formulated. For either approach the objective is to translate the problem statement in words into one or more simultaneous differential equations having the form

$$\frac{dx}{dt} = f(x, t) \tag{6.10}$$

Then, assuming this differential equation can be solved, x can be found as a function of t. Of course, we have to know some initial condition(s) or at one (or more) given time(s) know the value(s) of x.

If dt and dx are always considered positive when increasing, then you can use Eq. (6.1) without having any difficulties with signs. However, if you for some reason transfer an output to the left-hand side of the equation, or the equation is written in some other form, then you should take great

care in the use of signs (see Example 6.2 below). We are now going to examine some very simple unsteady-state problems which are susceptible to
reasonably elementary mathematical analysis. You can (and will) find more
complicated examples in texts dealing with all phases of mass transfer, heat
transfer, and fluid dynamics.

Example 6.1   Unsteady-State Material Balance Without Generation

A tank holds 100 gal of a water-salt solution in which 4.0 lb of salt are
dissolved. Water runs into the tank at the rate of 5 gal/min and salt solution
leaves at the same rate. If the mixing in the tank is adequate to keep
the concentration of salt in the tank uniform at all times, how much salt is in
the tank at the end of 50 min? Ignore any change in the density of water or
in the solution with concentration.

Solution:
We will set up the differential equations which describe the process from
scratch.

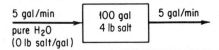

Step 1: Draw a picture, and put down the known data.
Step 2: Choose the independent and dependent variables. Time, of course,
is the independent variable, and either the salt quantity or concentration in the
tank can be the dependent variable. Suppose we make the mass (quantity) of
salt the dependent variable. Let $x = $ lb of salt in the tank at time t.
Step 3: Write down the known value of x at a given value of t. This is

$$\text{at } t = 0, \quad x = 4.0 \text{ lb} \quad \text{(the initial condition)}$$

Step 4: Make component material balances on the salt and on the water.
(No energy balance is needed because the system can be assumed to be
isothermal.)
H_2O balance:

accumulation   =   in

$$[H_2O \text{ (lb)}]_{t+\Delta t} - [H_2O \text{ (lb)}]_t = \frac{5 \text{ gal}}{\text{min}} \left| \frac{1 \text{ ft}^3}{7.48 \text{ gal}} \right| \frac{\rho_{H_2O} \text{ lb}}{\text{ft}^3} \left| \Delta t \text{ min} \right.$$

— out

$$- \frac{5 \text{ gal}}{\text{min}} \left| \frac{1 \text{ ft}^3}{7.48 \text{ gal}} \right| \frac{\rho_{H_2O} \text{ lb}}{\text{ft}^3} \left| \Delta t \text{ min} \right. = 0$$

This equation tells us that the flow of water into the tank equals the flow of
water out of the tank, i.e., the flow of water is in the steady state.

Salt balance:

$$\underset{\text{accumulation}}{[x \, (\text{lb})]_{t+\Delta t} - [x \, (\text{lb})]_t} = \underset{\text{in}}{0} - \underset{\text{out}}{\frac{5 \text{ gal}}{\text{min}} \left| \frac{x \text{ lb}}{100 \text{ gal}} \right| \Delta t \text{ min}}$$

Dividing by Δt and taking the limit as Δt approaches zero,

$$\lim_{\Delta t \to 0} \frac{[x]_{t+\Delta t} - [x]_t}{\Delta t} = -0.05x$$

or

$$\frac{dx}{dt} = -0.05x \qquad (a)$$

Notice how we have kept track of the units in the normal fashion in setting up these equations. Because of our assumption of uniform concentration of salt in the tank, the concentration of salt leaving the tank is the same as that in the tank, or x lb/100 gal of solution.

Step 5: Solve the unsteady-state material balance on the salt. By separating the independent and dependent variables we get

$$\frac{dx}{x} = -0.05 \, dt$$

This equation is easily integrated between the definite limits of

$$t = 0, \qquad x = 4.0$$
$$t = 50, \qquad x = \text{the unknown value } X \text{ lb}$$

$$\int_{4.0}^{X} \frac{dx}{x} = -0.05 \int_{0}^{50} dt$$

$$\ln \frac{X}{4.0} = -2.5, \quad \ln \frac{4.0}{X} = 2.5$$

$$\frac{4.0}{X} = 12.2, \qquad X = \frac{4.0}{12.2} = 0.328 \text{ lb salt}$$

An equivalent differential equation to Eq. (a) can be obtained directly from the component mass balance in the form of Eq. (6.6) if we let ρ_A = concentration of salt in the tank at any time t in terms of lb/gal.

$$\frac{d(\rho_A V)}{dt} = -\left(\frac{5 \text{ gal}}{\text{min}} \left| \frac{\rho_A \text{ lb}}{\text{gal}} \right| - 0 \right)$$

If the tank holds 100 gal of solution at all times, V is a constant and equal to 100, so that

$$\frac{d\rho_A}{dt} = -\frac{5\rho_A}{100} \qquad (b)$$

The initial conditions are

$$\text{at } t = 0, \qquad \rho_A = 0.04$$

The solution of Eq. (b) would be carried out exactly as the solution of Eq. (a).

Example 6.2   Unsteady-State Material Balance Without Generation

A square tank 4 ft on a side and 10 ft high is filled to the brim with water. Find the time required for it to empty through a hole in the bottom 1 in.^{2} in area.

Solution:
Step 1: Draw a diagram of the process, and put down the data.

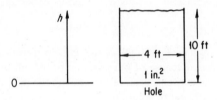

Step 2: Select the independent and dependent variables. Again, time will be the independent variable. We could select the quantity of water in the tank as the dependent variable, but since the cross section of the tank is constant, let us choose h, the height of the water in the tank, as the dependent variable.
Step 3: Write down the known value of h at a given value of t.

$$\text{at } t = 0, \qquad h = 10 \text{ ft}$$

Step 4: Develop the unsteady-state balance(s) for the process. In an elemental time Δt, the height of the water in the tank drops Δh. The mass of water leaving the tank is in the form of a cylinder 1 in.^{2} in area, and we can calculate the quantity as

$$\frac{1 \text{ in.}^2}{} \left| \frac{1 \text{ ft}^2}{144 \text{ in.}^2} \right| \frac{v^* \text{ ft}}{\text{sec}} \left| \frac{\rho \text{ lb}}{\text{ft}^3} \right| \frac{\Delta t \text{ sec}}{} = \rho \frac{v^* \, \Delta t}{144} \text{ lb}$$

where $\rho =$ the density of water
$v^* =$ the average velocity of the water leaving the tank

Also the depletion of water inside the tank in terms of the variable Δh [i.e., the value of h at $(t + \Delta t)$ minus the value of h at t], expressed in lb, is

$$\frac{16 \text{ ft}^2}{} \left| \frac{\Delta h \text{ ft}}{} \right| \frac{\rho \text{ lb}}{\text{ft}^3} = 16\rho \, \Delta h$$

An over-all material balance indicates

$$\textbf{accumulation} = \textbf{in} - \textbf{out}$$
$$16\rho \, \Delta h = 0 - \frac{\rho v^* \, \Delta t}{144} \tag{a}$$

Although Δh is a negative value, our equation takes account of this automatically. The accumulation is positive if the right-hand side is positive, and the accumulation is negative if the right-hand side is negative. Here the accumulation is really a depletion. You can see that the term ρ, the density of water, cancels out, and we could just as well have made our material balance on a volume of water.
Equation (a) becomes

$$\frac{\Delta h}{\Delta t} = -\frac{v^*}{(16)(144)}$$

Taking the limit as Δh and Δt approach zero, we get

$$\frac{dh}{dt} = -\frac{v^*}{(16)(144)} \tag{b}$$

Unfortunately, this is an equation with one independent variable, t, and two dependent variables, h and v^*. We must find another equation to eliminate either h or v^* if we want to obtain a solution. Since we want our final equation to be expressed in terms of h, the next step is to find some function that relates v^* to h and t, and then we can substitute for v^* in the unsteady-state equation.

We will employ the steady-state mechanical energy balance for an incompressible fluid, discussed in Chap. 4, to relate v^* and h. Recall from Eq. (4.30) with $W = 0$ and $E_v = 0$ that

$$\Delta\left(\frac{v^2}{2} + gh\right) = 0 \tag{c}$$

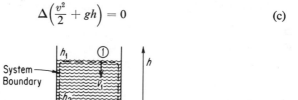

We assume that the pressures are the same at sections ① and ② of the system consisting of the water in the tank. Equation (c) reduces to

$$\frac{v_2^2 - v_1^2}{2} + g(h_2 - h_1) = 0 \tag{d}$$

where v_2 = the exit velocity through the 1-in.² hole at boundary ②
v_1 = the velocity of the water in the tank at boundary ①

If $v_1 \cong 0$, a reasonable assumption for the water in the large tank at any time, at least compared to v_2, and the reference plane is located at the 1-in.² hole,

$$v_2^2 = -2g(0 - h_1) = 2gh$$
$$v_2 = \sqrt{2gh} \tag{e}$$

Because the exit-stream flow is not frictionless and because of turbulence and orifice effects in the exit hole, we must correct the value of v given by Eq. (e) for frictionless flow by an empirical adjustment factor as follows:

$$v_2 = c\sqrt{2gh} = v^* \tag{f}$$

where c is an orifice correction which we could find (from a text discussing fluid dynamics) has a value of 0.62 for this case. In the American engineering system ($g = 32.2$ ft/sec²), $v^* = 0.62\sqrt{2(32.2)h} = 4.97\sqrt{h}$ ft/sec. Let us substitute this into Eq. (b) in place of v^*. Then we obtain

$$\frac{dh}{dt} = -\frac{4.97(h)^{1/2}}{(16)(144)}$$

or

$$-464\frac{dh}{h^{1/2}} = dt \tag{g}$$

Equation (g) can be integrated between

$$h = 10 \text{ ft} \quad \text{at } t = 0$$

and

$$h = 0 \text{ ft} \quad \text{at } t = \theta, \quad \text{the unknown time}$$

$$-464\int_{10}^{0}\frac{dh}{h^{1/2}} = \int_{0}^{\theta} dt$$

to yield θ,

$$\theta = 464\int_{0}^{10}\frac{dh}{h^{1/2}} = 464\left[2\sqrt{h}\,\right]_{0}^{10} = 2940 \text{ sec}$$

Example 6.3   Material Balance in Batch Distillation

A small still is separating propane and butane at 275°F and initially contains 10 lb moles of a mixture whose composition is $x = 0.30$ ($x = $ mole fraction butane). Additional mixture ($x_F = 0.30$) is fed at the rate of 5 lb

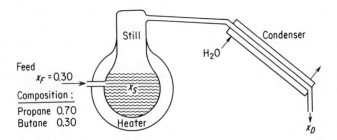

moles/hr. If the total volume of the liquid in the still is constant, and the concentration of the vapor from the still (x_D) is related to x_S as follows:

$$x_D = \frac{x_S}{1 + x_S}$$

how long will it take for the value of x_S to change from 0.30 to 0.40? What is the steady-state ("equilibrium") value of x_S in the still (i.e., when x_S becomes constant)?

Solution:

Since butane and propane form ideal solutions, we do not have to worry about volume changes on mixing or separation. Only the material balance is needed to answer the questions posed. If t is the independent variable and x_S the dependent variable, we can say:

Butane balance (C_4):

The input to the still is

$$\frac{5 \text{ moles feed}}{\text{hr}} \left| \frac{0.30 \text{ moles } C_4}{\text{mole feed}} \right| \Delta t \text{ hr}$$

The output from the still is equal to the amount condensed,

$$\frac{5 \text{ moles cond.}}{\text{hr}} \left| \frac{x_D \text{ moles C}_4}{\text{mole cond.}} \right| \Delta t \text{ hr}$$

The accumulation is

$$\frac{10 \text{ moles in still}}{} \left| \frac{\Delta x_S \text{ moles C}_4}{\text{mole in still}} \right.$$

where $\Delta x_S = [x_S]_{t+\Delta t} - [x_S]_t$.

Our unsteady-state material balance is then

$$\textbf{accumulation = in} \quad - \quad \textbf{out}$$
$$10 \, \Delta x_S \quad = 1.5 \, \Delta t - 5 x_D \, \Delta t$$

or, dividing by Δt and taking the limit as Δt approaches zero,

$$\frac{dx_S}{dt} = 0.15 - 0.5 x_D$$

As in the previous example, it is necessary to reduce the equation to two variables by substituting for x_D:

$$x_D = \frac{x_S}{1 + x_S}$$

Then

$$\frac{dx_S}{dt} = 0.15 - \frac{x_S}{1 + x_S}(0.5)$$

$$\frac{dx_S}{0.15 - \dfrac{0.5 x_S}{1 + x_S}} = dt$$

The integration limits are

$$\text{at } t = 0, \quad x_S = 0.30$$
$$t = \theta, \quad x_S = 0.40$$

$$\int_{0.30}^{0.40} \frac{dx_S}{0.15 - \dfrac{0.5 x_S}{1 + x_S}} = \int_0^{\theta} dt = \theta$$

$$\int_{0.30}^{0.40} \frac{(1 + x_S) \, dx_S}{0.15 - 0.35 x_S} = \theta = \left[-\frac{x_S}{0.35} - \frac{1}{(0.35)^2} \ln (0.15 - 0.35 x_S) \right]_{0.30}^{0.40}$$

$$\theta = 5.85 \text{ hr}$$

If you did not know how to integrate the equation analytically, or if you only had experimental data for x_D as a function of x_S instead of the given equation, you could always integrate the equation graphically as shown in Example 6.6.

The steady state value of x_S is established at infinite time or, alternatively, when the rate of change is zero. At this time,

$$0.15 = \frac{0.5 x_S}{1 + x_S} \quad \text{or} \quad x_S = 0.428$$

The value of x_S could never be greater than 0.428 for the given conditions.

Example 6.4   Unsteady-State Chemical Reaction

A compound dissolves in water at a rate proportional to the product of the amount undissolved and the difference between the concentration in a saturated solution and the concentration in the actual solution at any time. A saturated solution of compound contains 40 g/100 g H_2O. In a test run starting with 20 lb of undissolved compound in 100 lb of pure water it is found that 5 lb are dissolved in 3 hr. If the test continues, how many pounds of compound will remain undissolved after 7 hr? Assume the system is isothermal.

Solution:
Step 1:

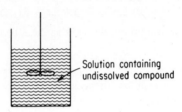

Solution containing undissolved compound

Step 2: Let the dependent variable $x =$ the pounds of *undissolved* compound at time t (the independent variable).

Step 3: At any time t the concentration of dissolved compound is

$$\frac{(20 - x)}{100} \frac{\text{lb compound}}{\text{lb } H_2O}$$

The rate of dissolution of compound according to the problem statement is

$$\text{rate } \frac{\text{lb}}{\text{hr}} = k(x \text{ lb})\left(\frac{40 \text{ lb compound}}{100 \text{ lb } H_2O} - \frac{(20 - x) \text{ lb compound}}{100 \text{ lb } H_2O}\right)$$

We could have utilized a concentration measured on a volume basis rather than one measured on a weight basis, but this would just change the value and units of the constant k.

Next we make an unsteady-state balance for the compound in the solution (the system):

accumulation = in — out + generation

$$\frac{dx}{dt} = 0 - 0 + kx\left(\frac{40}{100} - \frac{20 - x}{100}\right)$$

or

$$\frac{dx}{dt} = \frac{kx}{100}(20 + x)$$

Step 4: Solution of the unsteady-state equation

$$\frac{dx}{x(20 + x)} = \frac{k}{100} dt$$

This equation can be split into two parts and integrated

$$\frac{dx}{x} - \frac{dx}{x + 20} = \frac{k}{5} dt$$

or integrated directly for the conditions:

$$t_0 = 0, \qquad x_0 = 20$$
$$t_1 = 3, \qquad x_1 = 15$$
$$t_2 = 7, \qquad x_2 = ?$$

Since k is an unknown, the one extra pair of conditions is needed in order to evaluate k.

To find k we integrate between the limits stated in the test run.

$$\int_{20}^{15} \frac{dx}{x} - \int_{20}^{15} \frac{dx}{x+20} = \frac{k}{5} \int_0^3 dt$$

$$\left[\ln \frac{x}{x+20} \right]_{20}^{15} = \frac{k}{5}(3-0)$$

$$k = -0.257$$

(Note that the negative value of k corresponds to the actual physical situation.) To find the unknown amount of undissolved compound we have to integrate again.

$$\int_{20}^{x_2} \frac{dx}{x} - \int_{20}^{x_2} \frac{dx}{x+20} = \frac{-0.257}{5} \int_0^7 dt$$

$$\left[\ln \frac{x}{x+20} \right]_{20}^{x_2} = \frac{-0.257}{5}(7-0)$$

$$x_2 = 10.7 \text{ lb}$$

Example 6.5   Over-All Unsteady-State Process

A 15% Na_2SO_4 solution is fed at the rate of 12 lb/min into a mixer which initially holds 100 lb of a 50-50 mixture of Na_2SO_4 and water. The exit solution leaves at the rate of 10 lb/min. Assuming uniform mixing, what is the concentration of Na_2SO_4 in the mixer at the end of 10 min? Ignore any volume changes on mixing.

Solution:

In contrast to Example 6.1, both the water and the salt concentrations, and the total quantities, change with time in this problem.

Step 1:

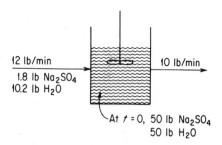

12 lb/min
1.8 lb Na_2SO_4
10.2 lb H_2O

10 lb/min

At $t = 0$, 50 lb Na_2SO_4
50 lb H_2O

Step 2:

Let x = fraction Na_2SO_4 in the tank at time t in $\left(\dfrac{lb\ Na_2SO_4}{lb\ total}\right)$

y = total lb of material in the tank at time t

Step 3: At time $t = 0$, $x = 0.50$, $y = 100$.

Step 4: Material balances between time t and $t + \Delta t$:

(a) Total balance:

$$\text{accumulation} \quad = \quad \text{in} \quad - \quad \text{out}$$

$$[y]_{t+\Delta t} - [y]_t = \Delta y = \frac{12\ lb}{min}\bigg|\ \Delta t\ min - \frac{10\ lb}{min}\bigg|\ \Delta t\ min$$

or

$$\frac{dy}{dt} = 2 \tag{a}$$

(b) Na_2SO_4 balance:

$$\text{accumulation}$$

$$\left[\frac{x\ lb\ Na_2SO_4}{lb\ total}\bigg|\ y\ lb\ total\right]_{t+\Delta t} - \left[\frac{x\ lb\ Na_2SO_4}{lb\ total}\bigg|\ y\ lb\ total\right]_t$$

$$= \quad \text{in} \quad - \quad \text{out}$$

$$= \frac{1.8\ lb\ Na_2SO_4}{min}\bigg|\ \Delta t\ min - \frac{10\ lb\ total}{min}\bigg|\ \frac{x\ lb\ Na_2SO_4}{lb\ total}\bigg|\ \Delta t\ min$$

or

$$\frac{d(xy)}{dt} = 1.8 - 10x \tag{b}$$

Step 5: There are a number of ways to handle the solution of these two differential equations with two unknowns. Perhaps the easiest is to differentiate the xy product in Eq. (b) and substitute Eq. (a) into the appropriate term containing dy/dt

$$\frac{d(xy)}{dt} = x\frac{dy}{dt} + y\frac{dx}{dt}$$

To get y we have to integrate Eq. (a)

$$\int_{100}^{y} dy = \int_{0}^{t} 2\ dt$$

$$y - 100 = 2t$$

$$y = 100 + 2t$$

Then

$$\frac{d(xy)}{dt} = x(2) + (100 + 2t)\frac{dx}{dt} = 1.8 - 10x$$

$$\frac{dx}{dt}(100 + 2t) = 1.8 - 12x$$

$$\int_{0.50}^{x} \frac{dx}{1.8 - 12x} = \int_{0}^{10} \frac{dt}{100 + 2t}$$

$$-\frac{1}{12}\ln\frac{1.8 - 12x}{1.8 - 6.0} = \frac{1}{2}\ln\frac{100 + 20}{100}$$

$$x = 0.267 \frac{\text{lb Na}_2\text{SO}_4}{\text{lb total solution}}$$

An alternate method of setting up the dependent variable would have been to let $x = $ lb Na_2SO_4 in the tank at the time t. Then,

$$\frac{dx}{dt} \frac{\text{lb Na}_2\text{SO}_4}{\text{min}} = \frac{1.8 \text{ lb Na}_2\text{SO}_4}{\text{min}} - \frac{10 \text{ lb total}}{\text{min}} \left| \frac{x \text{ lb Na}_2\text{SO}_4}{y \text{ lb total}} \right.$$

$$\frac{dx}{dt} = 1.8 - \frac{10x}{100 + 2t}$$

or

$$\frac{dx}{dt} + \frac{10}{100 + 2t} x = 1.8$$

The solution to this linear differential equation gives the pounds of Na_2SO_4 after 10 min; the concentration then can be calculated as x/y.

$$x e^{\int \frac{dt}{10+0.2t}} = \int \left(e^{\int \frac{dt}{10+0.2t}} \right)(1.8) \, dt + C$$

$$x(10 + 0.2t)^5 = 1.8 \int (10 + 0.2t)^5 dt + C$$

at $x = 50$, $t = 0$, and $C = 35 \times 10^5$;

$$x = 1.5(10 + 0.2t) + \frac{35 \times 10^5}{(10 + 0.2t)^5}$$

at $t = 10$ min;

$$x = 1.5(12) + \frac{35 \times 10^5}{(12)^5} = 32.1$$

The concentration is

$$\frac{x}{y} = \frac{32.1}{100 + 20} = 0.267 \frac{\text{lb Na}_2\text{SO}_4}{\text{lb total solution}}$$

Example 6.6   Unsteady-State Energy Balance With Graphical Integration

Five thousand pounds of oil initially at 60°F are being heated in a stirred (perfectly mixed) tank by saturated steam which is condensing in the steam coils at 40 psia. If the rate of heat transfer is given by Newton's heating law—i.e.,

$$\tilde{Q} = \frac{dQ}{dt} = h(T_{\text{steam}} - T_{\text{oil}})$$

where Q is the heat transferred in Btu and h is the heat transfer coefficient in the proper units, how long does it take for the discharge from the tank to rise from 60 to 90°F? What is the maximum temperature that can be achieved in the tank?

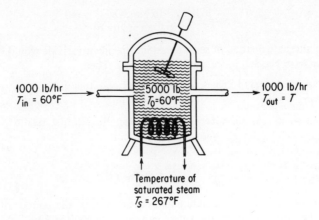

1000 lb/hr
$T_{in} = 60°F$

5000 lb
$T_0 = 60°F$

1000 lb/hr
$T_{out} = T$

Temperature of
saturated steam
$T_S = 267°F$

Additional data:

entering oil flow rate $= 1000$ lb/hr   (the temperature $= 60°F$)

discharge oil flow rate $= 1000$ lb/hr   (at temperature $= T$)

$$h = 300 \text{ Btu/(hr)(°F)}$$

$$C_{p_{oil}} = 0.5 \text{ Btu/(lb)(°F)}$$

Solution:
The process looks as diagramed. The independent variable will be t, the time; the dependent variable will be the temperature of the oil in the tank which is the same as the temperature of the oil discharged.

Our next step is to set up the unsteady-state energy balance for the interval Δt. Let $T_S =$ the steam temperature and $T =$ the oil temperature.

$$\text{accumulation} = \text{input} - \text{output}$$

A good choice for a reference temperature for the enthalpies is $60°F$ because this makes the input enthalpy zero.

enthalpy in input stream	$\dfrac{1000 \text{ lb}}{\text{hr}} \left| \dfrac{0.5 \text{ Btu}}{(\text{lb})(°F)} \right| \overbrace{(T_{in} - T_{ref})}^{60°F - 60°F} \left| \Delta t \text{ hr} \right. = 0$	input (Btu)
heat transfer	$h(T_S - T) = \dfrac{300 \text{ Btu}}{(\text{hr})(°F)} \left| (267 - T)°F \right| \Delta t \text{ hr}$	
enthalpy in output stream	$\dfrac{1000 \text{ lb}}{\text{hr}} \left| \dfrac{0.5 \text{ Btu}}{(\text{lb})(°F)} \right| (T - 60)°F \left| \Delta t \text{ hr} \right.$	output (Btu)
enthalpy change inside tank	$\left\{ \begin{array}{l} \left[\dfrac{5000 \text{ lb}}{} \left\| \dfrac{0.5 \text{ Btu}}{(\text{lb})(°F)} \right\| (T - 60)°F \right]_{t+\Delta t} \\[2em] \left[\dfrac{5000 \text{ lb}}{} \left\| \dfrac{0.5 \text{ Btu}}{(\text{lb})(°F)} \right\| (T - 60)°F \right]_{t} \end{array} \right.$	accumulation (Btu)

$$2500 \frac{dT}{dt} = 300(267 - T) - 500(T - 60)$$

$$\frac{dT}{dt} = 44.1 - 0.32T$$

$$\int_{60}^{90} \frac{dT}{44.1 - 0.32T} = \int_{0}^{\theta} dt = \theta$$

An analytical solution to this equation gives $\theta = 1.52$ hr. For illustrative purposes, so you can see how equations too complex to integrate directly can be handled, let us graphically integrate the left-hand side of the equation. We set up a table and choose values of T. We want to calculate $1/(44.1 - 0.32T)$ and plot this quantity vs. T. The area under the curve from $T = 60°$ to $T = 90°F$ should be 1.52 hr.

T	$0.32T$	$44.1 - 0.32T$	$\dfrac{1}{44.1 - 0.32T} = \phi$
60	19.2	24.9	0.0402
70	22.4	21.7	0.0462
80	25.6	18.5	0.0540
90	28.8	15.3	0.0655

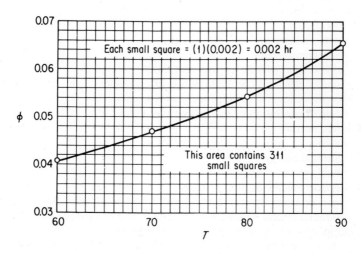

These data are plotted in the accompanying diagram. The area below $\phi = 0.030$ contains:

$$(90 - 60)(0.030 - 0) = 0.90 \text{ hr}$$

The area above $\phi = 0.030$ but under the curve contains:

$$(311)(0.002) = 0.622 \text{ hr}$$

The total area $= 0.90 + 0.622 = 1.522$ hr.

WHAT YOU SHOULD HAVE LEARNED FROM THIS CHAPTER

This chapter was intended to acquaint you with the basic concepts under-
lying unsteady-state material and energy balances and to enable you to
set up the necessary differential equations for very simple physical systems.

NOMENCLATURE
(Units are discussed in the text)

$\tilde{B}$ = rate of energy transfer accompanying $\tilde{w}$

C_p = heat capacity

E = total energy in system $= U + K + P$

g = acceleration of gravity

h = distance above reference plane for potential energy

$H, \hat{H}$ = enthalpy, enthalpy per unit mass or mole

K = kinetic energy

$\tilde{m}$ = rate of mass transport through defined surfaces

p = pressure

P = potential energy

Q = heat transferred

$\tilde{Q}$ = rate of heat transferred (per unit time)

r_A = rate of generation or consumption of component A (by chemical reaction)

S = cross-sectional area perpendicular to material flow

$\tilde{S}_R$ = rate of generation of energy (per unit time)

T = temperature

t = time

U = internal energy

v = fluid velocity

V = system volume or fluid volume

$\tilde{w}_A, \tilde{w}$ = rate of mass flow of component A and total mass flow, respectively, through system boundary other than a defined surface

$\tilde{W}$ = rate of work done by system (per unit time)

ρ_A, ρ = mass of component A, or total mass, respectively, per unit volume

Δ = difference between exit and entering stream; also used for final minus initial times or small time increments

SUPPLEMENTARY REFERENCES

1. Himmelblau, D. M., and K. B. Bischoff, *Process Analysis and Simulation*, John Wiley & Sons, Inc., New York, 1967.

2. Marshall, W. R., and R. L. Pigford, *The Application of Differential Equations to Chemical Engineering Problems*, University of Delaware, Newark, Delaware, 1942.
3. Sherwood, T. K., and C. E. Reid, *Applied Mathematics in Chemical Engineering*, 2nd ed., McGraw-Hill Book Coompany, New York, 1957.

PROBLEMS

6.1. A 2 per cent uranium oxide slurry (2 lb UO_2/100 lb H_2O) flows into a 100-gal tank at the rate of 2 gal/min. The tank initially contains 500 lb of H_2O and no UO_2. The slurry is well mixed and flows out at the same rate at which it enters. Find the concentration of slurry in the tank at the end of 1 hr.

6.2. An advertising firm wants to get a spherical inflated sign out of a warehouse. The sign is 20 ft in diameter and is filled with H_2 at 15 psig. Unfortunately the door to the warehouse is only 19 ft high by 20 ft wide. The maximum rate of H_2 that can be safely vented from the balloon is 5 ft³/min (measured at room conditions). How long will it take to get the sign small enough to just pass through the door?
   (a) First, assume the pressure inside the balloon (i.e., the flow rate) is constant.
   (b) Then assume the amount of H_2 escaping is proportional to the volume of the balloon and initially is 5 ft³/min.
   (c) Question: Could a solution to this problem be obtained if the amount of escaping H_2 were proportional to the pressure difference inside and outside the balloon?

6.3. A bubble of CH_4 is formed at the bottom of a lake at a uniform temperature of 70°F, and is 1 mm in diameter. What is its volume just as it reaches the surface? Assume the initial bubble and final bubble are both saturated with H_2O. The barometer reads 29.8 in. Hg.

6.4. A mixer containing 100 gal of Na_2SO_4 solution (4 lb of Na_2SO_4/gal) is attached to a reservoir containing a solution of 1 lb of Na_2SO_4/gal. If the solution is pumped from the reservoir at the rate of 5 gal/min and the mixed solution runs out of the mixer at the rate of 5 gal/min, how long will it take to reduce the concentration of salt in the tank to 1/2 its original value? To 1/4 its original value?

6.5. If the average person takes 18 breaths per minute and on each breath exhales 100 in.³ containing 4% CO_2, find the per cent CO_2 in the air of a bomb shelter $\frac{1}{2}$ hr after a group of 50 enters. Assume the air in the shelter was fresh to start with and the ventilation system introduces 100 ft³ of fresh air (CO_2 content is 0.04% by volume) per minute. The shelter size is 10^4 ft³.

6.6. A sewage disposal plant has a big concrete holding tank of 100,000 gal capacity. It is 3/4 full of liquid to start with and contains 60,000 lb of organic material in suspension. Water runs into the holding tank at the rate of 20,000 gal/hr and the solution leaves at the rate of 15,000 gal/hr. How much organic material is in the tank at the end of 3 hr?

6.7. Suppose that in Prob. 6.6 the bottom of the tank is covered with sludge (precipitated organic material) and that the stirring of the tank causes the sludge to go into suspension at a rate proportional to the difference between the concentration of sludge in the tank at any time and 10 lb sludge/gal. If no organic material were present, the sludge would go into suspension at the rate of 0.05 lb/(min)(gal solution) when 75,000 gal of solution are in the tank. How much organic material is in the tank at the end of 3 hr?

6.8. Water flows from a conical tank at the rate of $5(2 + h^2)$ gal/min. If the tank is initially full, how long will it take for 75% of the water to flow out of the tank? What is the flow rate at that time?

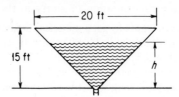

6.9. As a chemical engineer in a nuclear reactor design group, you have been asked to design a holding tank for a 10 gal/min effluent stream from a homogeneous reactor (one with the fuel in solution in water). Normally the concentration of a dangerous isotope, having a half-life of 10 min, is 0.010 mg/ft³ in the reactor. If you design the holding tank in such a way that mixing is complete inside the tank and the solution overflows at the top, how big does the tank have to be to reduce the normal concentration of the isotope at the overflow to 0.001 mg/ft³? *Note:* If the half-life of the isotope ($t_{1/2}$) is 10 min, its rate of decay is

$$\frac{dy}{dt} = \frac{0.693}{t_{1/2}} y$$

where y is the amount of material at any time t.

6.10. A radioactive waste that contains 1500 ppm of Sr^{92} is pumped into a holding tank that contains 100 gal at the rate of 5 gal/min. Sr^{92} decays as follows:

$$Sr^{92} \longrightarrow Y^{92} \longrightarrow Zr^{92}$$

half-life: 2.7 hr   3.5 hr

If the tank contains clear water initially and the solution runs out at the rate of 5 gal/min, assuming perfect mixing, what is the concentration of Sr, Y, and Zr after one day? What is the equilibrium concentration of Sr and Y in the tank?

Additional information: The rate of decay of such isotopes is $dN/dt = -\lambda N$, where $\lambda = 0.693/t_{1/2}$ and the half-life is $t_{1/2}$. $N =$ moles.

6.11. A tank containing 100 lb of a 60% brine (60% salt) is filled with a 10% salt solution at the rate of 10 lb/min. Solution is removed from the tank at the rate of 15 lb/min. Assuming complete mixing, find the lbs of salt in the tank after 10 min.

6.12. Suppose an organic compound decomposes as follows:

$$C_6H_{12} \longrightarrow C_4H_8 + C_2H_4$$

If 1 mole of C_6H_{12} exists at $t = 0$ but no C_4H_8 and C_2H_4, set up equations showing the moles of C_4H_8 and C_2H_4 as a function of time. The rates of formation of C_4H_8 and C_2H_4 are each proportional to the number of moles of C_6H_{12} present.

6.13. In a chemical reaction the products X and Y are formed according to the equation

$$C \longrightarrow X + Y$$

The rate at which each of these products is being formed is proportional to the amount of C present. Initially, $C = 1$, $X = 0$, $Y = 0$. Find the time for the amount of X to equal the amount of C.

6.14. Suppose you have two tanks in series as diagramed. The volume of liquid in each tank remains constant because of the design of the overflow lines. Assume that each tank is filled with a solution containing 10 lb of A and that

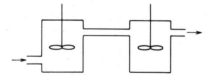

the tanks contain 100 gal of aqueous solution each. If fresh water enters at the rate of 10 gal/hr, what is the concentration of A in each tank at the end of 3 hr? Assume complete mixing in each tank, and ignore any change of volume with concentration.

6.15. A large tank is connected to a smaller tank by means of a valve. The large tank contains N_2 at 100 psia, while the small tank is evacuated. If the valve leaks between the two tanks and the rate of leakage of gas is proportional to the pressure difference between the two tanks $(p_1 - p_2)$, how long does it take for the pressure in the small tank to be one-half its final value? The instantaneous initial flow rate with the small tank evacuated is 0.2 lb mole/hr.

Other data:

	tank 1	*tank* 2
initial pressure (psia)	100	0
volume	1000 ft³	500 ft³

Assume the temperature in both tanks is constant and is 70°F.

6.16. A cylinder contains 3 ft³ of pure oxygen at atmospheric pressure. Air is slowly pumped into the tank and mixes uniformly with the contents, an equal volume of which is forced out of the tank. What is the concentration of oxygen in the tank after 9 ft^3 of air has been admitted?

6.17. Two well-mixed tanks are connected in series as shown in the diagram.

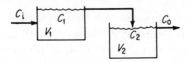

The entering concentration of a substance in tank 1 is c_i. No reactions occur. Tanks 1 and 2 both overflow. Set up an equation which will predict the concentration c_0 as a function of c_i.

6.18. The following chain reactions take place in a constant-volume batch tank:

$$A \xrightarrow{k_1} B \xrightarrow{k_2} C$$

Each reaction is first order and irreversible. If the initial concentration of A is C_{A_0} and if only A is present initially, find an expression for C_B as a function of time. Under what conditions will the concentration of B be dependent primarily on the rate of reaction of A?

6.19. Consider the following chemical reaction in a constant-volume batch tank:

$$A \underset{k_2}{\overset{k_1}{\rightleftarrows}} B$$
$$k_3 \Big\downarrow$$
$$C$$

All of the indicated reactions are first order. The initial concentration of A is C_{A_0}, and nothing else is present at that time. Determine the concentrations of A, B, and C as functions of time.

6.20. A ground material is to be suspended in water and heated in preparation for a chemical reaction. It is desired to carry out the mixing and heating simultaneously in a tank equipped with an agitator and a steam coil. The cold liquid and solid are to be added continuously and the heated suspension will be withdrawn at the same rate. One method of operation for starting up is to (1) fill the tank initially with water and solid in the proper proportions, (2) start the agitator, (3) introduce fresh water and solid in the proper proportions and simultaneously begin to withdraw the suspension for reaction, and (4) turn on the steam. An estimate is needed of the time required, after the steam is turned on, for the temperature of the effluent suspension to reach a certain elevated temperature.

(a) Using the nomenclature given below, formulate a differential equation for this process. Integrate this equation to obtain n as a function of B and ϕ (see nomenclature).

(b) Calculate the time required for the effluent temperature to reach 180°F if the initial contents of the tank and the inflow are both at 120°F and the steam temperature is 220°F. The surface area for heat transfer is

23.9 ft², and the heat transfer coefficient is 100 Btu/(hr)(ft²)(°F). The tank contains 6000 lb, and the rate of flow of both streams is 1200 lb/hr. In the proportions used, the specific heat of the suspension may be assumed to be 1.00.

If the area available for heat transfer is doubled, how will the time required be affected? Why is the time with the larger area less than half that obtained previously? The heat transferred is $\tilde{Q} = UA \, (T_{\text{tank}} - T_{\text{steam}})$.

Nomenclature

W = weight of tank contents, lb
G = rate of flow of suspension lb/hr
T_s = temperature of steam, °F
T = temperature in tank at any instant, perfect mixing assumed, °F
T_0 = temperature of suspension introduced into tank; also initial temperature of tank contents, °F
U = heat-transfer coefficient Btu/(hr)(ft²)(°F)
A = area of heat-transfer surface, ft²
C_p = specific heat of suspension, Btu/(lb)(°C)
t = time elapsed from the instant the steam is turned on, hr
n = dimensionless time Gt/W
B = dimensionless ratio, UA/GC_p
ϕ = dimensionless temperature (relative approach to the steam temperature) $(T - T_0)/(T_s - T_0)$

6.21. Tanks A, B, and C are each filled with 1000 gal of water. Workmen have instructions to dissolve 2000 lb of salt in each tank. By mistake, 3000 lb are dissolved in each of tanks A and C and none in B.

You wish to bring all of the compositions to within 5% of the specified 2 lb/gal. If the units are connected A-B-C-A by three 50-gpm pumps:
(a) Express concentrations C_A, C_B, and C_C in terms of t (time).
(b) Find the shortest time at which all concentrations are within the specified range.

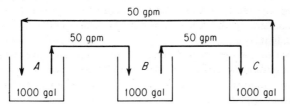

6.22. Consider a well-agitated cylindrical tank in which the heat-transfer surface is in the form of a coil which is distributed uniformly from the bottom of the tank to the top of the tank. The tank itself is completely insulated. Liquid is introduced into the tank at a uniform rate, starting with no liquid in the tank, and the steam is turned on at the instant that liquid flows into the tank.
(a) Using the nomenclature of Prob. 6.20 above, formulate a differential

equation for this process. Integrate this expression to obtain an equation for ϕ as a function of B and f, where $f =$ fraction filled $= W/W_{\text{filled}}$.

(b) If the heat transfer surface consists of a coil of 10 turns of 1-in. OD tubing 4 ft in diameter, the feed rate is 1200 lb/hr, the heat capacity of the liquid is 1.0 Btu/(lb)(°F), the heat-transfer coefficient is 100 Btu/ (hr)(°F)(ft²) of covered area, the steam temperature is 200°F, and the temperature of the liquid introduced into the tank is 70°F, what is the temperature in the tank when it is completely full? What is the temperature when the tank is half full? The heat transfer is given by $\bar{Q} = UA(T_{\text{tank}} - T_{\text{steam}})$.

6.23. A cylindrical tank 5 ft in diameter and 5 ft high is full of water at 70°F. The water is to be heated by means of a steam jacket around the sides only. The steam temperature is 230°F, and the over-all coefficient of heat transfer is constant at 40 Btu/(hr)(ft²)(°F). Use Newton's law of cooling (heating) to estimate the heat transfer. Neglecting the heat losses from the top and the bottom, calculate the time necessary to raise the temperature of the tank contents to 170°F. Repeat, taking the heat losses from the top and the bottom into account. The air temperature around the tank is 70°F, and the over-all coefficient of heat transfer for both the top and the bottom is constant at 10 Btu/(hr)(ft²)(°F).

6.24. A desired chemical B is manufactured according to the reaction

$$A \underset{k_2}{\overset{k_1}{\rightleftarrows}} B + H_2O$$

where k is in hr⁻¹. The forward reaction is first order, and, under the conditions of a large excess of water present, the reverse reaction may be taken to be first order also, depending only on the B present.

The following procedure is usually employed: 100 ft³ of the initial water-A mixture is added to a well-stirred tank (concentration of $A = C_A$ lb moles/ft³), and the catalyst to initiate the reaction is then added. During the next 4 hr, further water-A mixture is added to the tank at a rate of 100 ft³/hr while the reaction proceeds; and, after the complete charge of 500 ft³ has been added, the reaction is allowed to proceed for 6 hr. At the end of this time, the contents of the reactor are dumped into a chiller (to stop the reaction immediately).

(a) Set up the necessary differential equations, and give the necessary initial condition needed to calculate the concentration of B when the material was dumped into the chiller. (Assume the volume change on reaction to be negligible.)

(b) On a particular day the operator notices after a period of 2 hr that the valve in the line to the chiller was not closed and that the chiller contains 100 ft³ of material. The operator closes the valve. He then decides to carry out the rest of the run but to allow more time so as to bring the over-all concentration of B (material in the reactor + material already in chiller) up to the usual level. Assuming that the 100 ft³ of material had leaked into the chiller at a *uniform rate* during the first 2 hr after the catalyst was placed in the tank, set up the necessary differential equations and initial conditions to determine how long he should let the reaction proceed before dumping the remainder of the material into the chiller. *Define all your symbols (and units).*

6.25. Consider a flow process in which a precipitation is being formed by mixing two streams A and B to form a third stream C in which the precipitate is carried away. The reaction is extremely rapid, and agitation will be assumed to be so efficient that the material in the tank has substantially the same composition at all points. Streams A and B enter at the rate of a and b cfm, respectively. Change in volume due to reaction may be neglected, so that stream C leaves at the rate of $a + b$ cfm. To ensure proper quality of the precipitate, it is necessary to maintain the acidity of the tank contents at n_0 lb/ft^3 acid, with an allowable variation of $\pm$lb/ft^3. The acidity of the bath is maintained by a negligibly small volume of acid carried by stream A. On the assumption that the acid supply fails suddenly at a time when the concentration is n_0, it is desired to develop the law relating acid concentration and time in order to estimate what time would elapse before this concentration falls below the allowable level. During this time, all other flows will be assumed constant.

6.26. Determine the time required to heat a 10,000-lb batch of liquid from 60 to 120°F using an external, counterflow heat exchanger having an area of 300 ft^2. Water at 180°F is used as the heating medium and flows at a rate of 6000 lb/hr. An over-all heat-transfer coefficient of 40 Btu/(hr)(ft^2)(°F) may be assumed; use Newton's law of heating. The liquid is circulated at a rate of 6000 lb/hr, and the specific heat of the liquid is the same as that of water (1.0). Assume that the residence time of the liquid in the external heat exchanger is very small and that there is essentially no hold-up of liquid in this circuit.

Appendix A

CONVERSION FACTORS

TABLE A.1 VOLUME EQUIVALENTS*

	cu in.	cu ft	U.S. gal	liter
cu in.	1	5.787×10^{-4}	4.329×10^{-3}	1.639×10^{-2}
cu ft	1.728×10^{3}	1	7.481	28.32
U.S. gal	2.31×10^{2}	0.1337	1	3.785
liter	61.03	3.531×10^{-2}	0.2642	1

TABLE A.2 MASS EQUIVALENTS*

	avoir oz	pounds	grains	grams
avoir oz	1	6.25×10^{-2}	4.375×10^{2}	28.35
pounds	16	1	7×10^{3}	4.536×10^{2}
grains	2.286×10^{-3}	1.429×10^{-4}	1	6.48×10^{-2}
grams	3.527×10^{-2}	2.20×10^{-3}	15.432	1

TABLE A.3 LINEAR MEASURE EQUIVALENTS*

	meter	inch	foot	mile
meter	1	39.37	3.2808	6.214×10^{-4}
inch	2.54×10^{-2}	1	8.333×10^{-2}	1.58×10^{-5}
foot	0.3048	12	1	1.8939×10^{-4}
mile	1.61×10^{3}	6.336×10^{4}	5280	1

TABLE A.4 POWER EQUIVALENTS*

	hp	kw	ft-lb/sec	Btu/sec
hp	1	0.7457	550	0.7068
kw	1.341	1	737.56	0.9478
ft-lb/sec	1.818×10^{-3}	1.356×10^{-3}	1	1.285×10^{-3}
Btu/sec	1.415	1.055	778.16	1

*Source: J. H. Perry, *Chemical Engineers' Handbook*, 3rd ed., McGraw-Hill Book Company, New York, 1950.

TABLE A.5 HEAT, ENERGY, OR WORK EQUIVALENTS*

joules = 10^7 ergs	kg-m	ft-lb	kw-hr	hp-hr	liter-atm	kcal	Btu	gram-calorie†
1	0.10197	0.7376	2.773×10^{-7}	3.725×10^{-7}	9.869×10^{-3}	2.390×10^{-4}	9.478×10^{-4}	0.2390
9.80665	1	7.233	2.724×10^{-6}	3.653×10^{-6}	9.678×10^{-2}	2.344×10^{-3}	9.296×10^{-3}	2.3438
1.356	0.1383	1	3.766×10^{-7}	5.0505×10^{-7}	1.338×10^{-2}	3.24×10^{-4}	1.285×10^{-3}	0.3241
3.6×10^6	3.671×10^5	2.655×10^6	1	1.341	3.5534×10^4	8.6057×10^2	3.4128×10^3	8.6057×10^5
2.6845×10^6	2.7375×10^5	1.98×10^6	0.7455	1	2.6494×10^4	6.4162×10^2	2.545×10^3	6.4162×10^5
1.0133×10^2	10.333	74.73	2.815×10^{-5}	3.774×10^{-5}	1	2.422×10^{-2}	9.604×10^{-2}	24.218
4.184×10^3	4.267×10^2	3.086×10^3	1.162×10^{-3}	1.558×10^{-3}	41.29	1	3.9657	1×10^3
1.055×10^3	1.0758×10^2	7.7816×10^2	2.930×10^{-4}	3.930×10^{-4}	10.41	0.252	1	2.52×10^2
4.184	0.4267	3.086	1.162×10^{-6}	1.558×10^{-6}	4.129×10^{-2}	1×10^{-3}	3.97×10^{-3}	1

*Source: J. H. Perry, Chemical Engineers' Handbook, 3rd ed., McGraw-Hill Book Company, New York, 1950.
1 therm = 100,000 Btu.
†Gram-calorie. Thermochemical calorie is defined as 4.1840 absolute joules.

Appendix B
ATOMIC WEIGHTS AND NUMBERS

TABLE B.1 RELATIVE ATOMIC WEIGHTS, 1965

Based on the Atomic Mass of $^{12}C = 12$

The values for atomic weights given in the Table apply to elements as they exist in nature, without artificial alteration of their isotopic composition, and, further, to natural mixtures that do not include isotopes of radiogenic origin.

Name	Symbol	Atomic number	Atomic weight	Name	Symbol	Atomic number	Atomic weight
Actinium	Ac	89	.....	Mercury	Hg	80	200.59
Aluminium	Al	13	26.9815	Molybdenum	Mo	42	95.94
Americium	Am	95	.....	Neodymium	Nd	60	144.24
Antimony	Sb	51	121.75	Neon	Ne	10	20.183
Argon	Ar	18	39.948	Neptunium	Np	93	.....
Arsenic	As	33	74.9216	Nickel	Ni	28	58.71
Astatine	At	85	.....	Niobium	Nb	41	92.906
Barium	Ba	56	137.34	Nitrogen	N	7	14.0067
Berkelium	Bk	97	.....	Nobelium	No	102	.....
Beryllium	Be	4	9.0122	Osmium	Os	75	190.2
Bismuth	Bi	83	208.980	Oxygen	O	8	15.9994
Boron	B	5	10.811	Palladium	Pd	46	106.4
Bromine	Br	35	79.904	Phosphorus	P	15	30.9738
Cadmium	Cd	48	112.40	Platinum	Pt	78	195.09
Caesium	Cs	55	132.905	Plutonium	Pu	94	.....
Calcium	Ca	20	40.08	Polonium	Po	84	.....
Californium	Cf	98	.....	Potassium	K	19	39.102
Carbon	C	6	12.01115	Praseodym	Pr	59	140.907
Cerium	Ce	58	140.12	Promethium	Pm	61	.....
Chlorine	Cl	17	35.453[b]	Protactinium	Pa	91	.....
Chromium	Cr	24	51.996[b]	Radium	Ra	88	.....
Cobalt	Co	27	58.9332	Radon	Rn	86	.....
Copper	Cu	29	63.546[b]	Rhenium	Re	75	186.2
Curium	Cm	96	.....	Rhodium	Rh	45	102.905
Dysprosium	Dy	66	162.50	Rubidium	Rb	37	84.57
Einsteinium	Es	99	.....	Ruthenium	Ru	44	101.07
Erbium	Er	68	167.26	Samarium	Sm	62	150.35
Europium	Eu	63	151.96	Scandium	Sc	21	44.956
Fermium	Fm	100	.....	Selenium	Se	34	78.96
Fluorine	F	9	18.9984	Silicon	Si	14	28.086
Francium	Fr	87	.....	Silver	Ag	47	107.868
Gadolinium	Gd	64	157.25	Sodium	Na	11	22.9898
Gallium	Ga	31	69.72	Strontium	Sr	38	87.62
Germanium	Ge	32	72.59	Sulfur	S	16	32.064
Gold	Au	79	196.967	Tantalum	Ta	73	180.948
Hafnium	Hf	72	178.49	Technetium	Tc	43	.....
Helium	He	2	4.0026	Tellurium	Te	52	127.60
Holmium	Ho	67	164.930	Terbium	Tb	65	158.924
Hydrogen	H	1	1.00797	Thallium	Tl	81	204.37
Indium	In	49	114.82	Thorium	Th	90	232.038
Iodine	I	53	126.9044	Thulium	Tm	59	168.934
Iridium	Ir	77	192.2	Tin	Sn	50	118.69
Iron	Fe	26	55.847	Titanium	Ti	22	47.90
Krypton	Kr	36	83.80	Tungsten	W	74	183.85
Lanthanum	La	57	138.91	Uranium	U	92	238.03
Lawrencium	Lr	103	.....	Vanadium	V	23	50.942
Lead	Pb	82	207.19	Xenon	Xe	54	131.30
Lithium	Li	3	6.939	Ytterbium	Yb	70	173.04
Lutetium	Lu	71	174.97	Yttrium	Y	39	88.905
Magnesium	Mg	12	24.312	Zinc	Zn	30	65.37
Manganese	Mn	25	54.9380	Zirconium	Zr	40	91.22
Mendelevium	Md	101	.....				

Source: Comptes Rendus, 23rd IUPAC Conference, 1965, Butterworth's, London, 1965, pp. 177–78.

Appendix C

STEAM TABLES

Source: Combustion Engineering, Inc.
Absolute Pressure = atmospheric pressure − vacuum.

Barometer and vacuum columns may be corrected to mercury at 32°F by subtracting $0.00009 \times (t - 32) \times$ column height, where t is the column temperature in °F.

One inch of mercury at 32°F = 0.4912 lb/in.^{2}

Example:

Barometer reads 30.17 in. at 70°F. Vacuum column reads 28.26 in. at 80°F. Pounds pressure = $(30.17 - 0.00009 \times 38 \times 30.17) - 28.26 - 0.00009 \times 48 \times 28.26) = 1.93$ in. of mercury at 32°F.

Saturation temperature (from table) = 100°F.

TABLE C.1 SATURATED STEAM: TEMPERATURE TABLE

Temp. Fahr. t	Absolute pressure		Specific volume			Enthalpy		
	Lb/in.^{2} p	In. Hg 32°F	Sat. liquid v_f	Evap. v_{fg}	Sat. vapor v_g	Sat. liquid h_f	Evap. h_{fg}	Sat. vapor h_g
32	0.0886	0.1806	0.01602	3305.7	3305.7	0	1075.1	1075.1
34	0.0961	0.1957	0.01602	3060.4	3060.4	2.01	1074.9	1076.0
36	0.1041	0.2120	0.01602	2836.6	2836.6	4.03	1072.9	1076.9
38	0.1126	0.2292	0.01602	2632.2	2632.2	6.04	1071.7	1077.7
40	0.1217	0.2478	0.01602	2445.1	2445.1	8.05	1070.5	1078.6
42	0.1315	0.2677	0.01602	2271.8	2271.8	10.06	1069.3	1079.4
44	0.1420	0.2891	0.01602	2112.2	2112.2	12.06	1068.2	1080.3
46	0.1532	0.3119	0.01602	1965.5	1965.5	14.07	1067.1	1081.2
48	0.1652	0.3364	0.01602	1829.9	1829.9	16.07	1065.9	1082.0
50	0.1780	0.3624	0.01602	1704.9	1704.9	18.07	1064.8	1082.9
52	0.1918	0.3905	0.01603	1588.4	1588.4	20.07	1063.6	1083.7
54	0.2063	0.4200	0.01603	1482.4	1482.4	22.07	1062.5	1084.6
56	0.2219	0.4518	0.01603	1383.5	1383.5	24.07	1061.4	1085.5
58	0.2384	0.4854	0.01603	1292.7	1292.7	26.07	1060.2	1086.3
60	0.2561	0.5214	0.01603	1208.1	1208.1	28.07	1059.1	1087.2
62	0.2749	0.5597	0.01604	1129.7	1129.7	30.06	1057.9	1088.0
64	0.2949	0.6004	0.01604	1057.1	1057.1	32.06	1056.8	1088.9
66	0.3162	0.6438	0.01604	989.6	989.6	34.06	1055.7	1089.8
68	0.3388	0.6898	0.01605	927.0	927.0	36.05	1054.5	1090.6
70	0.3628	0.7387	0.01605	868.9	868.9	38.05	1053.4	1091.5
72	0.3883	0.7906	0.01606	814.9	814.9	40.04	1052.3	1092.3
74	0.4153	0.8456	0.01606	764.7	764.7	42.04	1051.2	1093.2
76	0.4440	0.9040	0.01607	718.0	718.0	44.03	1050.1	1094.1
78	0.4744	0.9659	0.01607	674.4	674.4	46.03	1048.9	1094.9
80	0.5067	1.032	0.01607	633.7	633.7	48.02	1047.8	1095.8
82	0.5409	1.101	0.01608	595.8	595.8	50.02	1046.6	1096.6
84	0.5772	1.175	0.01608	560.4	560.4	52.01	1045.5	1097.5
86	0.6153	1.253	0.01609	527.6	527.6	54.01	1044.4	1098.4
88	0.6555	1.335	0.01609	497.0	497.0	56.00	1043.2	1099.2
90	0.6980	1.421	0.01610	468.4	468.4	58.00	1042.1	1100.1
92	0.7429	1.513	0.01611	441.7	441.7	59.99	1040.9	1100.9
94	0.7902	1.609	0.01611	416.7	416.7	61.98	1039.8	1101.8
96	0.8403	1.711	0.01612	393.2	393.2	63.98	1038.7	1102.7
98	0.8930	1.818	0.01613	371.3	371.3	65.98	1037.5	1103.5

v = specific volume, ft^3/lb. h = enthalpy, Btu/lb.

TABLE C.1 (CONT.)

| Temp. Fahr. t | Absolute pressure | | Specific volume | | | Enthalpy | | |
	Lb/in.^{2} p	In. Hg 32°F	Sat. liquid v_f	Evap. v_{fg}	Sat. vapor v_g	Sat. liquid h_f	Evap. h_{fg}	Sat. vapor h_g
100	0.9487	1.932	0.01613	350.8	350.8	67.97	1036.4	1104.4
102	1.0072	2.051	0.01614	331.5	331.5	69.96	1035.2	1105.2
104	1.0689	2.176	0.01614	313.5	313.5	71.96	1034.1	1106.1
106	1.1338	2.308	0.01615	296.5	296.5	73.95	1033.0	1107.0
108	1.2020	2.447	0.01616	280.7	280.7	75.94	1032.0	1107.9
110	1.274	2.594	0.01617	265.7	265.7	77.94	1030.9	1108.8
112	1.350	2.749	0.01617	251.6	251.6	79.93	1029.7	1109.6
114	1.429	2.909	0.01618	238.5	238.5	81.93	1028.6	1110.5
116	1.512	3.078	0.01619	226.2	226.2	83.92	1027.5	1111.4
118	1.600	3.258	0.01620	214.5	214.5	85.92	1026.4	1112.3
120	1.692	3.445	0.01620	203.45	203.47	87.91	1025.3	1113.2
122	1.788	3.640	0.01621	193.16	193.18	89.91	1024.1	1114.0
124	1.889	3.846	0.01622	183.44	183.46	91.90	1023.0	1114.9
126	1.995	4.062	0.01623	174.26	174.28	93.90	1021.8	1115.7
128	2.105	4.286	0.01624	165.70	165.72	95.90	1020.7	1116.6
130	2.221	4.522	0.01625	157.55	157.57	97.89	1019.5	1117.4
132	2.343	4.770	0.01626	149.83	149.85	99.89	1018.3	1118.2
134	2.470	5.029	0.01626	142.59	142.61	101.89	1017.2	1119.1
136	2.603	5.300	0.01627	135.73	135.75	103.88	1016.0	1119.9
138	2.742	5.583	0.01628	129.26	129.28	105.88	1014.9	1120.8
140	2.887	5.878	0.01629	123.16	123.18	107.88	1013.7	1121.6
142	3.039	6.187	0.01630	117.37	117.39	109.88	1012.5	1122.4
144	3.198	6.511	0.01631	111.88	111.90	111.88	1011.3	1123.2
146	3.363	6.847	0.01632	106.72	106.74	113.88	1010.2	1124.1
148	3.536	7.199	0.01633	101.82	101.84	115.87	1009.0	1124.9
150	3.716	7.566	0.01634	97.18	97.20	117.87	1007.8	1125.7
152	3.904	7.948	0.01635	92.79	92.81	119.87	1006.7	1126.6
154	4.100	8.348	0.01636	88.62	88.64	121.87	1005.5	1127.4
156	4.305	8.765	0.01637	84.66	84.68	123.87	1004.4	1128.3
158	4.518	9.199	0.01638	80.90	80.92	125.87	1003.2	1129.1
160	4.739	9.649	0.01639	77.37	77.39	127.87	1002.0	1129.9
162	4.970	10.12	0.01640	74.00	74.02	129.88	1000.8	1130.7
164	5.210	10.61	0.01642	70.79	70.81	131.88	999.7	1131.6
166	5.460	11.12	0.01643	67.76	67.78	133.88	998.5	1132.4
168	5.720	11.65	0.01644	64.87	64.89	135.88	997.3	1133.2
170	5.990	12.20	0.01645	62.12	62.14	137.89	996.1	1134.0
172	6.272	12.77	0.01646	59.50	59.52	139.89	995.0	1134.9
174	6.565	13.37	0.01647	57.01	57.03	141.89	993.8	1135.7
176	6.869	13.99	0.01648	54.64	54.66	143.90	992.6	1136.5
178	7.184	14.63	0.01650	52.39	52.41	145.90	991.4	1137.3
180	7.510	15.29	0.01651	50.26	50.28	147.91	990.2	1138.1
182	7.849	15.98	0.01652	48.22	48.24	149.92	989.0	1138.9
184	8.201	16.70	0.01653	46.28	46.30	151.92	987.8	1139.7
186	8.566	17.44	0.01654	44.43	44.45	153.93	986.6	1140.5
188	8.944	18.21	0.01656	42.67	42.69	155.94	985.3	1141.3
190	9.336	19.01	0.01657	40.99	41.01	157.95	984.1	1142.1
192	9.744	19.84	0.01658	39.38	39.40	159.95	982.8	1142.8
194	10.168	20.70	0.01659	37.84	37.86	161.96	981.5	1143.5
196	10.605	21.59	0.01661	36.38	36.40	163.97	980.3	1144.3
198	11.057	22.51	0.01662	34.98	35.00	165.98	979.0	1145.0
200	11.525	23.46	0.01663	33.65	33.67	167.99	977.8	1145.8
202	12.010	24.45	0.01665	32.37	32.39	170.01	976.6	1146.6
204	12.512	25.47	0.01666	31.15	31.17	172.02	975.3	1147.3
206	13.031	26.53	0.01667	29.99	30.01	174.03	974.1	1148.1
208	13.568	27.62	0.01669	28.88	28.90	176.04	972.8	1148.8
210	14.123	28.75	0.01670	27.81	27.83	178.06	971.5	1149.6
212	14.696	29.92	0.01672	26.81	26.83	180.07	970.3	1150.4
215	15.591		0.01674	25.35	25.37	186.10	968.3	1151.4
220	17.188		0.01677	23.14	23.16	188.14	965.2	1153.3
225	18.915		0.01681	21.15	21.17	193.18	961.9	1155.1
230	20.78		0.01684	19.371	19.388	198.22	958.7	1156.9
235	22.80		0.01688	17.761	17.778	203.28	955.3	1158.6
240	24.97		0.01692	16.307	16.324	208.34	952.1	1160.4
245	27.31		0.01696	15.010	15.027	213.41	948.7	1162.1
250	29.82		0.01700	13.824	13.841	218.48	945.3	1163.8

v = specific volume, ft^3/lb. h = enthalpy, Btu/lb.

TABLE C.1 (CONT.)

Temp. Fahr. t	Absolute pressure Lb/in² p	Absolute pressure In. Hg 32°F	Sat. liquid v_f	Evap. v_{fg}	Sat. vapor v_g	Sat. liquid h_f	Evap. h_{fg}	Sat. vapor h_g
	Absolute pressure		Specific volume			Enthalpy		
255	32.53		0.01704	12.735	12.752	223.56	942.0	1165.6
260	35.43		0.01708	11.754	11.771	228.65	938.6	1167.3
265	38.54		0.01713	10.861	10.878	233.74	935.3	1169.0
270	41.85		0.01717	10.053	10.070	238.84	931.8	1170.6
275	45.40		0.01721	9.313	9.330	243.94	928.2	1172.1
280	49.20		0.01726	8.634	8.651	249.06	924.6	1173.7
285	53.25		0.01731	8.015	8.032	254.18	921.0	1175.2
290	57.55		0.01735	7.448	7.465	259.31	917.4	1176.7
295	62.13		0.01740	6.931	6.948	264.45	913.7	1178.2
300	67.01		0.01745	6.454	6.471	269.60	910.1	1179.7
305	72.18		0.01750	6.014	6.032	274.76	906.3	1181.1
310	77.68		0.01755	5.610	5.628	279.92	902.6	1182.5
315	83.50		0.01760	5.239	5.257	285.10	898.8	1183.9
320	89.65		0.01765	4.897	4.915	290.29	895.0	1185.3
325	96.16		0.01771	4.583	4.601	295.49	891.1	1186.6
330	103.03		0.01776	4.292	4.310	300.69	887.1	1187.8
335	110.31		0.01782	4.021	4.039	305.91	883.2	1189.1
340	117.99		0.01788	3.771	3.789	311.14	879.2	1190.3
345	126.10		0.01793	3.539	3.557	316.38	875.1	1191.5
350	134.62		0.01799	3.324	3.342	321.64	871.0	1192.6
355	143.58		0.01805	3.126	3.144	326.91	866.8	1193.7
360	153.01		0.01811	2.940	2.958	332.19	862.5	1194.7
365	162.93		0.01817	2.768	2.786	337.48	858.2	1195.7
370	173.33		0.01823	2.607	2.625	342.79	853.8	1196.6
375	184.23		0.01830	2.458	2.476	348.11	849.4	1197.5
380	195.70		0.01836	2.318	2.336	353.45	844.9	1198.4
385	207.71		0.01843	2.189	2.207	358.80	840.4	1199.2
390	220.29		0.01850	2.064	2.083	364.17	835.7	1199.9
395	233.47		0.01857	1.9512	1.9698	369.56	831.0	1200.6
400	247.25		0.01864	1.8446	1.8632	374.97	826.2	1201.2
405	261.67		0.01871	1.7445	1.7632	380.40	821.4	1201.8
410	276.72		0.01878	1.6508	1.6696	385.83	816.6	1202.4
415	292.44		0.01886	1.5630	1.5819	391.30	811.7	1203.0
420	308.82		0.01894	1.4806	1.4995	396.78	806.7	1203.5
425	325.91		0.01902	1.4031	1.4221	402.28	801.6	1203.9
430	343.71		0.01910	1.3303	1.3494	407.80	796.5	1204.3
435	362.27		0.01918	1.2617	1.2809	413.35	791.2	1204.6
440	381.59		0.01926	1.1973	1.2166	418.91	785.9	1204.8
445	401.70		0.01934	1.1367	1.1560	424.49	780.4	1204.9
450	422.61		0.01943	1.0796	1.0990	430.11	774.9	1205.0
455	444.35		0.0195	1.0256	1.0451	435.74	769.3	1205.0
460	466.97		0.0196	0.9745	0.9941	441.42	763.6	1205.0
465	490.43		0.0197	0.9262	0.9459	447.10	757.8	1204.9
470	514.70		0.0198	0.8808	0.9006	452.84	751.9	1204.7
475	539.90		0.0199	0.8379	0.8578	458.59	745.9	1204.5
480	566.12		0.0200	0.7972	0.8172	464.37	739.8	1204.2
485	593.28		0.0201	0.7585	0.7786	470.18	733.6	1203.8
490	621.44		0.0202	0.7219	0.7421	476.01	727.3	1203.3
495	650.59		0.0203	0.6872	0.7075	481.90	720.8	1202.7
500	680.80		0.0204	0.6544	0.6748	487.80	714.2	1202.0
505	712.19		0.0206	0.6230	0.6436	493.8	707.5	1201.3
510	744.55		0.0207	0.5932	0.6139	499.8	700.6	1200.4
515	777.96		0.0208	0.5651	0.5859	505.8	693.6	1199.4
520	812.68		0.0209	0.5382	0.5591	511.9	686.5	1198.4
525	848.37		0.0210	0.5128	0.5338	518.0	679.2	1197.2
530	885.20		0.0212	0.4885	0.5097	524.2	671.9	1196.1
535	923.45		0.0213	0.4654	0.4867	530.4	664.4	1194.8
540	962.80		0.0214	0.4433	0.4647	536.6	656.7	1193.3
545	1003.6		0.0216	0.4222	0.4438	542.9	648.9	1191.8
550	1045.6		0.0218	0.4021	0.4239	549.3	640.9	1190.2
555	1088.8		0.0219	0.3830	0.4049	555.7	632.6	1188.3
560	1133.4		0.0221	0.3648	0.3869	562.2	624.1	1186.3
565	1179.3		0.0222	0.3472	0.3694	568.8	615.4	1184.2
570	1226.7		0.0224	0.3304	0.3528	575.4	606.5	1181.9

v = specific volume, ft³/lb. h = enthalpy, Btu/lb.

TABLE C.1 (CONT.)

Temp. Fahr. t	Absolute pressure Lb/in² p	Specific volume Sat. liquid v_f	Specific volume Evap. v_{fg}	Specific volume Sat. vapor v_g	Enthalpy Sat. liquid h_f	Enthalpy Evap. h_{fg}	Enthalpy Sat. vapor h_g
575	1275.7	0.0226	0.3143	0.3369	582.1	597.4	1179.5
580	1326.1	0.0228	0.2989	0.3217	588.9	588.1	1177.0
585	1378.1	0.0230	0.2840	0.3070	595.7	578.6	1174.3
590	1431.5	0.0232	0.2699	0.2931	602.6	568.8	1171.4
595	1486.5	0.0234	0.2563	0.2797	609.7	558.7	1168.4
600	1543.2	0.0236	0.2432	0.2668	616.8	548.4	1165.2
605	1601.5	0.0239	0.2306	0.2545	624.1	537.7	1161.8
610	1661.6	0.0241	0.2185	0.2426	631.5	526.6	1158.1
615	1723.4	0.0244	0.2068	0.2312	638.9	515.3	1154.2
620	1787.0	0.0247	0.1955	0.2202	646.5	503.7	1150.2
625	1852.4	0.0250	0.1845	0.2095	654.3	491.5	1145.8
630	1919.8	0.0253	0.1740	0.1993	662.2	478.8	1141.0
635	1989.0	0.0256	0.1638	0.1894	670.4	465.5	1135.9
640	2060.3	0.0260	0.1539	0.1799	678.7	452.0	1130.7
645	2133.5	0.0264	0.1441	0.1705	687.3	437.6	1124.9
650	2208.8	0.0268	0.1348	0.1616	696.0	422.7	1118.7
655	2286.4	0.0273	0.1256	0.1529	705.2	407.0	1112.2
660	2366.2	0.0278	0.1167	0.1445	714.4	390.5	1104.9
665	2448.0	0.0283	0.1079	0.1362	724.5	372.1	1096.6
670	2532.4	0.0290	0.0991	0.1281	734.6	353.3	1087.9
675	2619.2	0.0297	0.0904	0.1201	745.5	332.8	1078.3
680	2708.4	0.0305	0.0810	0.1115	757.2	310.0	1067.2
685	2800.4	0.0316	0.0716	0.1032	770.1	284.5	1054.6
690	2895.0	0.0328	0.0617	0.0945	784.2	254.9	1039.1
695	2992.7	0.0345	0.0511	0.0856	801.3	219.1	1020.4
700	3094.1	0.0369	0.0389	0.0758	823.9	171.7	995.6
705	3199.1	0.0440	0.0157	0.0597	870.2	77.6	947.8
705.34*	3206.2	0.0541	0	0.0541	910.3	0	910.3

*Critical temperature. v = specific volume, ft³/lb. h = enthalpy, Btu/lb.

TABLE C.2 SUPERHEATED STEAM

Abs. press. lb/in² (sat. temp.)		Sat. water	Sat. steam	200°	250°	300°	350°	400°	450°	500°	600°	700°	800°	900°	1000°	1100°	1200°
										Temperature—Degrees Fahrenheit							
1 (101.76)	Sh	0.0161	333.79	98.24	148.24	198.24	248.24	298.24	348.24	398.24	498.24	598.24	698.24	798.24	898.24	998.24	1098.24
	v	69.72	1105.2	392.5	422.5	452.1	482.1	511.7	541.8	571.7	630.9	690.6	750.2	809.8	869.4	929.1	988.7
	h			1149.2	1171.9	1194.4	1217.3	1240.2	1263.5	1286.7	1333.9	1382.1	1431.0	1480.8	1531.4	1583.0	1635.4
5 (162.25)	Sh	0.0164	73.600	37.75	87.75	137.75	187.75	237.75	287.75	337.75	437.75	537.75	637.75	737.75	837.75	937.75	1037.75
	v	130.13	1130.8	78.17	84.24	90.21	96.26	102.19	108.23	114.16	126.11	138.05	149.99	161.91	173.83	185.80	197.72
	h			1148.3	1171.1	1193.6	1216.6	1239.8	1263.0	1286.1	1333.5	1381.8	1430.8	1480.6	1531.3	1582.9	1635.3
10 (193.21)	Sh	0.0166	38.462	6.79	56.79	106.79	156.79	206.79	256.79	306.79	406.79	506.79	606.79	706.79	806.79	906.79	1006.79
	v	161.17	1143.3	38.88	41.96	44.98	48.02	51.01	54.04	57.02	63.01	68.99	74.96	80.92	86.89	92.88	98.85
	h			1146.7	1170.2	1192.8	1216.0	1239.3	1262.5	1285.8	1333.3	1381.6	1430.6	1480.5	1531.2	1582.8	1635.2
14.696 (212.00)	Sh	0.0167	26.828		38.00	88.00	138.00	188.00	238.00	288.00	388.00	488.00	588.00	688.00	788.00	888.00	988.00
	v	180.07	1150.4		28.44	30.52	32.61	34.65	36.73	38.75	42.83	46.91	50.97	55.03	59.09	63.19	67.25
	h				1169.2	1192.0	1215.4	1238.9	1262.1	1285.4	1333.0	1381.4	1430.5	1480.4	1531.1	1582.7	1635.1
15 (213.03)	Sh	0.0167	26.320		36.97	86.97	136.97	186.97	236.97	286.97	386.97	486.97	586.97	686.97	786.97	886.97	986.97
	v	181.11	1150.7		27.86	29.90	31.94	33.95	35.98	37.97	41.98	45.97	49.95	53.93	57.91	61.91	65.89
	h				1169.2	1192.0	1215.4	1238.9	1262.1	1285.4	1333.0	1381.4	1430.5	1480.4	1531.1	1582.7	1635.1
20 (227.96)	Sh	0.0168	20.110		22.04	72.04	122.04	172.04	222.04	272.04	372.04	472.04	572.04	672.04	772.04	872.04	972.04
	v	196.16	1156.1		20.81	22.36	23.91	25.43	26.95	28.45	31.46	34.46	37.44	40.43	43.42	46.43	49.41
	h				1168.0	1191.1	1214.8	1238.4	1261.6	1285.0	1332.7	1381.2	1430.3	1480.2	1531.0	1582.6	1635.1
25 (240.07)	Sh	0.0169	16.321		9.93	59.93	109.93	159.93	209.93	259.93	359.93	459.93	559.93	659.93	759.93	859.93	959.93
	v	208.41	1160.4		16.58	17.84	19.08	20.30	21.53	22.73	25.15	27.55	29.94	32.33	34.73	37.14	39.52
	h				1166.3	1190.2	1214.1	1237.9	1261.1	1284.6	1332.4	1381.0	1430.1	1480.0	1530.9	1582.5	1635.0
30 (250.34)	Sh	0.0170	13.763			49.66	99.66	149.66	199.66	249.66	349.66	449.66	549.66	649.66	749.66	849.66	949.66
	v	218.83	1164.0			14.82	15.87	16.89	17.91	18.92	20.94	22.94	24.94	26.93	28.93	30.94	32.93
	h					1189.2	1213.4	1237.4	1260.6	1284.2	1332.1	1380.8	1429.9	1479.9	1530.8	1582.4	1634.9
35 (259.28)	Sh	0.0171	11.907			40.72	90.72	140.72	190.72	240.72	340.72	440.72	540.72	640.72	740.72	840.72	940.72
	v	227.92	1167.0			12.66	13.57	14.45	15.33	16.20	17.94	19.66	21.36	23.08	24.79	26.52	28.22
	h					1188.2	1212.7	1236.9	1260.1	1283.8	1331.9	1380.6	1429.8	1479.8	1530.7	1582.3	1634.8
40 (267.24)	Sh	0.0172	10.506			32.76	82.76	132.76	182.76	232.76	332.76	432.76	532.76	632.76	732.76	832.76	932.76
	v	236.02	1169.7			11.04	11.84	12.62	13.40	14.16	15.68	17.19	18.69	20.18	21.68	23.20	24.69
	h					1187.1	1211.9	1236.4	1259.6	1283.4	1331.6	1380.4	1429.6	1479.6	1530.6	1582.2	1634.8
45 (274.45)	Sh	0.0172	9.408			25.55	75.55	125.55	175.55	225.55	325.55	425.55	525.55	625.55	725.55	825.55	925.55
	v	243.38	1172.0			9.785	10.50	11.20	11.89	12.57	13.93	15.27	16.60	17.94	19.27	20.62	21.95
	h					1185.9	1211.1	1235.8	1259.1	1283.0	1331.3	1380.1	1429.4	1479.4	1530.5	1582.1	1634.7

Sh = superheat, °F. v = specific volume, ft³/lb. h = enthalpy, Btu/lb.

429

TABLE C.2 (CONT.)

Temperature—Degrees Fahrenheit (50–75 lb/in²)

Abs. press. lb/in² (sat. temp.)		Sat. water	Sat. steam	200°	250°	300°	350°	400°	450°	500°	600°	700°	800°	900°	1000°	1100°	1200°
50 (281.01)	Sh					18.99	68.99	118.99	168.99	218.99	318.99	418.99	518.99	618.99	718.99	818.99	918.99
	v	0.0173	8.522			8.777	9.430	10.06	10.69	11.30	12.53	13.74	14.93	16.14	17.34	18.55	19.75
	h	250.09	1174.0			1184.6	1210.3	1235.2	1258.6	1282.6	1331.0	1379.9	1429.3	1479.3	1530.4	1582.0	1634.6
55 (287.07)	Sh					12.93	62.93	112.93	162.93	212.93	312.93	412.93	512.93	612.93	712.93	812.93	912.93
	v	0.0173	7.792			7.950	8.553	9.130	9.703	10.26	11.38	12.48	13.57	14.67	15.76	16.86	17.95
	h	256.30	1175.8			1183.2	1209.4	1234.6	1258.2	1282.2	1330.7	1379.7	1429.1	1479.2	1530.3	1581.9	1634.5
60 (292.71)	Sh					7.29	57.29	107.29	157.29	207.29	307.29	407.29	507.29	607.29	707.29	807.29	907.29
	v	0.0174	7.179			7.260	7.821	8.353	8.882	9.398	10.42	11.44	12.44	13.44	14.44	15.45	16.45
	h	262.10	1177.5			1181.8	1208.5	1234.0	1257.7	1281.8	1330.4	1379.5	1428.9	1479.0	1530.2	1581.8	1634.4
65 (297.97)	Sh					2.03	52.03	102.03	152.03	202.03	302.03	402.03	502.03	602.03	702.03	802.03	902.03
	v	0.0174	6.654			6.674	7.202	7.696	8.187	8.665	9.614	10.55	11.48	12.40	13.33	14.26	15.19
	h	267.51	1179.1			1180.4	1207.6	1233.4	1257.2	1281.4	1330.1	1379.3	1428.8	1478.9	1530.1	1581.7	1634.4
70 (302.92)	Sh						47.08	97.08	147.08	197.08	297.08	397.08	497.08	597.08	697.08	797.08	897.08
	v	0.0175	6.210				6.671	7.132	7.592	8.036	8.920	9.791	10.65	11.51	12.37	13.24	14.10
	h	272.61	1180.5				1206.7	1232.8	1256.7	1281.0	1329.8	1379.0	1428.6	1478.7	1530.0	1581.6	1634.3
75 (307.60)	Sh						42.40	92.40	142.40	192.40	292.40	392.40	492.40	592.40	692.40	792.40	892.40
	v	0.0175	5.820				6.210	6.644	7.076	7.492	8.319	9.133	9.938	10.74	11.54	12.36	13.16
	h	277.44	1181.9				1205.8	1232.2	1256.2	1280.6	1329.6	1378.8	1428.4	1478.6	1529.8	1581.5	1634.2

Temperature—Degrees Fahrenheit (80–100 lb/in²)

Abs. press. lb/in² (sat. temp.)		Sat. water	Sat. steam	340°	360°	380°	400°	420°	450°	500°	600°	700°	800°	900°	1000°	1100°	1200°
80 (312.03)	Sh			27.97	47.97	67.97	87.97	107.97	137.97	187.97	287.97	387.97	487.97	587.97	687.97	787.97	887.97
	v	0.0176	5.476	5.738	5.889	6.055	6.217	6.384	6.623	7.015	7.793	8.558	9.313	10.07	10.82	11.58	12.33
	h	282.02	1183.1	1200.0	1211.0	1221.2	1231.2	1240.5	1255.7	1280.2	1329.3	1378.5	1428.2	1478.2	1529.7	1581.4	1634.1
85 (316.25)	Sh			23.75	43.75	63.75	83.75	103.75	133.75	183.75	283.75	383.75	483.75	583.75	683.75	783.75	883.75
	v	0.0176	5.169	5.368	5.528	5.685	5.839	5.995	6.226	6.594	7.329	8.050	8.762	9.472	10.18	10.90	11.61
	h	286.40	1184.3	1198.5	1209.5	1220.5	1230.5	1239.7	1255.1	1279.7	1328.9	1378.3	1428.0	1478.2	1529.6	1581.3	1634.0
90 (320.27)	Sh			19.73	39.73	59.73	79.73	99.73	129.73	179.73	279.73	379.73	479.73	579.73	679.73	779.73	879.73
	v	0.0177	4.898	5.055	5.208	5.357	5.504	5.653	5.869	6.220	6.916	7.599	8.272	8.943	9.626	10.22	10.96
	h	290.57	1185.4	1197.3	1209.0	1219.8	1230.0	1239.1	1254.5	1279.3	1328.7	1378.1	1427.9	1478.1	1529.5	1581.2	1634.0
95 (324.13)	Sh			15.87	35.87	55.87	75.87	95.87	125.87	175.87	275.87	375.87	475.87	575.87	675.87	775.87	875.87
	v	0.0177	4.653	4.773	4.921	5.063	5.205	5.346	5.552	5.886	6.547	7.195	7.834	8.481	9.117	9.751	10.38
	h	294.58	1186.4	1196.0	1208.0	1219.0	1229.3	1238.6	1254.0	1278.9	1328.4	1377.8	1427.7	1478.0	1529.4	1581.1	1633.9
100 (327.83)	Sh			12.17	32.17	52.17	72.17	92.17	122.17	172.17	272.17	372.17	472.17	572.17	672.17	772.17	872.17
	v	0.0177	4.433	4.520	4.663	4.801	4.936	5.070	5.266	5.589	6.217	6.836	7.448	8.055	8.659	9.262	9.862
	h	298.43	1187.3	1194.9	1207.0	1218.3	1228.4	1238.6	1253.7	1278.6	1327.9	1377.5	1427.5	1478.0	1529.2	1581.0	1633.7

Sh = superheat, °F.   v = specific volume, ft³/lb.   h = enthalpy, Btu/lb.

Superheated steam table (Sh = superheat, °F; v = specific volume, ft³/lb; h = enthalpy, Btu/lb)

Pressure, psia (Sat. temp, °F)		Sat. water	Sat. steam	340°	360°	380°	400°	420°	440°	450°	460°	480°	500°	550°	600°	700°	800°	900°	1000°	1100°	1200°
105 (331.38)	Sh			8.62	28.62	48.62	68.62	88.62		118.62			168.62		268.62	368.62	468.62	568.62	668.62	768.62	868.62
	v	0.0178	4.232	4.292	4.429	4.562	4.691	4.820		5.007			5.316		5.916	6.507	7.090	7.670	8.245	8.819	9.391
	h	302.13	1188.2	1193.5	1205.9	1217.2	1227.6	1237.5		1252.9			1278.0		1327.6	1377.4	1427.3	1477.7	1529.2	1580.9	1633.7
110 (334.79)	Sh			5.21	25.21	45.21	65.21	85.21		115.21			165.21		265.21	365.21	465.21	565.21	665.21	765.21	865.21
	v	0.0178	4.050	4.084	4.211	4.345	4.469	4.592		4.773			5.069		5.643	6.208	6.765	7.319	7.869	8.417	8.963
	h	305.69	1189.0	1192.2	1204.9	1216.4	1226.9	1236.9		1252.4			1277.5		1327.4	1377.1	1427.1	1477.5	1529.1	1580.8	1633.6
115 (338.08)	Sh				21.92	41.92	61.92	81.92		111.92			161.92		261.92	361.92	461.92	561.92	661.92	761.92	861.92
	v	0.0179	3.882		4.022	4.146	4.266	4.384		4.558			4.843		5.393	5.935	6.469	6.999	7.525	8.049	8.572
	h	309.13	1189.8		1203.8	1215.6	1226.2	1236.3		1251.9			1277.1		1327.1	1376.9	1427.0	1477.4	1528.9	1580.7	1633.6
120 (341.26)	Sh				18.74	38.74	58.74	78.74		108.74			158.74		258.74	358.74	458.74	558.74	658.74	758.74	858.74
	v	0.0179	3.728		3.845	3.963	4.079	4.194		4.361			4.635		5.165	5.685	6.197	6.705	7.210	7.713	8.215
	h	312.46	1190.6		1202.7	1214.7	1225.4	1235.7		1251.4			1276.7		1326.8	1376.7	1426.8	1477.2	1528.7	1580.6	1633.5
125 (344.34)	Sh				15.66	35.66	55.66	75.66		105.66			155.66		255.66	355.66	455.66	555.66	655.66	755.66	855.66
	v	0.0179	3.586		3.680	3.796	3.908	4.019		4.181			4.445		4.954	5.454	5.947	6.435	6.920	7.403	7.885
	h	315.69	1191.3		1201.6	1213.7	1224.5	1235.0		1250.8			1276.3		1326.5	1376.4	1426.6	1477.1	1528.7	1580.5	1633.4
130 (347.31)	Sh				12.69	32.69	52.69	72.69		102.69			152.69		252.69	352.69	452.69	552.69	652.69	752.69	852.69
	v	0.0180	3.455		3.528	3.641	3.750	3.857		4.013			4.268		4.760	5.242	5.716	6.186	6.653	7.117	7.581
	h	318.81	1192.0		1200.4	1212.7	1223.6	1234.3		1250.3			1275.8		1326.1	1376.1	1426.4	1476.9	1528.6	1580.4	1633.3
135 (350.21)	Sh				9.79	29.79	49.79	69.79		99.79			149.79		249.79	349.79	449.79	549.79	649.79	749.79	849.79
	v	0.0180	3.333		3.388	3.497	3.603	3.707		3.859			4.105		4.580	5.045	5.502	5.955	6.405	6.853	7.303
	h	321.86	1192.7		1199.2	1211.7	1222.7	1233.6		1249.7			1275.4		1325.8	1375.9	1426.2	1476.8	1528.5	1580.3	1633.2
140 (353.03)	Sh				6.97	26.97	46.97	66.97		96.97			146.97		246.97	346.97	446.97	546.97	646.97	746.97	846.97
	v	0.0180	3.220		3.258	3.364	3.467	3.567		3.715			3.954		4.413	4.862	5.303	5.741	6.175	6.607	7.037
	h	324.83	1193.3		1198.0	1210.6	1221.8	1232.9		1249.1			1275.0		1325.5	1375.7	1426.0	1476.6	1528.4	1580.2	1633.2
145 (355.76)	Sh				4.24	24.24	44.24	64.24		94.24			144.24		244.24	344.24	444.24	544.24	644.24	744.24	844.24
	v	0.0181	3.114		3.136	3.240	3.340	3.438		3.581			3.812		4.257	4.692	5.119	5.541	5.961	6.378	6.794
	h	327.71	1193.9		1196.7	1209.5	1220.9	1232.2		1248.5			1274.5		1325.1	1375.4	1425.8	1476.5	1528.3	1580.1	1633.1
150 (358.43)	Sh					21.57	41.57	61.57		91.57			141.57		241.57	341.57	441.57	541.57	641.57	741.57	841.57
	v	0.0181	3.016			3.124	3.221	3.317		3.456			3.681		4.112	4.533	4.946	5.355	5.761	6.164	6.567
	h	330.53	1194.4			1208.4	1220.0	1231.4		1248.0			1274.1		1324.9	1375.1	1425.6	1476.3	1528.1	1580.0	1633.0
155 (361.02)	Sh					18.98	38.98	58.98		88.98			138.98		238.98	338.98	438.98	538.98	638.98	738.98	838.98
	v	0.0181	2.921			3.015	3.110	3.203		3.340			3.558		3.976	4.384	4.785	5.181	5.574	5.964	6.354
	h	333.27	1195.0			1207.2	1219.1	1230.7		1247.5			1273.6		1324.5	1374.9	1425.4	1476.2	1528.0	1579.9	1632.9
160 (363.55)	Sh					16.45	36.45	56.45		86.45			136.45		236.45	336.45	436.45	536.45	636.45	736.45	836.45
	v	0.0182	2.834			2.913	3.006	3.097		3.230			3.443		3.849	4.245	4.633	5.018	5.398	5.777	6.155
	h	335.95	1195.5			1206.0	1218.3	1230.0		1246.9			1273.2		1324.1	1374.7	1425.2	1476.0	1527.9	1579.8	1632.8
165 (366.01)	Sh						33.99	53.99	73.99		93.99	113.99	133.99	183.99	233.99	333.99	433.99	533.99	633.99	733.99	833.99
	v	0.0182	2.752				2.909	2.997	3.084		3.170	3.251	3.334	3.533	3.729	4.114	4.491	4.864	5.234	5.601	5.967
	h	338.55	1195.9				1217.4	1229.3	1241.1		1251.8	1262.4	1272.8	1298.5	1323.8	1374.5	1425.0	1475.9	1527.8	1579.7	1632.7

Sh = superheat, °F.   v = specific volume, ft³/lb.   h = enthalpy, Btu/lb.

TABLE C.2 (CONT.)

Abs. press. lb./in.² (sat. temp.)		Sat. water	Sat. steam	400°	420°	440°	460°	480°	500°	550°	600°	700°	800°	900°	1000°	1100°	1200°
170 (368.42)	Sh			31.58	51.58	71.58	91.58	111.58	131.58	181.58	231.58	331.58	431.58	531.58	631.58	731.58	831.58
	v	0.0182	2.674	2.816	2.903	2.988	3.071	3.151	3.232	3.426	3.617	3.991	4.357	4.720	5.079	5.436	5.791
	h	341.11	1196.3	1216.5	1228.4	1240.5	1251.3	1261.3	1272.3	1298.2	1323.5	1374.2	1424.9	1475.7	1527.6	1579.6	1632.7
175 (370.77)	Sh			29.23	49.23	69.23	89.23	109.23	129.23	179.23	229.23	329.23	429.23	529.23	629.23	729.23	829.23
	v	0.0182	2.601	2.730	2.814	2.897	2.979	3.057	3.136	3.325	3.510	3.875	4.231	4.584	4.932	5.279	5.625
	h	343.61	1196.7	1215.6	1227.6	1239.9	1250.8	1261.3	1271.9	1297.8	1323.2	1374.0	1424.7	1475.6	1527.5	1579.5	1632.6
180 (373.08)	Sh			26.92	46.92	66.92	86.92	106.92	126.92	176.92	226.92	326.92	426.92	526.92	626.92	726.92	826.92
	v	0.0183	2.532	2.648	2.731	2.812	2.892	2.968	3.045	3.229	3.410	3.765	4.112	4.455	4.794	5.132	5.468
	h	346.07	1197.2	1214.6	1226.8	1239.2	1250.2	1260.8	1271.5	1297.5	1322.8	1373.7	1424.5	1475.5	1527.4	1579.4	1632.5
185 (375.34)	Sh			24.66	44.66	64.66	84.66	104.66	124.66	174.66	224.66	324.66	424.66	524.66	624.66	724.66	824.66
	v	0.0183	2.466	2.570	2.651	2.731	2.809	2.884	2.958	3.139	3.315	3.661	3.999	4.333	4.664	4.992	5.319
	h	348.47	1197.6	1213.7	1226.0	1238.4	1249.6	1260.3	1271.0	1297.0	1322.4	1373.4	1424.3	1475.3	1527.3	1579.3	1632.4
190 (377.55)	Sh			22.45	42.45	62.45	82.45	102.45	122.45	172.45	222.45	322.45	422.45	522.45	622.45	722.45	822.45
	v	0.0183	2.404	2.496	2.576	2.654	2.731	2.804	2.877	3.053	3.225	3.563	3.893	4.218	4.540	4.860	5.179
	h	350.83	1198.0	1212.7	1225.1	1237.7	1249.0	1259.8	1270.5	1296.6	1322.1	1373.1	1424.1	1475.2	1527.2	1579.2	1632.3
195 (379.70)	Sh			20.30	40.30	60.30	80.30	100.30	120.30	170.30	220.30	320.30	420.30	520.30	620.30	720.30	820.30
	v	0.0184	2.344	2.426	2.505	2.581	2.656	2.728	2.799	2.972	3.140	3.470	3.791	4.109	4.423	4.735	5.046
	h	353.13	1198.4	1211.7	1224.2	1237.0	1248.3	1259.3	1270.0	1296.2	1321.8	1372.9	1423.9	1475.0	1527.0	1579.1	1632.2
200 (381.82)	Sh			18.18	38.18	58.18	78.18	98.18	118.18	168.18	218.18	318.18	418.18	518.18	618.18	718.18	818.18
	v	0.0184	2.288	2.360	2.437	2.512	2.585	2.656	2.726	2.895	3.059	3.381	3.697	4.005	4.311	4.616	4.919
	h	355.40	1198.7	1210.8	1223.7	1236.3	1247.9	1258.7	1269.4	1295.6	1321.4	1372.5	1423.9	1474.9	1526.6	1579.0	1632.1
205 (383.89)	Sh			16.11	36.11	56.11	76.11	96.11	116.11	166.11	216.11	316.11	416.11	516.11	616.11	716.11	816.11
	v	0.0184	2.235	2.297	2.372	2.446	2.518	2.587	2.656	2.821	2.982	3.297	3.604	3.906	4.205	4.502	4.798
	h	357.61	1199.0	1209.7	1222.5	1235.4	1247.1	1258.2	1269.0	1295.4	1321.0	1372.4	1423.5	1474.7	1526.8	1578.9	1632.1
210 (385.93)	Sh			14.07	34.07	54.07	74.07	94.07	114.07	164.07	214.07	314.07	414.07	514.07	614.07	714.07	814.07
	v	0.0184	2.183	2.237	2.311	2.384	2.454	2.522	2.589	2.751	2.909	3.216	3.516	3.812	4.104	4.395	4.683
	h	359.80	1199.4	1208.8	1221.8	1234.7	1246.5	1257.7	1268.5	1295.0	1320.7	1372.1	1423.3	1474.6	1526.6	1578.8	1632.0
215 (387.93)	Sh			12.07	32.07	52.07	72.07	92.07	112.07	162.07	212.07	312.07	412.07	512.07	612.07	712.07	812.07
	v	0.0185	2.134	2.179	2.252	2.324	2.393	2.460	2.526	2.685	2.839	3.140	3.433	3.722	4.008	4.292	4.574
	h	361.95	1199.6	1207.8	1221.0	1234.0	1245.9	1257.2	1268.0	1294.6	1320.4	1371.9	1423.1	1474.4	1526.5	1578.7	1631.9
220 (389.89)	Sh			10.11	30.11	50.11	70.11	90.11	110.11	160.11	210.11	310.11	410.11	510.11	610.11	710.11	810.11
	v	0.0185	2.086	2.124	2.196	2.267	2.335	2.400	2.465	2.621	2.772	3.067	3.354	3.637	3.916	4.193	4.469
	h	364.05	1199.9	1206.8	1220.1	1233.2	1245.2	1256.7	1267.5	1294.1	1320.0	1371.6	1422.9	1474.2	1526.4	1578.6	1631.8

Sh = superheat, °F.   v = specific volume, ft³/lb.   h = enthalpy, Btu/lb.

Superheated steam table (pressure rows; each cell lists **Sh / v / h**).

Upper block (225–245 lb/sq in.)

Abs. Press. lb/sq in. (Sat. Temp °F)	Sat. water v / h	Sat. steam v / h	400°	420°	440°	460°	480°	500°	550°	600°	700°	800°	900°	1000°	1100°	1200°
225 (391.81)	0.0185 / 366.11	2.042 / 1200.2	8.19 2.072 1205.8	28.19 2.142 1219.2	48.19 2.212 1232.3	68.19 2.279 1244.5	88.19 2.344 1256.2	108.19 2.407 1267.1	158.19 2.560 1293.7	208.19 2.708 1319.6	308.19 2.997 1371.4	408.19 3.278 1422.7	508.19 3.555 1474.1	608.19 3.828 1526.3	708.19 4.100 1578.5	808.19 4.369 1631.7
230 (393.70)	0.0186 / 368.16	1.9989 / 1200.4	6.30 2.021 1204.9	26.30 2.091 1218.3	46.30 2.160 1231.6	66.30 2.226 1243.8	86.30 2.289 1255.6	106.30 2.352 1266.7	156.30 2.502 1293.3	206.30 2.647 1319.3	306.30 2.930 1371.1	406.30 3.205 1422.5	506.30 3.477 1474.0	606.30 3.744 1526.2	706.30 4.010 1578.4	806.30 4.274 1631.6
235 (395.56)	0.0186 / 370.17	1.9573 / 1200.7	4.44 1.973 1203.9	24.44 2.042 1217.5	44.44 2.110 1230.8	64.44 2.175 1243.2	84.44 2.237 1255.0	104.44 2.298 1266.2	154.44 2.446 1292.9	204.44 2.589 1319.0	304.44 2.866 1370.9	404.44 3.136 1422.3	504.44 3.402 1473.8	604.44 3.664 1526.0	704.44 3.924 1578.3	804.44 4.182 1631.6
240 (397.40)	0.0186 / 372.16	1.9176 / 1200.9		22.60 1.995 1216.6	42.60 2.062 1230.0	62.60 2.126 1242.5	82.60 2.187 1254.4	102.60 2.247 1265.7	152.60 2.392 1292.5	202.60 2.532 1318.6	302.60 2.805 1370.5	402.60 3.069 1422.1	502.60 3.330 1473.6	602.60 3.586 1525.9	702.60 3.841 1578.2	802.60 4.095 1631.5
245 (399.20)	0.0186 / 374.11	1.8797 / 1201.1		20.80 1.950 1215.6	40.80 2.015 1229.1	60.80 2.078 1241.8	80.80 2.139 1253.8	100.80 2.198 1265.2	150.80 2.341 1292.0	200.80 2.479 1318.3	300.80 2.746 1370.3	400.80 3.006 1421.9	500.80 3.261 1473.5	600.80 3.513 1525.8	700.80 3.762 1578.1	800.80 4.011 1631.4

Lower block (250–285 lb/sq in.)

Abs. Press. lb/sq in. (Sat. Temp °F)	Sat. water v / h	Sat. steam v / h	420°	440°	460°	480°	500°	520°	550°	600°	700°	800°	900°	1000°	1100°	1200°
250 (400.97)	0.0187 / 376.04	1.8431 / 1201.4	19.03 1.9065 1214.6	39.03 1.9711 1228.3	59.03 2.0334 1241.0	79.03 2.0932 1253.2	99.03 2.1515 1264.7	119.03 2.2085 1274.5	149.03 2.2920 1291.6	199.03 2.4272 1317.9	299.03 2.6897 1370.0	399.03 2.9444 1421.7	499.03 3.1949 1473.3	599.03 3.4416 1525.6	699.03 3.6867 1578.0	799.03 3.9299 1631.3
255 (402.71)	0.0187 / 377.91	1.8079 / 1201.6	17.29 1.8686 1213.7	37.29 1.9286 1227.5	57.29 1.9899 1240.3	77.29 2.0489 1252.6	97.29 2.1065 1264.2	117.29 2.1626 1274.2	147.29 2.2447 1291.2	197.29 2.3776 1317.5	297.29 2.6354 1369.8	397.29 2.8855 1421.5	497.29 3.1313 1473.2	597.29 3.3733 1525.5	697.29 3.6138 1577.9	797.29 3.8524 1631.2
260 (404.43)	0.0187 / 379.78	1.7742 / 1201.8	15.57 1.8246 1212.8	35.57 1.8876 1226.6	55.57 1.9482 1239.5	75.57 2.0063 1252.0	95.57 2.0631 1263.6	115.57 2.1185 1273.8	145.57 2.1991 1290.8	195.57 2.3299 1317.1	295.57 2.5833 1369.5	395.57 2.8289 1421.3	495.57 3.0701 1473.0	595.57 3.3077 1525.4	695.57 3.5437 1577.8	795.57 3.7778 1631.1
265 (406.12)	0.0187 / 381.62	1.7416 / 1202.0	13.88 1.7858 1211.9	33.88 1.8481 1225.7	53.88 1.9080 1238.7	73.88 1.9654 1251.2	93.88 2.0213 1263.0	113.88 2.0759 1273.4	143.88 2.1554 1290.4	193.88 2.2840 1316.8	293.88 2.5331 1369.3	393.88 2.7744 1421.1	493.88 3.0114 1472.9	593.88 3.2446 1525.3	693.88 3.4761 1577.7	793.88 3.7061 1631.1
270 (407.79)	0.0188 / 383.43	1.7101 / 1202.2	12.21 1.7486 1211.0	32.21 1.8101 1224.9	52.21 1.8692 1238.0	72.21 1.9259 1250.6	92.21 1.9810 1262.5	112.21 2.0350 1273.0	142.21 2.1131 1290.0	192.21 2.2399 1316.4	292.21 2.4847 1369.0	392.21 2.7219 1420.9	492.21 2.9548 1472.7	592.21 3.1838 1525.1	692.21 3.4112 1577.6	792.21 3.6370 1631.0
275 (409.44)	0.0188 / 385.22	1.6798 / 1202.3	10.56 1.7127 1210.0	30.56 1.7735 1224.1	50.56 1.8318 1237.3	70.56 1.8879 1250.0	90.56 1.9422 1262.0	110.56 1.9956 1272.6	140.56 2.0725 1289.5	190.56 2.1973 1316.1	290.56 2.4382 1368.7	390.56 2.6714 1420.7	490.56 2.9002 1472.6	590.56 3.1253 1525.0	690.56 3.3486 1577.5	790.56 3.5704 1630.9
280 (411.06)	0.0188 / 386.99	1.6504 / 1202.5	8.94 1.6780 1209.0	28.94 1.7381 1223.2	48.94 1.7957 1236.5	68.94 1.8512 1249.4	88.94 1.9048 1261.5	108.94 1.9575 1272.2	138.94 2.0334 1289.1	188.94 2.1562 1315.7	288.94 2.3932 1368.5	388.94 2.6226 1420.5	488.94 2.8475 1472.4	588.94 3.0688 1524.9	688.94 3.2883 1577.4	788.94 3.5062 1630.8
285 (412.66)	0.0188 / 388.74	1.6232 / 1202.7	7.34 1.6446 1208.0	27.34 1.7040 1222.3	47.34 1.7610 1235.6	67.34 1.8157 1248.7	87.34 1.8687 1260.9	107.34 1.9207 1271.8	137.34 1.9955 1288.6	187.34 2.1165 1315.4	287.34 2.3499 1368.2	387.34 2.5756 1420.3	487.34 2.7968 1472.2	587.34 3.0143 1524.7	687.34 3.2300 1577.3	787.34 3.4443 1630.7

Sh = superheat, °F. v = specific volume, ft³/lb. h = enthalpy, Btu/lb.

TABLE C.2 (CONT.)

Temperature—Degrees Fahrenheit

Abs. press. lb./in.² (sat. temp.)		Sat. water	Sat. steam	420°	440°	460°	480°	500°	520°	550°	600°	700°	800°	900°	1000°	1100°	1200°
290 (414.24)	Sh			5.76	25.76	45.76	65.76	85.76	105.76	135.76	185.76	285.76	385.76	485.76	585.76	685.76	785.76
	v	0.0189	1.5947	1.6122	1.6710	1.7273	1.7815	1.8338	1.8853	1.9590	2.0783	2.3080	2.5302	2.7478	2.9616	3.1738	3.3844
	h	390.47	1202.9	1207.0	1221.4	1234.8	1248.0	1260.4	1271.4	1288.2	1315.0	1367.0	1420.1	1472.1	1524.6	1577.2	1630.6
295 (415.80)	Sh			4.20	24.20	44.20	64.20	84.20	104.20	134.20	184.20	284.20	384.20	484.20	584.20	684.20	784.20
	v	0.0189	1.5684	1.5809	1.6391	1.6948	1.7484	1.8001	1.8510	1.9236	2.0413	2.2677	2.4863	2.7004	2.9108	3.1195	3.3267
	h	392.17	1203.0	1206.1	1220.5	1234.0	1247.4	1259.8	1271.0	1287.8	1314.7	1367.6	1419.9	1472.0	1524.5	1577.1	1630.5
300 (417.33)p	Sh			2.67	22.67	42.67	62.67	82.67	102.67	132.67	182.67	282.67	382.67	482.67	582.67	682.67	782.67
	v	0.0189	1.5426	1.5506	1.6082	1.6634	1.7164	1.7677	1.8172	1.8896	2.0056	2.2286	2.4447	2.6547	2.8634	3.0670	3.2707
	h	393.85	1203.2	1205.2	1219.5	1233.4	1246.6	1259.2	1270.5	1287.4	1314.4	1367.4	1419.7	1471.8	1524.4	1577.0	1630.4
310 (420.35)	Sh				19.65	39.65	59.65	79.65	99.65	129.65	179.65	279.65	379.65	479.65	579.65	679.65	779.65
	v	0.0189	1.4938		1.5495	1.6036	1.6555	1.7054	1.7546	1.8246	1.9375	2.1541	2.3631	2.5675	2.7682	2.9671	3.1645
	h	397.16	1203.5		1217.8	1231.5	1245.3	1258.0	1269.6	1286.4	1313.5	1366.9	1419.3	1471.5	1524.1	1576.8	1630.3
320 (423.29)	Sh				16.71	36.71	56.71	76.71	96.71	126.71	176.71	276.71	376.71	476.71	576.71	676.71	776.71
	v	0.0190	1.4479		1.4943	1.5473	1.5982	1.6472	1.6954	1.7637	1.8737	2.0844	2.2874	2.4857	2.6804	2.8735	3.0648
	h	400.40	1203.8		1216.0	1229.9	1244.0	1256.8	1268.6	1285.6	1312.8	1366.3	1418.9	1471.2	1523.8	1576.6	1630.1
330 (426.16)	Sh				13.84	33.84	53.84	73.84	93.84	123.84	173.84	273.84	373.84	473.84	573.84	673.84	773.84
	v	0.0190	1.4048		1.4424	1.4944	1.5445	1.5925	1.6397	1.7064	1.8138	2.0189	2.2163	2.4090	2.5981	2.7855	2.9712
	h	403.56	1204.0		1214.1	1228.2	1242.5	1255.5	1267.6	1284.7	1312.1	1365.8	1418.4	1470.8	1523.6	1576.4	1630.0
340 (428.96)	Sh				11.04	31.04	51.04	71.04	91.04	121.04	171.04	271.04	371.04	471.04	571.04	671.04	771.04
	v	0.0191	1.3640		1.3935	1.4446	1.4936	1.5409	1.5872	1.6525	1.7573	1.9572	2.1493	2.3368	2.5206	2.7027	2.8831
	h	406.65	1204.2		1212.2	1226.5	1241.0	1254.2	1266.6	1283.8	1311.4	1365.2	1418.0	1470.5	1523.3	1576.2	1629.8
350 (431.71)	Sh				8.29	28.29	48.29	68.29	88.29	118.29	168.29	268.29	368.29	468.29	568.29	668.29	768.29
	v	0.0191	1.3255		1.3472	1.3976	1.4460	1.4923	1.5377	1.6016	1.7041	1.8991	2.0863	2.2687	2.4475	2.6246	2.8000
	h	409.70	1204.4		1210.3	1224.8	1239.5	1252.9	1265.5	1282.9	1310.6	1364.7	1417.6	1470.2	1523.0	1576.0	1629.6
360 (434.39)	Sh				5.61	25.61	45.61	65.61	85.61	115.61	165.61	265.61	365.61	465.61	565.61	665.61	765.61
	v	0.0192	1.2889		1.3035	1.3532	1.4008	1.4463	1.4909	1.5536	1.6538	1.8441	2.0266	2.2044	2.3784	2.5506	2.7213
	h	412.67	1204.5		1208.5	1223.1	1238.0	1251.5	1264.5	1282.0	1309.9	1364.1	1417.2	1469.9	1522.8	1575.8	1629.4
370 (437.01)	Sh					22.99	42.99	62.99	82.99	112.99	162.99	262.99	362.99	462.99	562.99	662.99	762.99
	v	0.0192	1.2545			1.3111	1.3579	1.4028	1.4466	1.5286	1.6063	1.7921	1.9703	2.1435	2.3131	2.4809	2.6471
	h	415.58	1204.6			1221.4	1236.5	1250.2	1263.4	1286.7	1309.1	1363.6	1410.8	1469.6	1522.5	1575.6	1629.2
380 (439.59)	Sh					20.41	40.41	60.41	80.41	110.41	160.41	260.41	360.41	460.41	560.41	660.41	760.41
	v	0.0193	1.2217			1.2711	1.3173	1.3614	1.4045	1.4850	1.5612	1.7428	1.9168	2.0859	2.2512	2.4148	2.5768
	h	418.45	1204.7			1219.8	1235.0	1248.8	1262.3	1286.0	1308.4	1363.0	1416.4	1469.2	1522.2	1575.4	1629.1
390 (442.11)	Sh					17.89	37.89	57.89	77.89	107.89	157.89	257.89	357.89	457.89	557.89	657.89	757.89
	v	0.0193	1.1904			1.2332	1.2788	1.3222	1.3647	1.4436	1.5184	1.6961	1.8661	2.0311	2.1925	2.3521	2.5101
	h	421.27	1204.8			1218.0	1233.4	1247.4	1261.2	1285.1	1307.7	1362.5	1416.0	1468.9	1522.0	1575.2	1628.9
400 (444.58)	Sh					15.42	35.42	55.42	75.42	105.42	155.42	255.42	355.42	455.42	555.42	655.42	755.42
	v	0.0193	1.1609			1.1972	1.2422	1.2849	1.3269	1.4042	1.4777	1.6522	1.8219	1.9796	2.1367	2.2926	2.4475
	h	424.02	1204.9			1216.5	1231.6	1245.9	1259.9	1284.3	1307.0	1362.1	1415.5	1468.6	1521.5	1574.8	1628.8

Sh = superheat, °F.   *v* = specific volume, ft³/lb.   *h* = enthalpy, Btu/lb.

Appendix D

PHYSICAL PROPERTIES OF
VARIOUS ORGANIC AND
INORGANIC SUBSTANCES

General Sources of Data for Tables on the Physical Properties, Heat Capacities,
and Thermodynamic Properties in Appendices D, E, and F

1. Brown, G. G., et al., *Unit Operations*, John Wiley & Sons, Inc., New York, 1956. (Heat capacity; graph for various liquids and gases (p. 587) in Appendix E.)

2. Hodgeman, Charles D., *Handbook of Chemistry and Physics*, 40th ed., Chemical Rubber Publishing Co., Cleveland, 1958.

3. Kobe, Kenneth A., and Associates, "Thermochemistry of Petrochemicals," Reprint from *Petroleum Refiner*, Gulf Publishing Co., Houston, Texas, January, 1949–July, 1958. (Heat capacities of several gases in Table E.1, Appendix E.)

4. Lange, N. A., *Handbook of Chemistry*, 9th ed., Handbook Publishers, Sandusky, Ohio, 1956.

5. Maxwell, J. B., *Data Book on Hydrocarbons*, D. Van Nostrand Company, Inc., Princeton, N.J., 1950.

6. Perry, J. H., ed., *Chemical Engineers' Handbook*, 3rd ed., McGraw-Hill Book Company, New York, 1950.

7. Rossini, Frederick D., et al., "Selected Values of Chemical Thermodynamic Properties," from *National Bureau of Standards Circular* 500, U.S. Government Printing Office, Washington, D.C., 1952.

8. Rossini, Frederick D., et al., "Selected Values of Physical and Thermodynamic Properties of Hydrocarbons and Related Compounds," American Petroleum Institute Research Project 44, Carnegie Institute of Technology, Pittsburgh, 1953.

TABLE D.1 Physical Properties of Various Organic and Inorganic Substances*
Sp Gr = 20°C/4°C Unless Specified. Sp Gr for Gas Referred to Air (A) or Hydrogen (D)

Compound	Formula	Formula wt	Sp gr	Melting temp., °K	ΔH fusion kcal/g mole	Normal b.p., °K	ΔH vap. at b.p. kcal/g mole	T_c °K	p_c atm	V_c cm³/g mole	z_c
Acetaldehyde	C_2H_4O	44.05	$0.783^{18°/4°}$	149.5		293.2		461.0			
Acetic acid	CH_3CHO	60.05	1.049	328.9	2.89	391.4	5.83	594.8	57.1	171	0.200
Acetone	C_3H_6O	58.08	0.791	178.2		329.2		508.0	47.0	213	0.238
Acetylene	C_2H_2	26.04	0.9061(A)	191.7	0.9	191.7	4.2	309.5	61.6	113	0.274
Air			1.000					132.5	37.2		
Ammonia	NH_3	17.03	$0.817^{-79°}$ / 0.597(A)	195.40	1.351	239.73	5.581	405.5	111.3	72.5	0.243
Ammonium carbonate	$(NH_4)_2CO_3 \cdot H_2O$	114.11			(decomposes at 331°K)						
Ammonium chloride	NH_4Cl	53.50	$1.53^{17°}$		(decomposes at 623°K)						
Ammonium nitrate	NH_4NO_3	80.05	$1.725^{25°}$	442.8	1.3	(decomposes at 483.2°K)					
Ammonium sulfate	$(NH_4)_2SO_4$	132.14	1.769	786		(decomposes at 786°K after melting)					
Aniline	C_6H_7N	93.12	1.022	266.9		457.4		699	52.4		
Benzaldehyde	C_6H_5CHO	106.12	1.046	247.16		452.16	9.177				
Benzene	C_6H_6	78.11	0.879	278.693	2.351	353.26	7.353	562.6	48.6	260	0.274
Benzoic acid	$C_7H_6O_2$	122.12	$1.316^{28°/4°}$	395.4		523.0					
Benzyl alcohol	C_7H_8O	108.13	1.045	257.8		478.4					
Boron oxide	B_2O_3	69.64	1.85	723	5.27						
Bromine	Br_2	159.83	$3.119^{20°}$ / 5.87(A)	265.8		331.78		584	102	144	0.306
1,2-Butadiene	C_4H_6	54.09	$0.652^{20°}$	136.7		283.3		446			

*Sources of data are listed at the beginning of Appendix D.

Name	Formula										
1,3-Butadiene	C_4H_6	54.09	0.621	164.1		268.6		425	42.7	221	0.271
Butane	$n\text{-}C_4H_{10}$	58.12	0.579	134.83	1.114	272.66	5.331	425.17	37.47	255	0.274
iso-Butane	$iso\text{-}C_4H_{10}$	58.12	0.557	113.56	1.085	261.43	5.089	408.1	36.0	263	0.283
1-Butene	C_4H_8	56.10	0.60	87.81	0.9197	266.91	5.238	419.6	39.7	240	0.277
Butyl phthalate	see Dibutyl phthalate										
n-Butyric acid	$n\text{-}C_4H_8O_2$	88.10	0.958	267		437.1		628	52.0	290	0.293
iso-Butyric acid	$iso\text{-}C_4H_8O_2$	88.10	0.949	226		427.7		609			
Calcium arsenate	$Ca_3(AsO_4)_2$	398.06		1723							
Calcium carbide	CaC_2	64.10	2.22^{18}	2573							
Calcium carbonate	$CaCO_3$	100.09	2.93	(decomposes at 1098°K)							
Calcium chloride	$CaCl_2$	110.99	2.152^{15}	1055	6.78						
	$CaCl_2 \cdot H_2O$	129.01									
	$CaCl_2 \cdot 2\,H_2O$	147.03									
	$CaCl_2 \cdot 6\,H_2O$	219.09	1.68^{17}	303.4	8.92	$(-6\,H_2O$ at 473°K)					
Calcium cyanamide	$CaCN_2$	80.11	2.29								
Calcium cyanide	$Ca(CN)_2$	92.12									
Calcium hydroxide	$Ca(OH)_2$	74.10	2.24	$(-H_2O$ at 853°K) 2873							
Calcium oxide	CaO	56.08	2.62	2873	12	3123					
Calcium phosphate	$Ca_3(PO_4)_2$	310.19	3.14	1943							
Calcium silicate	$CaSiO_3$	116.17	2.915	1803	11.62						
Calcium sulfate (gypsum)	$CaSO_4 \cdot 2\,H_2O$	172.18	2.32	$(-1\tfrac{1}{2}\,H_2O$ at 301°K) 3873							
Carbon	C	12.010	2.26	4473	11.0		4473				

TABLE D.1 (CONT.)

Compound	Formula	Formula wt	Sp gr	Melting temp., °K	$\Delta\hat{H}$ fusion kcal/g mole	Normal b.p., °K	$\Delta\hat{H}$ vap. at b.p. kcal/g mole	T_c °K	p_c atm	V_c cm³/g mole	z_c
Carbon dioxide	CO_2	44.01	1.53(A)	$217.0^{5.2\,atm}$	1.99	(sublimes at 195°K)		304.2	72.9	94	0.275
Carbon disulfide	CS_2	76.14	$1.261^{22°/20°}$(A) 2.63(A)	161.1	1.05	319.41	6.40	552.0	78.0	170	0.293
Carbon monoxide	CO	28.01	0.968(A)	68.10	0.200	81.66	1.444	133.0	34.5	93	0.294
Carbon tetrachloride	CCl_4	153.84	1.595	250.3	0.60	349.9	7.17	556.4	45.0	276	0.272
Chlorine	Cl_2	70.91	2.49(A)	172.16	1.531	239.10	4.878	417.0	76.1	124	0.276
Chlorobenzene	C_6H_5Cl	112.56	1.107	228		405.26	8.73	632.4	44.6	308	0.265
Chloroform	$CHCl_3$	119.39	$1.489^{20°}$	209.5		334.2		536.0	54.0	240	0.294
Chromium	Cr	52.01	7.1								
Copper	Cu	63.54	8.92	1356.2	3.11	2855	72.8				
Cumene	C_9H_{12}	120.19	0.862	177.125	1.7	425.56	8.97	636	31.0	440	0.260
Cupric sulfate	$CuSO_4$	159.61	$3.606^{15°}$	(decomposes at 873°K)							
Cyclohexane	C_6H_{12}	84.16	0.779	279.83	0.6398	353.90	7.19	553.7	40.4	308	0.274
Cyclopentane	C_5H_{10}	70.13	0.745	179.71	0.1455	322.42	6.524	511.8	44.55	260	0.27
Decane	$C_{10}H_{22}$	142.28	$0.730^{20°}$	243.3		447.0		619.0	20.8	602	0.2476
Dibutyl phthalate	$C_8H_{22}O_4$	278.34	$1.045^{21°}$			613					
Diethyl ether	$(C_2H_5)_2O$	74.12	$0.708^{25°}$	156.86	1.745	307.76	6.226	467	35.6	281	0.261
Ethane	C_2H_6	30.07	1.049(A)	89.89	0.6834	184.53	3.517	305.4	48.2	148	0.285
Ethanol	C_2H_6O	46.07	0.789	158.6	1.200	351.7	9.22	516.3	63.0	167	0.248
Ethyl acetate	$C_4H_8O_2$	88.10	0.901	189.4		350.2		523.1	37.8	286	0.252
Ethyl benzene	C_8H_{10}	106.16	0.867	178.185	2.190	409.35	8.60	619.7	37.0	360	0.260
Ethyl bromide	C_2H_5Br	108.98	1.460	154.1		311.4		504	61.5	215	0.320

Name	Formula										
Ethyl chloride	CH_3CH_2Cl	64.52	$0.9030^{10°}$	134.83	1.064	285.43	5.9	460.4	52.0	199	0.274
3-Ethyl hexane	C_8H_{18}	114.22	0.7169			391.69	8.19	567.0	26.4	466	0.264
Ethylene	C_2H_4	28.05	0.975(A)	103.97	0.8008	169.45	3.237	283.1	50.5	124	0.270
Ethylene glycol	$C_2H_6O_2$	62.07	$1.113^{19°}$	260	2.685	470.4	13.6				
Ferric oxide	Fe_2O_3	159.70	5.12	1833		(decomposes at 1833°K)					
Ferrous sulfide	Fe_2S_3	207.90	4.3								
	FeS	87.92	4.84	1466		(decomposes)					
Formaldehyde	H_2CO	30.03	$0.815^{-20°}$	154.9		253.9	5.85				
Formic acid	CH_2O_2	46.03	1.220	281.46	3.03	373.7	5.32				
Glycerol	$C_3H_8O_3$	92.09	$1.260^{50°}$	291.36	4.373	563.2					
Helium	He	4.00	0.1368(A)	3.5	0.005	4.216	0.020	5.26	2.26	58	0.304
Heptane	C_7H_{16}	100.20	0.684	182.57	3.354	371.59	7.575	540.2	27.0	426	0.260
Hexane	C_6H_{14}	86.17	0.659	177.84	3.114	341.90	6.896	507.9	29.9	368	0.264
Hydrogen	H_2	2.016	0.06948(A)	13.96	0.028	20.39	0.216	33.3	12.8	65	0.304
Hydrogen chloride	HCl	36.47	1.268(A)	158.94	0.476	188.11	3.86	324.6	81.5	87	0.266
Hydrogen fluoride	HF	20.01	1.15	238		393		503.2			
Hydrogen sulfide	H_2S	34.08	1.1895(A)	187.63	0.568	212.82	4.463	373.6	88.9	98	0.284
Iodine	I_2	253.8	$4.93^{20°}$	386.5		457.4		826.0			
Iron	Fe	55.85	7.7	1808	3.6	3073	84.6				
Iron oxide	Fe_3O_4	231.55	5.2	1867	33.0	(decomposes at 1867° after melting)					
Lead	Pb	207.21	$11.337^{20°}$	600.6	1.22	2023	43.0				
Lead oxide	PbO	223.21	9.5	1159	2.8	1745	51				
Magnesium	Mg	24.32	1.74	923	2.2	1393	31.5				
Magnesium chloride	$MgCl_2$	95.23	$2.325^{25°}$	987	10.3	1691	32.7				
Magnesium hydroxide	$Mg(OH)_2$	58.34	2.4	(decomposes at 623°K)							
Magnesium oxide	MgO	40.32	3.65	3173	18.5	3873					

TABLE D.1 (CONT.)

Compound	Formula	Formula wt	Sp gr	Melting temp., °K	$\Delta \hat{H}$ fusion kcal/g mole	Normal b.p., °K	$\Delta \hat{H}$ vap. at b.p. kcal/g mole	T_c °K	P_c atm	V_c cm³/g mole	z_c
Mercury	Hg	200.61	13.546^{20}								
Methane	CH_4	16.04	0.554(A)	90.68	0.225	111.67	1.955	190.7	45.8	99	0.290
Methanol	CH_3OH	32.04	0.792	175.26	0.757	337.9	8.43	513.2	78.5	118	0.222
Methyl acetate	$C_3H_6O_2$	74.08	0.933	174.3		330.3		506.7	46.3	228	0.254
Methyl amine	CH_5N	31.06	$0.699^{-11°}$	180.5		266.3^{758mm}		429.9	73.6		
Methyl chloride	CH_3Cl	50.49	1.785(A)	175.3		249		416.1	65.8	143	0.276
Methyl ethyl ketone	C_4H_8O	72.10	0.805	186.1		352.6					
Methyl cyclohexane	C_7H_{14}	98.18	0.769	146.58	1.6134	374.10	7.58	572.2	34.32	344	0.251
Molybdenum	Mo	95.95	10.2								
Napthalene	$C_{10}H_8$	128.16	1.145	353.2		491.0					
Nickel	Ni	58.69	8.90^{20}								
Nitric acid	HNO_3	63.02	1.502	231.56	2.503	359	7.241				
Nitrobenzene	$C_6H_5O_2N$	123.11	1.203	278.7		483.9					
Nitrogen	N_2	28.02	12.5(D)	63.15	0.172	77.34	1.333	126.2	33.5	90	0.291
Nitrogen dioxide	NO_2	46.01	1.448	263.86	1.753	294.46	3.520	431.0	100.0	82	0.232
Nitrogen oxide	NO	30.01	1.0367(A)	109.51	0.550	121.39	3.293	179.2	65.0	58	0.256
Nitrogen pentoxide	N_2O_5	108.02	1.63^{18}	303		320					
Nitrogen tetraoxide	N_2O_4	92	$1.448^{20°}$	263.7		294.3		431.0	99.0		
Nitrogen trioxide	N_2O_3	76.02	$1.447^{2°}$	171		276.5					

440

Substance	Formula										
Nitrous oxide	N_2O	44.02	$1.226^{-89°}$ / 1.530(A)	182.1		184.4		309.5	71.7	96.3	0.272
n-Nonane	C_9H_{20}	128.25	0.718	219.4		423.8		595	23		
n-Octane	C_8H_{18}	114.22	0.703	216.2		398.7		595.0	22.5	543	0.250
Oxalic acid	$C_2H_2O_4$	90.04	1.90	(decomposes at 459°K)							
Oxygen	O_2	32.00	1.1053(A)	54.40	0.106	90.19	1.630	154.4	49.7	74	0.290
n-Pentane	C_5H_{12}	72.15	0.6301^{18}	143.49	2.006	309.23	6.160	469.8	33.3	311	0.269
iso-Pentane	iso-C_5H_{12}	72.15	$0.6219°$	113.1		300.9		461.0	32.9	308	0.268
1-Pentane	C_5H_{10}	70.13	0.641	107.96	1.180	303.13		474	39.9		
Phenol	C_6H_5OH	94.11	$1.071^{25°}$	315.66	2.732	454.56		692.1	60.5		
Phenyl hydrazine	$C_6H_8N_2$	108.14	$1.097^{23°}$	292.76	3.927	516.66					
Phosphoric acid	H_3PO_4	98.00	$1.834^{18°}$	315.51	2.52	$(-\tfrac{1}{2} H_2O$ at 486°K)					
Phosphorus (red)	P_4	123.90	2.20	863	19.40	863	10.00				
Phosphorus (white)	P_4	123.90	1.82	317.4	0.60	553	11.88				
Phosphorus pentoxide	P_2O_5	141.95	2.387	(sublimes at 523°K)							
Propane	C_3H_8	44.09	1.562(A)	85.47	0.8422	231.09	4.487	369.9	42.0	200	0.277
Propene	C_3H_6	42.08	1.498(A)	87.91	0.7176	225.46	4.402	365.1	45.4	181	0.274
Propionic acid	$C_3H_6O_2$	74.08	0.993	252.2		414.4		612.5	53.0		
n-Propyl alcohol	C_3H_8O	60.09	0.804	146		370.2		536.7	49.95	220	0.251
iso-Propyl alcohol	C_3H_8O	60.09	0.785	183.5		355.4		508.8	53.0	219	0.278
n-Propyl benzene	C_9H_{12}	120.19	0.862	173.660	2.04	432.38		638.7	31.3	429	0.257
Silicon dioxide	SiO_2	60.09	2.25	1883	2.04	2503	9.14				
Sodium bisulfate	$NaHSO_4$	120.07	2.742	455							
Sodium carbonate (sal soda)	$Na_2CO_3 \cdot 10\,H_2O$	286.15	1.46	306.5		$(-H_2O$ at 306.5°K)					
Sodium carbonate (soda ash)	Na_2CO_3	105.99	2.533	1127	8.0	(decomposes)					

TABLE D.1 (CONT.)

Compound	Formula	Formula wt	Sp gr	Melting temp., °K	$\Delta \hat{H}$ fusion kcal/g mole	Normal b.p., °K	$\Delta \hat{H}$ vap. at b.p. kcal/g mole	T_c °K	p_c atm	V_c cm³/g mole	z_c
Sodium chloride	NaCl	58.45	2.163	1081	6.8	1738	40.8				
Sodium cyanide	NaCN	49.01		835	4.0	1770	37				
Sodium nitrate	NaNO₃	85.00	2.257	583	3.8	(decomposes at 653°K)					
Sodium nitrite	NaNO₂	69.00	2.168°	544		(decomposes at 593°K)					
Sodium sulfate	Na₂SO₄	142.05	2.698	1163	5.8						
Sodium sulfide	Na₂S	78.05	1.856	1223	1.6						
Sodium sulfite	Na₂SO₃	126.05	2.633¹⁵°	(decomposes)							
Sodium thiosulfate	Na₂S₂O₃	158.11	1.667								
Sulfur (rhombic)	S₈	256.53	2.07	386	2.40	717.76	20.0				
Sulfur (monoclinic)	S₈	256.53	1.96	392	3.386	717.76	20.0				
Sulfur chloride (mono)	S₂Cl₂	135.05	1.687	193.0		411.2	8.61				
Sulfur dioxide	SO₂	64.07	2.264(A)	197.68	1.769	263.14	5.955	430.7	77.8	122	0.269
Sulfur trioxide	SO₃	80.07	2.75(A)	290.0	6.09	316.5	9.99	491.4	83.8	126	0.262
Sulfuric acid	H₂SO₄	98.08	1.834¹⁸°	283.51	2.36	(decomposes at 613°K)					
Toluene	C₆H₅CH₃	92.13	0.866	178.169	1.582	383.78	8.00	593.9	40.3	318	0.263
Water	H₂O	18.016	1.00⁴°	273.16	1.4363	373.16	9.7171	647.4	218.3	56	0.230
m-Xylene	C₈H₁₀	106.16	0.864	225.288	2.765	412.26	8.70	619	34.6	390	0.27
o-Xylene	C₈H₁₀	106.16	0.880	247.978	3.250	417.58	8.80	631.5	35.7	380	0.26
p-Xylene	C₈H₁₀	106.16	0.861	286.423	4.090	411.51	8.62	618	33.9	370	0.25
Zinc	Zn	65.38	7.140	692.7	1.595	1180	27.43				
Zinc sulfate	ZnSO₄	161.44	3.74¹⁵°	(decomposes at 1013°K)							

Appendix E

HEAT CAPACITY DATA

TABLE E.1 HEAT CAPACITY EQUATIONS FOR ORGANIC AND INORGANIC COMPOUNDS*

Units: cal/(g mole)(°K or °C); Btu/(lb mole)(°R or °F)

Forms:
1. $C_p° = a + b(t) + c(t)^2 + d(t)^3$
2. $C_p° = a + b(t) + c(t)^{-2}$
3. $C_p° = a + b(t) + c(t)^{-1/2}$

Compound	Formula	Mol. wt	State	Form	T	a	$b \cdot 10^2$	$c \cdot 10^5$	$d \cdot 10^9$	Range, °K
Acetone	CH_3COCH_3	58.08	g	1	°C	17.20	4.805	-3.056	8.307	0-1200
Acetylene	C_2H_2	26.04	g	1	°C	10.14	1.4468	-1.203	4.349	0-1200
			g	1	°F	9.89	0.8273	-0.3783	0.7457	32-2200
Air			g	1	°C	6.917	0.09911	0.07627	-0.4696	0-1500
			g	1	°K	6.713	0.04697	0.1147	-0.4696	273-1800
			g	1	°F	6.900	0.02884	0.02429	-0.08052	32-2700
			g	1	°R	6.713	0.02609	0.03540	-0.08052	492-3200
Ammonia	NH_3	17.03	g	1	°C	8.4017	0.70601	0.10567	-1.5981	0-1200
			g	1	°F	8.2765	0.39006	0.035245	-0.2740	32-2200
Ammonium sulfate	$(NH_4)_2SO_4$	132.15	c	1	°K	51.6	5.58			275-328
Benzene	C_6H_6	78.11	l	1	°K	14.95				279-350
			g	1	°C	17.700	7.875	-6.022	18.54	0-1200
Boron oxide	B_2O_3	69.64	l	1	°F	16.332	4.493	-1.888	3.179	32-2200
iso-Butane	C_4H_{10}	58.12	g	1	°C	21.382	7.202	-4.519	11.92	0-1200
n-Butane	C_4H_{10}	58.12	g	1	°C	22.060	6.663	-3.697	8.360	0-1200
iso-Butene	C_4H_8	56.10	g	1	°C	19.810	6.128	-4.127	12.07	0-1200
Calcium carbide	CaC_2	64.10	c	2	°K	16.40	0.284	-2.07×10^{10}		298-720
Calcium carbonate	$CaCO_3$	100.09	c	2	°K	19.68	1.189	-3.076×10^{10}		273-1033
Calcium hydroxide	$Ca(OH)_2$	74.10	c	1	°K	21.4				276-373
Calcium oxide	CaO	56.08	c	2	°K	10.00	0.484	-1.08×10^{10}		273-1173
Carbon	C	12.01	c^a	2	°K	2.673	0.2617	-1.169×10^{10}		273-1373
Carbon dioxide	CO_2	44.01	g	3	°K	18.036	-0.004474	-1.5808×10^7		273-3700

* Sources of data are listed at the beginning of Appendix D.

a Graphite.

444

Name	Formula	Mol. wt.	State	n	Temp. unit	a	b	c	d	Temp. range
Carbon monoxide	CO	28.01	g	1	°C	6.890	0.1436	−0.02387		0–3500
Carbon tetrachloride	CCl₄	153.84	1	1	°K	22.32	3.103			273–343
Chlorine	Cl₂	70.91	g	1	°C	8.031	0.3267	−0.3840	1.547	0–1200
Copper	Cu	63.54	c	1	°K	5.44	0.1462			273–1357
Cumene (isopropyl benzene)	C₆H₅CH(CH₃)₂	120.19	1	1	°F	50.48				50
					°F	64.91				300
Cyclohexane	C₆H₁₂	84.16	g	1	°C	33.280	12.850	−9.510	28.80	0–1200
			1		°F	37.05				50
					°F	41.26				150
			g		°C	22.500	11.860	−7.625	19.27	0–1200
Cyclopentane	C₅H₁₀	70.13	1	1	°F	30.84				50
					°F	32.95				100
			g		°C	17.540	9.388	−6.103	16.41	0–1200
Ethane	C₂H₆	30.07	g	1	°C	11.800	3.326	−1.390	1.740	0–1200
Ethyl alcohol	C₂H₆O	46.07	1	1	°C	24.65				0
					°C	37.96				100
Ethylene	C₂H₄	28.05	g	1	°C	14.66	3.758	−2.091	4.740	0–1200
			g		°C	9.740	2.741	−1.647	4.220	0–1200
Ferric oxide	Fe₂O₃	159.70	c	2	°K	24.72	1.604	-4.234×10^{10}		273–1097
Formaldehyde	H₂CO	30.03	g	1	°C	8.192	1.020	0.0000	−2.078	0–1200
Helium	He	4.00	g	1	°K	4.97				All
n-Hexane	C₆H₁₄	86.17	1	1	°C	51.702				20–100
			g		°C	32.850	9.763	−5.716	13.78	0–1200
Hydrogen	H₂	2.016	g	1	°C	6.702	0.0996	−0.007804		0–3500
Hydrogen bromide	HBr	80.92	g	1	°C	6.954	−0.00542	0.2363		0–1200
Hydrogen chloride	HCl	36.47	g	1	°C	6.962	−0.03206	0.2322	−1.161	0–1200
Hydrogen cyanide	HCN	27.03	g	1	°C	8.43	0.6950	−0.2611	−1.036	0–1200
Hydrogen sulfide	H₂S	34.08	g	1	°C	8.010	0.3697	0.07200	−0.7867	0–1500
Magnesium chloride	MgCl₂	95.23	c	1	°K	17.3	0.377			273–991
Magnesium oxide	MgO	40.32	c	2	°K	10.86	0.1197	-2.087×10^{10}		273–2073

TABLE E.1 (CONT.)

Compound	Formula	Mol. wt	State	Form	T	a	$b \cdot 10^2$	$c \cdot 10^5$	$d \cdot 10^9$	Range, °K
Methane	CH_4	16.04	g	1	°C	8.200	1.307	0.08750	-2.630	0–1200
			g	1	°K	4.750	1.200	0.3030	-2.630	273–1500
Methyl alcohol	CH_3OH	32.04	l	1	°C	18.13				0
						19.74				40
Methyl cyclohexane	C_7H_{14}	98.18	g	1	°C	10.26	1.984	-0.448	-1.92	0–700
			l	1	°F	45.17				50
					°F	53.03				200
Methyl cyclopentane	C_6H_{12}	84.16	g	1	°C	29.000	13.510	-9.016	24.09	0–1200
			l	1	°F	38.31				50
					°F	42.52				150
Nitric acid	HNO_3	63.02	g	1	°C	23.620	10.960	-7.275	20.03	0–1200
			l	1	°C	26.28				25
Nitric oxide	NO	30.01	g	1	°C	7.050	0.1957	-0.06990	0.08729	0–3500
Nitrogen	N_2	28.02	g	1	°C	6.919	0.1365	-0.02271		0–3500
			g	1	°K	6.529	0.1488	-0.02271		273–3700
Nitrogen dioxide	NO_2	46.01	g	1	°C	8.62	0.948	-0.688	1.88	0–1200
Nitrogen tetraoxide	N_2O_4	92.02	g	1	°C	18.1	2.98	-2.71		0–300
Nitrous oxide	N_2O	44.02	g	1	°C	9.000	0.9921	-0.6438	2.526	0–1200
Oxygen	O_2	32.00	g	1	°C	7.129	0.1407	-0.01791		0–3500
			g	1	°K	6.732	0.1505	-0.01791		273–3700
n-Pentane	C_5H_{12}	72.15		1	°F	38.21				50
						39.66				75
Propane	C_3H_8	44.09	g	1	°C	27.450	8.148	-4.538	10.10	0–1200
Propene	C_3H_6	42.08	g	1	°C	16.260	5.398	-3.134	7.580	0–1200
Sodium carbonate	Na_2CO_3	105.99	c	1	°C	14.240	4.233	-2.430	5.880	0–1200
					°K	28.9				288–371
Sodium carbonate	$Na_2CO_3 \cdot 10 H_2O$	286.15	c	1	°K	128.0				298
Sulfur	S	32.07	c[b]	1	°K	3.63	0.640			273–368
			c[c]	1	°K	4.38	0.440			368–392

Substance	Formula									
Sulfuric acid	H_2SO_4	1	1	98.08	°C	33.25	3.727	−0.7418		10-45
Sulfur dioxide	SO_2	g	1	64.07	°C	9.299	0.9330		2.057	0-1500
Sulfur trioxide	SO_3	g	1	80.07	°C	11.591	2.196	−2.041	7.744	0-1000
Toluene	$C_6H_5 \cdot CH_3$	1	1	92.13	°C	35.56				0
						43.30				100
		g			°C	22.509	9.292	−6.658	19.20	0-1200
			1		°F	20.869	5.293	−2.086	3.292	32-2200
Water	H_2O	g	1	18.016	°C	7.880	0.3200	−0.04833		0-3500

b Rhombic.

c Monoclinic.

447

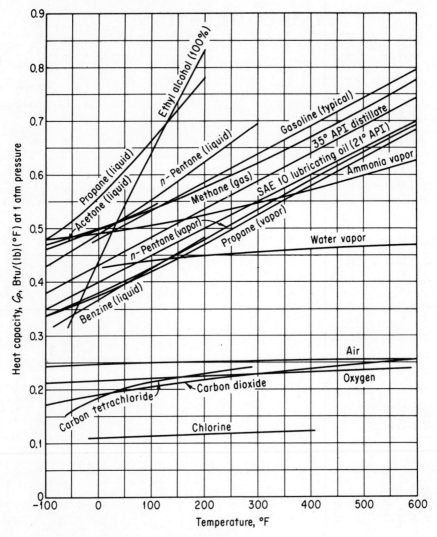

Source: Reference 1 in Appendix D.

Fig. E.1. Heat capacities of liquids and gases at one atmosphere.

HEATS OF FORMATION
AND COMBUSTION

TABLE F.1 HEATS OF FORMATION AND HEATS OF COMBUSTION OF COMPOUNDS AT 25°C*
Standard States of Products for $\Delta \hat{H}_c^\circ$ Are: $CO_2(g)$, $H_2O(l)$, $N_2(g)$, $SO_2(g)$, and $HCl(aq)$

Compound	Formula	Mol. wt	State	$-\Delta \hat{H}_f^\circ$ kcal/g mole	$-\Delta \hat{H}_c^\circ$ kcal/g mole
Acetic acid	CH_3COOH	60.05	l	97.800	208.34
			g		219.82
Acetaldethyde	CH_3CHO	40.052	g	39.76	284.980
Acetone	C_3H_6O	58.08	aq, 200	98.000	
			g	51.790	435.320
Acetylene	C_2H_2	26.04	g	−54.194	310.615
Ammonia	NH_3	17.032	l	16.06	
			g	11.040	91.440
Ammonium carbonate	$(NH_4)_2CO_3$	96.09	c	225.11	
			aq		
Ammonium chloride	NH_4Cl	53.50	c	75.38	
Ammonium hydroxide	NH_4OH	35.05	aq	87.59	
Ammonium nitrate	NH_4NO_3	80.05	c	87.27	
			aq	81.11	
Ammonium sulfate	$(NH_4)_2SO_4$	132.15	c	281.86	
			aq	280.38	
Benzaldehyde	C_6H_5CHO	106.12	l	21.23	
			g	9.57	
Benzene	C_6H_6	78.11	l	−11.63	780.98
			g	−19.820	789.08
Boron oxide	B_2O_3	69.64	c	302.0	
			l	297.6	
Bromine	Br_2	159.832	l	0	
			g	−7.340	
n-Butane	C_4H_{10}	58.12	l	35.29	682.51
			g	29.812	687.982

* Sources of data are given at the beginning of Appendix D, References 3, 6, and 7.

Isobutane	C$_4$H$_{10}$	58.12	l	37.87	680.93
			g	32.15	685.65
1-Butene	C$_4$H$_8$	56.104	g	−0.280	649.757
Calcium arsenate	Ca$_3$(AsO$_4$)$_2$	398.06	c	796.0	
Calcium carbide	CaC$_2$	64.10	c	15.0	
Calcium carbonate	CaCO$_3$	100.09	c	288.45	
Calcium chloride	CaCl$_2$	110.99	c	190.0	
Calcium cyanamide	CaCN$_2$	80.11	c	84.0	
Calcium hydroxide	Ca(OH)$_2$	74.10	c	235.80	
Calcium oxide	CaO	56.08	c	151.9	
Calcium phosphate	Ca$_3$(PO$_4$)$_2$	310.19	c	988.9	
Calcium silicate	CaSiO$_3$	116.17	c	378.6	
Calcium sulfate	CaSO$_4$	136.15	c	342.42	
			aq	346.67	
Calcium sulfate (gypsum)	CaSO$_4$·2 H$_2$O	172.18	c	483.06	
Carbon	C	12.01	c graphite (β)	0	94.052
Carbon dioxide	CO$_2$	44.01	g	94.052	
			l	98.69	
Carbon disulfide	CS$_2$	76.14	l	−21.0	256.97
			g	−27.55	263.52
Carbon monoxide	CO	28.01	g	26.416	67.636
Carbon tetrachloride	CCl$_4$	153.838	l	33.34	84.17
			g	25.500	92.01
Chloroethane	C$_2$H$_5$Cl	64.52	g	25.1	339.66
Cumene (isopropylbenzene)	C$_6$H$_5$CH(CH$_3$)$_2$	120.19	l	9.848	1246.52
			g	−0.940	1257.31
Cupric sulfate	CuSO$_4$	159.61	c	184.00	
			aq	201.51	
Cyclohexane	C$_6$H$_{12}$	84.16	l	37.34	936.88
			g	29.43	944.79
Cyclopentane	C$_5$H$_{10}$	70.130	l	25.30	786.54
			g	18.46	793.39

Table F.1 (Cont.)

Compound	Formula	Mol. wt	State	$-\Delta \hat{H}_f^\circ$ kcal/g mole	$-\Delta \hat{H}_c^\circ$ kcal/g mole
Ethane	C_2H_6	30.07	g	20.236	372.82
Ethyl alcohol	C_2H_5OH	46.068	l	66.356	326.700
			g	56.24	336.820
Ethyl benzene	$C_6H_5 \cdot C_2H_5$	106.16	g	2.977	1091.03
			l	−7.120	1101.13
Ethyl chloride	C_2H_5Cl	64.52	g	−25.1	
Ethylene	C_2H_4	28.052	g	−12.496	337.234
Ethylene chloride	C_2H_3Cl	62.50	g	−7.500	303.90
3-Ethyl hexane	C_8H_{18}	114.22	l	59.88	1307.39
			g	50.40	1316.87
Ferric oxide	Fe_2O_3	159.70	c	196.5	
Ferric sulfide	FeS_2	see Iron sulfide			
Ferrosoferric oxide	Fe_3O_4	231.55	c	267.0	
Ferrous oxide	FeO	71.85	c	63.7	
Ferrous sulfide	FeS	87.92	c	22.72	
Formaldehyde	H_2CO	30.026	g	27.700	134.670
n-Heptane	C_7H_{16}	100.20	l	53.63	1151.27
			g	44.89	1160.01
n-Hexane	C_6H_{14}	86.17	l	47.52	995.01
			g	39.96	1002.570
Hydrogen	H_2	2.016	g	0	68.317
Hydrogen bromide	HBr	80.924	g	8.660	
Hydrogen chloride	HCl	36.465	g	22.063	
Hydrogen cyanide	HCN	27.026	g	−31.200	
Hydrogen sulfide	H_2S	34.082	g	−4.815	134.462
Iron sulfide	FeS_2	119.98	c	42.52	
Lead oxide	PbO	223.21	c	52.40	
Magnesium chloride	$MgCl_2$	95.23	c	153.40	

452

Compound	Formula		State		
Magnesium hydroxide	Mg(OH)$_2$	58.34	c	221.00	
Magnesium oxide	MgO	40.32	c	143.84	
Methane	CH$_4$	16.041	g	17.889	212.80
Methyl alcohol	CH$_3$OH	32.042	l	57.036	173.650
			g	48.100	182.590
Methyl chloride	CH$_3$Cl	50.49	g	19.580	183.23*
Methyl cyclohexane	C$_7$H$_{14}$	98.182	l	45.45	1091.13
			g	36.99	1099.59
Methyl cyclopentane	C$_6$H$_{12}$	84.156	l	33.07	941.14
			g	25.50	948.72
Nitric acid	HNO$_3$	63.02	l	41.404	
			aq	49.372	
Nitric oxide	NO	30.01	g	−21.600	
Nitrogen dioxide	NO$_2$	46.01	g	−8.091	
Nitrous oxide	N$_2$O	44.02	g	−19.49	
n-Pentane	C$_5$H$_{12}$	72.15	l	41.36	838.80
			g	35.00	845.160
Phosphoric acid	H$_3$PO$_4$	98.00	c	306.2	
			aq (1 H$_2$O)	305.6	
Phosphorus	P$_4$	123.90	c	0	
Phosphorus pentoxide	P$_2$O$_5$	141.95	c	360.0	
Propane	C$_3$H$_8$	44.09	l	28.643	526.78
			g	24.820	530.60
Propene	C$_3$H$_6$	42.078	g	−4.879	491.987
n-Propyl alcohol	C$_3$H$_8$O	60.09	g	61.0	494.40
n-Propylbenzene	C$_6$H$_5$·CH$_2$·C$_2$H$_5$	120.19	l	9.178	1247.19
			g	−1.870	1258.24
Silicon dioxide	SiO$_2$	60.09	c	203.4	
Sodium bicarbonate	NaHCO$_3$	84.01	c	226.0	
Sodium bisulfate	NaHSO$_4$	120.07	c	269.2	
Sodium carbonate	Na$_2$CO$_3$	105.99	c	270.3	
Sodium chloride	NaCl	58.45	c	98.232	

* Standard state HCl(g).

TABLE F.1 (CONT.).

Compound	Formula	Mol. wt	State	$-\Delta \hat{H}_f^\circ$ kcal/g mole	$-\Delta \hat{H}_c^\circ$ kcal/g mole
Sodium cyanide	$NaCN$	49.01	c	21.46	
Sodium nitrate	$NaNO_3$	85.00	c	111.54	
Sodium nitrite	$NaNO_2$	69.00	c	85.9	
Sodium sulfate	Na_2SO_4	142.05	c	330.90	
Sodium sulfide	Na_2S	78.05	c	89.2	
Sodium sulfite	Na_2SO_3	126.05	c	260.6	
Sodium thiosulfate	$Na_2S_2O_3$	158.11	c	267.0	
Sulfur	S	32.07	(rhombic) c	0	
			(monoclinic) c	-0.071	
Sulfur chloride	S_2Cl_2	135.05	l	14.4	
Sulfur dioxide	SO_2	64.066	g	70.960	
Sulfur trioxide	SO_3	80.066	g	94.450	
Sulfuric acid	H_2SO_4	98.08	l	193.91	
			aq	216.90	
Toluene	$C_6H_5 \cdot CH_3$	92.13	l	-2.867	934.50
			g	-11.950	943.58
Water	H_2O	18.016	l	68.3174	
			g	57.7979	
m-Xylene	$C_6H_4(CH_3)_2$	106.16	l	6.075	1087.92
			g	-4.120	1098.12
o-Xylene	$C_6H_4(CH_3)_2$	106.16	l	5.841	1088.16
			g	-4.540	1098.54
p-Xylene	$C_6H_4(CH_3)_2$	106.16	l	5.838	1088.16
			g	-4.290	1098.29
Zinc sulfate	$ZnSO_4$	161.45	c	233.88	
			aq	253.33	

Appendix G

VAPOR PRESSURES

TABLE G.1 VAPOR PRESSURES OF VARIOUS SUBSTANCES

Antoine equation:

$$\log_{10} p^* = A - \frac{B}{C + t}$$

where p^* = vapor pressure in mm Hg
t = temperature in °C
A, B, C = constants

Name	Formula	Range, °C	A	B	C
Acetic acid	$C_2H_4O_2$	0 to 36	7.80307	1651.2	225
		36 to 170	7.18807	1416.7	211
Acetone	C_3H_6O	—	7.02447	1161.0	224
Ammonia	NH_3	−83 to +60	7.55466	1002.711	247.885
Benzene	C_6H_6	—	6.90565	1211.033	220.790
Carbon disulfide	CS_2	−10 to +160	6.85145	1122.50	236.46
Ethyl acetate	$C_4H_8O_2$	−20 to +150	7.09808	1238.71	217.0
Ethyl alcohol	C_2H_6O	—	8.04494	1554.3	222.65
Ethyl bromide	C_2H_5Br	−50 to +130	6.89285	1083.8	231.7
n-Heptane	C_7H_{16}	—	6.90240	1268.115	216.900
Methyl alcohol	CH_4O	−20 to +140	7.87863	1473.11	230.0
Sulfur dioxide	SO_2	—	7.32776	1022.80	240
Toluene	C_7H_8	—	6.95464	1344.800	219.482

Source: N. A. Lange et al., *Lange's Handbook of Chemistry*, 9th ed., Handbook Publishers, Inc., Sandusky, Ohio, 1956.

Appendix H

HEATS OF SOLUTION AND DILUTION

TABLE H.1 INTEGRAL HEATS OF SOLUTION AND DILUTION AT 25°C

Formula	Description			State	$-\Delta\hat{H}_f^\circ$ kcal/mole	$-\Delta\hat{H}_{soln}^\circ$ kcal/mole	$-\Delta\hat{H}_{dil}^\circ$ kcal/mole
HCl				g	22.063		
	in	1	H_2O	aq	28.331	6.268	6.268
		2		aq	33.731	11.668	5.400
		3		aq	35.651	13.588	1.920
		4		aq	36.691	14.628	1.040
		5		aq	37.371	15.308	0.680
		10		aq	38.671	16.608	1.300
		20		aq	39.218	17.155	0.547
		30		aq	39.413	17.350	0.195
		40		aq	39.516	17.448	0.098
		50		aq	39.577	17.509	0.061
		100		aq	39.713	17.650	0.141
		200		aq	39.798	17.735	0.085
		300		aq	39.837	17.774	0.039
		400		aq	39.859	17.796	0.022
		500		aq	39.874	17.811	0.015
		700		aq	39.895	17.832	0.021
		1000		aq	39.913	17.850	0.018
		2000		aq	39.946	17.883	0.033
		3000		aq	39.960	17.897	0.014
		4000		aq	39.968	17.905	0.108
		5000		aq	39.972	17.909	0.004
		7000		aq	39.982	17.919	0.010
		10,000		aq	39.987	17.924	0.005
		20,000		aq	39.998	17.935	0.011
		50,000		aq	40.007	17.944	0.009
		100,000		aq	40.012	17.949	0.005
		∞		aq	40.023	17.960	0.011
NaOH			crystalline, II		101.99		
	in	3	H_2O	aq	108.894	6.90	6.90
		4		aq	110.219	8.23	1.33
		5		aq	111.015	9.02	0.79
		10		aq	112.148	10.16	1.14
		20		aq	112.235	10.24	0.08
		30		30	112.203	10.21	−0.03
		40		aq	112.175	10.18	−0.03
		50		aq	112.154	10.16	−0.02
		100		aq	112.108	10.12	−0.04
		200		aq	112.1	10.10	−0.02
		300		aq	112.105	10.11	0.01
		500		aq	112.117	10.13	0.02

TABLE H.1 (CONT.)

Formula	Description		State	$-\Delta \hat{H}_f^\circ$ kcal/mole	$-\Delta \hat{H}_{soln}^\circ$ kcal/mole	$-\Delta \hat{H}_{dil}^\circ$ kcal/mole
	1000		aq	112.139	10.15	0.02
	2000		aq	112.162	10.17	0.02
	5000		aq	112.186	10.20	0.03
	10,000		aq	112.201	10.21	0.01
	50,000		aq	112.220	10.23	0.02
	∞		aq	112.236	10.25	0.02
H_2SO_4			liq	193.91		
	in	0.5 H_2O	aq	197.67	3.76	3.76
		1.0	aq	200.62	6.71	2.95
		1.5	aq	202.73	8.82	2.11
		2	aq	203.93	10.02	1.20
		3	aq	205.62	11.71	1.69
		4	aq	206.83	12.92	1.21
		5	aq	207.78	13.87	0.95
		10	aq	209.93	16.02	2.15
		25	aq	211.19	17.28	1.26
		50	aq	211.44	17.53	0.25
		100	aq	211.59	17.68	0.15
		500	aq	212.25	18.34	0.66
		1000	aq	212.69	18.78	0.44
		5000	aq	214.09	20.18	1.40
		10,000	aq	214.72	20.81	0.63
		100,000	aq	216.29	22.38	1.57
		500,000	aq	216.69	22.78	0.40
		∞	aq	216.90	22.99	0.21

Source: F. D. Rossini, et al., "Selected Values of Chem. Thermo. Properties," *Natl. Bur. Std. Circ.* 500, U.S. Government Printing Office, Washington, D.C., 1952.

Appendix I

ENTHALPY-CONCENTRATION DATA

TABLE I.1 ENTHALPY-CONCENTRATION DATA FOR THE SINGLE-PHASE LIQUID REGION AND ALSO THE SATURATED VAPOR OF THE ACETIC ACID-WATER SYSTEM AT ONE ATMOSPHERE

Liquid or vapor		Enthalpy—Btu/lb liquid solution						Enthalpy saturated vapor Btu/lb
Mole fraction water	Weight fraction water	20°C 68°F	40°C 104°F	80°C 140°F	80°C 176°F	100°C 212°F	Satu- rated liquid	
0.00	0.00	93.54	111.4	129.9	149.1	169.0	187.5	361.8
0.05	0.01555	93.96	112.2	130.9	150.4	170.6	186.9	
0.10	0.03225	93.82	112.3	131.5	151.3	172.0	186.5	374.6
0.20	0.0698	92.61	111.9	131.7	152.2	173.8	185.2	395.3
0.30	0.1140	90.60	110.7	131.3	152.6	175.0	183.8	423.7
0.40	0.1667	87.84	108.9	130.6	152.9	176.1	182.9	461.4
0.50	0.231	83.96	106.3	129.1	152.7	177.1	182.4	510.5
0.55	0.268	81.48	104.5	128.1	152.5	177.5	182.3	
0.60	0.3105	78.53	102.5	126.9	152.1	178.0	182.0	573.4
0.65	0.358	75.36	100.2	125.5	151.6	178.3	181.9	
0.70	0.412	71.72	97.71	123.9	151.1	178.8	181.7	656.0
0.75	0.474	67.59	94.73	122.2	149.9	179.3	182.1	
0.80	0.545	62.88	91.43	120.2	149.7	179.9	181.6	767.3
0.85	0.630	57.44	87.56	117.8	148.9	180.5	181.6	
0.90	0.730	51.03	83.02	115.1	147.8	180.8	181.7	921.6
0.95	0.851	43.74	77.65	111.7	146.4	181.2	181.5	
1.00	1.00	36.06	71.91	107.7	143.9	180.1	180.1	1150.4

Reference states: Liquid water at 32°F and 1 atm; solid acid at 32°F and 1 atm. Data calculated from miscellaneous literature sources and smoothed.

TABLE I.2 VAPOR-LIQUID EQUILIBRIUM DATA FOR THE ACETIC ACID-WATER SYSTEM; PRESSURE = 1 ATMOSPHERE*

x Mole fraction water in the liquid	y Mole fraction water in the vapor
0.020	0.035
0.040	0.069
0.060	0.103
0.080	0.135
0.100	0.165
0.200	0.303
0.300	0.425
0.400	0.531
0.500	0.627
0.600	0.715
0.700	0.796
0.800	0.865
0.900	0.929
0.940	0.957
0.980	0.985

*From data of L. W. Cornell and R. E. Montonna, *Ind. Eng. Chem.*, v. 25, pp. 1331–35 (1933).

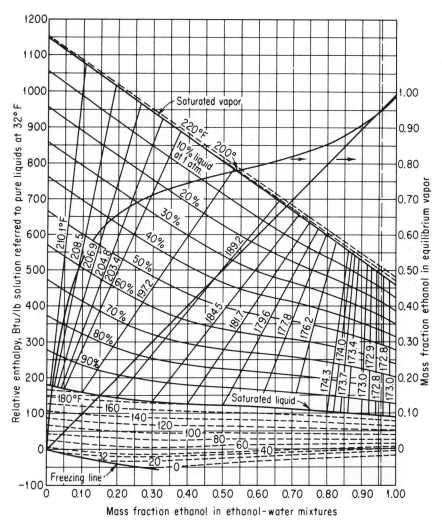

Fig. I.1. Enthalpy-composition diagram for the ethanol-water system, showing liquid and vapor phases in equilibrium at 1 atm.

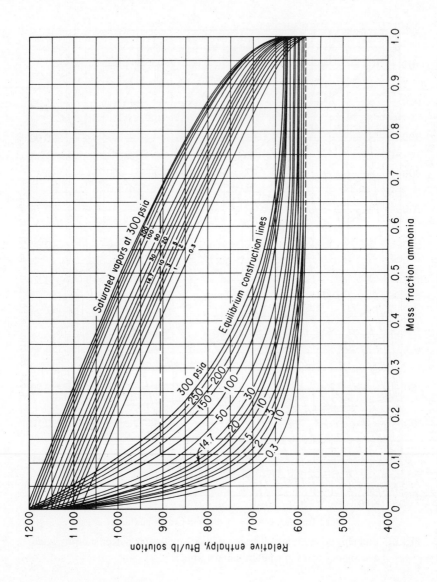

Saturated vapors at 300 psia

200
100
50
30 20
14.7 10 5
3
2
1
0.3

Equilibrium construction lines

300 psia
250 200
150 100
50 30
20 10
14.7 5
2 3
0.3 1.0

Relative enthalpy, Btu/lb solution

1200
1100
1000
900
800
700
600
500
400

0 0.1 0.2 0.3 0.4 0.5 0.6 0.7 0.8 0.9 1.0

Mass fraction ammonia

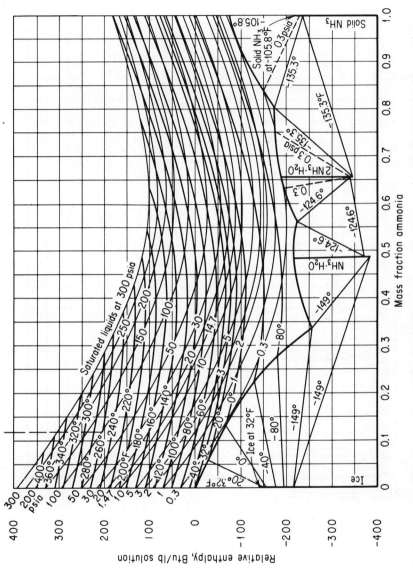

Reference states: water at 32°F and liquid ammonia at −40°F. To determine equilibrium compositions erect a vertical line from any liquid composition at its saturation or boiling point, and locate its intersection with the appropriate equilibrium construction line. A horizontal line from this intersection will intersect the appropriate saturated vapor line at the desired equilibrium vapor composition.

Fig. I.2. Enthalpy-concentration chart for NH₃-H₂O.

461

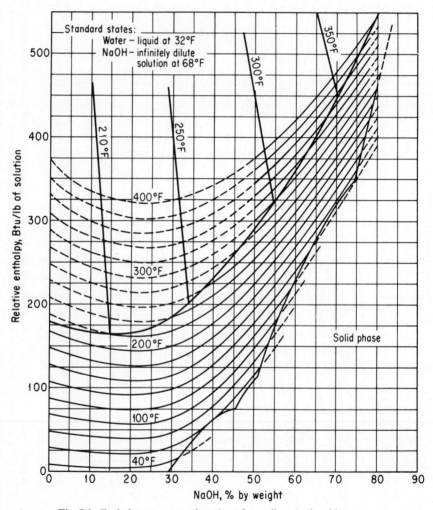

Fig. I.3. Enthalpy-concentration chart for sodium hydroxide-water.

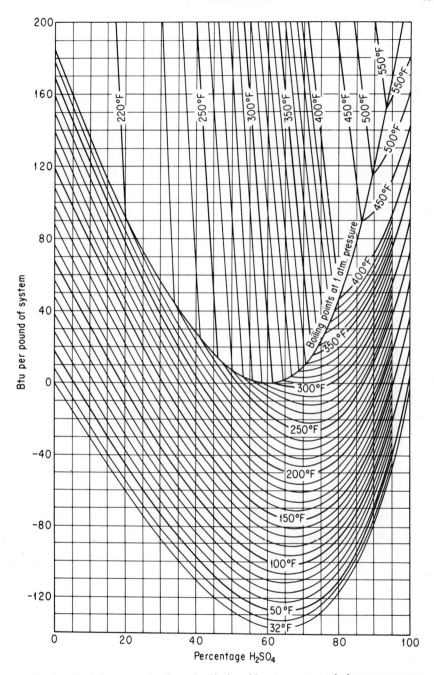

Fig. I.4. Enthalpy-concentration of sulfuric acid-water system relative to pure components. (Water and H_2SO_4 at 32°F and own vapor pressure.) Data from int. crit. tables © 1943 O. A. Hougen and K. M. Watson.

Appendix J

THERMODYNAMIC CHARTS

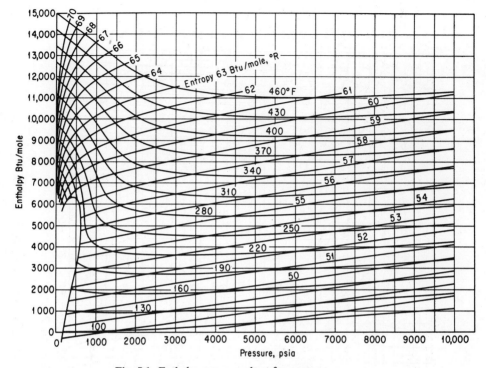

Fig. J.1. Enthalpy-pressure chart for propane.

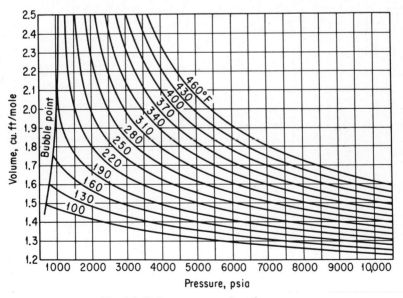

Fig. J.2. Volume-pressure chart for propane.

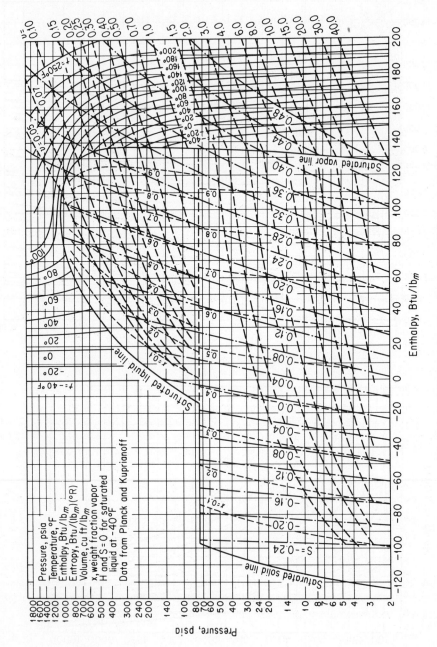

Fig. J.3. Pressure-enthalpy chart for carbon dioxide.

466

Appendix K

PHYSICAL PROPERTIES

OF PETROLEUM FRACTIONS

In the early 1930's tests were developed which would characterize petroleum oils and petroleum fractions, so that various physical characteristics of petroleum products could be related to these tests. Details of the tests can be found in *Petroleum Products and Lubricants,* an annual publication of the Committee D-2 of the American Society for Testing Materials.[1] These tests are not scientifically exact, hence the procedure used in the tests must be followed faithfully if reliable results are to be obtained. However, the tests have been adopted because they are quite easy to perform in the ordinary laboratory, and because the properties of petroleum fractions can be predicted from the results. The tests of particular consequence to us are:

1. API gravity, which has been mentioned in Chap. 1
2. The Reid vapor-pressure test (D323), which is used for volatile products such as gasoline
3. The ASTM or Engler distillation for various petroleum fractions

The specifications for fuels, oils, etc., are set out in terms of these tests plus many other properties, such as the flashpoint, the per cent sulfur, the viscosity, etc.

Another important technique developed in the early 1930's by Watson, Nelson, and associates[2,3,4] relates petroleum properties to a factor known as the *characterization factor* (sometimes called the *UOP characterization factor*). It is defined as

$$K = \frac{(T_B)^{1/3}}{S}$$

where $K =$ the UOP characterization factor
$T =$ the cubic average boiling point, °R
$S =$ the specific gravity at 60°F

This factor has been related to many of the other simple tests and properties of petroleum fractions, such as viscosity, molecular weight, critical temperature, and percentage of hydrogen, so that it is quite easy to estimate

[1] Report of Committee D-2, ASTM, Philadelphia, annually.
[2] R. L. Smith and K. M. Watson, *Ind. Eng. Chem.*, v. 29, p. 1408 (1937).
[3] K. M. Watson and E. F. Nelson, *Ind. Eng. Chem.*, v. 25, p. 880 (1933).
[4] K. M. Watson, E. F. Nelson, and G. B. Murphy, *Ind. Eng. Chem.*, v. 27, p. 1460 (1935).

the factor for any particular sample. Furthermore, tables of the UOP characterization factor are available for a wide variety of common types of petroleum fractions as shown in Table K.1 for typical liquids.

TABLE K.1 TYPICAL UOP CHARACTERIZATION FACTORS

Type of stock	K	Type of stock	K
Pennsylvania crude	12.2–12.5	Propane	14.7
Mid-Continent crude	11.8–12.0	Hexane	12.8
Gulf-Coast crude	11.0–11.8	Octane	12.7
East-Texas crude	11.9	Natural gasoline	12.7–12.8
California crude	10.8–11.9	Light gas oil	10.5
Benzene	9.5	Kerosene	10.5–11.5

Van Winkle[5] discusses the relationships among the volumetric average boiling point, the molal average boiling point, the cubic average boiling point, the weight average boiling point, and the mean average boiling point, and illustrates how the K and other properties of petroleum fractions can be evaluated from experimental data. In Table K.2 are shown the source, boiling point basis, and any special limitations of the various charts in this Appendix.

TABLE K.2 INFORMATION CONCERNING CHARTS IN APPENDIX K

1. *Specific heats of hydrocarbon liquids*
   Source: J. B. Maxwell, *Data Book on Hydrocarbons*, D. Van Nostrand Co., Inc., New York, 1950, p. 93 (original from M. W. Kellogg Co.).
   Description: A chart of C_p (0.4 to 0.8) vs. t (0 to 1000°F) for petroleum fractions from 0 to 120°API.
   Boiling point basis: Volumetric average boiling point, which is equal to graphical integration of the differential ASTM distillation curve (Van Winkle's "exact method").
   Limitations: This chart is not valid at temperatures within 50°F of the pseudocritical temperatures.

2. *Vapor pressure of hydrocarbons*
   Source: Maxwell, *op. cit.*, p. 42.
   Description: Vapor pressure (0.002 to 100 atm) vs. temperature (50 to 1200°F) for hydrocarbons with normal b.p. of 100 to 1200°F (C_4H_{10} and C_5H_{12} lines shown).
   Boiling point basis: Normal boiling points (pure hydrocarbons).
   Limitations: These charts apply well to all hydrocarbon series except the lowest-boiling members of each series.

3. *Heat of combustion of fuel oils and petroleum fractions*
   Source: Maxwell, *op. cit.*, p. 180.
   Description: Heats of combustion above 60°F (17,000 to 20,500 Btu/lb) vs. gravity (0 to 60°API) with correction for sulfur and inerts included (as shown on chart).

[5] M. Van Winkle, *Petroleum Refiner*, June, 1955.

TABLE K.2 (CONT.)

4. *Properties of petroleum fractions*
   Source: O. A. Hougen and K. M. Watson, *Chemical Process Principles Charts*, John
   Wiley & Sons, Inc., New York, 1946, Chart 3.
   Description: °API (−10 to 90°API) vs. b.p. (100 to 1000°F) with molecular weight,
   critical temperature, and *K* factors as parameters.
   Boiling point basis: Use cubic average b.p. when using the *K* values; use mean average
   b.p. when using the molecular weights.

5. *Heats of vaporization of hydrocarbons and petroleum fractions at 1.0 atm pressure*
   Source: Hougen and Watson, *op. cit.*, Chart 68.
   Description: Heats of vaporization (60 to 180 Btu/lb) vs. mean average b.p. (100 to
   1000°F) with molecular weight and API gravity as parameters.
   Boiling point basis: Mean average b.p.

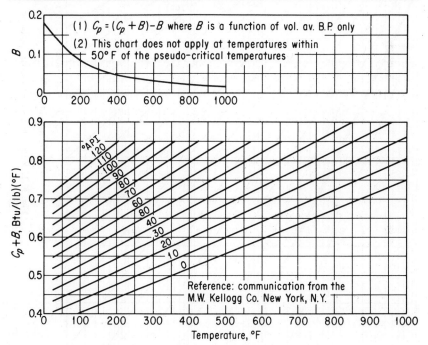

Fig. K.1. Specific heats of hydrocarbon liquids.

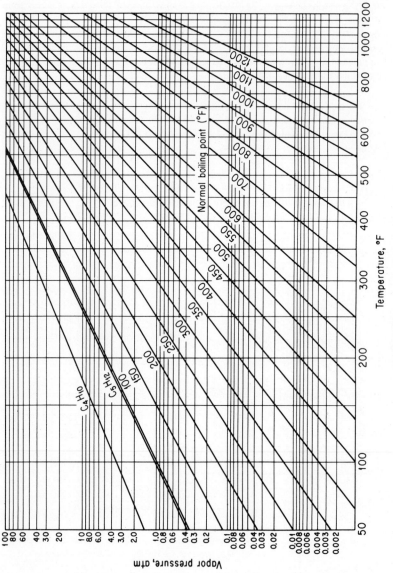

Fig. K.2. Vapor pressure of hydrocarbons.

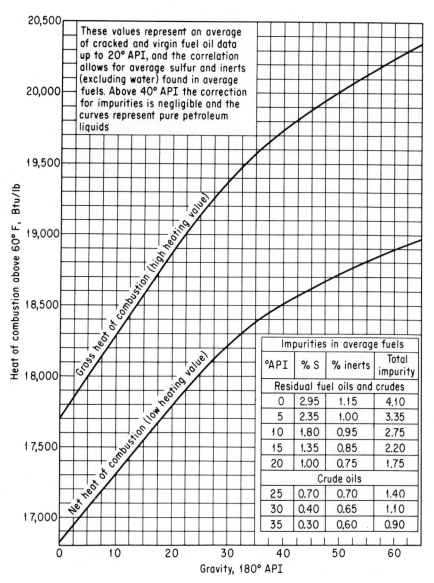

These values represent an average of cracked and virgin fuel oil data up to 20° API, and the correlation allows for average sulfur and inerts (excluding water) found in average fuels. Above 40° API the correction for impurities is negligible and the curves represent pure petroleum liquids

Gross heat of combustion (high heating value)

Net heat of combustion (low heating value)

°API	% S	% inerts	Total impurity
Impurities in average fuels			
Residual fuel oils and crudes			
0	2.95	1.15	4.10
5	2.35	1.00	3.35
10	1.80	0.95	2.75
15	1.35	0.85	2.20
20	1.00	0.75	1.75
Crude oils			
25	0.70	0.70	1.40
30	0.40	0.65	1.10
35	0.30	0.60	0.90

Heat of combustion above 60° F, Btu/lb

Gravity, 180° API

Fig. K.3. Heat of combustion of fuel oils and petroleum fractions.

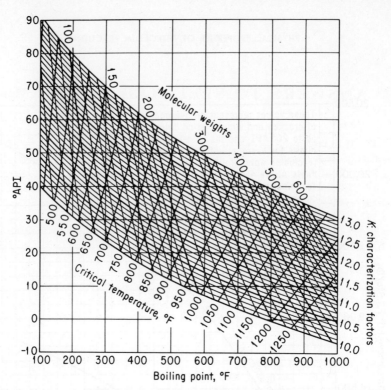

Fig. K.4. Properties of petroleum fractions.

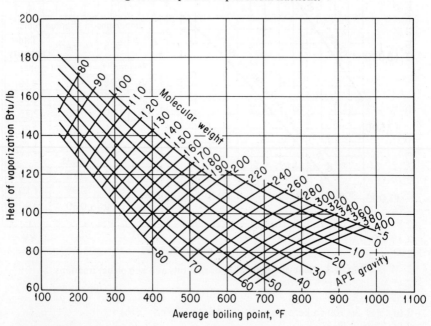

Fig. K.5. Heats of vaporization of hydrocarbons and petroleum fractions at 1.0 atm pressure.

Appendix L

ANSWERS TO SELECTED PROBLEMS

1.3 Petit larceny.
1.4 (a) 0.21 ft/sec².
1.8 0.271 m³/sec.
1.12 1.4×10^3 (lb$_f$)(ft).
1.13 3000 g.
1.16 (b) 3.265×10^{12} ergs.
1.17 7.11.
1.20 lb/(ft³)(°F).
1.25 cm²/(sec)(cm height).
1.26 (1) 14.8×10^5, (4) 2.38×10^7.
1.31 (d) 85.01 kg/kg mole. (g) 258.186 kg/kg mole.
1.35 (e) 21.0, (f) 15,950.
1.37 92.7%.
1.38 124.8 lb$_m$/ft³.
1.46 29.74 lb/lb mole.
1.51 $CaCO_3 - 15.7$, $MgCO_3 - 15.3$, CaO $- 29.4$, NaCl $- 36.7$, $K_2SO_4 - 2.9\%$
1.56 17.5°API. 7.94 lb/gal. 59.3 lb/ft³.
1.61 (h) 1832°F, 2292°R, 1273°K, 1000°C.
1.65 9.48 atm.
1.67 32.2ft H_2O.
1.72 (a) 26.5 psig.
1.80 (e) 2.04 g NaCl. (f) 3.44 g NaCl.
1.84 33.7 lb Pb_2O_5.
1.92 (a) 5210 lb CaO. (b) 0.438 lb CO_2/lb L.S.
1.94 1275 lb pyrites.
1.102 (a) 314 lb Cl_2. (b) 3.13%.

2.4 (a) 0.21 moles or 21% CO_2, 79% N_2. (b) $CO_2 - 14$, $O_2 - 7$, $N_2 - 79\%$.
2.7 (a) fg: $CO_2(11.7\%)$, $N_2(88.3\%)$; sg: $CO_2(9.5\%)$, $N_2(71.5\%)$, $H_2O(19\%)$.
2.12 Mole %: CH_4 (4.69), CS_2 (10.81), $CO_2(84.50)$
2.16 $CO_2 - 17.8$, $O_2 - 1.2$, $N_2 - 81.0\%$
2.21 (a) 3920 lb H_2O req'd. (c) 4356 lb H_2O req'd.
2.25 61,850 lb feed/hr.
2.33 (a) 38.0% B.D.L. (b) 1.555 lb H_2O/lb B.D.L.
2.37 $9.73/100 lb.
2.42 138 ft³ initial gas/min.
2.46 727 lb recl. rubber/ton crude.
2.47 3.12 lb air/lb pyrite.
2.51 44.5%.
2.61 (a) 39,700 lb kero/day. (b) 10,920 lb K/day.
2.66 3 lb R/lb F.
2.69 0.656.

3.1   4.75 ft³ at 29.92 in Hg

3.4 $-55°C$

3.10   75°F

3.12   751 mm Hg

3.14   388 psia

3.17   29,600 ft³/hr at S.C.

3.24   2790 ft³

3.26   (a) 1.248 ft³ air/ft³ gas. (b) 5.87 ft³ fg @ 750°F and 738 mm/ft³ gas at S.C.

3.28   (c) 395 ft³ at 690°F/lb coke

3.32   (a) $CO_2 - 15.85$, $N_2 - 84.15\%$. 14.2 lb air/lb fuel. 187 ft³ air at 60°F, 1 atm/lb fuel.

3.34   (a_1) mole %: $CO_2(15.85)$, $N_2(84.15)$; (a_2) 14.2 lb air/lb fuel

3.39   1300 ft³ gas in at 70°F, 740 mm Hg.

3.40   1230 ft³ initial gas at 60°F, 740 mm Hg/min

3.41   0.392 lb/min

3.45   (b) 20.22 lb/lb mole

3.51   (a) 0.447 psia. (b) 3.0 ft³ of N_2 at 20°C, 30 psig. (c) 0.128 lb/ft³ at 20°C, 30 psia.

3.55 $N_2 - 397$ psia. $O_2 - 284$ psia.

3.60   434°K

3.63   Van der Waals: 0.0212 ft³/lb; Compressibility: 0.0159 ft³/lb.

3.72   2.0 lb/ft³ at 500 psia and 250°F

3.76   (a) 3.85 ft³ at 180°F, 2415 psia. (b) 2.90 ft³ at 180°F, 2415 psia. (c) 1400 psia.

3.78   53.4 psia.

3.81   766.8 mm Hg.

3.82   3.68 liters.

3.85   3.87 ft³ BD air at 25°C, 760 mm.

3.93   (a) 50%. (b) 0.2435. (c) 0.678 lb B/lb N_2. (d) 19.6 mole%. (e) 37.9%. (f) 232 grain B/ft³ mix at 700 mm, 50°C.

3.101   (a) 48.6%. (b) 48.1%. (c) 130°F.

3.104   1840 lb BDA/hr.

3.113   (a) rel. satn = 0.588. (b) % satn = 58%. (c) 0.00158 lb H_2O/ft³ at 86°F, 745 mm.

3.118   (a) 750.0 lb H_2O. (b) 14,091 lb BD air.

3.125   (a) 968 ft³ dry exit gas. (b) 11.5%.

4.1   (d) Intensive.

4.8   (a) 254,000 Btu/hr. (b) 17,800 cal/sec. (c) 74.6 kW.

4.12   (a) $\Delta H = 4680$ cal/g mole. (b) $\Delta U = 3490$ cal/g mole.

4.15   (a) 1783 Btu. (b) 2225 Btu.

4.22   for SO_2: (a) 11.342. (b) 10.109. (c) 10.48.

4.24   7.519 cal/(g mole) (°C)

4.27 $Na_2CO_3 \cdot 10H_2O$: 0.394 vs. 0.447 by expt.

4.31   171 Btu/lb calculated.

4.35   (a) 8640 Btu/lb mole. (b) 9110 Btu/lb mole.

4.37   (a) 3576 Btu. (b) 3576 Btu. (i) 0.00216 ft³. (m) 0.34.

4.41 (a) $Q = 0$, $W = 0$, $\Delta U = 0$, $\Delta H = 0$. (b) The minimum work is -766 Btu/lb mole; actual work is greater.

4.50 Rev. flow: $W = 0$. Rev. non-flow: $W = 1313$ Btu/lb.

4.58 100°C.

4.62 (a) for CO_2: $W = 3264$ Btu/lb mole (on gas). (b) If $Q = 0$ and were rev., there would be a different set of final conditions. (c) $W = -Q + (17.2)(44)$.

4.65 324 hp

4.70 (a) 49.271 kcal. (b) -9.83 kcal.

4.71 (i) -26.76 kcal. (m) 47.72 kcal. (w) 22.07 kcal.

4.74 (a) $-23,600$ Btu/lb.

4.76 (a) -749.42 kcal/g mole.

4.81 16,763 Btu/lb mole.

4.85 7,220 cal evolved.

4.86 276%.

4.90 3250°F

4.93 (a) $C_6 - 9.5$, $O_2 - 19.1$, $N_2 - 71.4$. (b) $C_6H_5CH_3 - 8.20$, $CO_2 - 0.33$, $H_2O - 1.42$, $C_6H_5CHO - 1.23$, $O_2 - 17.30$, $N_2 - 71.52\%$. (c) 325 gal H_2O/hr.

4.96 27,732 cal/g mole feed.

4.99 (a) $-33,000$ Btu/lb mole. (b) -289.65 kcal/g mole. (c) -1440 Btu/lb mole.

5.3 9140 lb/hr.

5.4 For H_2O at 70°F: 148 lb ice and 38 lb H_2O.

5.7 1.45 lb steam/lb soln.

5.11 (a) 67%. (b) $Q = -580$ Btu/lb A; L = 67.5%.

5.14 (a_1) 0.081 lb H_2O/lb dry air. (a_2) 16.52 ft³/lb dry air. (a_3) 77°F. (a_4) 46.7%. (a_5) 0.579 lb H_2O/100 lb moist air.

5.22 (a_1) 0.0175. (a_2) 0.0188. (a_3) 0.0188. (a_4) 0.0377. (d) 163,580 ft³/hr.

5.25 0.19 lb wet glue/lb dry air recycled.

5.30 (b) 0.424 lb mix.

5.31 (a) 184°F. (b) 384 lb/hr.

6.1 0.0173 lb UO_2/lb H_2O.

6.5 0.58%.

6.6 34,700 lb.

6.13 $t = \dfrac{\ln 2}{K}$.

INDEX

477